Solutions Manual *for the* Mechanical Engineering Reference Manual

Tenth Edition

Michael R. Lindeburg, PE

Professional Publications, Inc. • Belmont, CA

Production Manager: Aline Sullivan Magee
Acquisitions Editors: Gerald R. Galbo and Catie Berkenfield
Copy Editor: Mia Laurence
Book Designer: Charles P. Oey
Typesetter: Kate Hayes
Illustrator: Yvonne M. Sartain
Proofreader: Jessica R. Whitney-Holden
Cover Designer: Charles P. Oey

SOLUTIONS MANUAL for the
MECHANICAL ENGINEERING REFERENCE MANUAL
Tenth Edition

Printed in the United States of America

Professional Publications, Inc.
1250 Fifth Avenue, Belmont, CA 94002
(650) 593-9119
www.ppi2pass.com

Current printing of this edition: 1

Library of Congress Cataloging-in-Publication Data
Lindeburg, Michael R.
    Solutions manual for the Mechanical engineering reference manual /
    Michael R. Lindeburg. -- 10th ed.
        p.   cm.
    ISBN 1-888577-15-0
    1. Mechanical engineering--Problems, exercises, etc.
    2. Mechanical engineering--Handbooks, manuals, etc. I. Lindeburg,
    Michael R. Mechanical engineering reference manual. II. Title.
    TJ159.L526   1997
    621'.076--dc21   97-28055
                                                            CIP

Table of Contents

Before You Begin...
Changes, *Mechanical Engineering Reference Manual*, 10th Edition, First Printing

Please check the printing number of your *Mechanical Engineering Reference Manual* (not this *Solutions Manual*). The printing number is located on the copyright page. If you have the first printing of the *Mechanical Engineering Reference Manual*, the following changes to the practice problem statements are necessary to use this *Solutions Manual*. No changes are needed if you have the second or any subsequent printing. We apologize for any inconvenience this may bring you.

Chap. 17, Prob. 8: Add "The water is at $70°F$ ($20°C$)."

Chap. 17, Prob. 12: Add "The water is at $70°F$ ($20°C$). The pipe's modulus of elasticity is 20×10^6 psi (140 GPa)."

Chap. 17, Prob. 13: Add "The air is at $70°F$ ($20°C$)."

Chap. 17, Prob. 16: Add to the problem illustration: "The outline branch consists of 1500 ft (450 m) of 12 in diameter pipe."

Chap. 18, Prob. 13: (1) Change the SI equivalent pressure drop from "63 to 160 Pa" to "0.021 to 0.054 m of water." (2) Change "300 kW" to "257 kW" in two places. (3) Omit part (c) entirely.

Chap. 20, in the Note before the problems: Add "Round all duct dimensions to multiples of 25 mm."

Chap. 20, Prob. 3: Change "1525 m" to "1500 m."

Chap. 20, Prob. 6: Add parts (b) and (c): "(b) What is the static pressure at the fan? (c) What is the total pressure at the fan?"

Chap. 20, Prob. 7: Add parts (b) and (c): "(b) What is the static pressure at the fan? (c) What is the total pressure at the fan?"

Chap. 20, Prob. 8: Only the Customary U.S. Solution is required.

Chap. 20, Prob. 9: Change part (c) to "(c) What is the regain in sections B and C?"

Chap. 21, Prob. 3: In part (a), change "100 mg/L" to "100 mg/L as $CaCO_3$."

Chap. 22, Prob. 2: The SI equivalent of 15 lbm/hr for this problem is 6.8 kg/hr.

Chap. 22, Prob. 9: Add "Evaluate flue gas volumes at $600°F$ ($320°C$)."

Chap. 22, Prob. 12: In the last line, change "carbon dioxide" to "carbon monoxide."

Chap. 22, Prob. 17: The SI equivalent of 250 SCFM for this problem is 118 L/s.

Chap. 22, Prob. 18: Add part (c): "(c) How much water is removed from the stack gas?"

Chap. 26, Prob. 1: Change part (c) to "(c) total temperature at the throat?"

Chap. 26, Prob. 4: Change the first line to "A wedge-shaped leading edge with a semivertex angle of $20°$ . . . "

Chap. 26, Prob. 5: The SI equivalent of 1 in^2 for this problem is 6.45×10^{-4} m^2.

Chap. 26, Prob. 7: Omit part (d) entirely.

Chap. 26, Prob. 12: $k = 1.31$ for steam.

Chap. 26, Prob. 13: $k = 1.30$ for steam.

Chap. 27, Prob. 9: Change "3.74 kg" to "8.23 kg" in the first line.

Chap. 27, Prob. 12: Omit part (c) entirely.

Chap. 27, Prob. 13: Add second question: "What power is developed in the turbine?"

Chap. 28, Prob. 8: The air is at $140°F$ ($60°C$).

Chap. 29, Prob. 3: Change "$40°$ past TDC" to "$40°$ past BDC."

Chap. 29, Prob. 5: Change "0.035 kg/s" to "0.0035 kg/s."

Chap. 32, Prob. 5: The SI equivalent of 1000 ft^3 for this problem is 27 m^3.

Chap. 35, Prob. 4: Change "2.5 W/m" to "25 W/m."

Chap. 38, Prob. 5: Change the question to "What are the (a) enthalpy change and (b) change in moisture content per cubic foot (meter) of air?"

Chap. 38, Prob. 6: Add "The air is discharged at 75% relative humidity."

Chap. 40, Prob. 6: (1) Change "30.2 kJ/kg" to "30.2 MJ/kg." (2) Change "1.9 MW" to "0.19 MW."

Chap. 40, Prob. 8: (1) Change the SI equivalent wall area from "1939 m^2" to "993 m^2." (2) Omit the 75% furnace efficiency entirely.

Chap. 46, Prob. 2: (1) Add part (g): "(g) toughness." (2) In the problem illustration, change "140" to "137.5," and change "410" to "412.5."

Chap. 46, Prob. 3: Omit part (b) entirely.

Chap. 51, Prob. 3: Omit part (a) entirely.

Chap. 52, Prob. 1: Add "The load is static."

Chap. 52, Prob. 6: (1) Add "Use the Lewis beam strength theory." (2) Change part (b) to "(b) Given a gear face width of 6 in (150 mm), what is the diametral pitch?" (3) Change part (c) to "(c) Given a diametral pitch of 1.5 (a module of 17 mm), what should be the face width of the gear?"

Chap. 52, Prob. 7: Add "Use the Lewis beam strength theory."

Chap. 52, Prob. 11: (1) The SI equivalent of a diametral pitch of 5 for this problem is a module of 5 mm. (2) Add "Use a factor of safety of 2. Assume static loading."

Chap. 57, Prob. 3: Change "run gear" to "sun gear."

Chap. 58, Prob. 5: (1) Change "$9 \cos 2t$ N" to "$18 \cos 2t$ N." (2) Add "What are the natural frequency, damping ratio, and maximum excursion?"

Preface and Acknowledgments

Putting out a solutions manual for one of my reference manuals has always been a major undertaking. For one thing, it's a lot of work. For another, "good enough" just won't do. Over the years, I have learned the amount of detail that will help you learn from a solution, as opposed to just presenting the numbers. (I have also learned that if I leave out certain steps or items, then I get a lot of inquisitive letters, phone calls, and E-mail!)

The style standards set by Professional Publications' Production Department are as strict as my content standards. There is a proper way to edit, typeset, illustrate, and proofread a book. The Production Department won't do it any other way.

Most textbook authors see their solutions manuals as a necessary evil: something required by their contract, something to bang out as quickly as possible, an afterthought stuck between two editions. The finished product seems to say, "Here are the numbers and the answer. Sure, we've been a little sloppy with units, and maybe we've omitted a few steps. But a little struggling is good for you. You can figure it all out. Somehow."

But not me. And not Professional Publications. All that struggling with vague content and sloppy production wastes your time. And before an exam, time is one thing that an examinee doesn't have much of. There was no way we were going to cut corners on this book.

Most of the problems in the tenth edition of the *Mechanical Engineering Reference Manual* were derived from similar problems in the ninth edition. However, each problem was changed in many subtle (and not-so-subtle) ways. One major change is that each problem is now dual-dimensioned so that you can work it in either English or SI units. Many problems were "improved" by explicitly stating required assumptions or by giving data that was necessary but time-consuming to locate. Some problems were rewritten to be more practical and less ideal or theoretical. Others were modified so that the answers were within reasonable ranges.

Along the way, a few of the problems became "unsolvable" due to the changes in the problem statement. Some became unsolvable because of changes in the *Mechanical Engineering Reference Manual*. Some solutions were developed before the *Mechanical Engineering Reference Manual* was even available, leading to "synchronization" errors between the solution and data in the book's various appendices.

Furthermore, all of the conditions that publishers groan about were present in this manuscript: it was large, handwritten, and late. The entire manuscript wasn't available at one time to begin working on. It consisted of primarily equations and illustrations. There was no electronic file, and everything had to be keyboarded. The schedule was ultra-tight.

Professional Publications certainly could not have brought out this solutions manual without Mahesh Aggarwal, PhD. Dr. Aggarwal and his team of assistants at Gannon University (Erie, Pennsylvania) took on this project late and worked tirelessly to produce the content for the book you are currently reading.

Since the problem statements in the tenth edition were derived from my ninth edition problems, I originally believed that reformatting the ninth edition solutions would be all that was required to bring out this edition. However, as I began my job of checking, cross-referencing, recalculating, and verifying, I realized that "reformatting" wasn't the path that had been taken.

In the best of worlds, each problem would be meticulously dissected. Any missing data would be taken from the tenth edition of the *Mechanical Engineering Reference Manual*. All steps in the solution would be shown. Units would be included in all calculations. The equations would be shown before inserting the numerical values. All numbers would be run though the calculator, and results would be compared to the original solution. Enough explanation would be provided to teach you something new if you needed it. And that's exactly what Dr. Aggarwal did. But not only that: he and his team did it while remaining on a tight schedule.

Professional Publications' Production Department took on this project while working on at least a zillion other books, labored valiantly without complaint, and managed to pull off a winner. My admiration and gratitude go to Mia Laurence who edited, Kate Hayes who typeset, Yvonne Sartain who illustrated, and Jessica Whitney-Holden who proofed this book under most difficult conditions and who held it all together with chewing gum, horse feathers, and large red rubber bands. And to Aline Sullivan Magee, Production Department Manager, who oversaw the printing and kept me on my toes.

For me, it's a little scary to retreat from the security of solutions whose kinks had already been ironed out in nine previous editions and now pass into the critical, hot spotlight of a new edition. You would think that after all these years of writing problems and solutions I would know virtually all of the ways you and I make mistakes. But even knowing the ways mistakes are made doesn't mean we can avoid them all.

If you think you've found something questionable in a solution, or if you think there is a better way to solve a problem, use one of the postcards in the back of this book. Or visit our website at www.ppi2pass.com and send me an E-mail. I like to learn new things, too.

Michael R. Lindeburg, PE

How to Use This Book

This *Solutions Manual* is a companion to *Mechanical Engineering Reference Manual*. Since it is a solutions manual, there are a few, but not many, ways to use it.

Since most of the problems in the book can be solved in either English or SI units, your first decision will be which set of units you will work in. Don't get me wrong: The exam doesn't give you such a choice. Exam problems are either in English or SI units, not both. So, you have to be proficient with both. I recommend that you solve half of the problems in English units and half in SI. Then, if you have time, go back to solve all of the problems a second time, using the alternate units.

The big decision you have to make is whether you really work the practice problems or not. Some people think they can read a problem statement, think about it for about ten seconds, read the solution, and then say "Yes, that's what I was thinking of, and that's what I would have done." Sadly, these people find out too late that the human brain doesn't learn very efficiently that way. Under pressure, they find they know and remember little. For real learning, you have to spend some time with a stubby pencil.

There are so many places where you can get messed up solving a problem. Maybe it's in the use of your calculator, like pushing log instead of ln, or forgetting to set the angle to radians instead of degrees, and so on. Maybe it's rusty math. What is $\ln(e^x)$, anyway? How do you factor a polynomial? Maybe it's in finding the data needed or the proper unit conversion. Maybe it's just trying to find out if that funky code equation expects L to be in feet or inches. These things take time. And you have to make the mistakes once so that you don't make them again.

If you do decide to get your hands dirty and actually work these problems, you'll have to decide how much reliance you place on the solutions manual. It's tempting to turn to a solution when you get slowed down by details or stumped by the subject material. You'll probably want to maximize the number of problems you solve by spending as little time as possible. I want you to struggle a little bit more than that.

Studying a new subject is analogous to using a machete to cut a path through a dense jungle. By doing the work, you develop pathways that weren't there before. It's a lot different than just looking at the route on a map. You actually get nowhere by looking at a map. But cut that path once, and you're in business until the jungle overgrowth closes in again.

So, do the problems. All of them. Do them in both sets of units. Don't look at the answers until you've sweated a little. And, let's not have any whining. Please.

1 Systems of Units

1. The conversion to degrees Celsius is given by

$$°C = \left(\frac{5}{9}\right)(°F - 32°F)$$

$$= \left(\frac{5}{9}\right)(250°F - 32°F)$$

$$= \left(\frac{5}{9}\right)(218°F)$$

$$= \boxed{121.1°C}$$

2. In U.S. customary units, the Stephan-Boltzmann constant, σ, is 0.1713×10^{-8} Btu/hr-ft^2-°R^4.

Use the following conversion factors.

$$1 \text{ Btu/hr} = 0.2931 \text{ W}$$

$$1 \text{ ft} = 0.3048 \text{ m}$$

$$°R = \frac{5}{9}K$$

Performing the conversion gives

$$\sigma = \left(0.1713 \times 10^{-8} \frac{\text{Btu}}{\text{hr-ft}^2\text{-°R}^4}\right)\left(0.2931 \frac{\text{W}}{\frac{\text{Btu}}{\text{hr}}}\right)$$

$$\times \left(\frac{1 \text{ ft}}{0.3048 \text{ m}}\right)^2 \left(\frac{1°R}{\frac{5}{9}K}\right)^4$$

$$= \boxed{5.67 \times 10^{-8} \text{ W/m}^2\text{·K}^4}$$

3. The energy produced from the nuclear conversion of any quantity of mass is given as

$$E = mc^2$$

The speed of light, c, is 3×10^8 m/s.

For a mass of 1 g (0.001 kg),

$$E = mc^2$$

$$= (0.001 \text{ kg})\left(3 \times 10^8 \frac{\text{m}}{\text{s}}\right)^2$$

$$= 9 \times 10^{13} \text{ J}$$

Convert to U.S. customary units with the conversion 1 Btu = 1055 J.

$$E = (9 \times 10^{13} \text{ J})\left(\frac{1 \text{ Btu}}{1055 \text{ J}}\right)$$

$$= 8.53 \times 10^{10} \text{ Btu}$$

The number of tons of 13,000 Btu/lbm coal is

$$\frac{8.53 \times 10^{10} \text{ Btu}}{\left(13{,}000 \frac{\text{Btu}}{\text{lbm}}\right)\left(2000 \frac{\text{lbm}}{\text{ton}}\right)} = \boxed{3281 \text{ tons}}$$

3 Algebra

1. Let $S_n = (j+1)^2 - 1$.

For $j = 1$,
$$S_1 = (1+1)^2 - 1 = 3$$

For $j = 2$,
$$S_2 = (2+1)^2 - 1 = 8$$

For $j = 3$,
$$S_3 = (3+1)^2 - 1 = 15$$

For $j = 4$,
$$S_4 = (4+1)^2 - 1 = 24$$

For $j = 5$,
$$S_5 = (5+1)^2 - 1 = 35$$

Substituting the above expressions gives

$$\sum_{j=1}^{5}\left((j+1)^2 - 1\right) = \sum_{j=1}^{5} S_j$$
$$= S_1 + S_2 + S_3 + S_4 + S_5$$
$$= 3 + 8 + 15 + 24 + 35$$
$$= \boxed{85}$$

2. Let n represent the number of elapsed periods of 0.1 sec, and let y_n represent the amount present after n periods.

y_0 represents the initial quantity.

$$y_1 = 1.001 y_0$$
$$y_2 = 1.001 y_1 = (1.001)\left((1.001)y_0\right) = (1.001)^2 y_0$$

Therefore, by deduction,

$$y_n = (1.001)^n y_0$$

The expression for a doubling of the original quantity is

$$2 y_0 = y_n$$

Substitute for y_n.

$$2 y_0 = (1.001)^n y_0$$
$$2 = (1.001)^n$$

Take the logarithm of both sides.

$$\log(2) = \log(1.001)^n$$
$$= n\log(1.001)$$

Solve for n.

$$n = \frac{\log(2)}{\log(1.001)} = 693.5$$

Since each period is 0.01 sec, the time is given by

$$t = n(0.01 \text{ sec})$$
$$= (693.5)(0.01 \text{ sec}) = \boxed{69.35 \text{ sec}}$$

4 Linear Algebra

1. Rearrange the equations.

$$\begin{aligned} x + y \quad\;\; &= -4 \\ x \quad\;\; + z &= 1 \\ 3x - y + 2z &= 4 \end{aligned}$$

Write the set of equations in matrix form: $\mathbf{AX} = \mathbf{B}$.

$$\begin{bmatrix} 1 & 1 & 0 \\ 1 & 0 & 1 \\ 3 & -1 & 2 \end{bmatrix} \begin{bmatrix} x \\ y \\ z \end{bmatrix} = \begin{bmatrix} -4 \\ 1 \\ 4 \end{bmatrix}$$

Find the determinant of the matrix $\mathbf{A}$.

$$\begin{aligned} |\mathbf{A}| &= \begin{vmatrix} 1 & 1 & 0 \\ 1 & 0 & 1 \\ 3 & -1 & 2 \end{vmatrix} \\ &= (1)\begin{vmatrix} 0 & 1 \\ -1 & 2 \end{vmatrix} - (1)\begin{vmatrix} 1 & 0 \\ -1 & 2 \end{vmatrix} + (3)\begin{vmatrix} 1 & 0 \\ 0 & 1 \end{vmatrix} \\ &= (1)\big((0)(2) - (1)(-1)\big) \\ &\quad - (1)\big((1)(2) - (-1)(0)\big) \\ &\quad + (3)\big((1)(1) - (0)(0)\big) \\ &= (1)(1) - (1)(2) + (3)(1) \\ &= 1 - 2 + 3 \\ &= 2 \end{aligned}$$

Find the determinant of the substitutional matrix $\mathbf{A_1}$.

$$\begin{aligned} |\mathbf{A_1}| &= \begin{vmatrix} -4 & 1 & 0 \\ 1 & 0 & 1 \\ 4 & -1 & 2 \end{vmatrix} \\ &= (-4)\begin{vmatrix} 0 & 1 \\ -1 & 2 \end{vmatrix} - (1)\begin{vmatrix} 1 & 0 \\ -1 & 2 \end{vmatrix} + (4)\begin{vmatrix} 1 & 0 \\ 0 & 1 \end{vmatrix} \\ &= (-4)\big((0)(2) - (1)(-1)\big) \\ &\quad - (1)\big((1)(2) - (-1)(0)\big) \\ &\quad + (4)\big((1)(1) - (0)(0)\big) \\ &= (-4)(1) - (1)(2) + (4)(1) \\ &= -4 - 2 + 4 \\ &= -2 \end{aligned}$$

Find the determinant of the substitutional matrix $\mathbf{A_2}$.

$$\begin{aligned} |\mathbf{A_2}| &= \begin{vmatrix} 1 & -4 & 0 \\ 1 & 1 & 1 \\ 3 & 4 & 2 \end{vmatrix} \\ &= (1)\begin{vmatrix} 1 & 1 \\ 4 & 2 \end{vmatrix} - (1)\begin{vmatrix} -4 & 0 \\ 4 & 2 \end{vmatrix} + (3)\begin{vmatrix} -4 & 0 \\ 1 & 1 \end{vmatrix} \\ &= (1)\big((1)(2) - (4)(1)\big) \\ &\quad - (1)\big((-4)(2) - (4)(0)\big) \\ &\quad + (3)\big((-4)(1) - (1)(0)\big) \\ &= (1)(-2) - (1)(-8) + (3)(-4) \\ &= -2 + 8 - 12 \\ &= -6 \end{aligned}$$

Find the determinant of the substitutional matrix $\mathbf{A_3}$.

$$\begin{aligned} |\mathbf{A_3}| &= \begin{vmatrix} 1 & 1 & -4 \\ 1 & 0 & 1 \\ 3 & -1 & 4 \end{vmatrix} \\ &= (1)\begin{vmatrix} 0 & 1 \\ -1 & 4 \end{vmatrix} - (1)\begin{vmatrix} 1 & -4 \\ -1 & 4 \end{vmatrix} + (3)\begin{vmatrix} 1 & -4 \\ 0 & 0 \end{vmatrix} \\ &= (1)\big((0)(4) - (-1)(1)\big) \\ &\quad - (1)\big((1)(4) - (-1)(-4)\big) \\ &\quad + (3)\big((1)(1) - (0)(-4)\big) \\ &= (1)(1) - (1)(0) + (3)(1) \\ &= 1 - 0 + 3 \\ &= 4 \end{aligned}$$

Use Cramer's rule.

$$x = \frac{|\mathbf{A_1}|}{|\mathbf{A}|} = \frac{-2}{2} = \boxed{-1}$$

$$y = \frac{|\mathbf{A_2}|}{|\mathbf{A}|} = \frac{-6}{2} = \boxed{-3}$$

$$z = \frac{|\mathbf{A_3}|}{|\mathbf{A}|} = \frac{4}{2} = \boxed{2}$$

6 Trigonometry

1.

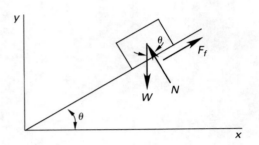

Customary U.S. Solution

The mass of the block is $m = 5$ lbm.

The angle of inclination is $\theta = 20°$.

The weight is

$$W = \frac{mg}{g_c}$$

$$= \frac{(5 \text{ lbm}) \left(32.2 \dfrac{\text{ft}}{\text{sec}^2}\right)}{32.2 \dfrac{\text{lbm-ft}}{\text{lbf-sec}^2}}$$

$$= \boxed{5 \text{ lbf}}$$

The normal force is

$$N = W \cos \theta$$

$$= (5 \text{ lbf})(\cos 20°)$$

$$= \boxed{4.70 \text{ lbf}}$$

The frictional force is

$$F_f = W \sin \theta$$

$$= (5 \text{ lbf})(\sin 20°)$$

$$= \boxed{1.71 \text{ lbf}}$$

SI Solution

The mass of the block is $m = 5$ kg.

The angle of inclination is $\theta = 20°$.

The gravitational force is

$$W = mg$$

$$= (5 \text{ kg}) \left(9.81 \dfrac{\text{m}}{\text{s}^2}\right)$$

$$= \boxed{49.1 \text{ N}}$$

The normal force is

$$N = W \cos \theta$$

$$= (49.1 \text{ N})(\cos 20°)$$

$$= \boxed{46.1 \text{ N}}$$

The frictional force is

$$F_f = W \sin \theta$$

$$= (49.1 \text{ N})(\sin 20°)$$

$$= \boxed{16.8 \text{ N}}$$

7 Analytic Geometry

1. Let d be the diameter of the sphere and the base of the cone.

The volume of the sphere is given by

$$V_{\text{sphere}} = \left(\frac{4}{3}\right)\pi r^3 = \left(\frac{4}{3}\right)\pi\left(\frac{d}{2}\right)^3$$
$$= \left(\frac{\pi}{6}\right)d^3$$

The volume of the circular cone is given by

$$V_{\text{cone}} = \left(\frac{1}{3}\right)\pi r^2 h = \left(\frac{1}{3}\right)\pi\left(\frac{d}{2}\right)^2 h$$
$$= \left(\frac{\pi}{12}\right)d^2 h$$

Since the volume of the sphere and cone are equal,

$$V_{\text{cone}} = V_{\text{sphere}}$$
$$\left(\frac{\pi}{12}\right)d^2 h = \left(\frac{\pi}{6}\right)d^3$$
$$h = 2d$$

The height of the cone must be 200% of the diameter.

8 Differential Calculus

1. If c is positive, then $n(\infty) = \infty$, which is contrary to the data given. Therefore, $c \leq 0$. If $c = 0$, then $n(\infty) = a/(1 + b) = 100$, which is possible depending on a and b. However, $n(0) = a/(1+b)$ would also equal 100, which is contrary to the given data. Therefore, $c \not< 0$.

c must be less than 0.

Since $c < 0$, then $n(\infty) = a$, so $\boxed{a = 100.}$

Applying the condition $t = 0$ gives

$$n(0) = \frac{a}{1 + b} = 10$$

Since $a = 100$,

$$n(0) = \frac{100}{1 + b}$$
$$100 = (10)(1 + b)$$
$$10 = 1 + b$$
$$\boxed{b = 9}$$

Substitute the results for a and b into the expression.

$$n(t) = \frac{100}{1 + 9e^{ct}}$$

Take the first derivative.

$$\frac{d}{dt}n(t) = \left(\frac{100}{(1 + 9e^{ct})^2} \right)(-9ce^{ct})$$

Apply the initial condition.

$$\frac{d}{dt}n(0) = \left(\frac{100}{(1 + 9e^{c(0)})^2} \right)\left(- 9ce^{c(0)} \right) = 0.5$$
$$\left(\frac{100}{(1 + 9)^2} \right)(-9c) = 0.5$$
$$(1)(-9c) = 0.5$$
$$c = \frac{-0.5}{9}$$
$$= \boxed{-0.0556}$$

Substitute the terms a, b, and c into the expression.

$$n(t) = \frac{100}{1 + 9e^{-0.0556t}}$$

2. Determine the critical points by taking the first derivative of the function and setting it equal to zero.

$$\frac{dy}{dx} = 3x^2 - 18x = 3x(x - 6)$$
$$3x(x - 6) = 0$$
$$x(x - 6) = 0$$

The critical points are at $x = 0$ and $x = 6$.

Determine the inflection points by setting the second derivative equal to zero. Take the second derivative.

$$\frac{d^2y}{dx^2} = \left(\frac{d}{dx} \right)\left(\frac{dy}{dx} \right) = \frac{d}{dx}(3x^2 - 18x)$$
$$= 6x - 18$$

Set the second derivative equal to zero.

$$\frac{d^2y}{dx^2} = 0 = 6x - 18 = (6)(x - 3)$$
$$(6)(x - 3) = 0$$
$$x - 3 = 0$$
$$x = 3$$

$\boxed{\text{This inflection point is at } x = 3.}$

Determine the local maximum and minimum by substituting the critical points into the expression for the second derivative.

At the critical point $x = 0$,

$$\left. \frac{d^2y}{dx^2} \right|_{x=0} = (6)(x - 3) = (6)(0 - 3)$$
$$= -18$$

Since $-18 < 0$, $\boxed{x = 0 \text{ is a local maximum.}}$

At the critical point $x = 6$,

$$\left.\frac{d^2y}{dx^2}\right|_{x=6} = (6)(x-3) = (6)(6-3)$$
$$= 18$$

Since $-18 > 0$, $\boxed{x = 6 \text{ is a local minimum.}}$

10 Differential Equations

1. Obtain the characteristic equation by replacing each derivative with a polynomial term of equal degree.

$$r^2 - 4r - 12 = 0$$

Find the roots of the characteristic equation.

$$(r - 6)(r + 2) = 0$$

The roots are $r_1 = 6$ and $r_2 = -2$.

Since the roots are real and distinct, the solution is

$$y = A_1 e^{r_1 x} + A_2 e^{r_2 x}$$

$$= \boxed{A_1 e^{6x} + A_2 e^{-2x}}$$

2. The equation is a first-order linear differential equation of the form

$$y' + p(x)y = g(x)$$
$$p(x) = -1$$
$$g(x) = 2xe^{2x}$$

The integration factor $u(x)$ is given by

$$u(x) = e\left(\int p(x)dx\right)$$
$$= e\left(\int (-1)dx\right)$$
$$= e^{-x}$$

The closed form of the solution is given by

$$y = \left(\frac{1}{u(x)}\right)\left(\int u(x)g(x)dx + C\right)$$
$$= \left(\frac{1}{e^{-x}}\right)\left(\int (e^{-x})(2xe^{2x})dx + C\right)$$
$$= e^x\left(2(xe^x - 2e^x) + C\right)$$
$$= e^x\left(2e^x(x - 1) + C\right)$$
$$= 2e^{2x}(x - 1) + Ce^x$$

Apply the initial condition $y(0) = 1$ to obtain the integration constant C.

$$y(0) = 2e^{(2)(0)}(0 - 1) + Ce^0 = 1$$
$$(2)(1)(-1) + C(1) = 1$$
$$-2 + C = 1$$
$$C = 3$$

Substituting in the value for the integration constant C, the solution is

$$y(x) = \boxed{2e^{2x}(x - 1) + 3e^x}$$

3. (a) The differential equation is a homogeneous second-order linear differential equation with constant coefficients. Write the characteristic equation.

$$r^2 + 2r + 2 = 0$$

This is a quadratic equation of the form $ar^2 + br + c = 0$ where $a = 1$, $b = 2$, and $c = 2$.

Solve for r.

$$r = \frac{-b \pm \sqrt{b^2 - 4ac}}{2a}$$
$$= \frac{-2 \pm \sqrt{(2)^2 - (4)(1)(2)}}{(2)(1)}$$
$$= \frac{-2 \pm \sqrt{4 - 8}}{2}$$
$$= \frac{-2 \pm \sqrt{-4}}{2}$$
$$= \frac{-2 \pm 2\sqrt{-1}}{2}$$
$$= -1 \pm \sqrt{-1}$$
$$= -1 \pm i$$
$$r_1 = -1 + i \text{ and } r_2 = 1 - i$$

Since the roots are imaginary and of the form $\alpha + i\omega$ and $\alpha - i\omega$ where $\alpha = -1$ and $\omega = 1$, the general form of the solution is given by

$$x(t) = A_1 e^{\alpha t}\cos \omega t + A_2 e^{\alpha t}\sin \omega t$$
$$= A_1 e^{-1t}\cos (1t) + A_2 e^{-1t}\sin (1t)$$
$$= A_1 e^{-t}\cos t + A_2 e^{-t}\sin t$$

Apply the initial conditions $x(0) = 0$ and $x'(0) = 1$ to solve for A_1 and A_2.

First, apply the initial condition $x(0) = 0$.

$$x(t) = A_1 e^0 \cos 0 + A_2 e^0 \sin 0 = 0$$
$$A_1(1)(1) + A_2(1)(0) = 0$$
$$A_1 = 0$$

Substituting, the solution of the differential equation becomes

$$x(t) = A_2 e^{-t} \sin t$$

To apply the second initial condition, take the first derivative.

$$x'(t) = \frac{d}{dt}\left(A_2 e^{-t}\sin t\right)$$
$$= A_2 \frac{d}{dt}\left(e^{-t}\sin t\right)$$
$$= A_2 \left(\sin t \frac{d}{dt}\left(e^{-t}\right) + e^{-t}\frac{d}{dt}\sin t\right)$$
$$= A_2 \left(\sin t(-e^{-t}) + e^{-t}(\cos t)\right)$$
$$= A_2 \left(e^{-t}\right)(-\sin t + \cos t)$$

Apply the initial condition, $x'(0) = 1$.

$$x(0) = A_2\left(e^0\right)(-\sin 0 + \cos 0) = 1$$
$$A_2(1)(0 + 1) = 1$$
$$A_2 = 1$$

The solution is

$$x(t) = A_2 e^{-t}\sin t$$
$$= (1)e^{-t}\sin t$$
$$= \boxed{e^{-t}\sin t}$$

(b) To determine the natural frequency, set the damping term to zero. The equation has the form

$$x'' + 2x = 0$$

This equation has a general solution of the form

$$x(t) = x_0 \cos \omega t + \left(\frac{v_0}{\omega}\right)\sin \omega t$$

ω is the natural frequency. Given the equation $x'' + 2x = 0$, the characteristic equation is

$$r^2 + 2 = 0$$
$$r = \sqrt{-2}$$
$$= \pm\sqrt{2}i$$

Since the roots are imaginary and of the form $\alpha + i\omega$ and $\alpha - i\omega$ where $\alpha = 0$ and $\omega = \sqrt{2}$, the general form of the solution is given by

$$x(t) = A_1 e^{\alpha t}\cos \omega t + A_2 e^{\alpha t}\sin \omega t$$
$$= A_1 e^{0t}\cos \sqrt{2}t + A_2 e^{0t}\sin \sqrt{2}t$$
$$= A_1(1)\cos \sqrt{2}t + A_2(1)\sin \sqrt{2}t$$
$$= A_1 \cos \sqrt{2}t + A_2 \sin \sqrt{2}t$$

Apply the initial conditions, $x(0) = 0$ and $x'(0) = 1$ to solve for A_1 and A_2. Applying the initial condition $x(0) = 0$ gives

$$x(0) = A_1 \cos\left(\sqrt{2}\right)(0) + A_2 \sin\left(\sqrt{2}\right)(0) = 0$$
$$A_1 \cos 0 + A_2 \sin 0 = 0$$
$$A_1(1) + A_2(0) = 0$$
$$A_1 = 0$$

Substituting, the solution of the different equation becomes

$$x(t) = A_2 \sin \sqrt{2}t$$

To apply the second initial condition, take the first derivative.

$$x'(t) = \frac{d}{dt}\left(A_2 \sin \sqrt{2}t\right)$$
$$= A_2\sqrt{2}\cos \sqrt{2}t$$

Apply the second initial condition, $x'(0) = 1$.

$$x'(0) = A_2\sqrt{2}\cos\left(\sqrt{2}\right)(0) = 1$$
$$A_2\sqrt{2}\cos(0) = 1$$
$$A_2(\sqrt{2})(1) = 1$$
$$A_2\sqrt{2} = 1$$
$$A_2 = \frac{1}{\sqrt{2}} = \frac{\sqrt{2}}{2}$$

Substituting, the undamped solution becomes

$$x(t) = \left(\frac{\sqrt{2}}{2}\right)\sin \sqrt{2}t$$

Therefore, the undamped natural frequency is $\boxed{\omega = \sqrt{2}.}$

(c) The amplitude of the oscillation is the maximum displacement.

Take the derivative of the solution, $x(t) = e(-t)\sin t$.

$$x'(t) = \frac{d}{dt}\left(e^{-t}\sin t\right)$$
$$= \sin t\frac{d}{dt}\left(e^{-t}\right) + e^{-t}\frac{d}{dt}\sin t$$
$$= \sin(t-1)\left(e^{-t}\right) + e^{-t}\cos t$$
$$= e^{-t}\cos t - \sin t$$

The maximum displacement occurs at $x'(t) = 0$.

Since $e^{-t} \neq 0$ except as t approaches infinity,

$$\cos t - \sin t = 0$$
$$\tan t = 1$$
$$t = \tan^{-1}(1)$$
$$= 0.785 \text{ rad}$$

At $t = 0.785$ rad, the displacement is maximum. Substitute into the orginal solution to obtain a value for the maximum displacement.

$$x(0.785) = e^{-0.785}\sin(0.785)$$
$$= 0.322$$

The amplitude is $\boxed{0.322.}$

(d) (An alternate solution using Laplace transforms follows this solution.) The application of a lateral wind load with the form $\sin t$ revises the differential equation to the form
$$x'' + 2x' + 2x = \sin t$$

Express the solution as the sum of the complementary x_c and particular x_p solutions.

$$x(t) = x_c(t) + x_p(t)$$

From part (a),

$$x_c(t) = A_1 e^{-t}\cos t + A_2 e^{-t}\sin t$$

The general form of the particular solution is given by

$$x_p(t) = x^s(A_3 \cos t + A_4 \sin t)$$

Determine the value of s; check to see if the terms of the particular solution solve the homogeneous equation.

Examine the term $A_3 \cos(t)$.

Take the first derivative.

$$\frac{d}{dx}(A_3 \cos t) = -A_3 \sin t$$

Take the second derivative.

$$\frac{d}{dx}\left(\frac{d}{dx}(A_3 \cos t)\right) = \frac{d}{dx}(-A_3 \sin t)$$
$$= -A_3\cos t$$

Substitute the terms into the homogenous equation.

$$x'' + 2x' + 2x = -A_3 \cos t + (2)(-A_3 \sin t)$$
$$+ (2)(-A_3 \cos t)$$
$$= A_3 \cos t - 2A_3 \sin t \neq 0$$

Except for the trival solution $A_3 = 0$, the term $A_3\cos t$ does not solve the homogenous equation.

Examine the second term $A_4 \sin t$.

Take the first derivative.

$$\frac{d}{dx}(A_4 \sin t) = A_4 \cos t$$

Take the second derivative.

$$\frac{d}{dx}\left(\frac{d}{dx}(A_4 \sin t)\right) = \frac{d}{dx}(A_4\cos t)$$
$$= -A_4 \sin t$$

Substitute the terms into the homogenous equation.

$$x'' + 2x' + 2x = -A_4 \sin t + (2)(A_4\cos t)$$
$$+ (2)(A_4 \sin t)$$
$$= A_4 \sin t + 2A_4\cos t \neq 0$$

Except for the trival solution $A_4 = 0$, the term $A_4 \sin t$ does not solve the homogenous equation.

Neither of the terms satisfy the homogenous equation $s = 0$; therefore, the particular solution is of the form

$$x_p(t) = A_3 \cos t + A_4 \sin t$$

Use the method of undetermined coefficients to solve for A_3 and A_4. Take the first derivative.

$$x'_p(t) = \frac{d}{dx}(A_3 \cos t + A_4 \sin t)$$
$$= -A_3 \sin t + A_4 \cos t$$

Take the second derivative.

$$x''_p(t) = \frac{d}{dx}\left(\frac{d}{dx}(A_3 \cos t + A_4 \sin t)\right)$$
$$= \frac{d}{dx}(-A_3 \sin t + A_4 \cos t)$$
$$= -A_3 \cos t - A_4 \sin t$$

Substitute the expressions for the derivatives into the differential equation.

$$x'' + 2x' + 2x = (-A_3 \cos t + A_4 \sin t)$$
$$+ (2)(-A_3 \sin t + A_4 \cos t)$$
$$+ (2)(A_3 \cos t + A_4 \sin t)$$
$$= \sin t$$

Rearranging terms gives

$$(-A_3 + 2A_4 + 2A_3)\cos t$$
$$+(-A_4 - 2A_3 + 2A_4)\sin t = \sin t$$
$$(A_3 + 2A_4)\cos t + (-2A_3 + A_4)\sin t = \sin t$$

Equating coefficients gives

$$A_3 + 2A_4 = 0$$
$$-2A_3 + A_4 = 1$$

Multiplying the first equation by 2 and adding equations gives

$$A_3 + 2A_4 = 0$$
$$+(-2A_3 + A_4) = 1$$
$$\overline{5A_4 = 1 \ \text{or} \ A_4 = \tfrac{1}{5}}$$

From the first equation for $A_4 = {}^1/_5$, $A_3 + (2)({}^1/_5) = 0$ and $A_3 = -{}^2/_5$.

Substituting for the coefficients, the particular solution becomes

$$x_p(t) = -\tfrac{2}{5}\cos t + \tfrac{1}{5}\sin t$$

Combining the complementary and particular solutions gives

$$x(t) = x_c(t) + x_p(t)$$
$$= A_1 e^{-t}\cos t + A_2 e^{-t}\sin t - \tfrac{2}{5}\cos t + \tfrac{1}{5}\sin t$$

Apply the initial conditions to solve for the coefficients A_1 and A_2; then apply the first initial condition, $x(0) = 0$.

$$x(t) = A_1 e^0 \cos 0 + A_2 e^0 \sin 0$$
$$- \tfrac{2}{5}\cos 0 + \tfrac{1}{5}\sin 0 = 0$$
$$A_1(1)(1) + A_2(1)(0) + \left(-\tfrac{2}{5}\right)(1) + \left(\tfrac{1}{5}\right)(0) = 0$$
$$A_1 - \tfrac{2}{5} = 0$$
$$A_1 = \tfrac{2}{5}$$

Substituting for A_1, the solution becomes

$$x(t) = \tfrac{2}{5}e^{-t}\cos t + A_2 e^{-t}\sin t - \tfrac{2}{5}\cos t + \tfrac{1}{5}\sin t$$

Take the first derivative.

$$x'(t) = \frac{d}{dx}\left(\tfrac{2}{5}e^{-t}\cos t + A_2 e^{-t}\right)\sin t$$
$$+ \left(\left(-\tfrac{2}{5}\right)\cot t + \tfrac{1}{5}\sin t\right)$$
$$= \left(\tfrac{2}{5}\right)\left(-e^{-t}\cos t - e^{-t}\sin t\right)$$
$$+ A_2\left(-e(-t)\sin t + e(-t)\cos t\right)$$
$$+ \left(-\tfrac{2}{5}\right)(-\sin t) + \tfrac{1}{5}\cos t$$

Apply the second initial condition, $x'(0) = 1$.

$$x'(0) = \left(\tfrac{2}{5}\right)\left(-e^0\cos 0 - e^0 \sin 0\right)$$
$$+ A_2\left(-e^0\sin 0 + e^0\cos 0\right)$$
$$+ \left(-\tfrac{2}{5}\right)(-\sin 0) + \tfrac{1}{5}\cos 0$$
$$= 1$$

$$\left(\tfrac{2}{5}\right)\left(-(1)(1) - (1)(0)\right) + A_2\left(-(1)(0)\right.$$
$$\left.+(1)(1)\right) + \left(\left(-\tfrac{2}{5}\right)(0) + \left(\tfrac{1}{5}\right)(1)\right) = 1$$
$$\left(\tfrac{2}{5}\right)(-1) + A_2(1) + \left(\tfrac{1}{5}\right) = 1$$
$$A_2 = \tfrac{6}{5}$$

Substituting for A_2, the solution becomes

$$x(t) = \tfrac{2}{5}e^{-t}\cos t + \tfrac{6}{5}e^{-t}\sin t$$
$$- \tfrac{2}{5}\cos t + \tfrac{1}{5}\sin t$$

(d) *Alternate solution:*

Use the Laplace transform method.

$$x'' + 2x' + 2x = \sin t$$
$$\mathcal{L}(x'') + 2\mathcal{L}(x') + 2\mathcal{L}(x) = \mathcal{L}(\sin t)$$
$$s^2\mathcal{L}(x) - 1 + 2s\mathcal{L}(x) + 2\mathcal{L}(x) = \frac{1}{s^2 + 1}$$
$$\mathcal{L}(x)(s^2 + 2s + 2) - 1 = \frac{1}{s^2 + 1}$$

$$\mathcal{L}(x) = \frac{1}{s^2 + 2s + 2} + \frac{1}{(s^2 + 1)(s^2 + 2s + 2)}$$
$$= \frac{1}{(s + 1)^2 + 1} + \frac{1}{(s^2 + 1)(s^2 + 2s + 2)}$$

Use partial fractions to expand the second term.

$$\frac{1}{(s^2 + 1)(s^2 + 2s + 2)} = \frac{A_1 + B_1 s}{s^2 + 1} + \frac{A_2 + B_2 s}{s^2 + 2s + 2}$$

Cross multiply.

$$\begin{aligned} &A_1 s^2 + 2A_1 s + 2A_1 + B_1 s^3 + 2B_1 s^2 \\ = &\frac{+2B_1 s + A_2 s^2 + A_2 + B_2 s^3 + B_2 s}{(s^2 + 1)(s^2 + 2s + 2)} \end{aligned}$$

$$\begin{aligned} &s^3(B_1 + B_2) + s^2(A_1 + A_2 + 2B_1) \\ = &\frac{+s(2A_1 + 2B_1 + B_2) + 2A_1 + A_2}{(s^2 + 1)(s^2 + 2s + 2)} \end{aligned}$$

Compare numerators to obtain the following four simultaneous equations.

$$\begin{aligned} B_1 + B_2 &= 0 \\ A_1 + A_2 + 2B_1 &= 0 \\ 2A_1 + 2B_1 + B_2 &= 0 \\ 2A_1 + A_2 &= 1 \end{aligned}$$

Use Cramer's rule to find A_1.

$$A_1 = \frac{\begin{vmatrix} 0 & 0 & 1 & 1 \\ 0 & 1 & 2 & 0 \\ 0 & 0 & 2 & 1 \\ 1 & 1 & 0 & 0 \end{vmatrix}}{\begin{vmatrix} 0 & 0 & 1 & 1 \\ 1 & 1 & 2 & 0 \\ 2 & 0 & 2 & 1 \\ 2 & 1 & 0 & 0 \end{vmatrix}} = \frac{-1}{-5} = \frac{1}{5}$$

The rest of the coefficients are found similarly.

$$A_1 = \tfrac{1}{5}$$
$$A_2 = \tfrac{3}{5}$$
$$B_1 = -\tfrac{2}{5}$$
$$B_2 = \tfrac{2}{5}$$

Then,

$$\mathcal{L}(x) = \frac{1}{(s+1)^2+1} + \frac{\tfrac{1}{5}}{s^2+1} + \frac{-\tfrac{2}{5}s}{s^2+1}$$
$$+ \frac{\tfrac{3}{5}}{s^2+2s+2} + \frac{\tfrac{2}{5}s}{s^2+2s+2}$$

Take the inverse transform.

$$x(t) = \mathcal{L}^{-1}\{\mathcal{L}(x)\}$$
$$= e^{-t}\sin t + \tfrac{1}{5}\sin t - \tfrac{2}{5}\cos t + \tfrac{3}{5}e^{-t}\sin t$$
$$+ \tfrac{2}{5}(e^{-t}\cos t - e^{-t}\sin t)$$
$$= \boxed{\tfrac{6}{5}e^{-t}\sin t + \tfrac{2}{5}e^{-t}\cos t + \tfrac{1}{5}\sin t - \tfrac{2}{5}\cos t}$$

4. *Customary U.S. Solution*

The differential equation is given as

$$m'(t) = a(t) - \frac{m(t)o(t)}{V(t)}$$

$a(t)$ = rate of addition of chemical
$m(t)$ = mass of chemical at time t
$o(t)$ = volumetric flow out of the lagoon
$\quad$ (= 30 gal/min)
$V(t)$ = volume in the lagoon at time t

Water flows into the lagoon at a rate of 30 gal/min, and a water-chemical mix flows out of the lagoon at rate of 30 gal/min. Therefore, the volume of the lagoon at time t is equal to the initial volume.

$$V(t) = \left(\frac{\pi}{4}\right)(\text{diameter of lagoon})^2(\text{depth of lagoon})$$
$$= \left(\frac{\pi}{4}\right)(120\text{ ft})^2(10\text{ ft})$$
$$= 113{,}097\text{ ft}^3$$

Use a conversion factor of 7.48 gal/ft^3.

$$o(t) = \frac{30\ \frac{\text{gal}}{\text{min}}}{7.48\ \frac{\text{gal}}{\text{ft}^3}}$$
$$= 4.01\text{ ft}^3/\text{min}$$

Substituting into the general form of the differential equation gives

$$m'(t) = a(t) - \frac{m(t)o(t)}{V(t)}$$
$$= (0) - m(t)\left(\frac{4.01\ \frac{\text{ft}^3}{\text{min}}}{113{,}097\text{ ft}^3}\right)$$
$$= -\left(\frac{3.55\times10^{-5}}{\text{min}}\right)m(t)$$
$$m'(t) + \left(\frac{3.55\times10^{-5}}{\text{min}}\right)m(t) = 0$$

The differential equation of the problem has a characteristic equation.

$$r + \frac{3.55\times10^{-5}}{\text{min}} = 0$$
$$r = -3.55\times10^{-5}/\text{min}$$

The general form of the solution is given by

$$m(t) = Ae^{rt}$$

Substituting for the root, r, gives

$$m(t) = Ae^{\left(\frac{-3.55\times10^{-5}}{\text{min}}\right)t}$$

Apply the initial condition $m(0) = 90$ lbm at time $t = 0$.

$$m(0) = Ae^{\left(\frac{-3.55\times10^{-5}}{\text{min}}\right)(0)} = 90\text{ lbm}$$
$$Ae^0 = 90\text{ lbm}$$
$$A = 90\text{ lbm}$$

Therefore,

$$m(t) = (90\text{ lbm})\,e^{\left(\frac{-3.55\times10^{-5}}{\text{min}}\right)t}$$

Solve for t.

$$\frac{m(t)}{90\text{ lbm}} = e^{\left(\frac{-3.55\times10^{-5}}{\text{min}}\right)t}$$
$$\ln\left(\frac{m(t)}{90\text{ lbm}}\right) = \ln\left(e^{\left(\frac{-3.55\times10^{-5}}{\text{min}}\right)t}\right)$$
$$= \left(\frac{-3.55\times10^{-5}}{\text{min}}\right)t$$
$$t = \frac{\ln\left(\frac{m(t)}{90\text{ lbm}}\right)}{\frac{-3.55\times10^{-5}}{\text{min}}}$$

The mass of the water in the lagoon is given by

$$m_i = V\rho$$

$$= (113{,}097 \text{ ft}^3)\left(62.4 \,\frac{\text{lbm}}{\text{ft}^3}\right)$$

$$= 7.05 \times 10^6 \text{ lbm}$$

The final mass of chemicals is achieved at a concentration of 1 ppb or

$$m_f = \frac{7.06 \times 10^6 \text{ lbm}}{1 \times 10^9}$$

$$= 7.06 \times 10^{-3} \text{ lbm}$$

Find the time required to achieve a mass of 7.06×10^{-3} lbm.

$$t = \left(\frac{\ln\left(\dfrac{m(t)}{90 \text{ lbm}}\right)}{\dfrac{-3.55 \times 10^{-5}}{\text{min}}}\right)\left(\frac{1 \text{ hr}}{60 \text{ min}}\right)\left(\frac{1 \text{ day}}{24 \text{ hr}}\right)$$

$$= \left(\frac{\ln\left(\dfrac{7.06 \times 10^{-3} \text{ lbm}}{90 \text{ lbm}}\right)}{\dfrac{-3.55 \times 10^{-5}}{\text{min}}}\right)\left(\frac{1 \text{ hr}}{60 \text{ min}}\right)\left(\frac{1 \text{ day}}{24 \text{ hr}}\right)$$

$$= \boxed{185 \text{ days}}$$

SI Solution

The differential equation is given as

$$m'(t) = a(t) - \frac{m(t)o(t)}{V(t)}$$

$a(t)$ = rate of addition of chemical
$m(t)$ = mass of chemical at time t
$o(t)$ = volumetric flow out of the lagoon
$\quad\quad (= 115 \text{ L/min})$
$V(t)$ = volume in the lagoon at time t

Water flows into the lagoon at a rate of 115 L/min, and a water-chemical mix flows out of the lagoon at rate of 115 L/min. Therefore, the volume of the lagoon at time t is equal to the initial volume.

$$V(t) = \left(\frac{\pi}{4}\right)(\text{diameter of lagoon})^2(\text{depth of lagoon})$$

$$= \left(\frac{\pi}{4}\right)(35 \text{ m})^2(3 \text{ m})$$

$$= 2886 \text{ m}^3$$

Using a conversion factor of 1 m³/1000 L gives

$$o(t) = \left(115 \,\frac{\text{L}}{\text{min}}\right)\left(\frac{1 \text{ m}^3}{1000 \text{ L}}\right)$$

$$= 0.115 \text{ m}^3/\text{min}$$

Substitute into the general form of the differential equation.

$$m'(t) = a(t) - \frac{m(t)o(t)}{V(t)}$$

$$= 0 - m(t)\left(\frac{0.115 \,\dfrac{\text{m}^3}{\text{min}}}{2886 \text{ m}^3}\right)$$

$$= -\left(\frac{3.985 \times 10^{-5}}{\text{min}}\right)m(t)$$

$$m'(t) + \left(\frac{3.985 \times 10^{-5}}{\text{min}}\right)m(t) = 0$$

The differential equation of the problem has the following characteristic equation.

$$r + \frac{3.985 \times 10^{-5}}{\text{min}} = 0$$

$$r = -3.985 \times 10^{-5}/\text{min}$$

The general form of the solution is given by

$$m(t) = Ae^{rt}$$

Substituting in for the root, r, gives

$$m(t) = Ae^{\left(\frac{-3.985 \times 10^{-5}}{\text{min}}\right)t}$$

Apply the initial condition $m(0) = 40$ kg at time $t = 0$.

$$m(0) = Ae^{\left(\frac{-3.985 \times 10^{-5}}{\text{min}}\right)(0)} = 40 \text{ kg}$$

$$Ae^0 = 40 \text{ kg}$$

$$A = 40 \text{ kg}$$

Therefore,

$$m(t) = (40 \text{ kg})e^{\left(\frac{-3.985 \times 10^{-5}}{\text{min}}\right)t}$$

Solve for t.

$$\frac{m(t)}{40 \text{ kg}} = e^{\left(\frac{-3.985 \times 10^{-5}}{\text{min}}\right)t}$$

$$\ln\left(\frac{m(t)}{40 \text{ kg}}\right) = \ln\left(e^{\left(\frac{-3.985 \times 10^{-5}}{\text{min}}\right)t}\right)$$

$$= \left(\frac{-3.985 \times 10^{-5}}{\text{min}}\right)t$$

$$t = \ln\left(\frac{\dfrac{m(t)}{40 \text{ kg}}}{\dfrac{-3.985 \times 10^{-5}}{\text{min}}}\right)$$

The mass of water in the lagoon is given by

$$m_i = V\rho$$
$$= (2886 \text{ m}^3)\left(1000 \ \frac{\text{kg}}{\text{m}^3}\right)$$
$$= 2.886 \times 10^6 \text{ kg}$$

The final mass of chemicals is achieved at a concentration of 1 ppb or

$$m_f = \frac{2.886 \times 10^6 \text{ kg}}{1 \times 10^9}$$
$$= 2.886 \times 10^{-3} \text{ kg}$$

Find the time required to achieve a mass of 2.886×10^{-3} kg.

$$t = \left(\frac{\ln\left(\frac{m(t)}{40 \text{ kg}}\right)}{\frac{-3.985 \times 10^{-5}}{\text{min}}}\right)\left(\frac{1 \text{ h}}{60 \text{ min}}\right)\left(\frac{1 \text{ day}}{24 \text{ h}}\right)$$

$$= \left(\frac{\ln\left(\frac{2.886 \times 10^{-3} \text{ kg}}{40 \text{ kg}}\right)}{\frac{-3.985 \times 10^{-5}}{\text{min}}}\right)\left(\frac{1 \text{ h}}{60 \text{ min}}\right)\left(\frac{1 \text{ day}}{24 \text{ h}}\right)$$

$$= \boxed{166 \text{ days}}$$

11 Probability and Statistical Analysis of Data

Mathematics

1. For an exponential distribution function, the mean is given as

$$\mu = \frac{1}{\lambda}$$

For a mean of 23,

$$\mu = 23 = \frac{1}{\lambda}$$
$$\lambda = 0.0435$$

For an exponential distribution function,

$$p\{X < x\} = F(x) = 1 - e^{-\lambda x}$$
$$p\{x > X\} = 1 - p\{X < x\}$$
$$= 1 - F(x)$$
$$= 1 - \left(1 - e^{-\lambda x}\right)$$
$$= e^{-\lambda x}$$

The probability of a random vehicle being processed in 25 sec or more is given by

$$p\{x > 25\} = e^{-(0.0435)(25)}$$
$$= e^{-1.0875}$$
$$= \boxed{0.337}$$

2. Find the average.

$$\bar{x} = \frac{\sum x_i}{n}$$
$$= \frac{1249.529 + 1249.494 + 1249.384 + 1249.348}{4}$$
$$= 1249.439$$

Since the sample population is small, $n < 50$, use the sample standard deviation.

$$s = \sqrt{\frac{\sum(x_i - \bar{x})^2}{n-1}}$$
$$= \sqrt{\frac{\begin{array}{c}(1249.529-1249.439)^2 + (1249.494-1249.439)^2\\ +(1249.384-1249.439)^2 + (1249.348-1249.439)^2\end{array}}{4-1}}$$
$$= 0.08647$$

From the standard deviation table, a 90% confidence limit falls within $1.645s$ of $\bar{x}$.

$$1249.439 \pm (1.645)(0.08647) = 1249.439 \pm 0.142$$

Therefore, (1249.297, 1249.581) is a 90% confidence range.

(a) By observation, all the readings fall within the 90% confidence range.

(b) All readings are acceptable.

(c) Any readings outside the range determined for the 90% confidence limit are unacceptable.

(d) The unbiased estimate of the most probable distance is 1249.439.

(e) The error for the 90% confidence range is 0.142.

(f) If the surveying crew places a marker, measures a distance x, places a second marker, and then measures the same distance x back to the original marker, the ending point should coincide with the original marker. If, due to measurement errors, the ending and starting points do not coincide, the difference is the closure error.

In this example, the survey crew moves around the four sides of a square, so there are two measurements in the x-direction and two measurements in the y-direction. If the errors E_1 and E_2 are known for two measurements, x_1 and x_2, the error associated with the sum or difference $x_1 \pm x_2$ is

$$E\{x_1 \pm x_2\} = \sqrt{E_1^2 + E_2^2}$$

In this case, the error in the x-direction is

$$E_x = \sqrt{(0.1422)^2 + (0.1422)^2}$$
$$= 0.2011$$

The error in the y-direction is calculated the same way and is also 0.2011. E_x and E_y are combined by the Pythagorean theorem to yield

$$E_{\text{closure}} = \sqrt{(0.2011)^2 + (0.2011)^2}$$
$$= \boxed{0.2844}$$

(g) In surveying, error may be expressed as a fraction of one or more legs of the traverse. Assume that the total of all four legs is to be used as the basis.

$$\frac{0.2844}{(4)(1249)} = \boxed{\frac{1}{17,567}}$$

PROFESSIONAL PUBLICATIONS, INC. BELMONT, CA

(h) In surveying, a second-order error is smaller than 1/10,000. The error of 1/17,567 is smaller than the second-order error; therefore, the error is within the second-order accuracy.

(i) An experiment is accurate if it is unchanged by experimental error. Precision is concerned with the repeatability of the experimental results. If an experiment is repeated with identical results, the experiment is said to be precise. However, it is possible to have a highly precise experiment with a large bias.

(j) A systematic error is one that is always present and is unchanged from sample to sample. For example, a steel tape that is 0.02 ft short introduces a systematic error.

3. ((a) and (d)) Tabulate the frequency distribution data.

(Note that the lowest speed is 20 mi/hr and the highest speed is 48 mi/hr; therefore, the range is 28 mi/hr. Choose 10 cells with a width of 3 mi/hr.)

midpoint	interval (mi/hr)	frequency	cumulative frequency	cumulative percent
21	20–22	1	1	3
24	23–25	3	4	10
27	26–28	5	9	23
30	29–31	8	17	43
33	32–34	3	20	50
36	35–37	4	24	60
39	38–40	3	27	68
42	41–43	8	35	88
45	44–46	3	38	95
48	47–49	2	40	100

(b)

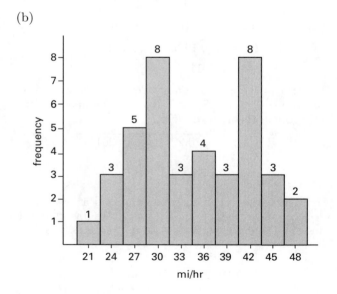

(c)

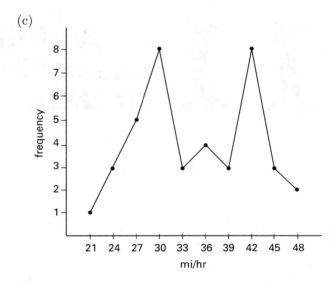

(e)

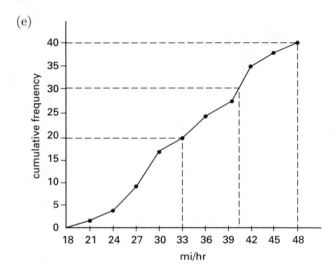

(f) From the cumulative frequency graph in part (e), the upper quartile speed occurs at 30 cars or 75%, which corresponds to approximately 40 mi/hr.

(g) The mode occurs at two speeds (the frequency at each of the two speeds is 8), which are 30 mi/hr and 42 mi/hr.

From the cumulative frequency chart, the median occurs at 50% or 20 cars and corresponds to 33 mi/hr.

$$\sum x_i = 1390 \text{ mi/hr}$$
$$n = 40$$

The mean is computed as

$$\overline{x} = \frac{\sum x_i}{n}$$

$$= \frac{1390 \dfrac{\text{mi}}{\text{hr}}}{40}$$

$$= \boxed{34.75 \text{ mi/hr}}$$

(h) The standard deviation of the sample data is given as

$$\sigma = \sqrt{\frac{\sum x^2}{N} - \mu^2}$$

$$\sum x^2 = 50{,}496 \text{ mi}^2/\text{hr}^2$$

Use the sample mean as an unbiased estimator of the population mean, μ.

$$\sigma = \sqrt{\frac{\sum x^2}{N} - \mu^2}$$

$$= \sqrt{\frac{50{,}496 \dfrac{\text{mi}^2}{\text{hr}^2}}{40} - \left(34.75 \dfrac{\text{mi}}{\text{hr}}\right)^2}$$

$$= \boxed{7.405 \text{ mi/hr}}$$

(i) The standard deviation is given by

$$s = \sqrt{\frac{\sum x^2 - \dfrac{(\sum x)^2}{n}}{n-1}}$$

$$= \sqrt{\frac{50{,}496 \dfrac{\text{mi}^2}{\text{hr}^2} - \dfrac{\left(1390 \dfrac{\text{mi}}{\text{hr}}\right)^2}{40}}{40-1}}$$

$$= \boxed{7.500 \text{ mi/hr}}$$

(j) The sample variance is given by the square of the sample standard deviation.

$$s^2 = \left(7.500 \frac{\text{mi}}{\text{hr}}\right)^2$$

$$= \boxed{56.25 \text{ mi}^2/\text{hr}^2}$$

4. (a) The distribution is a Poisson distribution with an average of $\lambda = 20$.

The probability for a Poisson distribution is given by

$$p\{x\} = f(x) = \frac{e^{-\lambda}\lambda^x}{x!}$$

The probability of 17 cars is

$$p\{x = 17\} = f(17) = \frac{e^{-20} \times 20^{17}}{17!}$$

$$= \boxed{0.076 \quad (7.6\%)}$$

(b) The probability of three or fewer cars is given by

$$p\{x \leq 3\} = p\{x = 0\} + p\{x = 1\} + p\{x = 2\} + p\{x = 3\}$$

$$= f(0) + f(1) + f(2) + f(3)$$

$$= \frac{e^{-20} \times 20^0}{0!} + \frac{e^{-20} \times 20^1}{1!} + \frac{e^{-20} \times 20^2}{2!} + \frac{e^{-20} \times 20^3}{3!}$$

$$= (2 \times 10^{-9}) + (4.1 \times 10^{-8}) + (4.12 \times 10^{-7}) + (2.75 \times 10^{-6})$$

$$= \boxed{3.2 \times 10^{-6} \quad (3.2 \times 10^{-4}\%)}$$

5. This is a typical hypothesis test of two sample population means. The two populations are the original population the manufacturer used to determine the 1600 hr average life value and the new population the sample was taken from. The mean ($\overline{x} = 1520$ hr) of the sample and its standard deviation ($s = 120$ hr) are known, but the mean and standard deviation of a population of average lifetimes are unknown.

(a) Assume that the average lifetime population mean and the sample mean are identical.

$$\overline{x} = \mu = \boxed{1520 \text{ hr}}$$

(b) The standard deviation of the average lifetime population is

$$\sigma_{\overline{x}} = \frac{s}{\sqrt{n}} = \frac{120}{\sqrt{100}} = 12$$

The manufacturer can be reasonably sure that the claim of a 1600 hr average life is justified if the average test life is near 1600 hr. "Reasonably sure" must be evaluated based on acceptable probability of being incorrect. If the manufacturer is willing to be wrong with a 5% probability, then a 95% confidence level is required.

Since the direction of bias is known, a one-tailed test is required. To determine if the mean has shifted downward, test the hypothesis that 1600 hr is within the 95% limit of a distribution with a mean of 1520 hr and a standard deviation of 12 hr. From a standard normal table, 5% of a standard normal distribution is outside of $z = 1.645$. Therefore, the 95% confidence limit is

$$1520 + (1.645)(12) = 1540$$

The manufacturer can be 95% certain that the average lifetime of the bearings is less than 1600 hr.

If the manufacturer is willing to be wrong with a probability of only 1%, then a 99% confidence limit is required. From the normal table, $z = 2.33$ and the 99% confidence limit is

$$1520 + (2.33)(12) = 1548$$

The manufacturer can be 99% certain that the average bearing life is less than 1600 hr.

6. (a) Plot the data points to determine if the relationship is linear.

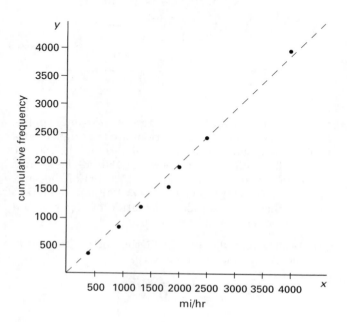

The data appear to be essentially linear. The slope, m, and the y-intercept, b, can be determined using linear regression.

The individual terms are

$$n = 7$$

$$\sum x_i = 400 + 800 + 1250 + 1600 + 2000 + 4000$$
$$= 12{,}550$$

$$\left(\sum x_i\right)^2 = (12{,}550)^2$$
$$= 1.575 \times 10^8$$

$$\bar{x} = \frac{\sum x_i}{n}$$
$$= \frac{12{,}550}{7}$$
$$= 1792.9$$

$$\sum x_i^2 = (400)^2 + (800)^2 + (1250)^2 + (1600)^2$$
$$+ (2000)^2 + (2500)^2 + (4000)^2$$
$$= 3.117 \times 10^7$$

Similarly,

$$\sum y_i = 370 + 780 + 1210 + 1560 + 1980$$
$$+ 2450 + 3950$$
$$= 12{,}300$$

$$\left(\sum y_i\right)^2 = (12{,}300)^2 = 1.513 \times 10^8$$

$$\bar{y} = \frac{\sum y_i}{n} = \frac{12{,}300}{7} = 1757.1$$

$$\sum y_i^2 = (370)^2 + (780)^2 + (1210)^2 + (1560)^2$$
$$+ (1980)^2 + (2450)^2 + (3950)^2$$
$$= 3.017 \times 10^7$$

Also,

$$\sum x_i y_i = (400)(370) + (800)(780) + (1250)(1210)$$
$$+ (1600)(1560) + (2000)(1980)$$
$$+ (2500)(2450) + (4000)(3950)$$
$$= 3.067 \times 10^7$$

The slope is

$$m = \frac{n \sum x_i y_i - \sum x_i \sum y_i}{n \sum x_i^2 - \left(\sum x_i\right)^2}$$
$$= \frac{(7)(3.067 \times 10^7) - (12{,}550)(12{,}300)}{(7)(3.117 \times 10^7) - (12{,}550)^2}$$
$$= 0.994$$

The y intercept is

$$b = \bar{y} - m\bar{x}$$
$$= 1757.1 - (0.994)(1792.9)$$
$$= -25.0$$

The least squares equation of the line is

$$y = mx + b$$
$$= \boxed{0.994x - 25.0}$$

(b) The correlation coefficient is

$$r = \frac{n \sum (x_i y_i) - \left(\sum x_i\right)\left(\sum y_i\right)}{\sqrt{[n \sum x_i^2 - (\sum x_i)^2][n \sum y_i^2 - (\sum y_i)^2]}}$$
$$= \frac{(7)(3.067 \times 10^7) - (12{,}500)(12{,}300)}{\sqrt{\begin{array}{l}[(7)(3.117 \times 10^7) - (12{,}500)^2] \\ \times [(7)(3.017 \times 10^7) - (12{,}300)^2]\end{array}}}$$
$$\approx \boxed{1.00}$$

7. Plotting the data shows that the relationship is nonlinear.

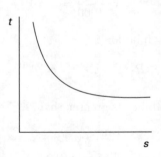

This appears to be an exponential with the form

$$t = ae^{bs}$$

Take the natural log of both sides.

$$\ln t = \ln(ae^{bs})$$
$$= \ln a + \ln(e^{bs})$$
$$= \ln a + bs$$

But, $\ln a$ is just a constant, c.

$$\ln t = c + bs$$

Make the transformation $R = \ln t$.

$$R = c + bs$$

S	R
20	3.76
18	4.95
16	5.95
14	7.00

This is linear.

$$n = 4$$
$$\sum s_i = 20 + 18 + 16 + 14 = 68$$
$$\bar{s} = \frac{\sum s}{n} = \frac{68}{4} = 17$$
$$\sum s_i^2 = (20)^2 + (18)^2 + (16)^2 + (14)^2 = 1176$$
$$\left(\sum s_i\right)^2 = (68)^2 = 4624$$
$$\sum R_i = 3.76 + 4.95 + 5.95 + 7.00 = 21.66$$
$$\bar{R} = \frac{\sum R_i}{n} = \frac{21.66}{4} = 5.415$$
$$\sum R_i^2 = (3.76)^2 + (4.95)^2 + (5.95)^2 + (7.00)^2$$
$$= 123.04$$
$$\left(\sum R_i\right)^2 = (21.66)^2 = 469.16$$
$$\sum s_i R_i = (20)(3.76) + (18)(4.95) + (16)(5.95)$$
$$+ (14)(7.00)$$
$$= 357.5$$

The slope, b, of the transformed line is

$$b = \frac{n\sum s_i R_i - \sum s_i \sum R_i}{n\sum s_i^2 - (\sum s_i)^2}$$
$$= \frac{(4)(357.5) - (68)(21.66)}{(4)(1176) - (68)^2} = -0.536$$

The intercept is

$$c = \bar{R} - b\bar{s} = 5.415 - (-0.536)(17)$$
$$= 14.527$$

The transformed equation is

$$R = c + bs$$
$$= 14.527 - 0.536s$$

$$\boxed{\ln t = 14.527 - 0.536s}$$

8. The first step is to graph the data.

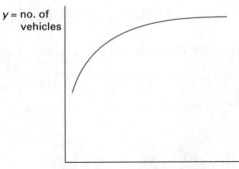

It is assumed that the relationship between the variables has the form $y = a + b\log x$. Therefore, the variable change $z = \log x$ is made, resulting in the following set of data.

z	y
0.301	14.8
0.699	18.0
0.903	20.4
1.079	23.0
1.431	29.9

$$\sum z_i = 4.413$$
$$\sum y_i = 106.1$$
$$\sum z_i^2 = 4.6082$$
$$\sum y_i^2 = 2382.2$$

$$\left(\sum z_i\right)^2 = 19.475$$
$$\left(\sum y_i\right)^2 = 11{,}257.2$$
$$\overline{z} = 0.8826$$
$$\overline{y} = 21.22$$
$$\sum z_i y_i = 103.06$$
$$n = 5$$

The slope is

$$m = \frac{n \sum z_i y_i - \sum z_i \sum y_i}{n \sum z_i^2 - \left(\sum z_i\right)^2}$$
$$= \frac{(5)(103.06) - (4.413)(106.1)}{(5)(4.6082) - 19.475}$$
$$= 13.20$$

The y-intercept is

$$b = \overline{y} - m\overline{z}$$
$$= 21.22 - (13.20)(0.8826)$$
$$= 9.570$$

The resulting equation is

$$y = 9.570 + 13.20z$$

The relationship between x and y is approximately

$$\boxed{y = 9.570 + 13.20 \log x}$$

9.

$$\lambda = \frac{1}{\text{MTTF}}$$
$$= \frac{1}{1000} = 0.001$$

The reliability function is

$$R\{t\} = e^{-\lambda t} = e^{-0.001t}$$

Since the reliability is greater than 99%,

$$e^{-0.001t} > 0.99$$
$$\ln(e^{-0.001t}) > \ln(0.99)$$
$$-0.001t > \ln(0.99)$$
$$t < -1000 \ln(0.99)$$
$$\boxed{t < 10.05}$$

The maximum operating time such that the reliability remains above 99% is 10.05 hr.

13 Numerical Analysis

1. The actual value at $x = 2.7$ is given by

$$y(x) = 3x^{0.93} + 4.2$$
$$y(2.7) = (3)(2.7)^{0.93} + 4.2$$
$$= 11.756$$

At $x = 3$,

$$y(3) = (3)(3)^{0.93} + 4.2$$
$$= 12.534$$

At $x = 2$,

$$y(2) = (3)(2)^{0.93} + 4.2$$
$$= 9.916$$

Use straight-line interpolation.

$$\frac{x_2 - x}{x_2 - x_1} = \frac{y_2 - y}{y_2 - y_1}$$
$$\frac{3 - 2.7}{3 - 2} = \frac{12.534 - y}{12.534 - 9.916}$$
$$y = 11.749$$

The relative error is given by

$$\frac{\text{actual value} - \text{predicted value}}{\text{actual value}} = \frac{11.756 - 11.749}{11.756}$$

$$= \boxed{0.0006 \ (0.06\%)}$$

2. Let $x_1 = 2$; therefore, from the table of data points, $y_1 = 6$. Let $x_2 = 3$; therefore, from the table of data points, $y_2 = 2$.

Let $x = 2.75$. By straight-line interpolation,

$$\frac{x_2 - x}{x_2 - x_1} = \frac{y_2 - y}{y_2 - y_1}$$
$$\frac{3 - 2.75}{3 - 2} = \frac{2 - y}{2 - 6}$$

$$\boxed{y = 3}$$

14 Fluid Properties

1. *Customary U.S. Solution*

$$p_{\text{gage}} = -8.7 \text{ lbf/in}^2$$

$$p_{\text{atmospheric}} = 14.7 \text{ lbf/in}^2$$

The relationship between absolute, gage, and atmospheric pressure is given by

$$p_{\text{absolute}} = p_{\text{gage}} + p_{\text{atmospheric}}$$

$$= -8.7 \frac{\text{lbf}}{\text{in}^2} + 14.7 \frac{\text{lbf}}{\text{in}^2}$$

$$= \boxed{6 \text{ lbf/in}^2 \quad (6 \text{ psi})}$$

SI Solution

$$p_{\text{gage}} = -60 \text{ kPa}$$

$$p_{\text{atmospheric}} = 101.3 \text{ kPa}$$

The relationship between absolute, gage, and atmospheric pressure is given by

$$p_{\text{absolute}} = p_{\text{gage}} + p_{\text{atmospheric}}$$

$$= -60 \text{ kPa} + 101.3 \text{ kPa}$$

$$= \boxed{41.3 \text{ kPa}}$$

2. *Customary U.S. Solution*

For air at 14.7 psia and 80°F, the absolute viscosity independent of pressure is $\mu = 3.85 \times 10^{-7}$ lbf-sec/ft^2.

Determine the density of air at 70 psia and 80°F. (Assume an ideal gas.)

$$\rho = \frac{p}{RT}$$

For air, $R = 53.3$ lbf-ft/lbm-°R.

Substituting gives

$$\rho = \frac{\left(70 \frac{\text{lbf}}{\text{in}^2}\right)\left(144 \frac{\text{in}^2}{\text{ft}^2}\right)}{\left(53.3 \frac{\text{lbf-ft}}{\text{lbm-°R}}\right)(80°\text{F} + 460)}$$

$$= 0.350 \text{ lbm/ft}^3$$

The kinematic viscosity, ν, is related to the absolute viscosity by

$$\nu = \frac{\mu g_c}{\rho}$$

$$= \frac{\left(3.85 \times 10^{-7} \frac{\text{lbf-sec}}{\text{ft}^2}\right)\left(32.2 \frac{\text{lbm-ft}}{\text{lbf-sec}^2}\right)}{0.350 \frac{\text{lbm}}{\text{ft}^3}}$$

$$= \boxed{3.54 \times 10^{-5} \text{ ft}^2/\text{sec}}$$

SI Solution

For air at 480 kPa and 27°C, the absolute viscosity independent of pressure is $\mu = 1.84 \times 10^{-5}$ Pa·s.

Determine the density of air at 480 kPa and 27°C. (Assume an ideal gas.)

$$\rho = \frac{p}{RT}$$

For air, $R = 287$ J/kg·K.

Substituting gives

$$\rho = \frac{(480 \text{ kPa})\left(1000 \frac{\text{Pa}}{\text{kPa}}\right)}{\left(287 \frac{\text{J}}{\text{kg·K}}\right)(27°\text{C} + 273)}$$

$$= 5.575 \text{ kg/m}^3$$

The kinematic viscosity, ν, is related to the absolute viscosity by

$$\nu = \frac{\mu}{\rho}$$

$$= \frac{1.84 \times 10^{-5} \text{ Pa·s}}{5.575 \frac{\text{kg}}{\text{m}^3}}$$

$$= \boxed{3.30 \times 10^{-6} \text{ m}^2/\text{s}}$$

15 Fluid Statics

1. *Customary U.S. Solution*

Assume the weight of the blimp structure is small (negligible) compared with the weight of the hydrogen.

The lift of the hydrogen-filled blimp (F_{lift}) is equal to the difference between the buoyancy force (F_b) and the weight of the hydrogen contained in the blimp (w_{H}).

$$F_{\text{lift}} = F_b - w_{\text{H}}$$

The weight of the hydrogen is calculated from the mass of hydrogen by

$$w_{\text{H}} = \frac{mg}{g_c}$$

$$= \frac{(10{,}000 \text{ lbm}) \left(32.2 \dfrac{\text{ft}}{\text{sec}^2}\right)}{32.2 \dfrac{\text{lbm-ft}}{\text{lbf-sec}^2}}$$

$$= 10{,}000 \text{ lbf}$$

The buoyancy force is equal to the weight of the displaced air. The weight of the displaced air is calculated by knowing that the volume of the air displaced is equal to the volume of hydrogen enclosed in the blimp. Compute the volume of the hydrogen contained in the blimp by assuming the hydrogen behaves like an ideal gas.

$$V_{\text{H}} = \frac{mRT}{p}$$

For hydrogen, $R = 766.5$ ft-lbf/lbm-°R.

The temperature of the hydrogen is given as 56°F. Convert to absolute temperature (degrees Rankine).

$$T = 56°\text{F} + 460 = 516°\text{R}$$

The pressure of the hydrogen is given as 30.2 in Hg. Convert the pressure to units of pounds per square foot.

$$p = (30.2 \text{ in Hg}) \left(\frac{1 \dfrac{\text{lbf}}{\text{in}^2}}{2.036 \text{ in Hg}}\right) \left(144 \dfrac{\text{in}^2}{\text{ft}^2}\right)$$

$$= 2136 \text{ lbf/ft}^2$$

Compute the volume of hydrogen.

$$V_{\text{H}} = \frac{mRT}{p}$$

$$= \frac{(10{,}000 \text{ lbm}) \left(766.5 \dfrac{\text{ft-lbf}}{\text{lbm-°R}}\right) (516°\text{R})}{2136 \dfrac{\text{lbf}}{\text{ft}^2}}$$

$$= 1.85 \times 10^6 \text{ ft}^3$$

Since the volume of the hydrogen contained in the blimp is equal to the air displaced, the air displaced can be computed from the ideal gas equation by assuming the air behaves like an ideal gas.

$$m = \frac{pV_{\text{H}}}{RT}$$

Since the air and hydrogen are assumed to be in thermal and pressure equilibrium, the temperature and pressure are equal to the value given for the hydrogen.

For air, $R = 53.3$ ft-lbf/lbm-°R.

Substituting gives

$$m_{\text{air}} = \frac{pV_{\text{H}}}{RT}$$

$$= \frac{\left(2136 \dfrac{\text{lbf}}{\text{ft}^2}\right) (1.85 \times 10^6 \text{ ft}^3)}{\left(53.3 \dfrac{\text{ft-lbf}}{\text{lbm-°R}}\right) (516°\text{R})}$$

$$= 1.437 \times 10^5 \text{ lbm}$$

Recall that the buoyancy force is equal to the weight of the air.

$$F_b = w_{\text{air}} = \frac{mg}{g_c}$$

$$= \frac{(1.437 \times 10^5 \text{ lbm}) \left(32.2 \dfrac{\text{ft}}{\text{sec}^2}\right)}{32.2 \dfrac{\text{lbm-ft}}{\text{lbf-sec}^2}}$$

$$= 1.437 \times 10^5 \text{ lbf}$$

Therefore, the lift can be calculated as

$$F_{\text{lift}} = F_b - w_{\text{H}}$$

$$= 1.437 \times 10^5 \text{ lbf} - 10{,}000 \text{ lbf}$$

$$= \boxed{1.337 \times 10^5 \text{ lbf}}$$

Fluids

SI Solution

Assume the mass of the blimp structure is small (negligible) compared with the mass of the hydrogen.

The lift of the hydrogen-filled blimp (F_{lift}) is equal to the difference between the buoyancy force (F_b) and the weight of the hydrogen contained in the blimp (w_{H}).

$$F_{\text{lift}} = F_b - w_{\text{H}}$$

The weight of the hydrogen is calculated from the mass of hydrogen by

$$\begin{aligned} w_{\text{H}} &= mg \\ &= (4500 \text{ kg})\left(9.81 \frac{\text{m}}{\text{s}^2}\right) \\ &= 44\,145 \text{ N} \end{aligned}$$

The buoyancy force is equal to the weight of the displaced air. The weight of the displaced air is calculated by knowing that the volume of the air displaced is equal to the volume of hydrogen enclosed in the blimp. Compute the volume of the hydrogen contained in the blimp by assuming the hydrogen behaves like an ideal gas.

$$V_{\text{H}} = \frac{mRT}{p}$$

For hydrogen, $R = 4124$ J/kg·K.

The temperature of the hydrogen is given as 13°C. Convert to absolute temperature (degrees Kelvin).

$$T = 13°\text{C} + 273 = 286\text{K}$$

The pressure of the hydrogen is given as 770 mm Hg. Convert the pressure to units of pascals.

$$\begin{aligned} p &= \frac{(770 \text{ mm Hg})\left(133.4 \frac{\text{kPa}}{\text{m}}\right)}{1000 \frac{\text{mm}}{\text{m}}} \\ &= 102.7 \text{ kPa} \end{aligned}$$

The volume of hydrogen is

$$\begin{aligned} V_{\text{H}} &= \frac{mRT}{p} \\ &= \frac{(4500 \text{ kg})\left(4124 \frac{\text{J}}{\text{kg·K}}\right)(286\text{K})}{(102.7 \text{ kPa})\left(1000 \frac{\text{Pa}}{\text{kPa}}\right)} \\ &= 5.168 \times 10^4 \text{ m}^3 \end{aligned}$$

Since the volume of the hydrogen contained in the blimp is equal to the air displaced, the air displaced can be computed from the ideal gas equation assuming the air behaves like an ideal gas.

$$m = \frac{pV_{\text{H}}}{RT}$$

Since the air and hydrogen are assumed to be in thermal and pressure equilibrium, the temperature and pressure are equal to the value given for the hydrogen.

For air, $R = 287$ J/kg·K.

Substituting gives

$$\begin{aligned} m_{\text{air}} &= \frac{pV_{\text{H}}}{RT} \\ &= \frac{(102.7 \text{ kPa})\left(1000 \frac{\text{Pa}}{\text{kPa}}\right)(5.168 \times 10^4 \text{ m}^3)}{\left(287 \frac{\text{J}}{\text{kg·K}}\right)(286\text{K})} \\ &= 6.466 \times 10^4 \text{ kg} \end{aligned}$$

The buoyancy force is equal to the weight of the air, so

$$\begin{aligned} F_b &= w_{\text{air}} = mg \\ &= (6.466 \times 10^4 \text{ kg})\left(9.81 \frac{\text{m}}{\text{s}^2}\right) \\ &= 6.34 \times 10^5 \text{ N} \end{aligned}$$

Therefore, the lift can be calculated as

$$\begin{aligned} F_{\text{lift}} &= F_b - w_{\text{H}} \\ &= 6.34 \times 10^5 \text{ N} - 44\,145 \text{ N} \\ &= \boxed{5.90 \times 10^5 \text{ N}} \end{aligned}$$

2. *Customary U.S. Solution*

The weight of the sphere is equal to the difference in the buoyancy force of the fully submerged sphere (F_{fs}) and the buoyancy force of the half-submerged sphere (F_{hs}).

The buoyancy force is given by

$$F_{\text{buoyancy}} = \frac{\rho g V_{\text{displaced}}}{g_c}$$

Since the volume of the half-submerged sphere is equal to half of the fully submerged sphere,

$$\begin{aligned} w_{\text{sphere}} &= F_{\text{fs}} - F_{\text{hs}} \\ &= \left(\tfrac{1}{2}\right)\left(\frac{\rho g V_{\text{sphere}}}{g_c}\right) \end{aligned}$$

For seawater, $\rho = 64.0$ lbm/ft^3.

The volume of the sphere is given by

$$V_{\text{sphere}} = \left(\frac{\pi}{6}\right) d^3$$

$$= \left(\frac{\pi}{6}\right) (6 \text{ ft})^3$$

$$= 113.1 \text{ ft}^3$$

The weight of the sphere is

$$w_{\text{sphere}} = \left(\tfrac{1}{2}\right) \left(\frac{\rho g V_{\text{sphere}}}{g_c}\right)$$

$$= \left(\tfrac{1}{2}\right) \left(\frac{\left(64.0 \ \dfrac{\text{lbm}}{\text{ft}^3}\right) \left(32.2 \ \dfrac{\text{ft}}{\text{sec}^2}\right) \times (113.1 \text{ ft}^3)}{32.2 \ \dfrac{\text{lbm-ft}}{\text{lbf-sec}^2}} \right)$$

$$= 3619 \text{ lbf}$$

The buoyant force equation for a fully submerged sphere and anchor can be solved for the concrete volume.

$$w_{\text{sphere}} + w_{\text{concrete}} = (V_{\text{sphere}} + V_{\text{concrete}})\rho_{\text{water}}$$

$$w_{\text{sphere}} + \rho_{\text{concrete}} V_{\text{concrete}} \left(\frac{g}{g_c}\right)$$

$$= (V_{\text{sphere}} + V_{\text{concrete}})\rho_{\text{water}}$$

$$\times \left(\frac{g}{g_c}\right)$$

$$3619 \text{ lbf} + \left(150 \ \frac{\text{lbm}}{\text{ft}^3}\right) V_{\text{concrete}} \left(\frac{32.2 \ \dfrac{\text{ft}}{\text{sec}^2}}{32.2 \ \dfrac{\text{ft-lbm}}{\text{lbf-sec}^2}}\right)$$

$$= (113.1 \text{ ft}^3 + V_{\text{concrete}})$$

$$\times \left(64.0 \ \frac{\text{lbm}}{\text{ft}^3}\right)$$

$$\times \left(\frac{32.2 \ \dfrac{\text{ft}}{\text{sec}^2}}{32.2 \ \dfrac{\text{ft-lbm}}{\text{lbf-sec}^2}}\right)$$

$$V_{\text{concrete}} = 42.09 \text{ ft}^3$$

$$m_{\text{concrete}} = \rho_{\text{concrete}} V_{\text{concrete}}$$

$$= \left(150 \ \frac{\text{lbm}}{\text{ft}^3}\right) (42.09 \text{ ft}^3)$$

$$\boxed{= 6314 \text{ lbm}}$$

SI Solution

The weight of the sphere is equal to the difference in the buoyancy force of the fully submerged sphere (F_{fs}) and the buoyancy force of the half-submerged sphere (F_{hs}).

The buoyancy force is given by

$$F_{\text{buoyancy}} = \rho g V_{\text{displaced}}$$

Since the volume of the half-submerged sphere is equal to half of the fully submerged sphere,

$$w_{\text{sphere}} = F_{\text{fs}} - F_{\text{hs}}$$

$$= \tfrac{1}{2}\rho g V_{\text{sphere}}$$

For seawater, $\rho = 1024 \text{ kg/m}^3$.

The volume of the sphere is given by

$$V_{\text{sphere}} = \left(\frac{\pi}{6}\right) d^3$$

$$= \left(\frac{\pi}{6}\right) (1.8 \text{ m})^3$$

$$= 3.054 \text{ m}^3$$

The weight of the sphere required is

$$w_{\text{sphere}} = \tfrac{1}{2}\rho g V_{\text{sphere}}$$

$$= \left(\tfrac{1}{2}\right) \left(1024 \ \frac{\text{kg}}{\text{m}^3}\right) \left(9.81 \ \frac{\text{m}}{\text{s}^2}\right) (3.054 \text{ m}^3)$$

$$= 15\,339 \text{ N}$$

The buoyant force equation for a fully submerged sphere and anchor can be solved for the concrete volume.

$$w_{\text{sphere}} + w_{\text{concrete}} = (V_{\text{sphere}} + V_{\text{concrete}})\rho_{\text{water}}$$

$$w_{\text{sphere}} + \rho_{\text{concrete}} g V_{\text{concrete}} = (V_{\text{sphere}} + V_{\text{concrete}})\rho_{\text{water}} g$$

$$15\,339 \text{ N} + \left(2400 \ \frac{\text{kg}}{\text{m}^3}\right) \left(9.81 \ \frac{\text{m}}{\text{s}^2}\right) V_{\text{concrete}}$$

$$= (3.054 \text{ m}^3 + V_{\text{concrete}})$$

$$\times \left(1024 \ \frac{\text{kg}}{\text{m}^3}\right) \left(9.81 \ \frac{\text{m}}{\text{s}^2}\right)$$

$$V_{\text{concrete}} = 1.136 \text{ m}^3$$

$$m_{\text{concrete}} = \rho_{\text{concrete}} V_{\text{concrete}}$$

$$= \left(2400 \ \frac{\text{kg}}{\text{m}^3}\right) (1.136 \text{ m}^3)$$

$$\boxed{= 2726 \text{ kg}}$$

16 Fluid Flow Parameters

1. *Customary U.S. Solution*

The perimeter of the pipe is

$$p = \pi d = \pi(10 \text{ in})$$
$$= 31.42 \text{ in}$$

If the pipe is flowing half-full, the wetted perimeter becomes

$$\text{wetted perimeter} = \tfrac{1}{2}p = \left(\tfrac{1}{2}\right)(31.42 \text{ in})$$
$$= 15.71 \text{ in}$$

Assume the compressed pipe is an elliptical cross-section. The ellipse will have a minor axis, b, equal to one-half the height of the compressed pipe or

$$b = \frac{7.2 \text{ in}}{2} = 3.6 \text{ in}$$

When the pipe is compressed, the perimeter of the pipe will remain constant. The perimeter of an ellipse is given by

$$p = 2\pi\sqrt{\left(\tfrac{1}{2}\right)(a^2 + b^2)}$$

Solve for the major axis.

$$a = \sqrt{(2)\left(\frac{p}{2\pi}\right)^2 - b^2}$$
$$= \sqrt{(2)\left(\frac{31.42 \text{ in}}{2\pi}\right)^2 - (3.6 \text{ in})^2}$$
$$= 6.09 \text{ in}$$

The flow area or area of the ellipse is given by

$$\text{flow area} = \tfrac{1}{2}\pi ab$$
$$= \tfrac{1}{2}\pi(6.09 \text{ in})(3.6 \text{ in})$$
$$= 34.4 \text{ in}^2$$

The hydraulic radius is

$$r_h = \frac{\text{area in flow}}{\text{wetted perimeter}} = \frac{34.4 \text{ in}^2}{15.7 \text{ in}}$$
$$= \boxed{2.19 \text{ in}}$$

SI Solution

The perimeter of the pipe is

$$p = \pi d = \pi(25 \text{ cm})$$
$$= 78.54 \text{ cm}$$

If the pipe is flowing half-full, the wetted perimeter becomes

$$\text{wetted perimeter} = \tfrac{1}{2}p = \left(\tfrac{1}{2}\right)(78.54 \text{ cm})$$
$$= 39.27 \text{ cm}$$

Assume the compressed pipe is an elliptical cross-section. The ellipse will have a minor axis, b, equal to one-half the height of the compressed pipe or

$$b = \frac{18 \text{ cm}}{2} = 9 \text{ cm}$$

When the pipe is compressed, the perimeter of the pipe will remain constant. The perimeter of an ellipse is given by

$$p = 2\pi\sqrt{\left(\tfrac{1}{2}\right)(a^2 + b^2)}$$

Solve for the major axis.

$$a = \sqrt{(2)\left(\frac{p}{2\pi}\right)^2 - b^2}$$
$$= \sqrt{(2)\left(\frac{78.54 \text{ cm}}{2\pi}\right)^2 - (9 \text{ cm})^2}$$
$$= 15.2 \text{ cm}$$

The flow area or area of the ellipse is given by

$$\text{flow area} = \tfrac{1}{2}\pi ab = \tfrac{1}{2}\pi(15.2 \text{ cm})(9 \text{ cm})$$
$$= 214.9 \text{ cm}^2$$

The hydraulic radius is

$$r_h = \frac{\text{area in flow}}{\text{wetted perimeter}}$$
$$= \frac{214.9 \text{ cm}^2}{39.27 \text{ cm}}$$
$$= \boxed{5.47 \text{ cm}}$$

17 Fluid Dynamics

Fluids

1. *Customary U.S. Solution*

For 6 in schedule-40 pipe, the internal diameter, D_i, is 0.5054 ft. The internal area is 0.2006 ft^2.

The velocity, v, is calculated from the volumetric flow, $\dot{V}$, and the flow area, A_i, by

$$v = \frac{\dot{V}}{A_i}$$

$$= \frac{1.5 \frac{ft^3}{sec}}{0.2006 \ ft^2}$$

$$= 7.48 \ ft/sec$$

For water at 70°F, the kinematic viscosity, ν, is 1.059×10^{-5} ft^2/sec.

Calculate the Reynolds number.

$$Re = \frac{D_i v}{\nu}$$

$$= \frac{(0.5054 \ ft)\left(7.48 \ \frac{ft}{sec}\right)}{1.059 \times 10^{-5} \ \frac{ft^2}{sec}}$$

$$= 3.57 \times 10^5$$

Since Re > 2100, the flow is turbulent. The friction loss coefficient can be determined from the Moody diagram.

For new steel pipe, the specific roughness, ϵ, is 0.0002 ft.

The relative roughness is

$$\frac{\epsilon}{D_i} = \frac{0.0002 \ ft}{0.5054 \ ft}$$

$$= 0.0004$$

From the Moody diagram with Re = 3.57×10^5 and $e/D_i = 0.0004$, the friction factor, f, can be determined as 0.0174.

Use Darcy's equation to compute the frictional loss.

$$h_f = \frac{fLv^2}{2D_i g}$$

$$= \frac{(0.0174)(1200 \ ft)\left(7.48 \ \frac{ft}{sec}\right)^2}{(2)(0.5054 \ ft)\left(32.2 \ \frac{ft}{sec^2}\right)}$$

$$= \boxed{35.9 \ ft}$$

SI Solution

For 6 in pipe, the internal diameter is 154.1 mm and the internal area is 186.5×10^{-4} m^2.

The velocity, v, is calculated from the volumetric flow, $\dot{V}$, and the flow area, A_i, by

$$v = \frac{\dot{V}}{A_i}$$

$$= \frac{\left(40 \ \frac{L}{s}\right)\left(0.001 \ \frac{m^3}{L}\right)}{186.5 \times 10^{-4} \ m^2}$$

$$= 2.145 \ m/s$$

For water at 20°C, the kinematic viscosity is

$$\nu = \frac{\mu}{\rho} = \frac{1.0050 \times 10^{-3} \ Pa \cdot s}{998.23 \ \frac{kg}{m^3}}$$

$$= 1.007 \times 10^{-6} \ m^2/s$$

Calculate the Reynolds number.

$$Re = \frac{D_i v}{\nu}$$

$$= \frac{(154.1 \ mm)\left(0.001 \ \frac{m}{mm}\right)\left(2.145 \ \frac{m}{s}\right)}{1.007 \times 10^{-6} \ \frac{m^2}{s}}$$

$$= 3.282 \times 10^5$$

Since Re > 2100, the flow is turbulent. The friction loss coefficient can be determined from the Moody diagram.

For new steel pipe, the specific roughness, ϵ, is 6.0×10^{-5} m.

The relative roughness is

$$\frac{\epsilon}{D_i} = \frac{6.0 \times 10^{-5} \text{ m}}{0.1541 \text{ m}}$$
$$= 0.0004$$

From the Moody diagram with Re $= 3.28 \times 10^5$ and $e/D_i = 0.0004$, the friction factor, f, can be determined as 0.0175.

Use Darcy's equation to compute the frictional loss.

$$h_f = \frac{fLv^2}{2D_i g}$$
$$= \frac{(0.0175)(355 \text{ m})\left(2.145 \dfrac{\text{m}}{\text{s}}\right)^2}{(2)(0.1541 \text{ m})\left(9.81 \dfrac{\text{m}}{\text{s}^2}\right)}$$
$$= \boxed{9.45 \text{ m}}$$

2. *Customary U.S. Solution*

For 6 in schedule-40 pipe, the internal diameter, D_i, is 0.5054 ft. The internal area is 0.2006 ft^2.

The velocity, v, is calculated from the volumetric flow, $\dot{V}$, and the flow area, A_i.

Convert the volumetric flow rate from gal/min to ft^3/sec.

$$\dot{V} = \left(500 \dfrac{\text{gal}}{\text{min}}\right)\left(\dfrac{1 \text{ ft}^3}{7.48 \text{ gal}}\right)\left(\dfrac{1 \text{ min}}{60 \text{ sec}}\right)$$
$$= 1.114 \text{ ft}^3/\text{sec}$$

The velocity is

$$v = \frac{\dot{V}}{A_i}$$
$$= \frac{1.114 \dfrac{\text{ft}^3}{\text{sec}}}{0.2006 \text{ ft}^2}$$
$$= 5.55 \text{ ft/sec}$$

For water at 100°F, the kinematic viscosity, ν, is 0.739×10^{-5} ft^2/sec.

Calculate the Reynolds number.

$$\text{Re} = \frac{D_i v}{\nu}$$
$$= \frac{(0.5054 \text{ ft})\left(5.55 \dfrac{\text{ft}}{\text{sec}}\right)}{0.739 \times 10^{-5} \dfrac{\text{ft}^2}{\text{sec}}}$$
$$= 3.80 \times 10^5$$

Since Re > 2100, the flow is turbulent. The friction loss coefficient can be determined from the Moody diagram.

For new steel pipe, the specific roughness, ϵ, is 0.0002 ft.

The relative roughness is

$$\frac{\epsilon}{D_i} = \frac{0.0002 \text{ ft}}{0.5054 \text{ ft}}$$
$$= 0.0004$$

From the Moody diagram with Re $= 3.80 \times 10^5$ and $e/D_i = 0.0004$, the friction factor, f, can be determined as 0.0173.

The equivalent length of the valves and fittings is

standard radius elbow	2×8.9 ft =	17.8 ft
gate valve (fully open)	2×3.2 ft =	6.4 ft
90° angle valve (fully open)	1×63.0 ft =	63.0 ft
back flow limiter		
swing check valve	1×63.0 ft =	63.0 ft
		150.2 ft

The equivalent pipe length is the sum of the straight run of pipe and the equivalent length of pipe for the valves and fittings.

$$L_e = L + L_{\text{fittings}}$$
$$= 300 \text{ ft} + 150.2 \text{ ft}$$
$$= 450.2 \text{ ft}$$

Use Darcy's equation to compute the frictional loss.

$$h_f = \frac{fL_e v^2}{2D_i g}$$
$$= \frac{(0.0173)(450.2 \text{ ft})\left(5.55 \dfrac{\text{ft}}{\text{sec}}\right)^2}{(2)(0.5054 \text{ ft})\left(32.2 \dfrac{\text{ft}}{\text{sec}^2}\right)}$$
$$= 7.37 \text{ ft}$$

The total difference in head is the sum of the head loss through the pipe, valves, and fittings and the change in elevation.

$$\Delta h = h_f + \Delta z$$
$$= 7.37 \text{ ft} + 20 \text{ ft}$$
$$= 27.37 \text{ ft}$$

The pressure difference between the entrance and discharge can be determined from

$$\Delta p = \gamma \Delta h = \rho h \left(\frac{g}{g_c}\right)$$
$$= \frac{\left(62.4 \dfrac{\text{lbm}}{\text{ft}^3}\right)(27.37 \text{ ft})\left(32.2 \dfrac{\text{ft}}{\text{sec}^2}\right)\left(\dfrac{1 \text{ ft}^2}{144 \text{ in}^2}\right)}{32.2 \dfrac{\text{lbm-ft}}{\text{lbf-sec}^2}}$$
$$= \boxed{11.9 \text{ lbf/in}^2 \ (11.9 \text{ psi})}$$

SI Solution

For 6 in pipe, the internal diameter is 154.1 mm (0.1541 m).

The internal area is 186.5×10^{-4} m².

The velocity, v, is calculated from the volumetric flow, $\dot{V}$, and the flow area, A_i.

$$v = \frac{\dot{V}}{A_i}$$
$$= \frac{\left(30\ \dfrac{L}{s}\right)\left(0.001\ \dfrac{m^3}{L}\right)}{186.5 \times 10^{-4}\ m^2}$$
$$= 1.61\ m/s$$

For water at 40°C, the kinematic viscosity is

$$\nu = \frac{\mu}{\rho} = \frac{0.6560 \times 10^{-3}\ Pa \cdot s}{992.25\ \dfrac{kg}{m^3}}$$
$$= 6.611 \times 10^{-7}\ m^2/s$$

Calculate the Reynolds number.

$$Re = \frac{D_i v}{\nu}$$
$$= \frac{(0.1541\ m)\left(1.61\ \dfrac{m}{s}\right)}{6.611 \times 10^{-7}\ \dfrac{m^2}{s}}$$
$$= 3.75 \times 10^5$$

Since Re > 2100, the flow is turbulent. The friction loss coefficient can be determined from the Moody diagram.

For new steel pipe, the specific roughness is 6.0×10^{-5} m.

The relative roughness is

$$\frac{\epsilon}{D_i} = \frac{6.0 \times 10^{-5}\ m}{0.1541\ m}$$
$$= 0.0004$$

From the Moody diagram with Re = 3.75×10^5 and $e/D_i = 0.0004$, the friction factor, f, can be determined as 0.0173.

The equivalent length of the valves and fittings is

standard radius elbow	2×2.7 m =	5.4 m
gate valve (fully open)	2×1.0 m =	2.0 m
90° angle valve (fully open)	1×18.9 m =	18.9 m
back flow limiter		
swing check valve	1×18.9 m =	18.9 m
		45.2 m

The equivalent pipe length is the sum of the straight run of pipe and the equivalent length of pipe for the valves and fittings.

$$L_e = L + L_{\text{fittings}}$$
$$= 90\ m + 45.2\ m$$
$$= 135.2\ m$$

Use Darcy's equation to compute the frictional loss.

$$h_f = \frac{fLv^2}{2D_i g}$$
$$= \frac{(0.0173)(135.2\ m)\left(1.61\ \dfrac{m}{s^2}\right)^2}{(2)(0.1541\ m)\left(9.81\ \dfrac{m}{s^2}\right)}$$
$$= 2.01\ m$$

The total difference in head is the sum of the head loss through the pipe, valves, and fittings, and the change in elevation.

$$\Delta h = h_f + \Delta z$$
$$= 2.01\ m + 6\ m$$
$$= 8.01\ m$$

The pressure difference between the entrance and discharge can be determined from

$$\Delta p = \rho h g$$
$$= \left(992.25\ \frac{kg}{m^3}\right)(8.01\ m)\left(9.81\ \frac{m}{s^2}\right)$$
$$= \boxed{77\,969\ Pa\quad (78\ kPa)}$$

3. *Customary U.S. Solution*

For 6 in schedule-40 pipe, the internal diameter, D_i, is 0.5054 ft. The internal area is 0.2006 ft².

For air at 70°F, the kinematic viscosity is 16.15×10^{-5} ft²/sec.

Calculate the Reynolds number.

$$Re = \frac{D_i v}{\nu}$$
$$= \frac{(0.5054\ ft)\left(60\ \dfrac{ft}{sec}\right)}{16.15 \times 10^{-5}\ \dfrac{ft^2}{sec}}$$
$$= 1.88 \times 10^5$$

Since Re > 2100, the flow is turbulent. The friction loss coefficient can be determined from the Moody diagram.

For new steel pipe, the specific roughness, ϵ, is 0.0002 ft.

The relative roughness is

$$\frac{\epsilon}{D_i} = \frac{0.0002 \text{ ft}}{0.5054 \text{ ft}}$$
$$= 0.0004$$

From the Moody diagram with $\text{Re} = 1.88 \times 10^5$ and $e/D_i = 0.0004$, the friction factor, f, can be determined as 0.0184.

The equivalent length of the valves and fittings is

standard radius elbow	2×8.9 ft $=$	17.8 ft
gate valve (fully open)	2×3.2 ft $=$	6.4 ft
90° angle valve (fully open)	1×63.0 ft $=$	63.0 ft
back flow limiter		
swing check valve	1×63.0 ft $=$	63.0 ft
		150.2 ft

The equivalent pipe length is the sum of the straight run of pipe and the equivalent length of pipe for the valves and fittings.

$$L_e = L + L_{\text{fittings}}$$
$$= 300 \text{ ft} + 150.2 \text{ ft}$$
$$= 450.2 \text{ ft}$$

Use Darcy's equation to compute the frictional loss.

$$h_f = \frac{f L_e \text{v}^2}{2 D_i g}$$
$$= \frac{(0.0184)(450.2 \text{ ft}) \left(60 \, \frac{\text{ft}}{\text{sec}} \right)^2}{(2)(0.5054 \text{ ft}) \left(32.2 \, \frac{\text{ft}}{\text{sec}^2} \right)}$$
$$= 916.2 \text{ ft}$$

The difference in head is the sum of the head loss through the pipe, valves, and fittings and the change in elevation.

$$h = h_f + \Delta z$$
$$= 916.2 \text{ ft} + 20 \text{ ft}$$
$$= 936.2 \text{ ft}$$

Assume the density of the air, ρ, is approximately 0.075 lbm/ft³.

The pressure difference between the entrance and discharge can be determined from

$$\Delta p = \gamma h = \rho h \left(\frac{g}{g_c} \right)$$
$$= \left(0.075 \, \frac{\text{lbm}}{\text{ft}^3} \right) (936.2 \text{ ft})$$
$$\times \left(\frac{32.2 \, \frac{\text{ft}}{\text{sec}^2}}{32.2 \, \frac{\text{lbm-ft}}{\text{lbf-sec}^2}} \right) \left(\frac{1 \text{ ft}^2}{144 \text{ in}^2} \right)$$
$$= \boxed{0.49 \text{ lbf/in}^2 \quad (0.49 \text{ psi})}$$

SI Solution

For 6 in pipe, the internal diameter, D_i, is 154.1 mm (0.1541 m) and the internal area is $186.5 \times 10^{-4} \text{ m}^2$.

For air at 20°C, the kinematic viscosity, ν, is $1.51 \times 10^{-5} \text{ m}^2/\text{s}$.

Calculate the Reynolds number.

$$\text{Re} = \frac{D_i \text{v}}{\nu}$$
$$= \frac{(0.1541 \text{ m}) \left(18 \, \frac{\text{m}}{\text{s}} \right)}{1.51 \times 10^{-5} \, \frac{\text{m}^2}{\text{s}}}$$
$$= 1.84 \times 10^5$$

Since $\text{Re} > 2100$, the flow is turbulent. The friction loss coefficient can be determined from the Moody diagram.

For new steel pipe, the specific roughness, ϵ, is 6.0×10^{-5} m.

The relative roughness is

$$\frac{\epsilon}{D_i} = \frac{6.0 \times 10^{-5}}{0.1541 \text{ m}}$$
$$= 0.0004$$

From the Moody diagram with $\text{Re} = 1.84 \times 10^5$ and $e/D_i = 0.0004$, the friction factor, f, can be determined as 0.0185.

Compute the equivalent length of the valves and fittings.

standard radius elbow	2×2.7 m $=$	5.4 m
gate valve (fully open)	2×1.0 m $=$	2.0 m
90° angle valve (fully open)	1×18.9 m $=$	18.9 m
back flow limiter		
swing check valve	1×18.9 m $=$	18.9 m
		45.2 m

The equivalent pipe length is the sum of the straight run of pipe and the equivalent length of pipe for the valves and fittings.

$$L_e = L + L_{\text{fittings}}$$
$$= 90 \text{ m} + 45.2 \text{ m}$$
$$= 135.2 \text{ m}$$

Use Darcy's equation to compute the frictional loss.

$$h_f = \frac{fLv^2}{2D_ig}$$
$$= \frac{(0.0185)(135.2 \text{ m})\left(18 \frac{\text{m}}{\text{s}}\right)^2}{(2)(0.1541 \text{ m})\left(9.81 \frac{\text{m}}{\text{s}^2}\right)}$$
$$= 268.0 \text{ m}$$

The difference in head is the sum of the head loss through the pipe, valves, and fittings and the change in elevation.

$$\Delta h = h_f + \Delta z$$
$$= 268.0 \text{ m} + 6 \text{ m}$$
$$= 274.0 \text{ m}$$

Assume the density of the air, ρ, is approximately 1.20 kg/m^3.

The pressure difference between the entrance and discharge can be determined from

$$\Delta p = \rho h g$$
$$= \left(1.20 \frac{\text{kg}}{\text{m}^3}\right)(274.0 \text{ m})\left(9.81 \frac{\text{m}}{\text{s}^2}\right)$$
$$= \boxed{3226 \text{ Pa} \quad (3.23 \text{ kPa})}$$

4. *Customary U.S. Solution*

Assume schedule-40 pipe.

$$D_A = 0.5054 \text{ ft}$$
$$D_B = 1.4063 \text{ ft}$$

Let point A be at zero elevation.

The total energy at point A from Bernoulli's equation is

$$E_{tA} = E_p + E_v + E_z$$
$$= \frac{p_A}{\rho} + \frac{v_A}{2g_c} + \frac{z_Ag}{g_c}$$

At point A, the diameter is 6 in. The velocity at point A is

$$Q = v_A A_A$$
$$= v_A\left(\frac{\pi}{4}\right)d_A^2$$
$$v_A = \left(\frac{4}{\pi}\right)\left(\frac{Q}{D_A^2}\right)$$
$$= \left(\frac{4}{\pi}\right)\left(\frac{5.0 \frac{\text{ft}^3}{\text{sec}}}{(0.5054 \text{ ft})^2}\right)$$
$$= 24.9 \text{ ft/sec}$$
$$p_A = \left(10 \frac{\text{lbf}}{\text{in}^2}\right)\left(\frac{144 \text{ in}^2}{1 \text{ ft}^2}\right) = 1440 \text{ lbf/ft}^2$$
$$z_A = 0$$

For water, $\rho \approx 62.4$ lbm/ft^3.

$$E_{tA} = \frac{p_A}{\rho} + \frac{v_A^2}{2g_c} + \frac{z_Ag}{g_c}$$
$$= \frac{1440 \frac{\text{lbf}}{\text{ft}^2}}{62.4 \frac{\text{lbm}}{\text{ft}^3}} + \frac{\left(24.9 \frac{\text{ft}}{\text{sec}}\right)^2}{(2)\left(32.2 \frac{\text{lbm-ft}}{\text{lbf-sec}^2}\right)} + 0$$
$$= 32.7 \text{ ft-lbf/lbm}$$

Similarly, the total energy at point B is

$$v_B = \left(\frac{4}{\pi}\right)\left(\frac{Q}{D_B^2}\right)$$
$$= \left(\frac{4}{\pi}\right)\left(\frac{5.0 \frac{\text{ft}^3}{\text{sec}}}{(1.4063 \text{ ft})^2}\right)$$
$$= 3.22 \text{ ft/sec}$$
$$p_B = \left(7 \frac{\text{lbf}}{\text{in}^2}\right)\left(\frac{144 \text{ in}^2}{1 \text{ ft}^2}\right) = 1008 \text{ lbf/ft}^2$$
$$z_B = 15 \text{ ft}$$
$$E_{tB} = \frac{p_B}{\rho} + \frac{v_B^2}{2g_c} + \frac{z_Bg}{g_c}$$
$$= \frac{1008 \frac{\text{lbf}}{\text{ft}^2}}{62.4 \frac{\text{lbm}}{\text{ft}^3}} + \frac{\left(3.22 \frac{\text{ft}}{\text{sec}}\right)^2}{(2)\left(32.2 \frac{\text{lbm-ft}}{\text{lbf-sec}^2}\right)}$$
$$+ \frac{(15 \text{ ft})\left(32.2 \frac{\text{ft}}{\text{sec}^2}\right)}{32.2 \frac{\text{lbm-ft}}{\text{lbf-sec}^2}}$$
$$= 31.3 \text{ ft-lbf/lbm}$$

Since $E_{tA} > E_{tB}$, the flow is from point A to point B.

SI Solution

Let point A be at zero elevation.

The total energy at point A from Bernoulli's equation is

$$E_{tA} = E_p + E_v + E_z$$
$$= \frac{p_A}{\rho} + \frac{v_A^2}{2} + z_A g$$

At point A, the diameter is 150 mm (0.15 m). The velocity at point A is

$$Q = v_A A_A$$
$$= v_A \left(\frac{\pi}{4}\right) d_A^2$$
$$v_A = \left(\frac{4}{\pi}\right)\left(\frac{Q}{d_A^2}\right)$$
$$= \left(\frac{4}{\pi}\right)\left[\frac{\left(130 \frac{L}{s}\right)\left(\frac{1 \text{ m}^3}{1000 \text{ L}}\right)}{(0.15 \text{ m})^2}\right]$$
$$= 7.36 \text{ m/s}$$
$$p_A = 69 \text{ kPa } (69\,000 \text{ Pa})$$
$$z_A = 0$$

For water, $\rho = 1000$ kg/m^3.

$$E_{tA} = \frac{p_A}{\rho} + \frac{v_A^2}{2} + z_A g$$
$$= \frac{69\,000 \text{ Pa}}{1000 \frac{kg}{m^3}} + \frac{\left(7.36 \frac{m}{s}\right)^2}{2} + 0$$
$$= 96.08 \text{ J/kg}$$

Similarly, the total energy at point B is

$$v_B = \left(\frac{4}{\pi}\right)\left(\frac{Q}{d_B^2}\right)$$
$$= \left(\frac{4}{\pi}\right)\left(\frac{\left(130 \frac{L}{s}\right)\left(\frac{1 \text{ m}^3}{1000 \text{ L}}\right)}{(0.46 \text{ m})^2}\right)$$
$$= 0.78 \text{ m/s}$$
$$p_B = 48.3 \text{ kPa } (48\,300 \text{ Pa})$$
$$z_B = 4.6 \text{ m}$$

$$E_{tB} = \frac{p_B}{\rho} + \frac{v_B^2}{2} + z_B g$$
$$= \frac{48\,300 \text{ Pa}}{1000 \frac{kg}{m^3}} + \frac{\left(0.78 \frac{m}{s}\right)^2}{2}$$
$$+ (4.6 \text{ m})\left(9.81 \frac{m}{s^2}\right)$$
$$= 93.7 \text{ J/kg}$$

Since $E_{tA} > E_{tB}$, the flow is from point A to point B.

5. *Customary U.S. Solution*

Use projectile equations.

The maximum range of the discharge is given by

$$R = v_o^2 \left(\frac{\sin 2\phi}{g}\right)$$
$$= \left(50 \frac{ft}{sec}\right)^2 \left(\frac{\sin ((2)(45°))}{32.2 \frac{ft}{sec^2}}\right)$$
$$= \boxed{77.64 \text{ ft}}$$

SI Solution

Use projectile equations.

The maximum range of the discharge is given by

$$R = v_o^2 \left(\frac{\sin 2\phi}{g}\right)$$
$$= \frac{\left(15 \frac{m}{s}\right)^2 \sin ((2)(45°))}{9.81 \frac{m}{s^2}}$$
$$= \boxed{22.94 \text{ m}}$$

6. *Customary U.S. Solution*

The volumetric flow rate of benzene through the venturi meter is given by

$$\dot{V} = C_f A_2 \sqrt{\frac{2g(\rho_m - \rho)h}{\rho}}$$

The density of mercury, ρ_m, at 60°F is approximately 848 lbm/ft^3.

The density of the benzene at 60°F is

$$\rho = (SG)\rho_{\text{water}}$$
$$= (0.885)\left(62.4 \ \frac{\text{lbm}}{\text{ft}^3}\right)$$
$$= 55.22 \ \text{lbm/ft}^3$$

The throat area is

$$A_2 = \left(\frac{\pi}{4}\right)d_2^2$$
$$= \left(\frac{\pi}{4}\right)(3.5 \ \text{in})^2\left(\frac{1 \ \text{ft}^2}{144 \ \text{in}^2}\right) = 0.0668 \ \text{ft}^2$$

The flow coefficient is defined as

$$C_f = \frac{C_d}{\sqrt{1 - \beta^4}}$$

β is the ratio of the throat to inlet diameters.

$$\beta = \frac{3.5 \ \text{in}}{8 \ \text{in}}$$
$$= 0.4375$$

$$C_f = \frac{C_d}{\sqrt{1 - \beta^4}}$$
$$= \frac{0.99}{\sqrt{1 - (0.4375)^4}}$$
$$= 1.00865$$

Find the volumetric flow of benzene.

$$\dot{V} = C_f A_2 \sqrt{\frac{2g(\rho_m - \rho)h}{\rho}}$$
$$= (1.00865)(0.0668 \ \text{ft}^2)$$

$$\times \sqrt{\frac{(2)\left(32.2 \ \dfrac{\text{ft}}{\text{sec}^2}\right)\left(848 \ \dfrac{\text{lbm}}{\text{ft}^3}\right.}{\left. - 55.22 \ \dfrac{\text{lbm}}{\text{ft}^3}\right)(4 \ \text{in})\left(\dfrac{1 \ \text{ft}}{12 \ \text{in}}\right)}{55.22 \ \dfrac{\text{lbm}}{\text{ft}^3}}}$$

$$= \boxed{1.183 \ \text{ft}^3/\text{sec}}$$

SI Solution

The volumetric flow rate of benzene through the venturi meter is given by

$$\dot{V} = C_f A_2 \sqrt{\frac{2g(\rho_m - \rho)h}{\rho}}$$

ρ_m is the density of mercury at 15°C; ρ_m is approximately $13\,600 \ \text{kg/m}^3$.

The density of the benzene at 15°C is

$$\rho = (SG)\rho_{\text{water}}$$
$$= (0.885)\left(1000 \ \frac{\text{kg}}{\text{m}^3}\right)$$
$$= 885 \ \text{kg/m}^3$$

The throat area is

$$A_2 = \left(\frac{\pi}{4}\right)d_2^2$$
$$= \left(\frac{\pi}{4}\right)(0.09 \ \text{m})^2$$
$$= 0.0064 \ \text{m}^2$$

The flow coefficient is defined as

$$C_f = \frac{C_d}{\sqrt{1 - \beta^4}}$$

β is the ratio of the throat to inlet diameters.

$$\beta = \frac{9 \ \text{cm}}{20 \ \text{cm}}$$
$$= 0.45$$

$$C_f = \frac{C_d}{\sqrt{1 - \beta^4}}$$
$$= \frac{0.99}{\sqrt{1 - (0.45)^4}}$$
$$= 1.01094$$

Find the volumetric flow of benzene.

$$\dot{V} = C_f A_2 \sqrt{\frac{2g(\rho_m - \rho)h}{\rho}}$$
$$= (1.01094)(0.0064 \ \text{m}^2)$$

$$\times \sqrt{\frac{(2)\left(9.81 \ \dfrac{\text{m}}{\text{s}^2}\right)}{\times \left(13\,600 \ \dfrac{\text{kg}}{\text{m}^3} - 885 \ \dfrac{\text{kg}}{\text{m}^3}\right)(0.1 \ \text{m})}{885 \ \dfrac{\text{kg}}{\text{m}^3}}}$$

$$= \boxed{0.0344 \ \text{m}^3/\text{s} \ \ (34.4 \ \text{L/s})}$$

7. *Customary U.S. Solution*

The pressure differential across the orifice meter is given by

$$\Delta p = p_1 - p_2 = (\rho_{\text{mercury}} - \rho_{\text{water}})h\left(\frac{g}{g_c}\right)$$

The densities of mercury and water are

$$\rho_{\text{mercury}} = 848 \text{ lbm/ft}^3$$
$$\rho_{\text{water}} = 62.4 \text{ lbm/ft}^3$$

Substituting gives

$$\Delta p = (\rho_{\text{mercury}} - \rho_{\text{water}})h\left(\frac{g}{g_c}\right)$$

$$= \frac{\left(848 \frac{\text{lbm}}{\text{ft}^3} - 62.4 \frac{\text{lbm}}{\text{ft}^3}\right)(7 \text{ in})}{32.2 \frac{\text{lbm-ft}}{\text{lbf-sec}^2}}$$

$$\boxed{= 458.3 \text{ lbf/ft}^2 \quad (3.18 \text{ psi})}$$

SI Solution

The pressure differential across the orifice meter is given by
$$\Delta p = p_1 - p_2 = (\rho_{\text{mercury}} - \rho_{\text{water}})hg$$

The densities of mercury and water are

$$\rho_{\text{mercury}} = 13\,600 \text{ kg/m}^3$$
$$\rho_{\text{water}} = 1000 \text{ kg/m}^3$$

Substituting gives

$$\Delta p = (\rho_{\text{mercury}} - \rho_{\text{water}})h\left(\frac{g}{g_c}\right)$$

$$= \left(13\,600 \frac{\text{kg}}{\text{m}^3} - 1000 \frac{\text{kg}}{\text{m}^3}\right)(0.178 \text{ m})\left(9.81 \frac{\text{m}}{\text{s}^2}\right)$$

$$\boxed{= 22\,002 \text{ Pa} \quad (22.0 \text{ kPa})}$$

8. *Customary U.S. Solution*

For 12 in pipe (assuming schedule-40),

$$D_i = 0.99483 \text{ ft}$$
$$A_i = 0.7773 \text{ ft}^2$$

The velocity is

$$v = \frac{\dot{V}}{A}$$

$$= \frac{10 \frac{\text{ft}^3}{\text{sec}}}{0.7773 \text{ ft}^2}$$

$$= 12.87 \text{ ft/sec}$$

For water at 70°F, $\nu = 1.059 \times 10^{-5} \text{ ft}^2/\text{sec}$.

The Reynolds number in the pipe is

$$\text{Re} = \frac{vD_i}{\nu}$$

$$= \frac{\left(12.87 \frac{\text{ft}}{\text{sec}}\right)(0.99483 \text{ ft})}{1.059 \times 10^{-5} \frac{\text{ft}^2}{\text{sec}}}$$

$$= 1.21 \times 10^6$$

The volumetric flow rate through a sharp-edged orifice is given by

$$\dot{V} = C_f A_o \sqrt{\frac{2g(\rho_m - \rho)h}{\rho}}$$

In terms of pressure,

$$\dot{V} = C_f A_o \sqrt{\frac{2g_c(p_1 - p_2)}{\rho}}$$

Rearranging gives

$$C_f A_o = \frac{\dot{V}}{\sqrt{\frac{2g_c(p_1 - p_2)}{\rho}}}$$

p_1 is the upstream pressure, and p_2 is the downstream pressure.

The maximum head loss must not exceed 25 ft; therefore,

$$\frac{\left(\frac{g_c}{g}\right)(p_1 - p_2)}{\rho} = 25 \text{ ft}$$

$$\frac{(g_c)(p_1 - p_2)}{\rho} = (25 \text{ ft})g$$

Substituting gives

$$C_f A_0 = \frac{10 \frac{\text{ft}^3}{\text{sec}}}{\sqrt{(2)\left(32.2 \frac{\text{ft}}{\text{sec}^2}\right)(25 \text{ ft})}}$$

$$= 0.249 \text{ ft}^2$$

Both C_f and A_o depend on the orifice diameter.

For a 7 in diameter orifice,

$$A_o = \frac{\pi}{4}D_o^2 = \frac{\pi\left((7\text{ in})\left(\dfrac{1\text{ ft}}{12\text{ in}}\right)\right)^2}{4}$$
$$= 0.267\text{ ft}^2$$

$$\frac{A_o}{A_1} = \frac{0.267\text{ ft}^2}{0.7768\text{ ft}^2} = 0.344$$

From a chart of flow coefficients (Fig. 17.28), for $A_o/A_1 = 0.344$ and $\text{Re} = 1.21 \times 10^6$,

$$C_f = 0.645$$

$$C_f A_o = (0.645)(0.267\text{ ft}^2) = 0.172\text{ ft}^2 < 0.249\text{ ft}^2$$

Therefore, a 7 in diameter orifice is too small.

Try a 9 in diameter orifice.

$$A_o = \frac{\pi D_o^2}{4} = \frac{\pi\left((9\text{ in})\left(\dfrac{1\text{ ft}}{12\text{ in}}\right)\right)^2}{4}$$
$$= 0.442\text{ ft}^2$$

$$\frac{A_o}{A_1} = \frac{0.442\text{ ft}^2}{0.7768\text{ ft}^2} = 0.569$$

From Fig. 17.28, for $A_o/A_1 = 0.568$ and $\text{Re} = 1.21 \times 10^6$,

$$C_f = 0.73$$

$$C_f A_o = (0.73)(0.442\text{ ft}^2) = 0.323\text{ ft}^2 > 0.249\text{ ft}^2$$

Therefore, a 9 in orifice is too large.

Interpolating gives

$$D_o = 7\text{ in} + \frac{(9\text{ in} - 7\text{ in})(0.249\text{ ft}^2 - 0.172\text{ ft}^2)}{0.323\text{ ft}^2 - 0.172\text{ ft}^2}$$
$$= 8.0\text{ in}$$

Further iterations yield

$$\boxed{D_o = 8.1\text{ in}}$$
$$C_f A_o = 0.243\text{ ft}^2$$

SI Solution

For 300 mm pipe (assume the nominal diameter is the inner diameter), $D_i = 0.30$ m.

The velocity is

$$\text{v} = \frac{\dot{V}}{A} = \frac{\dot{V}}{\dfrac{\pi D_i^2}{4}}$$

$$= \frac{\left(250\ \dfrac{\text{L}}{\text{s}}\right)\left(\dfrac{1\text{ m}^3}{1000\text{ L}}\right)}{\dfrac{\pi(0.3\text{ m})^2}{4}}$$

$$= 3.54\text{ m/s}$$

For water at 20°C, $\nu = 1.007 \times 10^{-6}\text{ m}^2/\text{s}$.

The Reynolds number in the pipe is

$$\text{Re} = \frac{\text{v}D_i}{\nu}$$

$$= \frac{\left(3.54\ \dfrac{\text{m}}{\text{s}}\right)(0.3\text{ m})}{1.007 \times 10^{-6}\ \dfrac{\text{m}^2}{\text{s}}}$$

$$= 1.05 \times 10^6$$

The volumetric flow rate through a sharp-edged orifice is given by

$$\dot{V} = C_f A_o \sqrt{\frac{2g(\rho_m - \rho)h}{\rho}}$$

In terms of pressure,

$$\dot{V} = C_f A_o \sqrt{\frac{2(p_1 - p_2)}{\rho}}$$

Rearranging gives

$$C_f A_o = \frac{\dot{V}}{\sqrt{\dfrac{2(p_1 - p_2)}{\rho}}}$$

p_1 is the upstream pressure, and p_2 is the downstream pressure.

The maximum head loss must not exceed 7.5 m; therefore,

$$\frac{p_1 - p_2}{g\rho} = 7.5\text{ m}$$

$$\frac{p_1 - p_2}{\rho} = (7.5\text{ ft})g$$

Substituting gives

$$C_f A_o = \frac{0.25\ \dfrac{\text{m}^3}{\text{s}}}{\sqrt{(2)\left(9.81\ \dfrac{\text{m}}{\text{s}^2}\right)(7.5\text{ m})}}$$

$$= 0.021\text{ m}^2$$

Both C_f and A_o depend on the orifice diameter.

For an 18 cm diameter orifice,

$$A_o = \frac{\pi D_o^2}{4} = \frac{\pi (0.18 \text{ m})^2}{4} = 0.0254 \text{ m}^2$$

$$\frac{A_o}{A_1} = \frac{0.0254 \text{ m}^2}{0.0707 \text{ m}^2} = 0.359$$

From a chart of flow coefficients (Fig. 17.28), for $A_o/A_1 = 0.359$ and Re $= 1.07 \times 10^6$,

$$C_f = 0.65$$

$$C_f A_o = (0.65)(0.0254 \text{ m}^2) = 0.0165 \text{ m}^2 < 0.021 \text{ m}^2$$

Therefore, an 18 cm diameter orifice is too small.

Try a 23 cm diameter orifice.

$$A_o = \frac{\pi D_o^2}{4} = \frac{\pi (0.23 \text{ m})^2}{4} = 0.0415 \text{ m}^2$$

$$\frac{A_o}{A_1} = \frac{0.0415 \text{ m}^2}{0.707 \text{ m}^2} = 0.587$$

From Fig. 17.28, for $A_o/A_1 = 0.587$ and Re $= 1.07 \times 10^6$,

$$C_f = 0.73$$

$$C_f A_o = (0.73)(0.0415 \text{ m}^2) = 0.0303 \text{ m}^2 > 0.021 \text{ m}^2$$

Therefore, a 23 cm orifice is too large.

Interpolating gives

$$D_o = 18 \text{ cm}$$

$$+ (23 \text{ cm} - 18 \text{ cm}) \left(\frac{0.021 \text{ m}^2 - 0.0165 \text{ m}^2}{0.0303 \text{ m}^2 - 0.0165 \text{ m}^2} \right)$$

$$= 19.6 \text{ cm}$$

Further iteration yields

$$D_o = \boxed{20.0 \text{ cm}}$$

$$C_f = 0.675$$

$$C_f A_o = 0.021 \text{ m}^2$$

9. *Customary U.S. Solution*

The power that must be added to the pump is given by

$$P = \frac{\Delta h \dot{m} \left(\dfrac{g}{g_c} \right)}{\eta}$$

Assume schedule-40 pipe.

$$D_i = 0.9948 \text{ ft}$$

$$A_i = 0.7773 \text{ ft}^2$$

$$v_i = \frac{\dot{V}}{A_i}$$

$$= \frac{\left(2000 \dfrac{\text{gal}}{\text{min}} \right) \left(\dfrac{0.002228 \dfrac{\text{ft}^3}{\text{sec}}}{1 \dfrac{\text{gal}}{\text{min}}} \right)}{0.7773 \text{ ft}^2}$$

$$= 5.73 \text{ ft/sec}$$

(Note the pressures are in terms of gage pressure, and the density of mercury is 0.491 lbm/in^3.)

$$p_i = \left[14.7 \frac{\text{lbf}}{\text{in}^2} - \frac{(6 \text{ in}) \left(0.491 \dfrac{\text{lbm}}{\text{in}^3} \right) \left(32.2 \dfrac{\text{ft}}{\text{sec}^2} \right)}{32.2 \dfrac{\text{lbm-ft}}{\text{lbf-sec}^2}} \right]$$

$$\times \left(\frac{144 \text{ in}^2}{1 \text{ ft}^2} \right)$$

$$= 1692.6 \text{ lbf/ft}^2$$

$$E_{ti} = \frac{p_i}{\rho} + \frac{v_i^2}{2g_c} + \frac{z_i g}{g_c}$$

Since the pump inlet and outlet are at the same elevation, use $z = 0$ and $\rho = (\text{SG})\rho_{\text{water}}$.

$$E_{ti} = \frac{p_i}{(\text{SG})\rho_{\text{water}}} + \frac{v_i^2}{2g_c} + 0$$

$$= \frac{1692.6 \dfrac{\text{lbf}}{\text{ft}^2}}{(1.2) \left(62.4 \dfrac{\text{lbm}}{\text{ft}^3} \right)} + \frac{\left(5.73 \dfrac{\text{ft}}{\text{sec}} \right)^2}{(2) \left(32.2 \dfrac{\text{lbm-ft}}{\text{lbf-sec}^2} \right)}$$

$$= 23.11 \text{ ft-lbf/lbm}$$

Calculate the total head at the inlet.

$$h_{ti} = E_{ti} \left(\frac{g_c}{g} \right)$$

$$= \frac{\left(23.11 \dfrac{\text{ft-lbf}}{\text{lbm}} \right) \left(32.2 \dfrac{\text{lbm-ft}}{\text{lbf-sec}^2} \right)}{32.2 \dfrac{\text{ft}}{\text{sec}^2}}$$

$$= 23.11 \text{ ft-lbf/lbm}$$

At the outlet side of the pump,

$$D_o = 0.6651 \text{ ft}$$
$$A_o = 0.3474 \text{ ft}^2$$
$$Q = v_o A_o$$
$$v_o = \frac{Q}{A_o}$$

$$= \frac{\left(2000 \ \frac{\text{gal}}{\text{min}}\right)\left(\frac{0.002228 \ \frac{\text{ft}^3}{\text{sec}}}{1 \ \frac{\text{gal}}{\text{min}}}\right)}{0.3474 \text{ ft}^2}$$

$$= 12.83 \text{ ft/sec}$$

(Note that the pressures are in terms of gage pressure and the gage is located 4 ft above the pump outlet, which adds 4 ft of pressure head at the pump outlet.)

$$p_o = \left(14.7 \ \frac{\text{lbf}}{\text{in}^2} + 20 \ \frac{\text{lbf}}{\text{in}^2}\right)\left(\frac{144 \text{ in}^2}{1 \text{ ft}^2}\right)$$

$$+ 4 \text{ ft} \left[\frac{(1.2)\left(62.4 \ \frac{\text{lbm}}{\text{ft}^3}\right)\left(32.2 \ \frac{\text{ft}}{\text{sec}^2}\right)}{32.2 \ \frac{\text{lbm-ft}}{\text{lbf-sec}^2}}\right]$$

$$= 5296 \text{ lbf/ft}^2$$

$$E_{to} = \frac{p_o}{\rho} + \frac{v_o^2}{2g_c} + \frac{z_o g}{g_c}$$

Since the pump inlet and outlet are at the same elevation, use $z = 0$ and $\rho = (\text{SG})\rho_{\text{water}}$.

$$E_{to} = \frac{p_o}{(\text{SG})\rho_{\text{water}}} + \frac{v_o^2}{2g_c} + 0$$

$$= \frac{5296 \ \frac{\text{lbf}}{\text{ft}^2}}{(1.2)\left(62.4 \ \frac{\text{lbm}}{\text{ft}^3}\right)} + \frac{\left(12.83 \ \frac{\text{ft}}{\text{sec}}\right)^2}{(2)\left(32.2 \ \frac{\text{lbm-ft}}{\text{lbf-sec}^2}\right)}$$

$$= 73.28 \text{ ft-lbf/lbm}$$

Calculate the total head at the outlet.

$$h_{to} = E_{to}\left(\frac{g_c}{g}\right)$$

$$= \left(73.28 \ \frac{\text{ft-lbf}}{\text{lbm}}\right)\left(\frac{32.2 \ \frac{\text{lbm-ft}}{\text{lbf-sec}^2}}{32.2 \ \frac{\text{ft}}{\text{sec}^2}}\right)$$

$$= 73.28 \text{ ft}$$

Compute the total head required across the pump.

$$\Delta h = h_{to} - h_{ti}$$
$$= 73.28 \text{ ft} - 23.11 \text{ ft}$$
$$= 50.17 \text{ ft}$$

The mass flow rate is

$$\dot{m} = \rho \dot{V}$$

In terms of the specific gravity, the mass flow rate is

$$\dot{m} = (\text{SG})\rho_{\text{water}}\dot{V}$$

$$= (1.2)\left(62.4 \ \frac{\text{lbm}}{\text{ft}^3}\right)\left(2000 \ \frac{\text{gal}}{\text{min}}\right)\left(\frac{0.002228 \ \frac{\text{ft}^3}{\text{sec}}}{1 \ \frac{\text{gal}}{\text{min}}}\right)$$

$$= 333.7 \text{ lbm/sec}$$

The power that must be added to the pump is

$$P = \frac{\Delta h \dot{m}\left(\frac{g}{g_c}\right)}{\eta}$$

$$= \frac{(50.17 \text{ ft})\left(333.7 \ \frac{\text{lbm}}{\text{sec}}\right)\left(\frac{32.2 \ \frac{\text{lbm-ft}}{\text{lbf-sec}^2}}{32.2 \ \frac{\text{ft}}{\text{sec}^2}}\right)}{(0.85)\left(550 \ \frac{\text{ft-lbf}}{\text{hp-sec}}\right)}$$

$$= \boxed{35.8 \text{ hp}}$$

SI Solution

The power that must be added to the pump is given by

$$P = \frac{\Delta h \dot{m} g}{\eta}$$

Assume the pipe nominal diameter is equal to the internal diameter.

$$D_i = 0.30 \text{ m}$$
$$A_i = \frac{\pi D_i^2}{4} = \frac{\pi(0.30 \text{ m})^2}{4} = 0.0707 \text{ m}^2$$
$$v = \frac{\dot{V}}{A_i}$$
$$= \frac{0.125 \ \frac{\text{m}^3}{\text{sec}}}{0.0707 \text{ m}^2}$$
$$= 1.77 \text{ m/s}$$

(Note that the pressures are in terms of gage pressure, and the density of mercury is $13\,600$ kg/m³.)

$$p_i = 1.013 \times 10^5 \text{ Pa}$$
$$- (0.15 \text{ m}) \left(13\,600 \ \frac{\text{kg}}{\text{m}^3} \right) \left(9.81 \ \frac{\text{m}}{\text{s}^2} \right)$$
$$= 8.13 \times 10^4 \text{ Pa}$$

$$E_{ti} = \frac{\rho}{\rho} + \frac{v_i^2}{2} + z_i g$$

Since the pump inlet and outlet are at the same elevation, use $z = 0$ and $\rho = (\text{SG})\rho_{\text{water}}$.

$$E_{ti} = \frac{\rho}{(\text{SG})\rho_{\text{water}}} + \frac{v_i^2}{2} + 0$$
$$= \frac{8.13 \times 10^4 \text{ Pa}}{(1.2) \left(1000 \ \frac{\text{kg}}{\text{m}^3} \right)} + \frac{\left(1.77 \ \frac{\text{m}}{\text{s}} \right)^2}{2}$$
$$= 69.3 \text{ J/kg}$$

The total head at the inlet is

$$h_{ti} = \frac{E_{ti}}{g}$$
$$= \frac{69.3 \ \frac{\text{J}}{\text{kg}}}{9.81 \ \frac{\text{m}}{\text{s}^2}}$$
$$= 7.06 \text{ m}$$

Assume the pipe nominal diameter is equal to the internal diameter. On the outlet side of the pump,

$$D_i = 0.20 \text{ m}$$
$$A_o = \frac{\pi D_o^2}{4} = \frac{\pi (0.20 \text{ m})^2}{4} = 0.0314 \text{ m}^2$$
$$v_o = \frac{\dot{V}}{A_o}$$
$$= \frac{0.125 \ \frac{\text{m}^3}{\text{sec}}}{0.0314 \text{ m}^2}$$
$$= 3.98 \text{ m/s}$$

(Note that the pressures are in terms of gage pressure and the gage is located 1.2 m above the pump outlet, which adds 1.2 m of pressure head at the pump outlet.)

$$p_o = 1.013 \times 10^5 \text{ Pa} + 13.8 \times 10^3 \text{ Pa}$$
$$+ (1.2 \text{ m}) \left[(1.2) \left(1000 \ \frac{\text{kg}}{\text{m}^3} \right) \left(9.81 \ \frac{\text{m}}{\text{s}^2} \right) \right]$$
$$= 1.29 \times 10^5 \text{ Pa}$$

$$E_{to} = \frac{p_o}{\rho} + \frac{v_o^2}{2} + z_o g$$

Since the pump inlet and outlet are at the same elevation, use $z = 0$ and $\rho = (\text{SG})\rho_{\text{water}}$.

$$E_{to} = \frac{p_o}{(\text{SG})\rho_{\text{water}}} + \frac{v_o^2}{2} + 0$$
$$= \frac{1.29 \times 10^5 \text{ Pa}}{(1.2) \left(1000 \ \frac{\text{kg}}{\text{m}^3} \right)} + \frac{\left(3.98 \ \frac{\text{m}}{\text{s}} \right)^2}{2}$$
$$= 115.4 \text{ J/kg}$$

The total head at the outlet is

$$h_{to} = \frac{E_{to}}{g}$$
$$= \frac{115.4 \ \frac{\text{J}}{\text{kg}}}{9.81 \ \frac{\text{m}}{\text{s}^2}}$$
$$= 11.76 \text{ m}$$

The total head required across the pump is

$$\Delta h = h_{to} - h_{ti}$$
$$= 11.76 \text{ m} - 7.04 \text{ m}$$
$$= 4.72 \text{ m}$$

The mass flow rate is

$$\dot{m} = \rho \dot{V}$$

In terms of the specific gravity, the mass flow rate is

$$\dot{m} = (\text{SG})\rho_{\text{water}} Q$$
$$= (1.2) \left(1000 \ \frac{\text{kg}}{\text{m}^3} \right) \left(0.125 \ \frac{\text{m}^3}{\text{s}} \right)$$
$$= 150 \text{ kg/s}$$

The power that must be added to the pump is

$$P = \frac{\Delta h \dot{m} g}{\eta}$$
$$= \frac{(4.72 \text{ m}) \left(150 \ \frac{\text{kg}}{\text{s}} \right) \left(9.81 \ \frac{\text{m}}{\text{s}^2} \right)}{0.85}$$
$$= \boxed{8171 \text{ W} \quad (8.2 \text{ kW})}$$

10. *Customary U.S. Solution*

The power developed by the horizontal turbine is given by

$$P = \dot{m} h_{\text{loss}} \left(\frac{g}{g_c} \right)$$

The mass flow rate is

$$\dot{m} = \dot{V} \rho$$
$$= \left(100 \ \frac{\text{ft}^3}{\text{sec}} \right) \left(62.4 \ \frac{\text{lbm}}{\text{ft}^3} \right)$$
$$= 6240 \ \text{lbm/sec}$$

The head loss across the horizontal turbine is given by

$$h_{\text{loss}} = \left(\frac{\Delta p}{\rho} \right) \left(\frac{g_c}{g} \right)$$
$$= \left(\frac{\left(30 \ \frac{\text{lbf}}{\text{in}^2} - \left(-5 \ \frac{\text{lbf}}{\text{in}^2} \right) \right) \left(\frac{144 \ \text{in}^2}{1 \ \text{ft}^2} \right)}{62.4 \ \frac{\text{lbm}}{\text{ft}^3}} \right)$$
$$\times \left(\frac{32.2 \ \frac{\text{lbm-ft}}{\text{lbf-sec}^2}}{32.2 \ \frac{\text{ft}}{\text{sec}^2}} \right)$$
$$= 80.77 \ \text{ft}$$

The power developed is

$$P = \dot{m} h_{\text{loss}} \left(\frac{g}{g_c} \right)$$
$$= \frac{\left(6240 \ \frac{\text{lbm}}{\text{sec}} \right) (80.77 \ \text{ft}) \left(32.2 \ \frac{\text{ft}}{\text{sec}^2} \right)}{\left(32.2 \ \frac{\text{lbm-ft}}{\text{lbf-sec}^2} \right) \left(550 \ \frac{\text{ft-lbf}}{\text{hp-sec}} \right)}$$
$$= \boxed{916 \ \text{hp}}$$

SI Solution

The power developed by the horizontal turbine is given by

$$P = \frac{\dot{m} h_{\text{loss}}}{g}$$

The mass flow rate is

$$\dot{m} = \dot{V} \rho$$
$$= \left(2.6 \ \frac{\text{m}^3}{\text{s}} \right) \left(1000 \ \frac{\text{kg}}{\text{m}^3} \right)$$
$$= 2600 \ \text{kg/s}$$

The head loss across the horizontal turbine is given by

$$h_{\text{loss}} = \frac{\Delta p}{\rho g}$$
$$= \frac{(210 \ \text{kPa} - (-35 \ \text{kPa})) \left(1000 \ \frac{\text{Pa}}{\text{kPa}} \right)}{\left(1000 \ \frac{\text{kg}}{\text{m}^3} \right) \left(9.81 \ \frac{\text{m}}{\text{s}^2} \right)}$$
$$= 25.0 \ \text{m}$$

The power developed is

$$P = \frac{\dot{m} h_{\text{loss}}}{g}$$
$$= \frac{\left(2600 \ \frac{\text{kg}}{\text{s}} \right) (25.0 \ \text{m})}{9.81 \ \frac{\text{m}}{\text{s}^2}}$$
$$= \boxed{6626 \ \text{W} \quad (6.63 \ \text{kW})}$$

11. *Customary U.S. Solution*

The mass flow rate of the water is

$$\dot{m} = \rho \dot{V} = \rho \text{v} A = \frac{\rho \text{v} \pi d^2}{4}$$
$$= \left(62.4 \ \frac{\text{lbm}}{\text{ft}^3} \right) \left(40 \ \frac{\text{ft}}{\text{sec}} \right) \left(\frac{\pi \left[(2 \ \text{in}) \left(\frac{1 \ \text{ft}}{12 \ \text{in}} \right) \right]^2}{4} \right)$$
$$= 54.45 \ \text{lbm/sec}$$

The effective mass flow rate of the water is

$$\dot{m}_{\text{eff}} = \left(\frac{\text{v} - \text{v}_b}{\text{v}} \right) \dot{m}$$
$$= \left(\frac{40 \ \frac{\text{ft}}{\text{sec}} - 15 \ \frac{\text{ft}}{\text{sec}}}{40 \ \frac{\text{ft}}{\text{sec}}} \right) \left(54.45 \ \frac{\text{lbm}}{\text{sec}} \right)$$
$$= 34.0 \ \text{lbm/sec}$$

The force in the (horizontal) x-direction is given by

$$F_x = \frac{\dot{m}_{\text{eff}} (\text{v} - \text{v}_b)(\cos \theta - 1)}{g_c}$$
$$= \frac{\left(34.0 \ \frac{\text{lbm}}{\text{sec}} \right) \left(40 \ \frac{\text{ft}}{\text{sec}} - 15 \ \frac{\text{ft}}{\text{sec}} \right) (\cos 60° - 1)}{32.2 \ \frac{\text{lbm-ft}}{\text{lbf-sec}^2}}$$
$$= -13.2 \ \text{lbf} \quad \text{[the force is acting to the left]}$$

The force in the (vertical) y-direction is given by

$$F_y = \frac{\dot{m}_{\text{eff}}(\text{v} - \text{v}_b)\sin\theta}{g_c}$$

$$= \frac{\left(34.0\ \dfrac{\text{lbm}}{\text{sec}}\right)\left(40\ \dfrac{\text{ft}}{\text{sec}} - 15\ \dfrac{\text{ft}}{\text{sec}}\right)(\sin 60°)}{32.2\ \dfrac{\text{lbm-ft}}{\text{lbf-sec}^2}}$$

$$= 22.9\ \text{lbf} \quad [\text{the force is acting upward}]$$

The net resultant force is

$$F = \sqrt{F_x^2 + F_y^2}$$

$$= \sqrt{(-13.2\ \text{lbf})^2 + (22.9\ \text{lbf})^2}$$

$$= \boxed{26.4\ \text{lbf}}$$

SI Solution

The mass flow rate of the water is

$$\dot{m} = \rho\dot{V} = \rho\text{v}A = \frac{\rho\text{v}\pi d^2}{4}$$

$$= \left(1000\ \frac{\text{kg}}{\text{m}^3}\right)\left(12\ \frac{\text{m}}{\text{s}}\right)\left(\frac{\pi(0.05\ \text{m})^2}{4}\right)$$

$$= 23.56\ \text{kg/s}$$

The effective mass flow rate of the water is

$$\dot{m}_{\text{eff}} = \left(\frac{\text{v} - \text{v}_b}{\text{v}}\right)\dot{m}$$

$$= \left(\frac{12\ \dfrac{\text{m}}{\text{s}} - 4.5\ \dfrac{\text{m}}{\text{s}}}{12\ \dfrac{\text{m}}{\text{s}}}\right)\left(23.56\ \frac{\text{kg}}{\text{s}}\right)$$

$$= 14.73\ \text{kg/s}$$

The force in the (horizontal) x-direction is given by

$$F_x = \dot{m}_{\text{eff}}(\text{v} - \text{v}_b)(\cos\theta - 1)$$

$$= \left(14.73\ \frac{\text{kg}}{\text{s}}\right)\left(12\ \frac{\text{m}}{\text{s}} - 4.5\ \frac{\text{m}}{\text{s}}\right)(\cos 60° - 1)$$

$$= -55.2\ \text{N} \quad [\text{the force is acting to the left}]$$

The force in the (vertical) y-direction is given by

$$F_y = \dot{m}_{\text{eff}}(\text{v} - \text{v}_b)\sin\theta$$

$$= \left(14.73\ \frac{\text{kg}}{\text{s}}\right)\left(12\ \frac{\text{m}}{\text{s}} - 4.5\ \frac{\text{m}}{\text{s}}\right)(\sin 60°)$$

$$= 95.7\ \text{N} \quad [\text{the force is acting upward}]$$

The net resultant force is

$$F = \sqrt{F_x^2 + F_y^2}$$

$$= \sqrt{(-55.2\ \text{N})^2 + (95.7\ \text{N})^2}$$

$$= \boxed{110.5\ \text{N}}$$

12. *Customary U.S. Solution*

The composite modulus of elasticity of the pipe and water is given by

$$E = \frac{E_{\text{water}}t_{\text{pipe}}E_{\text{pipe}}}{t_{\text{pipe}}E_{\text{pipe}} + d_{\text{pipe}}E_{\text{water}}}$$

For water at 70°F, $E_{\text{water}} = 320 \times 10^3\ \text{lbf/in}^2$.

For cast iron pipe, $E_{\text{pipe}} = 20 \times 10^6\ \text{lbf/in}^2$.

$$E = \frac{E_{\text{water}}t_{\text{pipe}}E_{\text{pipe}}}{t_{\text{pipe}}E_{\text{pipe}} + d_{\text{pipe}}E_{\text{water}}}$$

$$= \frac{\left(320 \times 10^3\ \dfrac{\text{lbf}}{\text{in}^2}\right)(0.75\ \text{in})\left(20 \times 10^6\ \dfrac{\text{lbf}}{\text{in}^2}\right)}{\begin{array}{c}(0.75\ \text{in})\left(20 \times 10^6\ \dfrac{\text{lbf}}{\text{in}^2}\right) \\[4pt] + (24\ \text{in})\left(320 \times 10^3\ \dfrac{\text{lbf}}{\text{in}^2}\right)\end{array}}$$

$$= 2.12 \times 10^5\ \text{lbf/in}^2$$

The speed of sound in the pipe is

$$a = \sqrt{\frac{Eg_c}{\rho}}$$

$$= \sqrt{\frac{\left(2.12 \times 10^5\ \dfrac{\text{lbf}}{\text{in}^2}\right)\left(\dfrac{144\ \text{in}^2}{1\ \text{ft}^2}\right)\left(32.2\ \dfrac{\text{lbm-ft}}{\text{lbf-sec}^2}\right)}{62.3\ \dfrac{\text{lbm}}{\text{ft}^3}}}$$

$$= \boxed{3972\ \text{ft/sec}}$$

(a) The maximum pressure is given by

$$\Delta p = \frac{\rho a \Delta \text{v}}{g_c}$$

$$= \left(\frac{\left(62.3\ \dfrac{\text{lbm}}{\text{ft}^3}\right)\left(3972\ \dfrac{\text{ft}}{\text{sec}}\right)\left(6\ \dfrac{\text{ft}}{\text{sec}}\right)}{32.2\ \dfrac{\text{lbm-ft}}{\text{lbf-sec}^2}}\right)$$

$$\times \left(\frac{1\ \text{ft}^2}{144\ \text{in}^2}\right)$$

$$= \boxed{320.2\ \text{lbf/in}^2 \quad (320.2\ \text{psi})}$$

(b) The length of time the pressure is constant at the valve is given by

$$t = \frac{2L}{a}$$

$$= \frac{(2)(500 \text{ ft})}{3972 \frac{\text{ft}}{\text{sec}}}$$

$$= \boxed{0.252 \text{ sec}}$$

SI Solution

The composite modulus of elasticity of the pipe and water is given by

$$E = \frac{E_{\text{water}} t_{\text{pipe}} E_{\text{pipe}}}{t_{\text{pipe}} E_{\text{pipe}} + d_{\text{pipe}} E_{\text{water}}}$$

For water at 20°C, $E_{\text{water}} = 2.2 \times 10^9$ Pa.

For cast iron pipe, $E_{\text{pipe}} = 1.4 \times 10^{11}$ Pa.

$$E = \frac{E_{\text{water}} t_{\text{pipe}} E_{\text{pipe}}}{t_{\text{pipe}} E_{\text{pipe}} + d_{\text{pipe}} E_{\text{water}}}$$

$$= \frac{(2.2 \times 10^9 \text{ Pa})(0.02 \text{ m})(1.4 \times 10^{11} \text{ Pa})}{(0.02 \text{ m})(1.4 \times 10^{11} \text{ Pa}) + (0.6 \text{ m})(2.2 \times 10^9 \text{ Pa})}$$

$$= 1.50 \times 10^9 \text{ Pa}$$

The speed of sound in the pipe is

$$a = \sqrt{\frac{E}{\rho}}$$

$$= \sqrt{\frac{1.50 \times 10^9 \text{ Pa}}{1000 \frac{\text{kg}}{\text{m}^3}}}$$

$$= 1225 \text{ m/s}$$

(a) The maximum pressure is given by

$$\Delta p = \rho a \Delta v$$

$$= \left(1000 \frac{\text{kg}}{\text{m}^3}\right)\left(1225 \frac{\text{m}}{\text{s}}\right)\left(2 \frac{\text{m}}{\text{s}}\right)$$

$$= \boxed{2.45 \times 10^6 \text{ Pa} \quad (2450 \text{ kPa})}$$

(b) The length of time the pressure is constant at the valve is given by

$$t = \frac{2L}{a}$$

$$= \frac{(2)(150 \text{ m})}{1225 \frac{\text{m}}{\text{s}}}$$

$$= \boxed{0.245 \text{ s}}$$

13. *Customary U.S. Solution*

(a) The drag on the car is given by

$$F_D = \frac{C_D A \rho v^2}{2g_c}$$

For air at 70°F,

$$\rho = \frac{p}{RT} = \frac{\left(14.7 \frac{\text{lbf}}{\text{in}^2}\right)\left(144 \frac{\text{in}^2}{\text{ft}^2}\right)}{\left(53.35 \frac{\text{ft-lbf}}{\text{lbm-}°\text{R}}\right)(70°\text{F} + 460)}$$

$$= 0.00749 \text{ lbm/ft}^3$$

$$v = \left(55 \frac{\text{mi}}{\text{hr}}\right)\left(5280 \frac{\text{ft}}{\text{mi}}\right)\left(\frac{1 \text{ hr}}{3600 \text{ sec}}\right)$$

$$= 80.67 \text{ ft/sec}$$

Substituting gives

$$F_D = \frac{C_D A \rho v^2}{2g_c}$$

$$= \frac{(0.42)(28 \text{ ft}^2)\left(0.0749 \frac{\text{lbm}}{\text{ft}^3}\right)\left(80.67 \frac{\text{ft}}{\text{sec}}\right)^2}{(2)\left(32.2 \frac{\text{lbm-ft}}{\text{lbf-sec}^2}\right)}$$

$$= 89.0 \text{ lbf}$$

The total resisting force is

$$F = F_D + \text{rolling resistance}$$

$$= 89.0 \text{ lbf} + (0.01)(3300 \text{ lbm})\left(\frac{g}{g_c}\right)$$

$$= 89.0 \text{ lbf} + \frac{(0.01)(3300 \text{ lbm})\left(32.2 \frac{\text{ft}}{\text{sec}^2}\right)}{32.2 \frac{\text{lbm-ft}}{\text{lbf-sec}^2}}$$

$$= 122.0 \text{ lbf}$$

The power consumed is

$$P_c = Fv$$

$$= \frac{(122.0 \text{ lbf})\left(80.67 \frac{\text{ft}}{\text{sec}}\right)}{778 \frac{\text{ft-lbf}}{\text{Btu}}}$$

$$= 12.65 \text{ Btu/sec}$$

The power available from the fuel is

$$P_A = (\text{engine thermal efficiency})(\text{fuel heating value})$$

$$= (0.28)\left(115,000 \frac{\text{Btu}}{\text{gal}}\right)$$

$$= 32,200 \text{ Btu/gal}$$

The fuel consumption at 55 mi/hr is

$$\frac{P_c}{P_A} = \frac{12.65 \, \frac{\text{Btu}}{\text{sec}}}{32{,}000 \, \frac{\text{Btu}}{\text{gal}}}$$

$$= 3.95 \times 10^{-4} \, \text{gal/sec}$$

The fuel consumption is

$$\frac{3.95 \times 10^{-4} \, \frac{\text{gal}}{\text{sec}}}{\left(55 \, \frac{\text{mi}}{\text{hr}}\right)\left(\frac{1 \, \text{hr}}{3600 \, \text{sec}}\right)} = \boxed{0.0259 \, \text{gal/mi}}$$

(b) Similarly, the fuel consumption at 65 mi/hr is

$$v = \left(65 \, \frac{\text{mi}}{\text{hr}}\right)\left(5280 \, \frac{\text{ft}}{\text{mi}}\right)\left(\frac{1 \, \text{hr}}{3600 \, \text{sec}}\right)$$

$$= 95.33 \, \text{ft/sec}$$

$$F_D = \frac{C_D A \rho v^2}{2 g_c}$$

$$= \frac{(0.42)(28 \, \text{ft}^2)\left(0.0749 \, \frac{\text{lbm}}{\text{ft}^3}\right)\left(95.33 \, \frac{\text{ft}}{\text{sec}}\right)^2}{(2)\left(32.2 \, \frac{\text{lbm-ft}}{\text{lbf-sec}^2}\right)}$$

$$= 124.3 \, \text{lbf}$$

The total resisting force is

$$F = F_D + \text{rolling resistance}$$

$$= 124.3 \, \text{lbf} + (0.01)(3300 \, \text{lbm})\left(\frac{g}{g_c}\right)$$

$$= 124.3 \, \text{lbf} + \frac{(0.01)(3300 \, \text{lbm})\left(32.2 \, \frac{\text{ft}}{\text{sec}^2}\right)}{32.2 \, \frac{\text{lbm-ft}}{\text{lbf-sec}^2}}$$

$$= 157.3 \, \text{lbf}$$

The power consumed is

$$P_c = Fv$$

$$= \frac{(157.3 \, \text{lbf})\left(95.33 \, \frac{\text{ft}}{\text{sec}}\right)}{778 \, \frac{\text{ft-lbf}}{\text{Btu}}}$$

$$= 19.27 \, \text{Btu/sec}$$

The fuel consumption at 65 mi/hr is

$$\frac{P_c}{P_A} = \frac{19.27 \, \frac{\text{Btu}}{\text{sec}}}{32{,}000 \, \frac{\text{Btu}}{\text{gal}}}$$

$$= 6.02 \times 10^{-4} \, \text{gal/sec}$$

The fuel consumption is

$$\frac{6.02 \times 10^{-4} \, \frac{\text{gal}}{\text{sec}}}{\left(65 \, \frac{\text{mi}}{\text{hr}}\right)\left(\frac{1 \, \text{hr}}{3600 \, \text{sec}}\right)} = 0.0333 \, \text{gal/mi}$$

The relative difference between the fuel consumption at 55 mi/hr and 65 mi/hr is

$$\frac{0.0333 \, \frac{\text{gal}}{\text{mi}} - 0.0259 \, \frac{\text{gal}}{\text{mi}}}{0.0259 \, \frac{\text{gal}}{\text{mi}}} = \boxed{0.286 \quad (28.6\%)}$$

SI Solution

(a) The drag on the car is given by

$$F_D = \frac{C_D A \rho v^2}{2}$$

For air at 20°C,

$$\rho = \frac{p}{RT} = \frac{1.013 \times 10^5 \, \text{Pa}}{\left(287 \, \frac{\text{J}}{\text{kg·K}}\right)(20°\text{C} + 273)}$$

$$= 1.205 \, \text{kg/m}^3$$

$$v = \left(90 \, \frac{\text{km}}{\text{h}}\right)\left(1000 \, \frac{\text{m}}{\text{km}}\right)\left(\frac{1 \, \text{h}}{3600 \, \text{s}}\right)$$

$$= 25.0 \, \text{m/s}$$

Substituting gives

$$F_D = \frac{C_D A \rho v^2}{2}$$

$$= \left(\tfrac{1}{2}\right)(0.42)(2.6 \, \text{m}^2)\left(1.205 \, \frac{\text{kg}}{\text{m}^3}\right)\left(25.0 \, \frac{\text{m}}{\text{s}}\right)^2$$

$$= 411.2 \, \text{N}$$

The total resisting force is

$$F = F_D + \text{rolling resistance}$$

$$= 411.2 \, \text{N} + (0.01)(1500 \, \text{kg})g$$

$$= 411.2 \, \text{N} + (0.01)(1500 \, \text{kg})\left(9.81 \, \frac{\text{m}}{\text{s}^2}\right)$$

$$= 558.4 \, \text{N}$$

The power consumed is

$$P = Fv$$

$$= (558.4 \, \text{N})\left(25 \, \frac{\text{m}}{\text{s}}\right)$$

$$= 13\,960 \, \text{W}$$

The power available from the fuel is

$$P_A = (\text{engine thermal efficiency})(\text{fuel heating value})$$
$$= (0.28)\left(4.6 \times 10^8 \ \frac{\text{J}}{\text{L}}\right)$$
$$= 1.288 \times 10^8 \ \text{J/L}$$

The fuel consumption at 90 km/h is

$$\frac{P}{P_A} = \frac{13\,960 \ \text{W}}{1.288 \times 10^8 \ \dfrac{\text{J}}{\text{L}}}$$
$$= 1.08 \times 10^{-4} \ \text{L/s}$$

The fuel consumption is

$$\frac{1.08 \times 10^{-4} \ \dfrac{\text{L}}{\text{s}}}{\left(90 \ \dfrac{\text{km}}{\text{h}}\right)\left(\dfrac{1 \ \text{h}}{3600 \ \text{s}}\right)} = \boxed{0.00434 \ \text{L/km}}$$

(b) Similarly, the fuel consumption at 65 mi/h is

$$\text{v} = \left(105 \ \frac{\text{km}}{\text{h}}\right)\left(1000 \ \frac{\text{m}}{\text{km}}\right)\left(\frac{1 \ \text{h}}{3600 \ \text{s}}\right)$$
$$= 29.2 \ \text{m/s}$$
$$D = \frac{C_D A \rho \text{v}^2}{2}$$
$$= \left(\tfrac{1}{2}\right)(0.42)(2.6 \ \text{m}^2)\left(1.205 \ \frac{\text{kg}}{\text{m}^3}\right)\left(29.2 \ \frac{\text{m}}{\text{s}}\right)^2$$
$$= 561.0 \ \text{N}$$

The total resisting force is

$$F = F_D + \text{rolling resistance}$$
$$= 561.0 \ \text{N} + (0.01)(1500 \ \text{kg})g$$
$$= 561.0 \ \text{N} + (0.01)(1500 \ \text{kg})\left(9.81 \ \frac{\text{m}}{\text{s}^2}\right)$$
$$= 708.2 \ \text{N}$$

The power consumed is

$$P_c = F\text{v}$$
$$= (708.2 \ \text{N})\left(29.2 \ \frac{\text{m}}{\text{s}}\right)$$
$$= 20\,679 \ \text{W}$$

The fuel consumption at 105 km/h is

$$\frac{P_c}{P_A} = \frac{20\,679 \ \text{W}}{1.288 \times 10^8 \ \dfrac{\text{J}}{\text{L}}}$$
$$= 1.61 \times 10^{-4} \ \text{L/s}$$

The fuel consumption is

$$\frac{1.61 \times 10^{-4} \ \dfrac{\text{L}}{\text{s}}}{\left(105 \ \dfrac{\text{km}}{\text{h}}\right)\left(\dfrac{1 \ \text{h}}{3600 \ \text{s}}\right)} = 0.00552 \ \text{L/km}$$

The relative difference between the fuel consumption at 90 km/h and 105 km/h is

$$\frac{0.00552 \ \dfrac{\text{L}}{\text{km}} - 0.00434 \ \dfrac{\text{L}}{\text{km}}}{0.00434 \ \dfrac{\text{L}}{\text{km}}} = \boxed{0.272 \ \ (27.2\%)}$$

14. To ensure similarity between the model and the true conditions of the full-scale airplane, the Reynolds numbers must be equal.

Substitute the definition for the Reynolds number where L is a characteristic length.

$$\left(\frac{\text{v}L}{\nu}\right)_{\text{model}} = \left(\frac{\text{v}L}{\nu}\right)_{\text{true}}$$

Use the absolute viscosity.

$$\mu = \frac{\rho\nu}{g_c}$$
$$\nu = \frac{\mu g_c}{\rho}$$

Substituting gives

$$\left(\frac{\text{v}L\rho}{\mu g_c}\right)_{\text{model}} = \left(\frac{\text{v}L\rho}{\mu g_c}\right)_{\text{true}}$$

Since g_c is a constant,

$$\left(\frac{\text{v}L\rho}{\mu}\right)_{\text{model}} = \left(\frac{\text{v}L\rho}{\mu}\right)_{\text{true}}$$

Assume the air behaves as an ideal gas.

$$\rho = \frac{p}{RT}$$

Substituting gives

$$\left(\frac{\text{v}Lp}{\mu RT}\right)_{\text{model}} = \left(\frac{\text{v}Lp}{\mu RT}\right)_{\text{true}}$$

Since the tunnel operates at true velocity and temperature,

$$\text{v}_{\text{model}} = \text{v}_{\text{true}}$$
$$T_{\text{model}} = T_{\text{true}}$$

Since both tunnels operate with air, R is a constant. The expression reduces to

$$\left(\frac{Lp}{\mu}\right)_{\text{model}} = \left(\frac{Lp}{\mu}\right)_{\text{true}}$$

Recall that the absolute viscosity is independent of pressure, so $\mu_{\text{model}} = \mu_{\text{true}}$.

Therefore,

$$(Lp)_{\text{model}} = (Lp)_{\text{true}}$$

Since the scale of the model is 1/20,

$$L_{\text{model}} = \frac{L_{\text{true}}}{20}$$

Substituting gives

$$(Lp)_{\text{model}} = (Lp)_{\text{true}}$$

$$\left(\frac{L_{\text{true}}}{20}\right) p_{\text{model}} = L_{\text{true}} p_{\text{true}}$$

$$\boxed{p_{\text{model}} = 20 p_{\text{true}}}$$

15. To ensure similarity between the two pumps, the Reynolds number, Re, of both pumps must be equal. (Let pump 1 represent the pump for the castor oil and pump 2 represent the pump for air.)

$$\text{Re}_1 = \text{Re}_2$$

Substitute the definition for the Reynolds number.

$$\frac{v_1 D_1}{\nu_1} = \frac{v_2 D_2}{\nu_2}$$

$$\frac{v_1}{v_2} = \left(\frac{\nu_1}{\nu_2}\right)\left(\frac{D_2}{D_1}\right)$$

v is the tangential velocity, and D is the impeller diameter.

$$v \propto nD$$

$$\frac{v_1}{v_2} = \left(\frac{n_1}{n_2}\right)\left(\frac{D_1}{D_2}\right)$$

Therefore,

$$\left(\frac{\nu_1}{\nu_2}\right)\left(\frac{D_2}{D_1}\right) = \left(\frac{n_1}{n_2}\right)\left(\frac{D_1}{D_2}\right)$$

$$n_2 = n_1 \left(\frac{\nu_2}{\nu_1}\right)\left(\frac{D_1}{D_2}\right)^2$$

Since the second pump has an impeller twice the size of the first pump, $D_2 = 2D_1$.

Substituting gives

$$n_2 = n_1 \left(\frac{\nu_2}{\nu_1}\right)\left(\frac{D_1}{D_2}\right)^2$$

$$= n_1 \left(\frac{\nu_2}{\nu_1}\right)\left(\frac{D_1}{2D_1}\right)^2$$

$$= \tfrac{1}{4} n_1 \left(\frac{\nu_2}{\nu_1}\right)$$

Customary U.S. Solution

For air at 68°F, $\nu_2 = 16.0 \times 10^{-5}$ ft^2/sec.

For castor oil at 68°F, $\nu_1 = 1110 \times 10^{-5}$ ft^2/sec (given).

Since $n_1 = 1000$ rpm,

$$n_2 = \tfrac{1}{4} n_1 \left(\frac{\nu_2}{\nu_1}\right)$$

$$= \left(\tfrac{1}{4}\right)(1000 \text{ rpm})\left(\frac{16.0 \times 10^{-5} \, \frac{\text{ft}^2}{\text{sec}}}{1110 \times 10^{-5} \, \frac{\text{ft}^2}{\text{sec}}}\right)$$

$$= \boxed{3.6 \text{ rpm}}$$

SI Solution

For air at 20°C, $\nu_2 = 1.48 \times 10^{-5}$ m^2/s.

For castor oil at 20°C, $\nu_1 = 103 \times 10^{-5}$ m^2/s (given).

Since $n_1 = 1000$ rpm,

$$n_2 = \tfrac{1}{4} n_1 \left(\frac{\nu_2}{\nu_1}\right)$$

$$= \left(\tfrac{1}{4}\right)(1000 \text{ rpm})\left(\frac{1.48 \times 10^{-5} \, \frac{\text{m}^2}{\text{s}}}{103 \times 10^{-5} \, \frac{\text{m}^2}{\text{s}}}\right)$$

$$= \boxed{3.6 \text{ rpm}}$$

16. *Customary U.S. Solution*

First it is necessary to collect data on schedule-40 pipe and water. The fluid viscosity, pipe dimensions, and other parameters can be found in App. 17.A. At 70°F water, $\nu = 1.059 \times 10^{-5}$ ft²/sec.

From Table 17.2, $\epsilon = 0.0002$ ft.

8 in pipe	$D = 0.6651$ ft	
	$A = 0.3474$ ft²	
12 in pipe	$D = 0.9948$ ft	
	$A = 0.7773$ ft²	
16 in pipe	$D = 1.25$ ft	
	$A = 1.2272$ ft²	

The flow quantity is converted from gallons per minute to cubic feet per second.

$$\dot{V} = \frac{(8 \text{ MGD})\left(10^6 \frac{\frac{\text{gal}}{\text{day}}}{\text{MGD}}\right)\left(0.002228 \frac{\frac{\text{ft}^3}{\text{sec}}}{\frac{\text{gal}}{\text{min}}}\right)}{\left(24 \frac{\text{hr}}{\text{day}}\right)\left(60 \frac{\text{min}}{\text{hr}}\right)}$$

$$= 12.378 \text{ ft}^3/\text{sec}$$

For the inlet pipe, the velocity is

$$\text{v} = \frac{\dot{V}}{A} = \frac{12.378 \frac{\text{ft}^3}{\text{sec}}}{0.3474 \text{ ft}^2} = 35.63 \text{ ft/sec}$$

The Reynolds number is

$$\text{Re} = \frac{D\text{v}}{\nu} = \frac{(0.6651 \text{ ft})\left(35.63 \frac{\text{ft}}{\text{sec}}\right)}{1.059 \times 10^{-5} \frac{\text{ft}^2}{\text{sec}}}$$

$$= 2.24 \times 10^6$$

The relative roughness is

$$\frac{\epsilon}{D} = \frac{0.0002 \text{ ft}}{0.6651 \text{ ft}} = 0.0003$$

From Fig. 17.4, $f = 0.015$.

Equation 17.23(b) is used to calculate the frictional energy loss.

$$E_{f,1} = h_f \times \left(\frac{g}{g_c}\right) = \frac{fL\text{v}^2}{2Dg_c}$$

$$= \frac{(0.015)(1000 \text{ ft})\left(35.63 \frac{\text{ft}}{\text{sec}}\right)^2}{(2)(0.6651 \text{ ft})\left(32.2 \frac{\text{lbm-ft}}{\text{lbf-sec}^2}\right)}$$

$$= 444.6 \text{ ft-lbf/lbm}$$

For the outlet pipe, the velocity is

$$\text{v} = \frac{\dot{V}}{A} = \frac{12.378 \frac{\text{ft}^3}{\text{sec}}}{0.7773 \text{ ft}^2} = 15.92 \text{ ft/sec}$$

The Reynolds number is

$$\text{Re} = \frac{D\text{v}}{\nu} = \frac{(0.9948 \text{ ft})\left(15.92 \frac{\text{ft}}{\text{sec}}\right)}{1.059 \times 10^{-5} \frac{\text{ft}^2}{\text{sec}}}$$

$$= 1.5 \times 10^6$$

The relative roughness is

$$\frac{\epsilon}{D} = \frac{0.0002 \text{ ft}}{0.9948 \text{ ft}} = 0.0002$$

From Fig. 17.4, $f = 0.014$.

Equation 17.23(b) is used to calculate the frictional energy loss.

$$E_{f,2} = h_f \times \left(\frac{g}{g_c}\right) = \frac{fL\text{v}^2}{2Dg_c}$$

$$= \frac{(0.014)(1500 \text{ ft})\left(15.92 \frac{\text{ft}}{\text{sec}}\right)^2}{(2)(0.9948 \text{ ft})\left(32.2 \frac{\text{lbm-ft}}{\text{lbf-sec}^2}\right)}$$

$$= 83.1 \text{ ft-lbf/lbm}$$

Assume a 50% split through the two branches. In the upper branch, the velocity is

$$\text{v} = \frac{\dot{V}}{A} = \frac{\left(\frac{1}{2}\right)\left(12.378 \frac{\text{ft}^3}{\text{sec}}\right)}{0.3474 \text{ ft}^2} = 17.81 \text{ ft/sec}$$

The Reynolds number is

$$\text{Re} = \frac{D\text{v}}{\nu} = \frac{(0.6651 \text{ ft})\left(17.81 \frac{\text{ft}}{\text{sec}}\right)}{1.059 \times 10^{-5} \frac{\text{ft}^2}{\text{sec}}}$$

$$= 1.1 \times 10^6$$

The relative roughness is

$$\frac{\epsilon}{D} = \frac{0.0002 \text{ ft}}{0.6651 \text{ ft}} = 0.0003$$

From Fig. 17.4, $f = 0.015$.

For the 16 in pipe in the lower branch, the velocity is

$$v = \frac{\dot{V}}{A} = \frac{\left(\frac{1}{2}\right)\left(12.378 \ \frac{ft^3}{sec}\right)}{1.2272 \ ft^2} = 5.04 \ ft/sec$$

The Reynolds number is

$$Re = \frac{Dv}{\nu} = \frac{(1.25 \ ft)\left(5.04 \ \frac{ft}{sec}\right)}{1.059 \times 10^{-5} \ \frac{ft^2}{sec}}$$
$$= 5.95 \times 10^5$$

The relative roughness is

$$\frac{\epsilon}{D} = \frac{0.0002 \ ft}{1.25 \ ft} = 0.00016$$

From Fig. 17.4, $f = 0.015$.

These values of f for the two branches are fairly insensitive to changes in $\dot{V}$, so they will be used for the rest of the problem in the upper branch.

Eq. 17.23(b) is used to calculate the frictional energy loss in the upper branch.

$$E_{f,\text{upper}} = h_f \times \left(\frac{g}{g_c}\right) = \frac{fLv^2}{2Dg_c}$$
$$= \frac{(0.015)(500 \ ft)\left(17.81 \ \frac{ft}{sec}\right)^2}{(2)(0.6651 \ ft)\left(32.2 \ \frac{lbm\text{-}ft}{lbf\text{-}sec^2}\right)}$$
$$= 55.5 \ ft\text{-}lbf/lbm$$

For the loss for any other flow in the upper branch,

$$E_{f,\text{upper 2}} = E_{f,\text{upper}}\left(\frac{\dot{V}}{\left(\frac{1}{2}\right)\left(12.378 \ \frac{ft^3}{sec}\right)}\right)^2$$
$$= \left(55.5 \ \frac{ft\text{-}lbf}{lbm}\right)\left(\frac{\dot{V}}{6.189 \ \frac{ft^3}{sec}}\right)^2$$
$$= 1.45 \ \dot{V}^2$$

Similarly, for the lower branch, in the 8 in section,

$$E_{f,\text{lower, 8 in}} = \frac{(0.015)(250 \ ft)\left(17.81 \ \frac{ft}{sec}\right)^2}{(2)(0.6651 \ ft)\left(32.2 \ \frac{lbm\text{-}ft}{lbf\text{-}sec^2}\right)}$$
$$= 27.8 \ ft\text{-}lbf/lbm$$

For the lower branch, in the 16 in section,

$$E_{f,\text{lower,16 in}} = \frac{(0.015)(1000 \ ft)\left(5.04 \ \frac{ft}{sec}\right)^2}{(2)(1.25 \ ft)\left(32.2 \ \frac{lbm\text{-}ft}{lbf\text{-}sec^2}\right)}$$
$$= 4.7 \ ft\text{-}lbf/lbm$$

The total loss in the lower branch is

$$E_{f,\text{lower}} = E_{f,\text{lower,8 in}} + E_{f,\text{lower,16 in}}$$
$$= 27.8 \ \frac{ft\text{-}lbf}{lbm} + 4.7 \ \frac{ft\text{-}lbf}{lbm}$$
$$= 32.5 \ ft\text{-}lbf/lbm$$

For the loss for any other flow in the lower branch,

$$E_{f,\text{lower 2}} = E_{f,\text{lower}}\left(\frac{\dot{V}}{\left(\frac{1}{2}\right)\left(12.378 \ \frac{ft^3}{sec}\right)}\right)^2$$
$$= \left(32.5 \ \frac{ft\text{-}lbf}{lbm}\right)\left(\frac{\dot{V}}{6.189 \ \frac{ft^3}{sec}}\right)^2$$
$$= 0.85\dot{V}^2$$

Let x be the fraction flowing in the upper branch. Then, because the friction losses are equal,

$$E_{f,\text{upper 2}} = E_{f,\text{lower 2}}$$
$$1.45x^2 = (0.85)(1-x)^2$$
$$x = 0.432$$

(a)
$$\dot{V}_{\text{upper}} = (0.432)\left(12.378 \ \frac{ft^3}{sec}\right)$$
$$= \boxed{5.347 \ ft^3/sec}$$

$$\dot{V}_{\text{lower}} = (1 - 0.432)\left(12.378 \ \frac{ft^3}{sec}\right)$$
$$= \boxed{7.03 \ ft^3/sec}$$

(b)
$$E_{f,\text{total}} = E_{f,1} + E_{f,\text{lower 2}} + E_{f,2}$$
$$E_{f,\text{lower 2}} = 0.85\dot{V}_{\text{lower}}^2$$
$$= (0.85)\left(7.03 \ \frac{ft^3}{sec}\right)^2$$
$$= 42.0 \ ft$$

$$E_{f,\text{total}} = 444.6 \ \frac{ft\text{-}lbf}{lbm} + 42.0 \ \frac{ft\text{-}lbf}{lbm} + 83.1 \ \frac{ft\text{-}lbf}{lbm}$$
$$= \boxed{569.7 \ ft\text{-}lbf/lbm}$$

SI Solution

First it is necessary to collect data on schedule-40 pipe and water. The fluid viscosity, pipe dimensions, and other parameters can be found in App. 17.B. At 20°C water, $\nu = 1.007 \times 10^{-6}$ m^2/s.

From Table 17.2, $\epsilon = 6 \times 10^{-5}$ m.

8 in pipe	$D = 202.7$ mm	$A = 322.7 \times 10^{-4}$ m^2
12 in pipe	$D = 303.2$ mm	$A = 721.9 \times 10^{-4}$ m^2
16 in pipe	$D = 381$ mm	$A = 1104 \times 10^{-4}$ m^2

For the inlet pipe, the velocity is

$$v = \frac{\dot{V}}{A} = \frac{\left(350 \frac{L}{s}\right)\left(\frac{1 \text{ m}^3}{1000 \text{ L}}\right)}{322.7 \times 10^{-4} \text{ m}^2} = 10.85 \text{ m/s}$$

The Reynolds number is

$$Re = \frac{Dv}{\nu} = \frac{(0.2027 \text{ m})\left(10.85 \frac{m}{s}\right)}{1.007 \times 10^{-6} \frac{m^2}{s}}$$
$$= 2.18 \times 10^6$$

The relative roughness is

$$\frac{\epsilon}{D} = \frac{6 \times 10^{-5} \text{ m}}{0.2027 \text{ m}} = 0.0003$$

From Fig. 17.4, $f = 0.015$.

Equation 17.23(a) is used to calculate the frictional energy loss.

$$E_{f,1} = h_f g = \frac{fLv^2}{2D}$$
$$= \frac{(0.015)(300 \text{ m})\left(10.85 \frac{m}{s}\right)^2}{(2)(0.2027 \text{ m})}$$
$$= 1307 \text{ J/kg}$$

For the outlet pipe, the velocity is

$$v = \frac{\dot{V}}{A} = \frac{\left(350 \frac{L}{s}\right)\left(\frac{1 \text{ m}^3}{1000 \text{ L}}\right)}{721.9 \times 10^{-4} \text{ m}^2} = 4.848 \text{ m/s}$$

The Reynolds number is

$$Re = \frac{Dv}{\nu} = \frac{(0.3032 \text{ m})\left(4.848 \frac{m}{s}\right)}{1.007 \times 10^{-6} \frac{m^2}{s}}$$
$$= 1.46 \times 10^6$$

The relative roughness is

$$\frac{\epsilon}{D} = \frac{6 \times 10^{-5} \text{ m}}{0.3032 \text{ m}} = 0.0002$$

From Fig. 17.4, $f = 0.014$.

Equation 17.23(b) is used to calculate the frictional energy loss.

$$E_{f,2} = h_f g = \frac{fLv^2}{2D}$$
$$= \frac{(0.014)(450 \text{ m})\left(4.848 \frac{m}{s}\right)^2}{(2)(0.3032 \text{ m})}$$
$$= 244.2 \text{ J/kg}$$

Assume a 50% split through the two branches. In the upper branch, the velocity is

$$v = \frac{\dot{V}}{A} = \frac{\left(\frac{1}{2}\right)\left(350 \frac{L}{s}\right)\left(\frac{1 \text{ m}^3}{1000 \text{ L}}\right)}{322.7 \times 10^{-4} \text{ m}^2} = 5.423 \text{ m/s}$$

The Reynolds number is

$$Re = \frac{Dv}{\nu} = \frac{(0.2027 \text{ m})\left(5.423 \frac{m}{s}\right)}{1.007 \times 10^{-6} \frac{m^2}{s}}$$
$$= 1.1 \times 10^6$$

The relative roughness is

$$\frac{\epsilon}{D} = \frac{6 \times 10^{-5} \text{ m}}{0.2027 \text{ m}} = 0.0003$$

From Fig. 17.4, $f = 0.015$.

For the 16 in pipe in the lower branch, the velocity is

$$v = \frac{\dot{V}}{A} = \frac{\left(\frac{1}{2}\right)\left(350 \frac{L}{s}\right)\left(\frac{1 \text{ m}^3}{1000 \text{ L}}\right)}{1104 \times 10^{-4} \text{ m}^2} = 1.585 \text{ m/s}$$

The Reynolds number is

$$Re = \frac{Dv}{\nu} = \frac{(0.381 \text{ m})\left(1.585 \frac{m}{s}\right)}{1.007 \times 10^{-6} \frac{m^2}{s}}$$
$$= 6.00 \times 10^5$$

The relative roughness is

$$\frac{\epsilon}{D} = \frac{6 \times 10^{-5} \text{ m}}{0.381 \text{ m}} = 0.00016$$

From Fig. 17.4, $f = 0.015$.

These values of f for the two branches are fairly insensitive to changes in $\dot{V}$, so they will be used for the rest of the problem in the upper branch.

Eq. 17.23(a) is used to calculate the frictional energy loss in the upper branch.

$$E_{f,\text{upper}} = h_f g = \frac{fLv^2}{2D}$$

$$= \frac{(0.015)(150 \text{ m})\left(5.423 \frac{\text{m}}{\text{s}}\right)^2}{(2)(0.2027 \text{ m})}$$

$$= 163.2 \text{ J/kg}$$

For the loss for any other flow in the upper branch,

$$E_{f,\text{upper 2}} = E_{f,\text{upper}} \left(\frac{\dot{V}}{\left(\frac{1}{2}\right)\left(0.350 \frac{\text{m}^3}{\text{s}}\right)}\right)^2$$

$$= \left(163.2 \frac{\text{J}}{\text{kg}}\right)\left(\frac{\dot{V}}{0.175 \frac{\text{m}^3}{\text{s}}}\right)^2$$

$$= 5329\dot{V}^2$$

Similarly, for the lower branch, in the 8 in section,

$$E_{f,\text{lower, 8 in}} = \frac{(0.015)(75 \text{ m})\left(5.423 \frac{\text{m}}{\text{s}}\right)^2}{(2)(0.2027 \text{ m})}$$

$$= 81.61 \text{ J/kg}$$

For the lower branch, in the 16 in section,

$$E_{f,\text{lower,16 in}} = \frac{(0.015)(300 \text{ m})\left(1.585 \frac{\text{m}}{\text{s}}\right)^2}{(2)(0.381 \text{ m})}$$

$$= 14.84 \text{ J/kg}$$

The total loss in the lower branch is

$$E_{f,\text{lower}} = E_{f,\text{lower,8 in}} + E_{f,\text{lower,16 in}}$$

$$= 81.61 \frac{\text{J}}{\text{kg}} + 14.84 \frac{\text{J}}{\text{kg}}$$

$$= 96.45 \text{ J/kg}$$

For the loss for any other flow in the lower branch,

$$E_{f,\text{lower 2}} = E_{f,\text{lower}} \left(\frac{\dot{V}}{\left(\frac{1}{2}\right)\left(0.350 \frac{\text{m}^3}{\text{s}}\right)}\right)^2$$

$$= \left(96.45 \frac{\text{J}}{\text{kg}}\right)\left(\frac{\dot{V}}{0.175 \frac{\text{m}^3}{\text{s}}}\right)^2$$

$$= 3149\dot{V}^2$$

Let x be the fraction flowing in the upper branch. Then, because the friction losses are equal,

$$E_{f,\text{upper 2}} = E_{f,\text{lower 2}}$$
$$5329x^2 = (3149)(1-x)^2$$
$$x = 0.435$$

(a) $$\dot{V}_{\text{upper}} = (0.435)\left(0.350 \frac{\text{m}^3}{\text{s}}\right)$$

$$= \boxed{0.152 \text{ m}^3/\text{s}}$$

$$\dot{V}_{\text{lower}} = (1 - 0.435)\left(0.350 \frac{\text{m}^3}{\text{s}}\right)$$

$$= \boxed{0.198 \text{ m}^3/\text{s}}$$

(b) $$E_{f,\text{total}} = E_{f,1} + E_{f,\text{lower 2}} + E_{f,2}$$

$$E_{f,\text{lower 2}} = 3149\dot{V}_{\text{lower}}^2$$

$$= (3149)\left(0.198 \frac{\text{m}^3}{\text{s}}\right)^2$$

$$= 123.5 \text{ J/kg}$$

$$E_{f,\text{total}} = 1307 \frac{\text{J}}{\text{kg}} + 123.5 \frac{\text{J}}{\text{kg}} + 244.2 \frac{\text{J}}{\text{kg}}$$

$$= \boxed{1675 \text{ J/kg}}$$

18 Hydraulic Machines

1. *Customary U.S. Solution*

From Table 18.4, the hydraulic horsepower is

$$\text{WHP} = \frac{\Delta p Q}{1714}$$

$$\Delta p = p_d - p_s$$

The absolute pressures are

$$p_d = 40 \text{ psig} + 14.7 = 54.7 \text{ psia}$$
$$p_s = 1 \text{ atm} = 14.7 \text{ psia}$$
$$\Delta p = 54.7 \text{ psia} - 14.7 \text{ psia} = 40 \text{ psia}$$

$$\text{WHP} = \frac{\left(40 \ \frac{\text{lbf}}{\text{in}^2}\right)\left(37 \ \frac{\text{gal}}{\text{min}}\right)}{1714 \ \frac{\text{in}^2\text{-min}}{\text{lbf-gal-hp}}} = \boxed{0.863 \text{ hp}}$$

SI Solution

From Table 18.5, the hydraulic kilowatts are

$$\text{WkW} = \frac{\Delta p Q}{1000}$$

$$\Delta p = p_d - p_s$$

The absolute pressures are

$$p_d = 275 \text{ kPa} + 101.3 \text{ kPa} = 376.3 \text{ kPa}$$
$$p_s = 1 \text{ atm} = 101.3 \text{ kPa}$$
$$\Delta p = 376.3 \text{ kPa} - 101.3 \text{ kPa} = 275 \text{ kPa}$$

$$\text{WkW} = \frac{(275 \text{ kPa})\left(65 \ \frac{\text{L}}{\text{s}}\right)}{1000 \ \frac{\text{W}}{\text{kW}}} = \boxed{17.88 \text{ kW}}$$

2. *Customary U.S. Solution*

From App. 16.B, data for 4 in schedule-40 steel pipe are

$$D_i = 0.3355 \text{ ft}$$
$$A_i = 0.08841 \text{ ft}^2$$

The velocity in the pipe is

$$\text{v} = \frac{Q}{A} = \frac{1.25 \ \frac{\text{ft}^3}{\text{sec}}}{0.08841 \text{ ft}^2} = 14.139 \text{ ft/sec}$$

From Table 17.3, typical equivalent lengths for schedule-40, screwed steel fittings for 4 in pipes are

90° elbow: 13 ft

gate valve: 2.5 ft

check valve: 38.0 ft

The total equivalent length is

$$(2)(13 \text{ ft}) + (1)(2.5 \text{ ft}) + (1)(38 \text{ ft}) = 66.5 \text{ ft}$$

At 70°F, from App. 14.A, the density of water is 62.3 lbm/ft³ and the kinematic viscosity of water, ν, is 1.059×10^{-5} ft²/sec. The Reynolds number is

$$\text{Re} = \frac{D\text{v}}{\nu} = \frac{(0.3355 \text{ ft})\left(14.139 \ \frac{\text{ft}}{\text{sec}}\right)}{1.059 \times 10^{-5} \ \frac{\text{ft}^2}{\text{sec}}}$$

$$= 4.479 \times 10^5$$

From App. 17.A, for steel, $\epsilon = 0.0002$ ft.
So,

$$\frac{\epsilon}{D} = \frac{0.0002 \text{ ft}}{0.3355 \text{ ft}} \approx 0.0006$$

From App. 17.B, the friction factor is $f = 0.01835$.

The friction head is

$$h_f = \frac{fL\text{v}^2}{2Dg}$$

$$= \frac{(0.01835)(700 \text{ ft} + 66.5 \text{ ft})\left(14.139 \ \frac{\text{ft}}{\text{sec}}\right)^2}{(2)(0.3355 \text{ ft})\left(32.2 \ \frac{\text{ft}}{\text{sec}^2}\right)}$$

$$= 130.1 \text{ ft}$$

The total dynamic head is

$$h = \frac{(p_d - p_s)g_c}{\rho g} + \frac{\text{v}_d^2 - \text{v}_s^2}{2g} + z_d - z_s$$

$$\text{v}_s \approx 0$$

$$z_d - z_s = 50 \text{ ft} \quad \text{[given as rise in elevation]}$$

The absolute discharge and suction pressures are

$$p_d = 20 \text{ psig} + 14.7 = 34.7 \text{ psia}$$
$$p_s = 50 \text{ psig} + 14.7 = 64.7 \text{ psia}$$

$$h = \frac{\left(34.7\,\frac{\text{lbf}}{\text{in}^2} - 64.7\,\frac{\text{lbf}}{\text{in}^2}\right) \times \left(144\,\frac{\text{in}^2}{\text{ft}^2}\right)\left(32.2\,\frac{\text{ft-lbm}}{\text{lbf-sec}^2}\right)}{\left(62.3\,\frac{\text{lbm}}{\text{ft}^3}\right)\left(32.2\,\frac{\text{ft}}{\text{sec}^2}\right)}$$
$$+ \frac{\left(14.139\,\frac{\text{ft}}{\text{sec}}\right)^2}{(2)\left(32.2\,\frac{\text{ft}}{\text{sec}^2}\right)} + 50 \text{ ft}$$

$$= -16.2 \text{ ft}$$

The head added is

$$h_A = h + h_f = -16.2 \text{ ft} + 130.1 \text{ ft}$$
$$= 113.9 \text{ ft}$$

The mass flow rate is

$$\dot{m} = \rho \dot{V}$$
$$= \left(62.3\,\frac{\text{lbm}}{\text{ft}^3}\right)\left(1.25\,\frac{\text{ft}^3}{\text{sec}}\right)$$
$$= 77.875 \text{ lbm/sec}$$

From Table 18.4, the hydraulic horsepower is

$$\text{WHP} = \left(\frac{h_A \dot{m}}{550}\right) \times \left(\frac{g}{g_c}\right)$$
$$= \left(\frac{(113.9 \text{ ft})\left(77.875\,\frac{\text{lbm}}{\text{sec}}\right)}{550\,\frac{\text{ft-lbf}}{\text{hp-sec}}}\right)$$
$$\times \left(\frac{32.2\,\frac{\text{ft}}{\text{sec}^2}}{32.2\,\frac{\text{ft-lbf}}{\text{lbm-sec}^2}}\right)$$
$$= \boxed{16.13 \text{ hp}}$$

SI Solution

From App. 16.C, data for 4 in schedule-40 steel pipe are

$$D_i = 102.3 \text{ mm}$$
$$A_i = 82.19 \times 10^{-4} \text{ m}^2$$

The velocity in the pipe is

$$v = \frac{\dot{V}}{A} = \frac{\left(35\,\frac{\text{L}}{\text{s}}\right)\left(\frac{1 \text{ m}^3}{1000 \text{ L}}\right)}{82.19 \times 10^{-4} \text{ m}^2} = 4.26 \text{ m/s}$$

From Table 17.3, typical equivalent lengths for schedule-40, screwed steel fittings for 4 in pipes are

90° elbow: 13 ft

gate valve: 2.5 ft

check valve: 38.0 ft

The total equivalent length is

$$(66.5 \text{ ft})\left(0.3048\,\frac{\text{m}}{\text{ft}}\right) = 20.27 \text{ m}$$

At 21°C, from App. 14.B, the water properties are

$$\rho = 998 \text{ kg/m}^3$$
$$\mu = 0.9827 \times 10^{-3} \text{ Pa·s}$$
$$\nu = \frac{\mu}{\rho} = \frac{0.9827 \times 10^{-3} \text{ Pa·s}}{998\,\frac{\text{kg}}{\text{m}^3}}$$
$$= 9.85 \times 10^{-7} \text{ m}^2/\text{s}$$

The Reynolds number is

$$\text{Re} = \frac{Dv}{\nu} = \frac{(102.3 \text{ mm})\left(\frac{1 \text{ m}}{1000 \text{ mm}}\right)\left(4.26\,\frac{\text{m}}{\text{s}}\right)}{9.85 \times 10^{-7}\,\frac{\text{m}^2}{\text{s}}}$$
$$= 4.424 \times 10^5$$

From Table 17.2, for steel, $\epsilon = 6 \times 10^{-5}$ m. So,

$$\frac{\epsilon}{D} = \frac{6.0 \times 10^{-5} \text{ m}}{(102.3 \text{ mm})\left(\frac{1 \text{ m}}{1000 \text{ mm}}\right)} = 0.0006$$

From App. 17.B, the friction factor is $f = 0.01836$.
From Eq. 18.6, the friction head is

$$h_f = \frac{fLv^2}{2Dg}$$
$$= \frac{(0.01836)(230 \text{ m} + 20.27 \text{ m})\left(4.26\,\frac{\text{m}}{\text{s}}\right)^2}{(2)(102.3 \text{ mm})\left(\frac{1 \text{ m}}{1000 \text{ mm}}\right)\left(9.81\,\frac{\text{m}}{\text{s}^2}\right)}$$
$$= 41.5 \text{ m}$$

The total dynamic head is

$$h = \frac{p_d - p_s}{\rho g} + \frac{v_d^2 + v_s^2}{2g} + z_d - z_s$$

$$v_s \approx 0$$

$$z_d - z_s = 15 \text{ m} \quad [\text{given as rise in elevation}]$$

The difference between discharge and suction pressure is

$$p_d - p_s = 140 \text{ kPa} - 345 \text{ kPa} = -205 \text{ kPa}$$

$$h = \frac{(-205 \text{ kPa})\left(1000 \frac{\text{Pa}}{\text{kPa}}\right)}{\left(998 \frac{\text{kg}}{\text{m}^3}\right)\left(9.81 \frac{\text{m}}{\text{s}^2}\right)}$$

$$+ \frac{\left(4.26 \frac{\text{m}}{\text{s}}\right)^2}{(2)\left(9.81 \frac{\text{m}}{\text{s}^2}\right)} + 15 \text{ m}$$

$$= -5.0 \text{ m}$$

The head added by the pump is

$$h_A = h + h_f = -5.0 \text{ m} + 41.5 \text{ m}$$

$$= 36.5 \text{ m}$$

The mass flow rate is

$$\dot{m} = \rho \dot{V}$$

$$= \left(998 \frac{\text{kg}}{\text{m}^3}\right)\left(35 \frac{\text{L}}{\text{s}}\right)\left(\frac{1 \text{ m}^3}{1000 \text{ L}}\right)$$

$$= 34.93 \text{ kg/s}$$

From Table 18.5, the hydraulic power is

$$\text{WkW} = \frac{(9.81)h_A \dot{m}}{1000}$$

$$= \frac{\left(9.81 \frac{\text{m}}{\text{s}^2}\right)(36.5 \text{ m})\left(34.93 \frac{\text{kg}}{\text{s}}\right)}{1000 \frac{\text{W}}{\text{kW}}}$$

$$= \boxed{12.51 \text{ kW}}$$

3. *Customary U.S. Solution*

The area of the rubber hose is

$$A = \left(\frac{\pi}{4}\right)D^2 = \left(\frac{\pi}{4}\right)\left(\frac{2 \text{ in}}{12 \frac{\text{in}}{\text{ft}}}\right)^2 = 0.0218 \text{ ft}^2$$

The velocity of water in the hose is

$$v = \frac{\dot{V}}{A} = \frac{\left(80 \frac{\text{gal}}{\text{min}}\right)\left(0.002228 \frac{\frac{\text{ft}^3}{\text{sec}}}{\frac{\text{gal}}{\text{min}}}\right)}{0.0218 \text{ ft}^2}$$

$$= 8.176 \text{ ft/sec}$$

At 80°F from App. 14.A, the kinematic viscosity of water is $\nu = 0.93 \times 10^{-5} \text{ ft}^2/\text{sec}$.

The Reynolds number is

$$\text{Re} = \frac{vD}{\nu} = \frac{\left(8.176 \frac{\text{ft}}{\text{sec}}\right)(2 \text{ in})\left(\frac{1 \text{ ft}}{12 \text{ in}}\right)}{0.93 \times 10^{-5} \frac{\text{ft}^2}{\text{sec}}}$$

$$= 1.47 \times 10^5$$

Assume that the rubber hose is smooth. From App. 17.B, the friction factor is $f = 0.0166$.

From Eq. 18.6, the friction head is

$$h_f = \frac{fLv^2}{2Dg}$$

$$= \frac{(0.0166)(50 \text{ ft})\left(8.176 \frac{\text{ft}}{\text{sec}}\right)^2}{(2)(2 \text{ in})\left(\frac{1 \text{ ft}}{12 \text{ in}}\right)\left(32.2 \frac{\text{ft}}{\text{sec}^2}\right)}$$

$$= 5.17 \text{ ft}$$

From Eq. 18.7, the velocity head is

$$h_v = \frac{v^2}{2g} = \frac{\left(8.176 \frac{\text{ft}}{\text{sec}}\right)^2}{(2)\left(32.2 \frac{\text{ft}}{\text{sec}^2}\right)} = 1.04 \text{ ft}$$

Neglecting entrance and exit losses, the head added by the pump is

$$h_A = h_f + h_v + h_z$$

$$= 5.17 \text{ ft} + 1.04 \text{ ft} + 12 \text{ ft} - 4 \text{ ft}$$

$$= \boxed{14.2 \text{ ft}}$$

SI Solution

The area of the rubber hose is

$$A = \left(\frac{\pi}{4}\right)D^2 = \left(\frac{\pi}{4}\right)(5.1 \text{ cm})^2 \left(\frac{1 \text{ m}}{100 \text{ cm}}\right)^2$$

$$= 0.00204 \text{ m}^2$$

The velocity of water in the hose is

$$v = \frac{\dot{V}}{A} = \frac{\left(5 \dfrac{\text{L}}{\text{s}}\right)\left(\dfrac{1 \text{ m}^3}{1000 \text{ L}}\right)}{0.00204 \text{ m}^2} = 2.45 \text{ m/s}$$

At 27°C from App. 14.B, the water data are

$$\rho = 996.5 \text{ kg/m}^3$$
$$\mu = 0.8565 \times 10^{-3} \text{ Pa·s}$$
$$\nu = \frac{\mu}{\rho} = \frac{0.8565 \times 10^{-3} \text{ Pa·s}}{996.5 \dfrac{\text{kg}}{\text{m}^3}}$$
$$= 8.60 \times 10^{-7} \text{ m}^2/\text{s}$$

The Reynolds number is

$$\text{Re} = \frac{vD}{\nu} = \frac{\left(2.45 \dfrac{\text{m}}{\text{s}}\right)(5.1 \text{ cm})\left(\dfrac{1 \text{ m}}{100 \text{ cm}}\right)}{8.60 \times 10^{-7} \dfrac{\text{m}^2}{\text{s}}}$$
$$= 1.45 \times 10^5$$

Assume that the rubber hose is smooth. From App. 17.B, the friction factor is $f \approx 0.0166$.

From Eq. 18.6, the friction head is

$$h_f = \frac{fLv^2}{2Dg}$$
$$= \frac{(0.0166)(15 \text{ m})\left(2.45 \dfrac{\text{m}}{\text{s}}\right)^2}{(2)(5.1 \text{ cm})\left(\dfrac{1 \text{ m}}{100 \text{ cm}}\right)\left(9.81 \dfrac{\text{m}}{\text{s}^2}\right)}$$
$$= 1.49 \text{ m}$$

From Eq. 18.7, the velocity head is

$$h_v = \frac{v^2}{2g} = \frac{\left(2.45 \dfrac{\text{m}}{\text{s}}\right)^2}{(2)\left(9.81 \dfrac{\text{m}}{\text{s}^2}\right)} = 0.31 \text{ m}$$

Neglecting entrance and exit losses, the head added by the pump is

$$h_A = h_f + h_v + h_z$$
$$= 1.49 \text{ m} + 0.31 \text{ m} + 4 \text{ m} - 1.2 \text{ m}$$
$$= \boxed{4.6 \text{ m}}$$

4. *Customary U.S. Solution*

From App. 16.B, the diameters (inside) for 6 in and 8 in steel, schedule-40 pipe are

$$D_1 = 7.981 \text{ in}$$
$$D_2 = 6.065 \text{ in}$$

At 60°F from App. 14.A, the density of water is 62.37 lbm/ft³.

The mass flow rate through 6 in pipe is

$$\dot{m} = A_2 v_2 \rho$$
$$= \left(\frac{\pi}{4}\right)(6.065 \text{ in})^2\left(\frac{1 \text{ ft}^2}{144 \text{ in}^2}\right)\left(12 \frac{\text{ft}}{\text{sec}}\right)\left(62.37 \frac{\text{lbm}}{\text{ft}^3}\right)$$
$$= 150.2 \text{ lbm/sec}$$

The inlet (suction) pressure is

$$14.7 - 5 \text{ psig} = 9.7 \text{ psia}$$
$$= \left(9.7 \frac{\text{lbf}}{\text{in}^2}\right)\left(144 \frac{\text{in}^2}{\text{ft}^2}\right)$$
$$= 1397 \text{ lbf/ft}^2$$

From Table 18.4, the head added by the pump is

$$h_A = \left(\frac{(550)(\text{WHP})\eta}{\dot{m}}\right) \times \left(\frac{g_c}{g}\right)$$
$$= \left(\frac{\left(550 \dfrac{\text{ft-lbf}}{\text{hp-sec}}\right)(20 \text{ hp})(0.70)}{150.2 \dfrac{\text{lbm}}{\text{sec}}}\right)\left(\frac{32.2 \dfrac{\text{ft-lbm}}{\text{lbf-sec}^2}}{32.2 \dfrac{\text{ft}}{\text{sec}^2}}\right)$$
$$= 51.26 \text{ ft}$$

At 1:

$$p_1 = 1397 \text{ lbf/in}^2$$
$$z_1 = 0$$
$$v_1 = \frac{v_2 A_2}{A_1}$$
$$v_1 = v_2\left(\frac{D_2}{D_1}\right)^2$$
$$= \left(12 \frac{\text{ft}}{\text{sec}}\right)\left(\frac{6.065 \text{ in}}{7.981 \text{ in}}\right)^2 = 6.93 \text{ ft/sec}$$

At 2:

$$p_2 = \left(14.7 \frac{\text{lbf}}{\text{in}^2}\right)\left(144 \frac{\text{in}^2}{\text{ft}^2}\right) = 2117 \text{ lbf/ft}^2$$
$$v_2 = 12 \text{ ft/sec} \quad [\text{given}]$$

From Eq. 18.9(b), the head added by the pump is

$$h_A = \frac{(p_2 - p_1)g_c}{\rho g} + \frac{v_2^2 - v_1^2}{2g} + z_2 - z_1 + h_f$$

$$51.26 \text{ ft} = \left(\frac{2117 \frac{\text{lbf}}{\text{ft}^2} - 1397 \frac{\text{lbf}}{\text{ft}^2}}{62.37 \frac{\text{lbm}}{\text{ft}^3}}\right) \times \left(\frac{32.2 \frac{\text{ft-lbm}}{\text{lbf-sec}^2}}{32.2 \frac{\text{ft}}{\text{sec}^2}}\right)$$

$$+ \frac{\left(12 \frac{\text{ft}}{\text{sec}}\right)^2 - \left(6.93 \frac{\text{ft}}{\text{sec}}\right)^2}{(2)\left(32.2 \frac{\text{ft}}{\text{sec}^2}\right)} + z_2 + 10 \text{ ft}$$

$$\boxed{z_2 = 28.2 \text{ ft}}$$

SI Solution

From App. 16.C, the inside diameters for 6 in and 8 in steel, schedule-40 pipe are

$$D_1 = 202.7 \text{ mm}$$
$$D_2 = 154.1 \text{ mm}$$

At 16°C from App. 14.B, the density of water is 998.83 kg/m³.

The mass flow rate through 15.2 cm pipe is

$$\dot{m} = A_2 v_2 \rho$$

$$= \left(\frac{\pi}{4}\right)(154.1 \text{ mm})^2 \left(\frac{1 \text{ m}}{1000 \text{ mm}}\right)^2 \left(4 \frac{\text{m}}{\text{s}}\right)$$

$$\times \left(998.83 \frac{\text{kg}}{\text{m3}}\right)$$

$$= 74.5 \text{ kg/s}$$

The inlet (suction) pressure is

$$101.3 \text{ kPa} - 35 \text{ kPa} = 66.3 \text{ kPa}$$

From Table 18.5, the head added by the pump is

$$h_A = \frac{(1000)(\text{WkW})\eta}{(9.81)\dot{m}}$$

$$= \frac{\left(1000 \frac{\text{W}}{\text{kW}}\right)(20 \text{ hp})\left(\frac{0.7457 \text{ kW}}{\text{hp}}\right)(0.70)}{\left(9.81 \frac{\text{m}}{\text{s}^2}\right)\left(74.5 \frac{\text{kg}}{\text{s}}\right)}$$

$$= 14.28 \text{ m}$$

At 1:

$$p_1 = 66.3 \text{ kPa}$$
$$z_1 = 0$$
$$v_1 = (v_2)\left(\frac{A_2}{A_1}\right) = (v_2)\left(\frac{D_2}{D_1}\right)^2$$

$$= \left(4 \frac{\text{m}}{\text{s}}\right)\left(\frac{154.1 \text{ mm}}{202.7 \text{ mm}}\right)^2 = 2.31 \text{ m/s}$$

At 2:

$$p_2 = 101.3 \text{ kPa}$$
$$v_2 = 4 \text{ m/s} \quad [\text{given}]$$

From Eq. 18.9(a), the head added by the pump is

$$h_A = \frac{p_2 - p_1}{\rho g} + \frac{v_2^2 - v_1^2}{2g} + z_2 - z_1 + h_f$$

$$14.28 \text{ m} = \frac{(101.3 \text{ kPa} - 66.3 \text{ kPa})\left(1000 \frac{\text{Pa}}{\text{kPa}}\right)}{\left(998.83 \frac{\text{kg}}{\text{m}^3}\right)\left(9.81 \frac{\text{m}}{\text{s}^2}\right)}$$

$$+ \frac{\left(4 \frac{\text{m}}{\text{s}}\right)^2 - \left(2.31 \frac{\text{m}}{\text{s}}\right)^2}{(2)\left(9.81 \frac{\text{m}}{\text{s}^2}\right)} + z_2 + 3.3 \text{ m}$$

$$\boxed{z_2 = 6.86 \text{ m}}$$

5. *Customary U.S. Solution*

The flow rate is

$$\dot{V} = \left(10{,}000 \frac{\text{gal}}{\text{hr}}\right)\left(0.1337 \frac{\text{ft}^3}{\text{gal}}\right) = 1337 \text{ ft}^3/\text{hr}$$

From App. 16.B, data for 4 in schedule-40 steel pipe are

$$D_i = 0.3355 \text{ ft}$$
$$A_i = 0.08841 \text{ ft}^2$$

The velocity in the pipe is

$$v = \frac{\dot{V}}{A} = \frac{\left(1337 \frac{\text{ft}^3}{\text{hr}}\right)\left(\frac{1 \text{ hr}}{3600 \text{ sec}}\right)}{0.08841 \text{ ft}^2} = 4.20 \text{ ft/sec}$$

At 60°F from App. 14.A, the kinematic viscosity of water is

$$\nu = 1.217 \times 10^5 \text{ ft}^2/\text{sec}$$
$$\rho = 62.37 \text{ lbm/ft}^3$$

The Reynolds number is

$$\text{Re} = \frac{Dv}{\nu} = \frac{(0.3355 \text{ ft})\left(4.20 \frac{\text{ft}}{\text{sec}}\right)}{1.217 \times 10^{-5} \frac{\text{ft}^2}{\text{sec}}}$$

$$= 1.16 \times 10^5$$

From App. 17.A, for welded and seamless steel, $\epsilon = 0.0002$ ft.

$$\frac{\epsilon}{D} = \frac{0.0002 \text{ ft}}{0.3355 \text{ ft}} \approx 0.0006$$

From App. 17.B, the friction factor, f, is 0.205. The friction head is

$$h_f = \frac{fLv^2}{2Dg}$$

$$= \frac{(0.0205)(7000 \text{ ft}) \left(4.2 \frac{\text{ft}}{\text{sec}}\right)^2}{(2)(0.3355 \text{ ft}) \left(32.2 \frac{\text{ft}}{\text{sec}^2}\right)}$$

$$= 117.2 \text{ ft}$$

From Eq. 18.7, the velocity head is

$$h_v = \frac{v^2}{2g} = \frac{\left(4.2 \frac{\text{ft}}{\text{sec}}\right)^2}{(2) \left(32.2 \frac{\text{ft}}{\text{sec}^2}\right)}$$

$$= 0.27 \text{ ft}$$

The head added by the pump is

$$h_A = h_f + h_v + h_z$$

$$= 117.2 \text{ ft} + 0.27 \text{ ft} + (12 \text{ ft} + 350 \text{ ft})$$

$$= 479.5 \text{ ft}$$

From Table 18.4, the hydraulic horsepower is

$$\text{WHP} = \frac{h_A Q (\text{SG})}{3956}$$

$$= \frac{(479.5 \text{ ft}) \left(10,000 \frac{\text{gal}}{\text{hr}}\right) \left(\frac{1 \text{ hr}}{60 \text{ min}}\right) (1)}{3956 \frac{\text{ft-gal}}{\text{hp-min}}}$$

$$= 20.2 \text{ hp}$$

From Eq. 18.16, the overall efficiency of the pump is

$$\eta = \frac{\text{WHP}}{\text{EHP}}$$

$$\text{EHP} = \frac{20.2 \text{ hp}}{0.7}$$

$$= 28.9 \text{ hp}$$

(a) At \$0.04/kW-hr, power costs for 1 hour are

$$(28.9 \text{ hp}) \left(\frac{0.7457 \text{ kW}}{\text{hp}}\right) (1 \text{ hr}) \left(\frac{\$0.04}{\text{kW-hr}}\right)$$

$$= \boxed{\$0.86 \text{ per hour}}$$

(b) The motor horsepower, EHP, is 28.9 hp. Select a

$$\boxed{30 \text{ hp motor.}}$$

(c) From Eq. 18.5(b),

$$h_{\text{atm}} = \left(\frac{p_{\text{atm}}}{\rho}\right) \times \left(\frac{g_c}{g}\right)$$

$$= \left(\frac{\left(14.7 \frac{\text{lbf}}{\text{in}^2}\right) \left(144 \frac{\text{in}^2}{\text{ft}^2}\right)}{62.37 \frac{\text{lbm}}{\text{ft}^3}}\right) \times \left(\frac{32.2 \frac{\text{ft}}{\text{sec}^2}}{32.2 \frac{\text{ft-lbf}}{\text{lbm-sec}^2}}\right)$$

$$= 33.94 \text{ ft}$$

The friction losses due to 300 ft is

$$h_{f(s)} = \left(\frac{300 \text{ ft}}{7000 \text{ ft}}\right) h_f$$

$$= \left(\frac{300 \text{ ft}}{7000 \text{ ft}}\right) (117.2 \text{ ft})$$

$$= 5.0 \text{ ft}$$

From App. 24.A, saturated pressure (vapor pressure) at $60°\text{F}$ is 0.2563 psia.

From Eq. 18.5(b),

$$h_{\text{vp}} = \left(\frac{p_{\text{vp}}}{\rho}\right) \times \left(\frac{g_c}{g}\right)$$

$$= \left(\frac{\left(0.2563 \frac{\text{lbf}}{\text{in}^2}\right) \left(144 \frac{\text{in}^2}{\text{ft}^2}\right)}{62.37 \frac{\text{lbm}}{\text{ft}^3}}\right)$$

$$\times \left(\frac{32.2 \frac{\text{ft}}{\text{sec}^2}}{32.2 \frac{\text{ft-lbf}}{\text{lbm-sec}^2}}\right)$$

$$= 0.59 \text{ ft}$$

The NPSHA from Eq. 18.30(a) is

$$\text{NPSHA} = h_{\text{atm}} + h_{z(s)} - h_{f(s)} - h_{\text{vp}}$$

$$= 33.94 \text{ ft} - 12 \text{ ft} - 5.0 \text{ ft} - 0.59 \text{ ft}$$

$$= \boxed{16.35 \text{ ft}}$$

SI Solution

From App. 16.C, data for 4 in schedule-40 steel pipe are

$$D_i = 102.3 \text{ mm}$$

$$A_i = 82.19 \times 10^{-4} \text{ m}^2$$

The velocity in the pipe is

$$v = \frac{\dot{V}}{A} = \frac{\left(10.5 \frac{\text{L}}{\text{s}}\right) \left(\frac{1 \text{ m}^3}{1000 \text{ L}}\right)}{82.19 \times 10^{-4} \text{ m}^2} = 1.28 \text{ m/s}$$

From App. 14.B, at 16°C the water data are

$$\rho = 998.83 \text{ kg/m}^3$$
$$\mu = 1.1261 \times 10^{-3} \text{ Pa·s}$$

The Reynolds number is

$$
\begin{aligned}
\text{Re} &= \frac{\rho v D}{\mu} \\
&= \frac{\left(998.83 \ \dfrac{\text{kg}}{\text{m}^3}\right)\left(1.28 \ \dfrac{\text{m}}{\text{s}}\right)}{1.1261 \times 10^{-3} \text{ Pa·s}} \\
&\qquad \times (102.3 \text{ mm})\left(\dfrac{1 \text{ m}}{1000 \text{ mm}}\right) \\
&= 1.16 \times 10^5
\end{aligned}
$$

From Table 17.2, for welded and seamless steel, $\epsilon = 6.0 \times 10^{-5}$ m.

$$\frac{\epsilon}{D} = \frac{6.0 \times 10^{-5} \text{ m}}{(102.3 \text{ mm})\left(\dfrac{1 \text{ m}}{1000 \text{ mm}}\right)} = 0.0006$$

From App. 17.B, the friction factor is $f = 0.0205$.

From Eq. 18.6, the friction head is

$$
\begin{aligned}
h_f &= \frac{fLv^2}{2Dg} \\
&= \frac{(0.0205)(2300 \text{ m})\left(1.28 \ \dfrac{\text{m}}{\text{s}}\right)^2}{(2)(102.3 \text{ mm})\left(\dfrac{1 \text{ m}}{1000 \text{ mm}}\right)\left(9.81 \ \dfrac{\text{m}}{\text{s}^2}\right)} \\
&= 38.5 \text{ m}
\end{aligned}
$$

From Eq. 18.7, the velocity head is

$$
h_v = \frac{v^2}{2g} = \frac{\left(1.28 \ \dfrac{\text{m}}{\text{s}}\right)^2}{(2)\left(9.81 \ \dfrac{\text{m}}{\text{s}^2}\right)} = 0.08 \text{ m}
$$

The head added by the pump is

$$
\begin{aligned}
h_A &= h_f + h_v + h_z \\
&= 38.5 \text{ m} + 0.08 \text{ m} + (4 \text{ m} + 115 \text{ m}) \\
&= 157.6 \text{ m}
\end{aligned}
$$

From Table 18.5, the hydraulic power is

$$
\begin{aligned}
\text{WkW} &= \frac{(9.81)h_A Q(\text{SG})}{1000} \\
&= \frac{\left(9.81 \ \dfrac{\text{m}}{\text{s}^2}\right)(157.6 \text{ m})\left(10.5 \ \dfrac{\text{L}}{\text{s}}\right)(1)}{1000 \ \dfrac{\text{W}}{\text{kW}}} \\
&= 16.23 \text{ kW}
\end{aligned}
$$

From Eq. 18.16,

$$
\begin{aligned}
\text{EHP} &= \frac{\text{WHP}}{\eta_{\text{overall}}} \\
&= \frac{16.23 \text{ kW}}{0.7} = 23.2 \text{ kW}
\end{aligned}
$$

(a) At \$0.04/kW·h, power costs for 1 hour

$$(23.2 \text{ kW})(1 \text{ h})\left(\frac{\$0.04}{\text{kW·h}}\right) = \boxed{\$0.93 \text{ per hour}}$$

(b) The required motor power is 23.2 kW. Select the next higher standard motor size.

(c) From Eq. 18.5(a),

$$
\begin{aligned}
h_{\text{atm}} &= \frac{p}{\rho g} \\
&= \frac{(101 \text{ kPa})(1000 \text{ Pa})}{\left(998.83 \ \dfrac{\text{kg}}{\text{m}^3}\right)\left(9.81 \ \dfrac{\text{m}}{\text{s}^2}\right)} \\
&= 10.31 \text{ m}
\end{aligned}
$$

The friction loss due to 100 m is

$$
\begin{aligned}
h_{f(s)} &= \left(\frac{100 \text{ m}}{2300 \text{ m}}\right) h_f \\
&= \left(\frac{100 \text{ m}}{2300 \text{ m}}\right)(38.5 \text{ m}) \\
&= 1.67 \text{ m}
\end{aligned}
$$

From App. 24.N, saturated pressure (vapor pressure) at 16°C is 0.01818 bar.

From Eq. 18.5(a),

$$
\begin{aligned}
h_{\text{vp}} &= \frac{p_{\text{vp}}}{g\rho} \\
&= \frac{(0.01818 \text{ bar})\left(1 \times 10^5 \ \dfrac{\text{Pa}}{\text{bar}}\right)}{\left(9.81 \ \dfrac{\text{m}}{\text{s}^2}\right)\left(998.83 \ \dfrac{\text{kg}}{\text{m}^3}\right)} \\
&= 0.19 \text{ m}
\end{aligned}
$$

The NPSHA from Eq. 18.30(a) is

$$
\begin{aligned}
\text{NPSHA} &= h_{\text{atm}} + h_{z(s)} - h_{f(s)} - h_{\text{vp}} \\
&= 10.31 \text{ m} - 4 \text{ m} - 1.67 \text{ m} - 0.19 \text{ m} \\
&= \boxed{4.45 \text{ m}}
\end{aligned}
$$

6. *Customary U.S. Solution*

(a) The equivalent lengths are assumed to be in feet of section's diameters. Since the diameters are different for many sections, the equivalent lengths cannot be added together. It is necessary to convert the lengths to pressure drop using the Darcy equation (Eq. 17.22). (A similar process can be carried out more expediently if a table of standard losses in copper tubing is used.)

The water temperature is not specified. Assume water at 70°F. From App. 14.A, the water data are

$$\rho = 62.3 \text{ lbm/ft}^3$$

$$\nu = 1.059 \times 10^{-5} \text{ ft}^2/\text{sec}$$

From App. 17.A, the pipe roughness is $\epsilon = 0.000005$ ft.

From App. 16.D, the data for $2^1/_2$ in type L pipe are

$$D_i = 2.465 \text{ in}$$

$$A_i = 4.77 \text{ in}^2$$

The flow rate is converted from gal/min to ft^3/sec.

$$\dot{V} = \left(60 \ \frac{\text{gal}}{\text{min}}\right)\left(0.002228 \ \frac{\frac{\text{ft}^3}{\text{sec}}}{\frac{\text{gal}}{\text{min}}}\right)$$

$$= 0.13368 \text{ ft}^3/\text{sec}$$

The velocity in the pipe is

$$v = \frac{\dot{V}}{A} = \frac{0.13368 \ \frac{\text{ft}^3}{\text{sec}}}{(4.77 \text{ in}^2)\left(\frac{1 \text{ ft}^2}{144 \text{ in}^2}\right)} = 4.04 \text{ ft/sec}$$

The Reynolds number is

$$Re = \frac{Dv}{\nu} = \frac{(2.465 \text{ in})\left(\frac{1 \text{ ft}}{12 \text{ in}}\right)\left(4.04 \ \frac{\text{ft}}{\text{sec}}\right)}{1.059 \times 10^{-5} \ \frac{\text{ft}^2}{\text{sec}}}$$

$$= 7.84 \times 10^4$$

$$\frac{\epsilon}{D} = \frac{0.000005 \text{ ft}}{(2.465 \text{ in})\left(\frac{1 \text{ ft}}{12 \text{ in}}\right)} \approx 0.000025$$

From the friction factor table (App. 17.B), $f \approx 0.019$.

From Eq. 17.22, the friction head loss is

$$h_f = \frac{fLv^2}{2Dg}$$

$$= \frac{(0.019)(40 \text{ ft})\left(4.04 \ \frac{\text{ft}}{\text{sec}}\right)^2}{(2)(2.465 \text{ in})\left(\frac{1 \text{ ft}}{12 \text{ in}}\right)\left(32.2 \ \frac{\text{ft}}{\text{sec}^2}\right)}$$

$$= 0.94 \text{ ft}$$

For all other sections, using the similar procedure, the following table can be constructed.

circuit	equivalent length (ft)	total loss (ft)
5-1-P-2	40	0.94
2-4	70	2.44
2-3	55	1.76
3-4	65	2.27
3-5	60	2.10
4-5	50	1.60

These head losses are for cold water and are greater than hot water losses. The pumping power will be less for hot water. However, the system may be tested with cold water. Therefore, horsepower must be adequate for this system.

Redraw the pipe network.

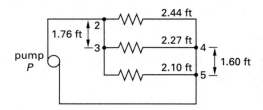

The pump must be able to handle the longest run.

run	total loss
2-4-5	2.44 ft + 1.60 ft = 4.04 ft
2-3-4-5	1.76 ft + 2.27 ft + 1.60 ft = 5.63 ft
2-3-5	1.76 ft + 2.10 ft = 3.86 ft

The longest run is 2-3-4-5 with a loss of 5.63 ft. The total circuit loss is 0.94 ft + 5.63 ft = 6.57 ft. Note that the loss between points 2 and 5 must be the same regardless of the path. Therefore, flow restriction valves must exist in the other two runs in order to match the longest run's loss.

From Table 18.4, the hydraulic horsepower is

$$\text{WHP} = \frac{h_A Q (\text{SG})}{3956}$$

$$= \frac{(6.57 \text{ ft})\left(60 \ \frac{\text{gal}}{\text{min}}\right)(1)}{3956 \ \frac{\text{ft-gal}}{\text{hp-min}}}$$

$$= 0.10 \text{ hp}$$

From Eq. 18.16, the motor horsepower is

$$P = \frac{\text{WHP}}{\eta} = \frac{0.10 \text{ hp}}{0.45} = \boxed{0.22 \text{ hp}}$$

(b) Use a $\boxed{{}^1\!/_4 \text{ hp or larger motor.}}$

(c) For water, the mass flow rate is

$$\dot{m} = \left(60 \; \frac{\text{gal}}{\text{min}}\right)\left(0.1337 \; \frac{\text{ft}^3}{\text{gal}}\right)\left(62.30 \; \frac{\text{lbm}}{\text{ft}^3}\right)$$

$$= 480 \; \text{lbm/min}$$

The heat added is

$$q = \dot{m}c_p\Delta T$$

$$= \left(480 \; \frac{\text{lbm}}{\text{min}}\right)\left(60 \; \frac{\text{min}}{\text{hr}}\right)\left(1 \; \frac{\text{Btu}}{\text{lbm-}^\circ\text{F}}\right)(20^\circ\text{F})$$

$$= \boxed{576{,}000 \; \text{Btu/hr}}$$

SI Solution

(a) Convert the lengths to pressure drop using the Darcy equation (Eq. 17.22).

Assume 20°C water. From App. 14.B, the water data at 20°C are

$$\rho = 998.23 \; \text{kg/m}^3$$

$$\mu = 1.0050 \times 10^{-3} \; \text{Pa·s}$$

From Table 17.2, the pipe roughness is $\epsilon = 1.5 \times 10^{-6}$ m.

From App. 16.D, the data for $2^1\!/_2$ in type-L pipe are

$$D_i = (2.465 \; \text{in})\left(2.540 \; \frac{\text{cm}}{\text{in}}\right)\left(\frac{1 \; \text{m}}{100 \; \text{cm}}\right)$$

$$= 0.0626 \; \text{m}$$

$$A_i = (4.77 \; \text{in}^2)\left(\frac{1 \; \text{ft}^2}{144 \; \text{in}^2}\right)\left(0.0929 \; \frac{\text{m}^2}{\text{ft}^2}\right)$$

$$= 3.08 \times 10^{-3} \; \text{m}^2$$

The velocity in the pipe is

$$v = \frac{\dot{V}}{A} = \frac{\left(3.9 \; \frac{\text{L}}{\text{s}}\right)\left(\frac{1 \; \text{m}^3}{1000 \; \text{L}}\right)}{3.08 \times 10^{-3} \; \text{m}^2} = 1.27 \; \text{m/s}$$

The Reynolds number is

$$\text{Re} = \frac{\rho v D}{\mu}$$

$$= \frac{\left(998.23 \; \frac{\text{kg}}{\text{m}^3}\right)\left(1.27 \; \frac{\text{m}}{\text{s}}\right)(0.0626 \; \text{m})}{1.0050 \times 10^{-3} \; \text{Pa·s}}$$

$$= 7.9 \times 10^4$$

$$\frac{\epsilon}{D} = \frac{1.5 \times 10^{-6} \; \text{m}}{0.0626 \; \text{m}} \approx 0.000025$$

From the friction factor table (App. 17.B), $f \approx 0.019$.

From Eq. 17.22, the friction head loss is

$$h_f = \frac{fLv^2}{2Dg} = \frac{(0.019)(13 \; \text{m})\left(1.27 \; \frac{\text{m}}{\text{s}}\right)^2}{(2)(0.0626 \; \text{m})\left(9.81 \; \frac{\text{m}}{\text{s}^2}\right)}$$

$$= 0.324 \; \text{m}$$

For all other sections, using the similar procedure, the following table can be constructed.

circuit	equivalent length (m)	total loss (m)
5-1-P-2	13	0.324
2-4	23	0.850
2-3	18	0.612
3-4	22	0.813
3-5	20	0.739
4-5	17	0.578

Redraw the pipe network.

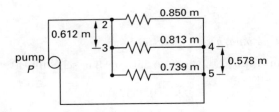

The pump must be able to handle the longest run.

run	total loss
2-4-5	0.850 m + 0.578 m = 1.43 m
2-3-4-5	0.612 m + 0.813 m + 0.578 m = 2.00 m
2-3-5	0.612 m + 0.739 m = 1.35 m

The longest run is 2-3-4-5 with a loss of 2.00 m. The total circuit loss is 0.324 m + 2.00 m = 2.324 m. Note that the loss between points 2 and 5 must be the same regardless of the path. Therefore, flow restriction valves must exist in the other two runs in order to match the longest run's loss.

From Table 18.5, hydraulic power is

$$\text{WkW} = \frac{9.81 h_A Q(\text{SG})}{1000}$$

$$= \frac{\left(9.81 \; \frac{\text{m}}{\text{s}^2}\right)(2.324 \; \text{m})\left(3.9 \; \frac{\text{L}}{\text{s}}\right)(1)}{1000 \; \frac{\text{W}}{\text{kW}}}$$

$$= 0.0889 \; \text{kW}$$

From Eq. 18.16, the motor power is

$$P = \frac{WkW}{\eta} = \frac{0.0889 \text{ kW}}{0.45}$$

$$= \boxed{0.198 \text{ kW}}$$

(b) Use a $\boxed{\text{0.2 kW or larger motor.}}$

(c) For water, the mass flow rate is

$$\dot{m} = \left(3.9 \frac{\text{L}}{\text{s}}\right)\left(\frac{1 \text{ m}^3}{1000 \text{ L}}\right)\left(998.23 \frac{\text{kg}}{\text{m}^3}\right)$$

$$= 3.89 \text{ kg/s}$$

The heat added is

$$q = \dot{m}c_p \Delta T$$

$$= \left(3.89 \frac{\text{kg}}{\text{s}}\right)\left(4.187 \frac{\text{kJ}}{\text{kg·C}}\right)(10°C)$$

$$= \boxed{162.9 \text{ kW}}$$

7. *Customary U.S. Solution*

From App. 16.B, the pipe data for 3 in schedule-40 steel pipe are

$$D_i = 0.2557 \text{ ft}$$
$$A_i = 0.05134 \text{ ft}^2$$

From App. 17.D, the equivalent length for various fittings is

$$\text{flanged elbow, } L_e = 4.4 \text{ ft}$$
$$\text{wide-open gate valve, } L_e = 2.8 \text{ ft}$$

The total equivalent length of pipe and fittings is

$$L_e = 500 \text{ ft} + (6)(4.4 \text{ ft}) + (2)(2.8 \text{ ft})$$
$$= 532 \text{ ft}$$

As a first estimate, assume the flow rate is 100 gal/min.

The velocity in the pipe is

$$v = \frac{\dot{V}}{A} = \frac{\left(100 \frac{\text{gal}}{\text{min}}\right)\left(0.002228 \frac{\frac{\text{ft}^3}{\text{sec}}}{\frac{\text{gal}}{\text{min}}}\right)}{0.05134 \text{ ft}^2}$$

$$= 4.34 \text{ ft/sec}$$

The Reynolds number is

$$\text{Re} = \frac{vD}{\nu} = \frac{\left(4.34 \frac{\text{ft}}{\text{sec}}\right)(0.2557 \text{ ft})}{6 \times 10^{-6} \frac{\text{ft}^2}{\text{sec}}}$$

$$= 1.85 \times 10^5$$

From App. 17.A, $\epsilon = 0.0002$ ft.

So,

$$\frac{\epsilon}{D} = \frac{0.0002 \text{ ft}}{0.2557 \text{ ft}} \approx 0.0008$$

From the friction factor table, $f \approx 0.0204$.

For higher flow rates, f approaches 0.0186. Since the chosen flow rate was almost the lowest, $f = 0.0186$ should be used.

From Eq. 17.22, the friction head loss is

$$h_f = \frac{fLv^2}{2Dg}$$

$$= \frac{(0.0186)(532 \text{ ft})\left(4.34 \frac{\text{ft}}{\text{sec}}\right)^2}{(2)(0.2557 \text{ ft})\left(32.2 \frac{\text{ft}}{\text{sec}^2}\right)}$$

$$= 11.3 \text{ ft of gasoline}$$

This neglects the small velocity head. The other system points can be found using

$$\frac{h_{f_1}}{h_{f_2}} = \left(\frac{Q_1}{Q_2}\right)^2$$

$$h_{f_2} = h_{f_1}\left(\frac{Q_2}{100 \frac{\text{gal}}{\text{min}}}\right)^2$$

$$= (11.3 \text{ ft})\left(\frac{Q_2}{100 \frac{\text{gal}}{\text{min}}}\right)^2$$

$$= 0.00113 Q_2^2$$

Q (gal/min)	h_f (ft)	$h_f + 60$ (ft)
100	11.3	71.3
200	45.2	105.2
300	101.7	161.7
400	180.8	240.8
500	282.5	342.5
600	406.8	466.8

(a) Plot the system and pump curves.

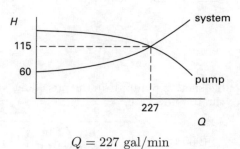

$$Q = 227 \text{ gal/min}$$
$$H = 115 \text{ ft}$$

(b) From Table 18.4, the hydraulic horsepower is

$$\text{WHP} = \frac{h_A Q (\text{SG})}{3956} = \frac{(115 \text{ ft}) \left(227 \frac{\text{gal}}{\text{min}}\right)(0.7)}{3956 \frac{\text{ft-gal}}{\text{hp-min}}}$$

$$= 4.62 \text{ hp}$$

$$\frac{(4.62 \text{ hp}) \left(0.7457 \frac{\text{kW}}{\text{hp}}\right)}{\times (1 \text{ hr}) \left(0.045 \frac{\$}{\text{kW-hr}}\right)}{(0.88)(0.88)} = \boxed{\$0.20}$$

SI Solution

From App. 16.C, the pipe data for 3 in schedule-40 pipe are

$$D_i = 77.92 \text{ mm}$$
$$A_i = 47.69 \times 10^{-4} \text{ m}^2$$

From App. 17.D, the equivalent length for various fittings is

$$\text{flanged elbow, } L_e = 4.4 \text{ ft}$$
$$\text{wide-open gate valve, } L_e = 2.8 \text{ ft}$$

The total equivalent length of pipe and fittings is

$$L_e = 170 \text{ m} + (6)(4.4 \text{ ft}) \left(0.3048 \frac{\text{m}}{\text{ft}}\right)$$
$$+ (2)(2.8 \text{ ft}) \left(0.3048 \frac{\text{m}}{\text{ft}}\right)$$
$$= 180 \text{ m}$$

As a first estimate, assume flow rate is 6 L/s. The velocity in the pipe is

$$v = \frac{\dot{V}}{A} = \frac{\left(6 \frac{\text{L}}{\text{s}}\right) \left(\frac{1 \text{ m}^3}{1000 \text{ L}}\right)}{47.69 \times 10^{-4} \text{ m}^2} = 1.26 \text{ m/s}$$

The Reynolds number is

$$\text{Re} = \frac{vD}{\nu}$$
$$= \frac{\left(1.26 \frac{\text{m}}{\text{s}}\right)(77.92 \text{ mm}) \left(\frac{1 \text{ m}}{1000 \text{ m}}\right)}{5.6 \times 10^{-7} \frac{\text{m}^2}{\text{s}}}$$
$$= 1.75 \times 10^5$$

From Table 17.2, $\epsilon = 6.0 \times 10^{-5}$ m.

$$\frac{\epsilon}{D} = \frac{6.0 \times 10^{-5} \text{ m}}{(77.92 \text{ mm}) \left(\frac{1 \text{ m}}{1000 \text{ mm}}\right)} \approx 0.0008$$

From the friction factor table (App. 17.B), $f = 0.0205$.

For higher flow rates, f approaches 0.0186. Since the chosen flow rate was almost the lowest, $f = 0.0186$ should be used.

From Eq. 17.22, the friction head loss is

$$h_f = \frac{fLv^2}{2Dg} = \frac{(0.0186)(180 \text{ m}) \left(1.32 \frac{\text{m}}{\text{s}}\right)^2}{(2)(77.92 \text{ mm}) \left(\frac{1 \text{ m}}{1000 \text{ mm}}\right) \left(9.81 \frac{\text{m}}{\text{s}^2}\right)}$$

$$= 3.82 \text{ m of gasoline}$$

This neglects the small velocity head. The other system points can be found using

$$\frac{h_{f_1}}{h_{f_2}} = \left(\frac{Q_1}{Q_2}\right)^2$$

$$h_{f_2} = h_{f_1} \left(\frac{Q_2}{Q_1}\right)^2 = (3.82 \text{ m}) \left(\frac{Q_2}{6.3 \frac{\text{L}}{\text{s}}}\right)^2$$

$$= 0.0962 Q_2^2$$

Q (L/s)	h_f (m)	$h_f + 20$ (m)
6.3	3.82	23.82
12	13.85	33.85
18	31.2	51.2
24	54.4	74.4
30	86.6	106.6
36	124.7	144.7

(a) Plot the system and pump curves.

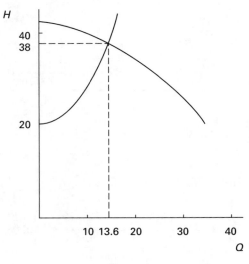

$$Q = 13.6 \text{ L/s}$$
$$H = 38.0 \text{ m}$$

(b) From Table 18.5, the hydraulic power is

$$\text{WkW} = \frac{9.81 h_A Q (\text{SG})}{1000}$$

$$= \frac{\left(9.81 \dfrac{\text{m}}{\text{s}^2}\right)(38.0 \text{ m})\left(13.6 \dfrac{\text{L}}{\text{s}}\right)(0.7)}{1000 \dfrac{\text{W}}{\text{kW}}}$$

$$= 3.55 \text{ kW}$$

The cost per hour is

$$= \left(\frac{3.55 \text{ kW}}{(0.88)(0.88)}\right)(1 \text{ h})\left(0.045 \frac{\$}{\text{kW·h}}\right)$$

$$= \boxed{\$0.21}$$

8. *Customary U.S. Solution*

From Eq. 18.28(b), the specific speed is

$$n_s = \frac{n\sqrt{Q}}{h_A^{0.75}}$$

For a double-suction pump, Q in the preceding equation is half of the full flow rate.

$$n_s = \frac{(900 \text{ rpm})\sqrt{\left(300 \dfrac{\text{gal}}{\text{sec}}\right)\left(60 \dfrac{\text{sec}}{\text{min}}\right)\left(\frac{1}{2}\right)}}{(20 \text{ ft})^{0.75}}$$

$$= \boxed{9028 \text{ rpm}}$$

SI Solution

From Eq. 18.28(a), the specific speed is

$$n_s = \frac{n\sqrt{\dot{V}}}{h_A^{0.75}}$$

For a double-suction pump, $\dot{V}$ in the preceding equation is half of the full flow rate.

$$n_s = \frac{(900 \text{ rpm})\sqrt{\left(1.1 \dfrac{\text{kL}}{\text{s}}\right)\left(\dfrac{1 \text{ m}^3}{1 \text{ kL}}\right)\left(\frac{1}{2}\right)}}{(7 \text{ m})^{0.75}}$$

$$= \boxed{155.1 \text{ rpm}}$$

9. *Customary U.S. Solution*

This problem is solved graphically using charts from *Standards of the Hydraulic Institute*.

Since each stage adds 150 ft of head and the suction lift is 10 ft, for a single-suction pump, $n_s \approx 2050$ rpm.

SI Solution

Since an SI chart is not available, the SI solution can only be obtained by converting all heads to feet and using the English-unit charts in the *Standards of the Hydraulic Institute*.

10.

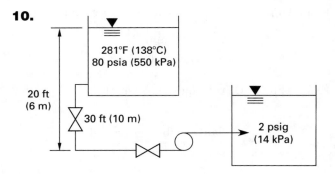

Customary U.S. Solution

From App. 16.B, data for 1.5 in schedule-40 steel pipe are

$$D_i = 0.1342 \text{ ft}$$
$$A_i = 0.01414 \text{ ft}^2$$

The velocity in the pipe is

$$\text{v} = \frac{\dot{V}}{A} = \frac{\left(100 \dfrac{\text{gal}}{\text{min}}\right)\left(0.002228 \dfrac{\text{ft}^3\text{-min}}{\text{sec-gal}}\right)}{0.01414 \text{ ft}^2}$$

$$= 15.76 \text{ ft/sec}$$

From App. 17.D, for screwed steel fittings, the approximate equivalent lengths for fittings are

> inlet (square mouth): $L_e = 3.1$ ft
>
> long radius 90° ell: $L_e = 3.4$ ft
>
> wide-open gate valves: $L_e = 1.2$ ft

The total equivalent length is

$$30 \text{ ft} + 3.1 \text{ ft} + (2)(3.4 \text{ ft}) + (2)(1.2 \text{ ft}) = 42.3 \text{ ft}$$

From App. 17.A, for steel, $\epsilon = 0.0002$ ft, so

$$\frac{\epsilon}{D} = \frac{0.0002 \text{ ft}}{0.1342 \text{ ft}} = 0.0015$$

At 281°F, $\nu = 0.239 \times 10^{-5}$ ft²/sec. The Reynolds number is

$$
\begin{aligned}
\text{Re} = \frac{D\text{v}}{\nu} &= \frac{(0.1342 \text{ ft}) \left(15.76 \dfrac{\text{ft}}{\text{sec}} \right)}{0.239 \times 10^{-5} \dfrac{\text{ft}^2}{\text{sec}}} \\
&= 8.85 \times 10^5
\end{aligned}
$$

From App. 17.B, the friction factor is $f = 0.022$.

From Eq. 18.6, the friction head is

$$
\begin{aligned}
h_f &= \frac{fL\text{v}^2}{2Dg} \\
&= \frac{(0.022)(42.3 \text{ ft}) \left(15.76 \dfrac{\text{ft}}{\text{sec}} \right)^2}{(2)(0.1342 \text{ ft}) \left(32.2 \dfrac{\text{ft}}{\text{sec}^2} \right)} \\
&= 26.74 \text{ ft}
\end{aligned}
$$

From App. 24.A, at 281°F,

$$p_{\text{vapor}} = 50.02 \text{ psia}$$

$$\rho = \frac{1}{v_f} = \frac{1}{0.01727 \dfrac{\text{ft}^3}{\text{lbm}}} = 57.9 \text{ lbm/ft}^3$$

From Eq. 18.5(b),

$$
\begin{aligned}
h_{\text{vp}} &= \left(\frac{p_{\text{vapor}}}{\rho} \right) \times \left(\frac{g_c}{g} \right) \\
&= \left(\frac{\left(50.02 \dfrac{\text{lbf}}{\text{in}^2} \right) \left(144 \dfrac{\text{in}^2}{\text{ft}^2} \right)}{57.9 \dfrac{\text{lbm}}{\text{ft}^3}} \right) \times \left(\frac{32.2 \dfrac{\text{ft-lbm}}{\text{lbf-sec}^2}}{32.2 \dfrac{\text{ft}}{\text{sec}^2}} \right) \\
&= 124.4 \text{ ft}
\end{aligned}
$$

From Eq. 18.5(b), the pressure head is

$$
\begin{aligned}
h_p &= \left(\frac{p}{\rho} \right) \times \left(\frac{g_c}{g} \right) \\
&= \left(\frac{\left(80 \dfrac{\text{lbf}}{\text{in}^2} \right) \left(144 \dfrac{\text{in}^2}{\text{ft}^2} \right)}{57.9 \dfrac{\text{lbm}}{\text{ft}^3}} \right) \times \left(\frac{32.2 \dfrac{\text{ft-lbm}}{\text{lbf-sec}^2}}{32.2 \dfrac{\text{ft}}{\text{sec}^2}} \right) \\
&= 199.0 \text{ ft}
\end{aligned}
$$

From Eq. 18.30(a), the NPSHA is

$$
\begin{aligned}
\text{NPSHA} &= h_p + h_{z(s)} - h_{f(s)} - h_{\text{vp}} \\
&= 199.0 \text{ ft} + 20 \text{ ft} - 26.74 \text{ ft} - 124.4 \text{ ft} \\
&= 67.9 \text{ ft}
\end{aligned}
$$

Since NPSHR = 10 ft, $\boxed{\text{the pump will not cavitate.}}$

SI Solution

From App. 16.C, data for 1.5 in schedule-40 steel pipe are

$$D_i = 40.89 \text{ mm}$$

$$A_i = 13.13 \times 10^{-4} \text{ m}^2$$

The velocity in the pipe is

$$
\begin{aligned}
\text{v} = \frac{\dot{V}}{A} &= \frac{\left(6.3 \dfrac{\text{L}}{\text{s}} \right) \left(\dfrac{1 \text{ m}^3}{1000 \text{ L}} \right)}{13.13 \times 10^{-4} \text{ m}^2} \\
&= 4.80 \text{ m/s}
\end{aligned}
$$

From App. 17.D, for screwed steel fittings, the approximate equivalent lengths for fittings are

> inlet (square mouth): $L_e = 3.1$ ft
>
> long radius 90° ell: $L_e = 3.4$ ft
>
> wide-open gate valves: $L_e = 1.2$ ft

The total equivalent length is

$$(42.3 \text{ ft}) \left(0.3048 \frac{\text{m}}{\text{ft}} \right) = 12.89 \text{ m}$$

From Table 17.2, for steel, $\epsilon = 6.0 \times 10^{-5}$ m.

$$\frac{\epsilon}{D} = \frac{6.0 \times 10^{-5} \text{ m}}{(40.89 \text{ mm}) \left(\dfrac{1 \text{ m}}{1000 \text{ m}} \right)} \approx 0.0015$$

At 138°C, $\nu = 0.222 \times 10^{-6}$ m²/s. The Reynolds number is

$$
\begin{aligned}
\text{Re} &= \frac{D\text{v}}{\nu} \\
&= \frac{(40.89 \text{ mm}) \left(\dfrac{1 \text{ m}}{1000 \text{ mm}} \right) \left(4.80 \dfrac{\text{m}}{\text{s}} \right)}{0.222 \times 10^{-6} \dfrac{\text{m}^2}{\text{s}}} \\
&= 8.84 \times 10^5
\end{aligned}
$$

From App. 17.B, the friction factor is $f = 0.022$.

From Eq. 18.6, the friction head is

$$h_f = \frac{fLv^2}{2Dg}$$

$$= \frac{(0.022)(12.89 \text{ m})\left(4.8 \frac{\text{m}}{\text{s}}\right)^2}{(2)(40.89 \text{ mm})\left(\frac{1 \text{ m}}{1000 \text{ mm}}\right)\left(9.81 \frac{\text{m}}{\text{s}^2}\right)}$$

$$= 8.14 \text{ m}$$

From Eq. 18.5(a),

$$h_{vp} = \frac{p_{vapor}}{\rho g}$$

From App. 24.N, at 138°C,

$$p_{vapor} = 3.431 \text{ bar}$$

$$\rho = \frac{1}{v_f}$$

$$= \frac{1}{\left(1.0777 \frac{\text{cm}^3}{\text{g}}\right)\left(1000 \frac{\text{g}}{\text{kg}}\right)\left(\frac{1 \text{ m}^3}{(100 \text{ cm})^3}\right)}$$

$$= 927.9 \text{ kg/m}^3$$

$$h_{vp} = \frac{(3.431 \text{ bar})\left(10^5 \frac{\text{Pa}}{\text{bar}}\right)}{\left(927.9 \frac{\text{kg}}{\text{m}^3}\right)\left(9.81 \frac{\text{m}}{\text{s}^2}\right)}$$

$$= 37.69 \text{ m}$$

From Eq. 18.5(a), the pressure head is

$$h_p = \frac{p}{\rho g}$$

$$= \frac{(550 \text{ kPa})\left(1000 \frac{\text{Pa}}{\text{kPa}}\right)}{\left(927.9 \frac{\text{kg}}{\text{m}^3}\right)\left(9.81 \frac{\text{m}}{\text{s}^2}\right)}$$

$$= 60.42 \text{ m}$$

From Eq. 18.30(a), the NPSHA is

$$\text{NPSHA} = h_p + h_{z(s)} - h_{f(s)} - h_{vp}$$

$$= 60.42 \text{ m} + 6 \text{ m} - 8.14 \text{ m} - 37.69 \text{ m}$$

$$= 20.6 \text{ m}$$

Since NPSHR is 3 m, the pump will not cavitate.

11. The solvent is the water (fresh), and the solution is the seawater. Since seawater contains $2\frac{1}{2}\%$ salt by weight, 100 lbm of seawater will yield 2.5 lbm salt and 97.5 lbm water. The molecular weight of salt is $23.0 + 35.5 = 58.5$ lbm/lbmol. The number of moles of salt in 100 lbm of seawater is

$$n_{salt} = \frac{2.5 \text{ lbm}}{58.5 \frac{\text{lbm}}{\text{lbmol}}} = 0.043 \text{ lbmol}$$

Similarly, the molecular weight of water is 18.016 lbm/lbmol. The number of moles of water is

$$n_{water} = \frac{97.5 \text{ lbm}}{18.016 \frac{\text{lbm}}{\text{lbmol}}} = 5.412 \text{ lbmol}$$

The mole fraction of water is

$$\frac{5.412 \text{ lbmol}}{5.412 \text{ lbmol} + 0.043 \text{ lbmol}} = 0.992$$

Customary U.S. Solution

Cavitation will occur when

$$h_{atm} - h_v < h_{vp}$$

The density of seawater is 64.0 lbm/ft³.

From Eq. 18.5(b), the atmospheric head is

$$h_{atm} = \left(\frac{p}{\rho}\right) \times \left(\frac{g}{g_c}\right)$$

$$= \left(\frac{\left(14.7 \frac{\text{lbf}}{\text{in}^2}\right)\left(144 \frac{\text{in}^2}{\text{ft}^2}\right)}{64.0 \frac{\text{lbm}}{\text{ft}^3}}\right) \times \left(\frac{32.2 \frac{\text{ft-lbm}}{\text{lbf-sec}^2}}{32.2 \frac{\text{ft}}{\text{sec}^2}}\right)$$

$$= 33.075 \text{ ft}$$

$$h_{depth} = 8 \text{ ft} \quad [\text{given}]$$

From Eq. 18.7, the velocity head is

$$h_v = \frac{v_{propeller}^2}{2g} = \frac{(4.2 \text{ v}_{boat})^2}{(2)\left(32.2 \frac{\text{ft}}{\text{sec}^2}\right)}$$

$$= 0.2739 v_{boat}^2$$

From steam tables (App. 24.A), the water pressure of 68°F freshwater is $p_{vp} = 0.3391$ psia.

From App. 14.A, the density of water at 68°F is 62.32 lbm/ft³. Raoult's law predicts the actual vapor pressure of the solution.

$$p_{vapor,solution} = (p_{vapor,solvent})\left(\begin{array}{c}\text{mole fraction}\\\text{of the solvent}\end{array}\right)$$

$$p_{vapor,seawater} = (0.992)(0.3391 \text{ psia})$$

$$= 0.3364 \text{ psia}$$

From Eq. 18.5(b), the vapor pressure head is

$$h_{\text{vapor,seawater}} = \left(\frac{p}{\rho}\right) \times \left(\frac{g_c}{g}\right)$$

$$= \left(\frac{\left(0.3364 \dfrac{\text{lbf}}{\text{in}^2}\right)\left(144 \dfrac{\text{in}^2}{\text{ft}^2}\right)}{62.32 \dfrac{\text{lbm}}{\text{ft}^3}}\right)$$

$$\times \left(\frac{32.2 \dfrac{\text{ft-lbm}}{\text{lbf-sec}^2}}{32.2 \dfrac{\text{ft}}{\text{sec}^2}}\right) = 0.7773 \text{ ft}$$

Then,

$$8 \text{ ft} + 33.075 \text{ ft} - 0.2739 v_{\text{boat}}^2 = 0.7773 \text{ ft}$$

$$\boxed{v_{\text{boat}} = \;\; 12.13 \text{ ft/sec}}$$

SI Solution

Cavitation will occur when

$$h_{\text{atm}} - h_{\text{v}} < h_{\text{vp}}$$

The density of seawater is 1024 kg/m^3.

From Eq. 18.5(a), the atmospheric head is

$$h_{\text{atm}} = \frac{p}{\rho g}$$

$$= \frac{(101.3 \text{ kPa})\left(1000 \dfrac{\text{Pa}}{\text{kPa}}\right)}{\left(1024 \dfrac{\text{kg}}{\text{m}^3}\right)\left(9.81 \dfrac{\text{m}}{\text{s}^2}\right)}$$

$$= 10.08 \text{ m}$$

$$h_{\text{depth}} = 3 \text{ m} \quad [\text{given}]$$

From Eq. 18.7, the velocity head is

$$h_{\text{v}} = \frac{v_{\text{propeller}}^2}{2g} = \frac{(4.2 \; v_{\text{boat}})^2}{(2)\left(9.81 \dfrac{\text{m}}{\text{s}^2}\right)}$$

$$= 0.899 v_{\text{boat}}^2$$

From steam tables (App. 24.N), the water pressure of 20°C freshwater is

$$p_{\text{vp}} = (0.02339 \text{ bar})\left(100 \dfrac{\text{kPa}}{\text{bar}}\right)$$

$$= 2.339 \text{ kPa}$$

From App. 14.B, the density of water at 20°C is 998.23 kg/m^3. Raoult's law predicts the actual vapor pressure of the solution.

$$p_{\text{vapor,solution}} = (p_{\text{vapor,solvent}})\left(\begin{array}{c}\text{mole fraction} \\ \text{of the solvent}\end{array}\right)$$

The solvent is the freshwater and the solution is the seawater.

The mole fraction of water is 0.992.

$$p_{\text{vapor,seawater}} = (0.992)(2.339 \text{ kPa}) = 2.320 \text{ kPa}$$

From Eq. 18.5(a), the vapor pressure head is

$$h_{\text{vapor,seawater}} = \frac{(2.320 \text{ kPa})\left(1000 \dfrac{\text{Pa}}{\text{kPa}}\right)}{\left(9.81 \dfrac{\text{m}}{\text{s}^2}\right)\left(998.23 \dfrac{\text{kg}}{\text{m}^3}\right)}$$

$$= 0.237 \text{ m}$$

Then,

$$3 \text{ m} + 10.08 \text{ m} - 0.899 \; v_{\text{boat}}^2 = 0.237 \text{ m}$$

$$\boxed{v_{\text{boat}} = \;\; 3.78 \text{ m/s}}$$

12.

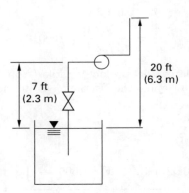

Customary U.S. Solution

From App. 17.D, the approximate equivalent lengths of various screwed steel fittings are

inlet: $L_e = 8.5$ ft

check valve: $L_e = 19$ ft

long radius elbows: $L_e = 3.6$ ft

The total equivalent length of the 2 in line is

$$L_e = 12 \text{ ft} + 8.5 \text{ ft} + 19.0 \text{ ft} + (3)(3.6 \text{ ft}) + 80 \text{ ft}$$

$$= 130.3 \text{ ft}$$

From App. 16.B, for schedule-40, 2 in pipe, the pipe data are

$$D_i = 0.1723 \text{ ft}$$

$$A_i = 0.0233 \text{ ft}^2$$

Since the flow rate is unknown, it must be assumed in order to find velocity. Assume 90 gal/min.

$$\dot{V} = \left(90 \ \frac{\text{gal}}{\text{min}}\right) \left(0.002228 \ \frac{\frac{\text{ft}^3}{\text{sec}}}{\frac{\text{gal}}{\text{min}}}\right) = 0.2005 \ \text{ft}^3/\text{sec}$$

The velocity is

$$\text{v} = \frac{\dot{V}}{A_i} = \frac{0.2005 \ \frac{\text{ft}^3}{\text{sec}}}{0.0233 \ \text{ft}^2} = 8.605 \ \text{ft/sec}$$

From App. 14.A, the kinematic viscosity of water at 70°F is $\nu = 1.059 \times 10^{-5} \ \text{ft}^2/\text{sec}$.

The Reynolds number is

$$Re = \frac{D\text{v}}{\nu} = \frac{(0.1723 \ \text{ft}) \left(8.605 \ \frac{\text{ft}}{\text{sec}}\right)}{1.059 \times 10^{-5} \ \frac{\text{ft}^2}{\text{sec}}}$$

$$= 1.4 \times 10^5$$

From App. 17.A, the specific roughness of steel pipe is

$$\epsilon = 0.0002 \ \text{ft}$$

$$\frac{\epsilon}{D} = \frac{0.0002 \ \text{ft}}{0.1723 \ \text{ft}} = 0.0012$$

From the Darcy friction factor table (App. 17.B), $f = 0.022$. At 90 gpm, the friction loss in the line from Eq. 18.6 is

$$h_L = \frac{fL\text{v}^2}{2Dg}$$

$$= \frac{(0.022)(130.3 \ \text{ft}) \left(8.605 \ \frac{\text{ft}}{\text{sec}}\right)^2}{(2)(0.1723 \ \text{ft}) \left(32.2 \ \frac{\text{ft}}{\text{sec}^2}\right)} = 19.1 \ \text{ft}$$

From Eq. 18.7, the velocity head at 90 gpm is

$$h_\text{v} = \frac{\text{v}^2}{2g} = \frac{\left(8.605 \ \frac{\text{ft}}{\text{sec}}\right)^2}{(2) \left(32.2 \ \frac{\text{ft}}{\text{sec}^2}\right)} = 1.1 \ \text{ft}$$

In general, the friction head and velocity head are

$$h_L = (19.1 \ \text{ft}) \left(\frac{Q_2}{90 \ \frac{\text{gal}}{\text{min}}}\right)^2$$

$$h_\text{v} = (1.1 \ \text{ft}) \left(\frac{Q_2}{90 \ \frac{\text{gal}}{\text{min}}}\right)^2$$

The total system head is

$$h = h_z + h_\text{v} + h_L$$

$$= 20 \ \text{ft} + (1.1 + 19.1 \ \text{ft}) \left(\frac{Q_2}{90 \ \frac{\text{gal}}{\text{min}}}\right)^2$$

From this equation, the following table for system head can be generated.

Q_2 (gal/min)	system head, h (ft)
0	20.0
10	20.2
20	21.0
30	22.2
40	24.0
50	26.2
60	29.0
70	32.2
80	36.0
90	40.2
100	44.9
110	50.2

(a) The intersection point of the system curve and the pump curve defines the operating flow rate. The flow rate is ⟩ 95 gal/min.

(b) The intersection point is not in an efficient range for the pump. A different pump should be used.

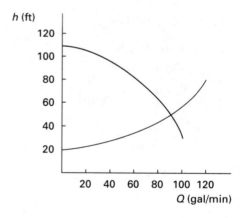

SI Solution

Use the approximate quivalent lengths of various screwed steel fittings from the Customary U.S. Solution. The total equivalent length of 5.08 cm schedule-40 pipe is

$$L_e = 4 \ \text{m} + \left(8.5 \ \text{ft} + 19.0 \ \text{ft} + (3)(3.6 \ \text{ft})\right) \left(0.3048 \ \frac{\text{m}}{\text{ft}}\right)$$

$$+ 27 \ \text{m}$$

$$= 42.67 \ \text{m}$$

From App. 16.C, for 2 in schedule-40 pipe, the pipe data are

$$D_i = 52.50 \text{ mm}$$
$$A_i = 21.65 \times 10^{-4} \text{ m}^2$$

Since the flow rate is unknown, it must be assumed in order to find velocity. Assume 6 L/s.

$$\dot{V} = \left(6 \, \frac{\text{L}}{\text{s}}\right) \left(\frac{1 \text{ m}^3}{1000 \text{ L}}\right) = 6 \times 10^{-3} \text{ m}^3/\text{s}$$

The velocity is

$$v = \frac{\dot{V}}{A_i} = \frac{6 \times 10^{-3} \, \frac{\text{m}^3}{\text{s}}}{21.65 \times 10^{-4} \text{ m}^2} = 2.77 \text{ m/s}$$

From App. 14.B, the absolute viscosity of water at 21°C is $\mu = 0.9827 \times 10^{-3}$ Pa·s.

The density of water is $\rho = 998 \text{ kg/m}^3$.

The Reynolds number is

$$\text{Re} = \frac{\rho v D_i}{\mu} = \frac{\left(998 \, \frac{\text{kg}}{\text{m}^3}\right) \left(2.77 \, \frac{\text{m}}{\text{s}}\right)}{0.9827 \times 10^{-3} \text{ Pa·s}}$$
$$\times (52.50 \text{ mm}) \left(\frac{1 \text{ m}}{1000 \text{ mm}}\right)$$
$$= 1.5 \times 10^5$$

From Table 17.2, the specific roughness of steel pipe is

$$\epsilon = 6.0 \times 10^{-5} \text{ m}$$

$$\frac{\epsilon}{D} = \frac{6.0 \times 10^{-5} \text{ m}}{(52.50 \text{ mm}) \left(\frac{1 \text{ m}}{1000 \text{ mm}}\right)} \approx 0.0012$$

From the friction factor table (App. 17.B), $f = 0.022$. At 6 L/s, the friction loss in the line from Eq. 18.6 is

$$h_L = \frac{f L v^2}{2Dg}$$
$$= \frac{(0.022)(42.67 \text{ m}) \left(2.77 \, \frac{\text{m}}{\text{s}}\right)^2}{(2)(52.50 \text{ mm}) \left(\frac{1 \text{ m}}{1000 \text{ mm}}\right) \left(9.81 \, \frac{\text{m}}{\text{s}^2}\right)}$$
$$= 6.99 \text{ m}$$

At 6 L/s, the velocity head from Eq. 18.7 is

$$h_v = \frac{v^2}{2g} = \frac{\left(2.77 \, \frac{\text{m}}{\text{s}}\right)^2}{(2) \left(9.81 \, \frac{\text{m}}{\text{s}^2}\right)} = 0.39 \text{ m}$$

In general, the friction head and velocity head are

$$h_L = (6.99 \text{ m}) \left(\frac{Q_2}{6 \, \frac{\text{L}}{\text{s}}}\right)^2$$

$$h_v = (0.39 \text{ m}) \left(\frac{Q_2}{6 \, \frac{\text{L}}{\text{s}}}\right)^2$$

The total system head is

$$h = h_z + h_v + h_L$$
$$= 6.3 \text{ m} + (0.39 \text{ m} + 6.99 \text{ m}) \left(\frac{Q_2}{6 \, \frac{\text{L}}{\text{s}}}\right)^2$$

From this equation the following table for the system head can be generated.

Q_2 (L/s)	h (m)
0	6.3
0.6	6.37
1.2	6.60
1.8	6.66
2.4	7.48
3.2	8.40
3.6	8.96
4.4	10.27
4.8	10.64
5.7	12.96
6.5	14.96
7.0	16.35
7.5	17.83

The intersection point of system curve and the pump curve will define the operating flow rate.

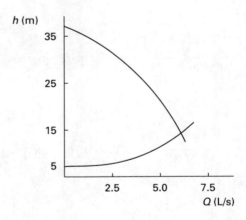

(a) The flow rate is $\boxed{6.2 \text{ L/s.}}$

(b) The intersection point is not in an efficient range of the pump. $\boxed{\text{A different pump should be used.}}$

13. *Customary U.S. Solution*

(a) From App. 24.A, the enthalpy of water at 200°F is 168.07 Btu/lbm and the enthalpy of the water at 180°F is 147.99 Btu/lbm. The mass flow rate through the system is

$$\dot{m} = \frac{q}{\Delta h}$$

$$= \frac{\left(1{,}000{,}000 \ \dfrac{\text{Btu}}{\text{hr}}\right)\left(\dfrac{1 \text{ hr}}{60 \text{ min}}\right)}{168.07 \ \dfrac{\text{Btu}}{\text{lbm}} - 147.99 \ \dfrac{\text{Btu}}{\text{lbm}}}$$

$$= 830.0 \text{ lbm/min}$$

The bulk temperature of the water is

$$\frac{200°\text{F} + 180°\text{F}}{2} = 190°\text{F}$$

From App. 14.A, the density of water at 190°F is $\rho = 60.36$ lbm/ft^3.

The volumetric flow rate is

$$Q = \frac{\left(830.0 \ \dfrac{\text{lbm}}{\text{min}}\right)\left(7.48 \ \dfrac{\text{gal}}{\text{ft}^3}\right)}{60.36 \ \dfrac{\text{lbm}}{\text{ft}^3}} = 102.9 \text{ gal/min}$$

From given pump data at 102.9 gal/min, head is

$$h_1 = 2.18 \text{ ft}$$
$$h_2 = 5.37 \text{ ft}$$
$$h_3 = 9.51 \text{ ft}$$

The loss per foot for the three pumps is as follows.

Pump 1:

$$\frac{(2.18 \text{ ft})\left(12 \ \dfrac{\text{in}}{\text{ft}}\right)}{420 \text{ ft}} = 0.062 \text{ in/ft} \quad [\text{too low}]$$

Pump 2:

$$\frac{(5.37 \text{ ft})\left(12 \ \dfrac{\text{in}}{\text{ft}}\right)}{420 \text{ ft}} = 0.15 \text{ in/ft} \quad [\text{too low}]$$

Pump 3:

$$\frac{(9.51 \text{ ft})\left(12 \ \dfrac{\text{in}}{\text{ft}}\right)}{420 \text{ ft}} = 0.27 \text{ in/ft} \quad [\text{OK}]$$

Choose pump 3.

(b) For noise, keep the velocity below 4 ft/sec.

The area of the pipe is

$$A = \frac{\dot{V}}{\text{v}} = \frac{\left(102.9 \ \dfrac{\text{gal}}{\text{min}}\right)\left(0.002228 \ \dfrac{\dfrac{\text{ft}^3}{\text{sec}}}{\dfrac{\text{gal}}{\text{min}}}\right)}{4 \ \dfrac{\text{ft}}{\text{sec}}}$$

$$= 0.057 \text{ ft}^2$$

The pipe diameter is

$$D = \sqrt{\frac{4A}{\pi}} = \sqrt{\frac{(4)(0.057 \text{ ft}^2)}{\pi}}\left(12 \ \dfrac{\text{in}}{\text{ft}}\right)$$

$$= \boxed{3.24 \text{ in} \quad \left[\text{say } 3\tfrac{1}{2} \text{ in}\right]}$$

SI Solution

(a) From App. 24.N, the enthalpy of the water at 90°C is 376.92 kJ/kg and at 80°C is 334.91 kJ/kg.

The mass flow rate through the system is

$$\dot{m} = \frac{q}{\Delta h}$$

$$= \frac{257 \text{ kW}}{376.92 \ \dfrac{\text{kJ}}{\text{kg}} - 334.91 \ \dfrac{\text{kJ}}{\text{kg}}} = 6.12 \text{ kg/s}$$

The bulk temperature of the water is

$$\frac{90°\text{C} + 80°\text{C}}{2} = 85°\text{C}$$

From App. 14.B, density of water at 85°C is $\rho = 968.59$ kg/m^3.

The volumetric flow rate is

$$Q = \frac{6.12 \ \dfrac{\text{kg}}{\text{s}}}{\left(968.59 \ \dfrac{\text{kg}}{\text{m}^3}\right)\left(\dfrac{1 \text{ m}^3}{1000 \text{ L}}\right)} = 6.32 \text{ L/s}$$

From given pump data at 6.32 L/s (equivalent to 100 gpm), head is

$$h_1 = 2.5 \text{ ft}$$
$$h_2 = 5.8 \text{ ft}$$
$$h_3 = 10.0 \text{ ft}$$

The loss for the three pumps is as follows.

Pump 1:

$$\frac{(2.5 \text{ ft})\left(0.305 \ \frac{\text{m}}{\text{ft}}\right)}{140 \text{ m}} = 0.0054 \text{ m/m} \quad [\text{too low}]$$

Pump 2:

$$\frac{(5.8 \text{ ft})\left(0.305 \ \frac{\text{m}}{\text{ft}}\right)}{140 \text{ m}} = 0.013 \text{ m/m} \quad [\text{too low}]$$

Pump 3:

$$\frac{(10.0 \text{ ft})\left(0.305 \ \frac{\text{m}}{\text{ft}}\right)}{140 \text{ m}} = 0.0217 \text{ m/m} \quad [\text{OK}]$$

Choose pump 3.

(b) For noise, keep the velocity below 1 m/s.

The area of the pipe is

$$A = \frac{\dot{V}}{\text{v}} = \frac{\left(6.32 \ \frac{\text{L}}{\text{s}}\right)\left(\frac{1 \text{ m}^3}{1000 \text{ L}}\right)}{1 \ \frac{\text{m}}{\text{s}}} = 0.00632 \text{ m}^2$$

The pipe diameter is

$$D = \sqrt{\frac{4A}{\pi}} = \sqrt{\frac{(4)(0.00632 \text{ m}^2)}{\pi}}$$

$$= \boxed{0.0897 \text{ m}}$$

14. From Eq. 18.52,

$$P_2 = P_1\left(\frac{\rho_2 n_2^3 D_2^5}{\rho_1 n_1^3 D_1^5}\right)$$

$$= P_1\left(\frac{n_2}{n_1}\right)^3 \quad [\rho_2 = \rho_1 \text{ and } D_2 = D_1]$$

Customary U.S. Solution

$$P_2 = (0.5 \text{ hp})\left(\frac{2000 \text{ rpm}}{1750 \text{ rpm}}\right)^3 = \boxed{0.746 \text{ hp}}$$

SI Solution

$$P_2 = P_1\left(\frac{n_2}{n_1}\right)^3$$

$$= (0.37 \text{ kW})\left(\frac{2000 \text{ rpm}}{1750 \text{ rpm}}\right)^3$$

$$= \boxed{0.55 \text{ kW}}$$

15. (a) Random values of Q are chosen, and the corresponding values of H are determined by the formula $H = 30 + 2Q^2$.

Q (ft^3/sec)	H (ft)
30	1830
25	1280
20	830
15	480
10	230
7.5	142.5
5	80
2.5	42.5
0	30

These points are plotted and connected to draw the system curve. The intersection of the system curve and the 1400 rpm pump curve defines the operating point at that rpm.

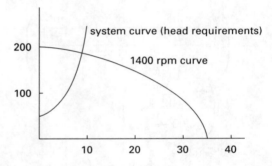

From the intersection of the graphs, at 1400 rpm the flow rate is approximately 9 ft^3/sec and the corresponding head is $30 + (2)(9)^2 \approx 192$ ft.

$$Q = \left(9 \ \frac{\text{ft}^3}{\text{sec}}\right)\left(448.8 \ \frac{\frac{\text{gal}}{\text{min}}}{\frac{\text{ft}^3}{\text{sec}}}\right) = \boxed{4039 \text{ gal/min}}$$

(b) From Table 18.4, the hydraulic horsepower is

$$\text{WHP} = \frac{h_A \dot{V}(\text{SG})}{8.814}$$

$$= \frac{(192 \text{ ft})\left(9 \ \frac{\text{ft}^3}{\text{sec}}\right)(1)}{8.814 \ \frac{\text{ft}^4}{\text{hp-sec}}}$$

$$= 196 \text{ hp}$$

From Eq. 18.28(b), the specific speed is

$$n_s = \frac{n\sqrt{Q}}{h_A^{0.75}}$$

$$= \frac{(1400 \text{ rpm})\sqrt{4039 \ \frac{\text{gal}}{\text{min}}}}{(192 \text{ ft})^{0.75}}$$

$$= 1725 \text{ rpm}$$

From Fig. 18.7, $\eta \approx 83\%$.

The minimum pump motor power should be

$$\frac{196 \text{ hp}}{0.83} = \boxed{236 \text{ hp}}$$

(c) From Eq. 18.41,

$$Q_2 = Q_1 \left(\frac{n_2}{n_1}\right) = \left(4039 \frac{\text{gal}}{\text{min}}\right)\left(\frac{1200 \text{ rpm}}{1400 \text{ rpm}}\right)$$

$$= \boxed{3462 \text{ gpm}}$$

16. *Customary U.S. Solution*

(a) From App. 14.A, the density of water at 60°F is 62.37 lbm/ft^3. From Eq. 18.5(b), the head dropped is

$$h = \left(\frac{\Delta p}{\rho}\right) \times \left(\frac{g_c}{g}\right)$$

$$= \left(\frac{\left(500 \frac{\text{lbf}}{\text{in}^2} - 30 \frac{\text{lbf}}{\text{in}^2}\right)\left(144 \frac{\text{in}^2}{\text{ft}^2}\right)}{62.37 \frac{\text{lbm}}{\text{ft}^3}}\right)$$

$$\times \left(\frac{32.2 \frac{\text{ft-lbm}}{\text{lbf-sec}^2}}{32.2 \frac{\text{ft}}{\text{sec}^2}}\right)$$

$$= 1085 \text{ ft}$$

From Eq. 18.55(b), the specific speed of a turbine is

$$n_s = \frac{n\sqrt{P \text{ in hp}}}{(h_t \text{ in ft})^{1.25}} = \frac{(1750 \text{ rpm})\sqrt{250 \text{ hp}}}{(1085 \text{ ft})^{1.25}}$$

$$= 4.443 \text{ rpm}$$

Since the lowest suggested value of n_s for a reaction turbine is 10 rpm, $\boxed{\text{recommend an impulse (Pelton) wheel.}}$

(b) The flow rate, $\dot{V}$, is

$$\dot{V} = Av = \left(\frac{\pi}{4}\right)\left(\frac{4 \text{ in}}{12 \frac{\text{in}}{\text{ft}}}\right)^2 \left(35 \frac{\text{ft}}{\text{sec}}\right)$$

$$= 3.054 \text{ ft}^3/\text{sec}$$

The flow rate due to the blade's moving away at 10 ft/sec is

$$\dot{V}' = \frac{\left(35 \frac{\text{ft}}{\text{sec}} - 10 \frac{\text{ft}}{\text{sec}}\right)\left(3.054 \frac{\text{ft}^3}{\text{sec}}\right)}{35 \frac{\text{ft}}{\text{sec}}}$$

$$= 2.181 \text{ ft}^3/\text{sec}$$

The forces in the x-direction and the y-direction are

$$F_x = \left(\frac{\dot{V}'\rho}{g_c}\right)(v_j - v_b)(\cos\theta - 1)$$

$$= \left(\frac{\left(2.181 \frac{\text{ft}^3}{\text{sec}}\right)\left(62.37 \frac{\text{lbm}}{\text{ft}^3}\right)}{32.2 \frac{\text{lbm-ft}}{\text{lbf-sec}^2}}\right)$$

$$\times \left(35 \frac{\text{ft}}{\text{sec}} - 10 \frac{\text{ft}}{\text{sec}}\right)(\cos 80° - 1)$$

$$= -87.27 \text{ lbf}$$

$$F_y = \left(\frac{\dot{V}'\rho}{g_c}\right)(v_j - v_b)(\sin\theta)$$

$$= \left(\frac{\left(2.181 \frac{\text{ft}^3}{\text{sec}}\right)\left(62.37 \frac{\text{lbm}}{\text{ft}^3}\right)}{32.2 \frac{\text{lbm-ft}}{\text{lbf-sec}^2}}\right)$$

$$\times \left(35 \frac{\text{ft}}{\text{sec}} - 10 \frac{\text{ft}}{\text{sec}}\right)(\sin 80°)$$

$$= 104.0 \text{ lbf}$$

$$R = \sqrt{F_x^2 + F_y^2}$$

$$= \sqrt{(-87.27 \text{ lbf})^2 + (104.0 \text{ lbf})^2} = \boxed{135.8 \text{ lbf}}$$

SI Solution

(a) From App. 14.B, the density of water at 16°C is 998.83 kg/m^3. From Eq. 18.5(a), the head dropped is

$$h = \frac{\Delta p}{\rho g}$$

$$= \frac{(3.5 \text{ MPa})\left(10^6 \frac{\text{Pa}}{\text{MPa}}\right) - (210 \text{ kPa})\left(1000 \frac{\text{Pa}}{\text{kPa}}\right)}{\left(998.83 \frac{\text{kg}}{\text{m}^3}\right)\left(9.81 \frac{\text{m}}{\text{s}^2}\right)}$$

$$= 335.8 \text{ m}$$

From Eq. 18.55(a), the specific speed of a turbine is

$$n_s = \frac{n\sqrt{P \text{ in kW}}}{(h_t \text{ in meters})^{1.25}}$$

$$= \frac{(1750 \text{ rpm})\sqrt{185 \text{ kW}}}{(335.8 \text{ m})^{1.25}}$$

$$= 16.56 \text{ rpm}$$

Since the lowest suggested value of n_s for a reaction turbine is 38 rpm, recommend an impeller (Pelton) wheel.

(b) The flow rate, $\dot{V}$, is

$$\dot{V} = Av = \left(\frac{\pi}{4}\right)\left[(100 \text{ mm})\left(\frac{1 \text{ m}}{1000 \text{ mm}}\right)\right]^2\left(10.5 \frac{\text{m}}{\text{s}}\right)$$
$$= 0.08247 \text{ m}^3/\text{s}$$

The flow rate due to the blade's moving away at 10 ft/sec is

$$\dot{V}' = \frac{\left(10.5 \frac{\text{m}}{\text{s}} - 3 \frac{\text{m}}{\text{s}}\right)\left(0.08247 \frac{\text{m}^3}{\text{s}}\right)}{10.5 \frac{\text{m}}{\text{s}}}$$
$$= 0.05891 \text{ m}^3/\text{s}$$

The forces in the x-direction and the y-direction are

$$F_x = \dot{V}'\rho(v_j - v_b)(\cos\theta - 1)$$
$$= \left(0.05891 \frac{\text{m}^3}{\text{s}}\right)\left(998.83 \frac{\text{kg}}{\text{m}^3}\right)$$
$$\times \left(10.5 \frac{\text{m}}{\text{s}} - 3 \frac{\text{m}}{\text{s}}\right)(\cos 80° - 1)$$
$$= -364.7 \text{ N}$$

$$F_y = \dot{V}'\rho(v_j - v_b)(\sin\theta)$$
$$= \left(0.05891 \frac{\text{m}^3}{\text{s}}\right)\left(998.83 \frac{\text{kg}}{\text{m}^3}\right)$$
$$\times \left(10.5 \frac{\text{m}}{\text{s}} - 3 \frac{\text{m}}{\text{s}}\right)(\sin 80°)$$
$$= 434.6 \text{ N}$$

$$R = \sqrt{F_x^2 + F_y^2}$$
$$= \sqrt{(-364.7 \text{ N})^2 + (434.6 \text{ N})^2} = \boxed{567.3 \text{ N}}$$

17. *Customary U.S. Solution*

(a) The total effective head is due to the pressure head, velocity head, and tailwater head.

$$h_{\text{eff}} = h_p + h_v - h_{z(\text{tailwater})}$$
$$= 92.5 \text{ ft} + \frac{\left(12 \frac{\text{ft}}{\text{sec}}\right)^2}{(2)\left(32.2 \frac{\text{ft}}{\text{sec}^2}\right)} - (-5.26 \text{ ft})$$
$$= \boxed{100 \text{ ft}}$$

(b) From Table 18.4, the theoretical hydraulic horsepower is

$$P_{\text{th}} = \frac{h_A\dot{V}(\text{SG})}{8.814} = \frac{(100 \text{ ft})\left(25 \frac{\text{ft}^3}{\text{sec}}\right)(1)}{8.814 \frac{\text{ft}^4}{\text{hp-sec}}}$$
$$= \boxed{283.6 \text{ hp}}$$

The overall turbine efficiency is

$$\eta = \frac{P_{\text{brake}}}{P_{\text{th}}} = \frac{250 \text{ hp}}{283.6 \text{ hp}} = \boxed{0.882 \ \ (88.2\%)}$$

(c) From Eq. 18.42 (the affinity laws),

$$n_2 = n_1\sqrt{\frac{h_2}{h_1}} = (610 \text{ rpm})\sqrt{\frac{225 \text{ ft}}{100 \text{ ft}}}$$
$$= \boxed{915 \text{ rpm}}$$

(d) Combine Eqs. 18.42 and 18.43.

$$P_2 = P_1\left(\frac{h_2}{h_1}\right)^{1.5} = (250 \text{ hp})\left(\frac{225 \text{ ft}}{100 \text{ ft}}\right)^{1.5}$$
$$= \boxed{843.8 \text{ hp}}$$

(e) Combine Eqs. 18.41 and 18.42.

$$Q_2 = Q_1\sqrt{\frac{h_2}{h_1}} = \left(25 \frac{\text{ft}^3}{\text{sec}}\right)\sqrt{\frac{225 \text{ ft}}{100 \text{ ft}}}$$
$$= \boxed{37.5 \text{ ft}^3/\text{sec}}$$

SI Solution

(a) The total effective head is due to the pressure head, velocity head, and tailwater head.

$$h_{\text{eff}} = h_p + h_v - h_{z(\text{tailwater})}$$
$$= 30.8 \text{ m} + \frac{\left(3.6 \frac{\text{m}}{\text{s}}\right)^2}{(2)\left(9.81 \frac{\text{m}}{\text{s}^2}\right)} - (-1.75 \text{ m})$$
$$= \boxed{33.21 \text{ m}}$$

(b) From Table 18.5, the theoretical hydraulic kilowatt is

$$P_{\text{th}} = \frac{9.81 h_A Q(\text{SG})}{1000}$$
$$= \frac{\left(9.81 \frac{\text{m}}{\text{s}^2}\right)(33.21 \text{ m})\left(700 \frac{\text{L}}{\text{s}}\right)(1)}{1000 \frac{\text{W}}{\text{kW}}}$$
$$= \boxed{228.1 \text{ kW}}$$

The overall turbine efficiency is

$$\eta = \frac{P_{\text{brake}}}{P_{\text{th}}} = \frac{185 \text{ kW}}{228.1 \text{ kW}}$$

$$= \boxed{0.811 \quad (81.1\%)}$$

(c) From Eq. 18.42 (the affinity laws),

$$h_2 = n_1 \sqrt{\frac{h_2}{h_1}} = (610 \text{ rpm}) \sqrt{\frac{75 \text{ m}}{33.21 \text{ m}}}$$

$$= \boxed{917 \text{ rpm}}$$

(d) Combine Eqs. 18.42 and 18.43.

$$P_2 = P_1 \left(\frac{h_2}{h_1}\right)^{1.5} = (185 \text{ kW}) \left(\frac{75 \text{ m}}{33.21 \text{ m}}\right)^{1.5}$$

$$= \boxed{627.3 \text{ kW}}$$

(e) Combine Eqs. 18.41 and 18.42.

$$Q_2 = Q_1 \sqrt{\frac{h_2}{h_1}} = \left(700 \text{ }\frac{\text{L}}{\text{s}}\right) \sqrt{\frac{75 \text{ m}}{33.21 \text{ m}}}$$

$$= \boxed{1051.9 \text{ L/s}}$$

20 Fans and Ductwork

1. Customary U.S. Solution

With aspect ratio $R = 4$, the short side is given by Eq. 20.31.

$$\text{short side} = \frac{D(1+R)^{\frac{1}{4}}}{1.3R^{\frac{5}{8}}}$$

$$= \frac{(18 \text{ in})(1+4)^{\frac{1}{4}}}{(1.3)(4)^{\frac{5}{8}}} = 8.7 \text{ in} \approx \boxed{9.0 \text{ in}}$$

From Eq. 20.32, the long side is

$$\text{long side} = R(\text{short side})$$

$$= (4)(8.7 \text{ in}) = 34.8 \text{ in} \approx \boxed{35 \text{ in}}$$

SI Solution

With aspect ratio $R = 4$, the short side is given by Eq. 20.31.

$$\text{short side} = \frac{D(1+R)^{\frac{1}{4}}}{1.3R^{\frac{5}{8}}}$$

$$= \frac{(457 \text{ mm})(1+4)^{\frac{1}{4}}}{(1.3)(4)^{\frac{5}{8}}} = \boxed{221 \text{ mm}}$$

From Eq. 20.32, the long side is

$$\text{long side} = R(\text{short side})$$

$$= (4)(221 \text{ mm}) = \boxed{884 \text{ mm}}$$

2. Customary U.S. Solution

Disregarding terminal pressure, the remainder of the points on the system curve can be found from Eq. 20.19.

$$\frac{p_2}{p_1} = \left(\frac{Q_2}{Q_1}\right)^2$$

$$Q_2 = Q_1\sqrt{\frac{p_2}{p_1}}$$

$$= (10{,}000 \text{ SCFM})\sqrt{\frac{p_2}{4 \text{ in wg}}}$$

$$= 5000\sqrt{p_2}$$

The following table can be generated from the preceding equation.

p_2 (in wg)	Q (SCFM)
1	5000
2	7071
3	8660
4	10,000
5	11,180
6	12,247

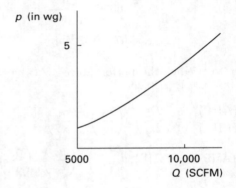

SI Solution

Disregarding terminal pressure, the remainder of the points on the system curve can be found from Eq. 20.19.

$$\frac{p_2}{p_1} = \left(\frac{Q_2}{Q_1}\right)^2$$

$$Q_2 = Q_1\sqrt{\frac{p_2}{p_1}}$$

$$= \left(4700 \ \frac{\text{L}}{\text{s}}\right)\sqrt{\frac{p_2}{1 \text{ kPa}}}$$

$$= 4700\sqrt{p_2}$$

The following table can be generated from the preceding equation.

p_2 (kPa)	Q (L/s)
1	4700
2	6647
3	8141
4	9400
5	10 510
6	11 513

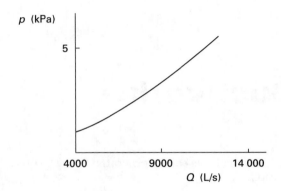

3. *Customary U.S. Solution*

The air horsepower is given by Eq. 20.11(b).

$$(AHP)_A = \frac{Q_{cfm}(TP_{in\ wg})}{6356}$$

$$= \frac{(40\ cfm)(0.5\ in\ wg)}{6356\ \frac{in\text{-}ft^3}{hp\text{-}min}}$$

$$= 3.147 \times 10^{-3}\ hp$$

In order to predict the performance of a dynamically similar fan, use Eq. 20.26.

$$\frac{(AHP)_1}{(AHP)_2} = \left(\frac{D_1}{D_2}\right)^5 \left(\frac{n_1}{n_2}\right)^3 \left(\frac{\gamma_1}{\gamma_2}\right)$$

$$(AHP)_2 = (AHP)_1 \left(\frac{D_2}{D_1}\right)^5 \left(\frac{n_2}{n_1}\right)^3 \left(\frac{\gamma_2}{\gamma_1}\right)$$

$$\frac{D_2}{D_1} = \frac{1}{\frac{1}{8}} = 8$$

$$\frac{n_2}{n_1} = \frac{1}{2}$$

At standard air conditions, $\rho_1 = 0.075\ lbm/ft^3$. Use standard atmospheric data from App. 26.E for 5000 ft altitude.

$$\rho_{5000} = \rho_2 = \frac{p}{RT} = \frac{\left(12.225\ \frac{lbf}{in^2}\right)\left(144\ \frac{in^2}{ft^2}\right)}{\left(53.3\ \frac{ft\text{-}lbf}{lbm\text{-}°R}\right)(500.9°R)}$$

$$= 0.06594\ lbm/ft^3$$

$$\frac{\gamma_2}{\gamma_1} = \frac{\rho_2 g}{\rho_1 g} = \frac{\rho_2}{\rho_1} = \frac{0.06594\ \frac{lbm}{ft^3}}{0.075\ \frac{lbm}{ft^3}}$$

$$= 0.8792$$

$$(AHP)_2 = (3.147 \times^{-3}\ hp)(8)^5 \left(\tfrac{1}{2}\right)^3 (0.8792)$$

$$= \boxed{11.33\ hp}$$

SI Solution

The air power is given by Eq. 20.11(a).

$$(AkW)_1 = \frac{Q_{L/s}(TP_{Pa})}{10^6}$$

$$= \frac{\left(19\ \frac{L}{s}\right)(125\ Pa)}{10^6\ \frac{L\cdot W}{m^3\cdot kW}}$$

$$= 2.375 \times 10^{-3}\ kW$$

In order to predict the performance of a dynamically similar fan, use Eq. 20.26.

$$\frac{(AkW)_1}{(AkW)_2} = \left(\frac{D_1}{D_2}\right)^5 \left(\frac{n_1}{n_2}\right)^3 \left(\frac{\gamma_1}{\gamma_2}\right)$$

$$(AkW)_2 = (AkW)_1 \left(\frac{D_2}{D_1}\right)^5 \left(\frac{n_2}{n_1}\right)^3 \left(\frac{\gamma_2}{\gamma_1}\right)$$

$$\frac{D_2}{D_1} = \frac{1}{\frac{1}{8}} = 8$$

$$\frac{n_2}{n_1} = \frac{1}{2}$$

At standard air conditions, $\rho = 1.2\ kg/m^3$. Use standard atmospheric data from App. 26.E for 1500 m altitude.

$$\rho_{1525} = \rho_2 = \frac{p}{RT} = \frac{(0.8456\ bar)\left(10^5\ \frac{Pa}{bar}\right)}{\left(287\ \frac{J}{kg\cdot K}\right)(278.4K)}$$

$$= 1.058\ kg/m^3$$

$$\frac{\gamma_2}{\gamma_1} = \frac{\rho_2 g}{\rho_1 g} = \frac{\rho_2}{\rho_1} = \frac{1.058\ \frac{kg}{m^3}}{1.2\ \frac{kg}{m^3}} = 0.88$$

$$(AkW)_2 = (2.375 \times 10^{-3}\ kW)(8)^5 \left(\tfrac{1}{2}\right)^3 (0.88)$$

$$= \boxed{8.56\ kW}$$

4. *Customary U.S. Solution*

From the standard friction loss in the standard duct chart (Fig. 20.4), the friction loss is 0.47 in of water per 100 ft of duct and v = 2700 ft/min. The friction loss due to the 750 ft of duct is

$$h_{f,1} = (0.47\ in\ wg)\left(\frac{750\ ft}{100\ ft}\right)$$

$$= 3.525\ in\ wg$$

The equivalent length of each round elbow (radius-to-diameter ratio of 1.5) can be found from Table 20.4.

$$L_e = 12D$$

For four round elbows,

$$L_e = (4)(12D)$$
$$= \frac{(4)(12D)(20 \text{ in})}{12 \frac{\text{in}}{\text{ft}}} = 80 \text{ ft}$$

The friction loss due to the 80 ft of equivalent length of the duct is

$$h_{f,2} = (0.47 \text{ in wg}) \left(\frac{80 \text{ ft}}{100 \text{ ft}} \right) = 0.376 \text{ in wg}$$

For a cross duct,

$$\frac{D_1}{D_2} = \frac{2 \text{ in}}{20 \text{ in}} = 0.1 \text{ in}$$

From Table 20.3, the loss coefficient is $K_{\text{up}} = 0.2$. For two cross pipes, the friction loss is given by Eq. 20.34.

$$h_{f,3} = (2)K_{\text{up}} \left(\frac{\text{v}}{4005} \right)^2$$
$$= (2)(0.2) \left(\frac{2700 \frac{\text{ft}}{\text{min}}}{4005 \frac{\text{ft}}{\text{min}}} \right)^2 = 0.182 \text{ in wg}$$

The total loss is

$$h_{f,1} + h_{f,2} + h_{f,3} = 3.525 \text{ in wg} + 0.376 \text{ in wg}$$
$$+ 0.182 \text{ in wg}$$
$$= \boxed{4.083 \text{ in wg}}$$

SI Solution

From the standard friction loss in the standard duct chart (Fig. 20.5), the friction loss is 9 Pa/m and v = 21.5 m/s. The friction loss due to the 230 m of the duct is

$$h_{f,1} = \left(9 \frac{\text{Pa}}{\text{m}} \right) (230 \text{ m}) = 2070 \text{ Pa}$$

The equivalent length of each round elbow (radius-to-diameter ratio of 1.5) can be found in Table 20.4.

$$L_e = 12D$$

For four round elbows,

$$L_e = (4)(12D)$$
$$= \frac{(4)(12D)(508 \text{ mm})}{1000 \frac{\text{mm}}{\text{m}}} = 24.38 \text{ m}$$

The friction loss due to the 24.38 m of equivalent length of duct is

$$h_{f,2} = \left(9 \frac{\text{Pa}}{\text{m}} \right) (24.38 \text{ m}) = 219.4 \text{ Pa}$$

For a cross duct,

$$\frac{D_1}{D_2} = \frac{51 \text{ mm}}{508 \text{ mm}} = 0.1$$

From Table 20.3, the loss coefficient K_{up} is 0.2. For two cross pipes, the friction loss is given by Eq. 20.34.

$$h_{f,3} = (2)K_{\text{up}}(\text{v}_{\text{m/s}})^2$$
$$= (2)(0.2) \left(21.5 \frac{\text{m}}{\text{s}} \right)^2 = 184.9 \text{ Pa}$$

The total loss is

$$h_{f,1} + h_{f,2} + h_{f,3} = 2070 \text{ Pa} + 219.4 \text{ Pa} + 184.9 \text{ Pa}$$
$$= \boxed{2474.3 \text{ Pa}}$$

5. *Customary U.S. Solution*

For the 18 in duct,

$$A = \frac{\pi}{4}D^2 = \left(\frac{\pi}{4} \right) \left(\frac{18 \text{ in}}{12 \frac{\text{in}}{\text{ft}}} \right)^2$$
$$= 1.767 \text{ ft}^2$$

$$\text{v}_1 = \frac{Q}{A} = \frac{1500 \frac{\text{ft}^3}{\text{min}}}{1.767 \text{ ft}^2}$$
$$= 848.9 \text{ ft/min}$$

For the 14 in duct,

$$A = \frac{\pi}{4}D^2 = \left(\frac{\pi}{4} \right) \left(\frac{14 \text{ in}}{12 \frac{\text{in}}{\text{ft}}} \right)^2 = 1.069 \text{ ft}^2$$

$$\text{v}_2 = \frac{Q}{A} = \frac{1500 \text{ cfm} - 300 \text{ cfm}}{1.069 \text{ ft}^2}$$
$$= 1122.5 \text{ ft/min}$$

Since $v_2 > v_1$, there is no regain. The regain will be a static pressure loss. Use $R = 1.1$ in that case. From Eq. 20.39, the static pressure loss is

$$SR_{actual} = R\left(\frac{v_{up}^2 - v_{down}^2}{(4005)^2}\right)$$

$$= (1.1)\left(\frac{\left(848.9\,\frac{ft}{min}\right)^2 - \left(1122.5\,\frac{ft}{min}\right)^2}{(4005)^2}\right)$$

$$= \boxed{-0.037\text{ in wg loss}}$$

SI Solution

For the 457 mm duct,

$$A = \frac{\pi}{4}D^2 = \left(\frac{\pi}{4}\right)\left(\frac{457\text{ mm}}{1000\,\frac{mm}{m}}\right)^2 = 0.164\text{ m}^2$$

$$v_1 = \frac{Q}{A} = \frac{\left(700\,\frac{L}{s}\right)\left(\frac{1\text{ m}^3}{1000\text{ L}}\right)}{0.164\text{ m}^2}$$

$$= 4.27\text{ m/s}$$

For 356 mm duct,

$$A = \frac{\pi}{4}D^2 = \left(\frac{\pi}{4}\right)\left(\frac{356\text{ mm}}{1000\,\frac{mm}{m}}\right)^2 = 0.1\text{ m}^2$$

$$v_2 = \frac{Q}{A} = \left(\frac{700\,\frac{L}{s} - 140\,\frac{L}{s}}{0.1\text{ m}^2}\right)\left(\frac{1\text{ m}^3}{1000\text{ L}}\right)$$

$$= 5.60\text{ m/s}$$

Since $v_2 > v_1$, there is no regain. The regain will be a static pressure loss. Use $R = 1.1$ in that case. From Eq. 20.5, the static pressure loss is

$$SR = R\left(0.6\,\frac{Pa\cdot s}{m}\right)(v_{up}^2 - v_{down}^2)$$

$$= (1.1)\left(0.6\,\frac{Pa\cdot s}{m}\right)\left(\left(4.27\,\frac{m}{s}\right)^2 - \left(5.60\,\frac{m}{s}\right)^2\right)$$

$$= \boxed{-8.66\text{ Pa loss}}$$

6. *Customary U.S. Solution*

(a) *step 1:* From Table 20.7, choose the main duct velocity as 1600 fpm.

step 2: The total air flow from the fan is 1500 cfm. From Fig. 20.4, the main duct diameter is 13 in. The friction loss is 0.27 in wg per 100 ft.

step 3: After the first takeoff at A, the flow rate in section A–B is

$$1500\text{ cfm} - 300\text{ cfm} = 1200\text{ cfm}$$

From Fig. 20.4, for 1200 cfm and 0.27 in wg per 100 ft, the diameter is 11.8 in (say 12 in) and the velocity is 1500 fpm. Similarly, the diameter and the velocity for other sections are obtained and listed in the following table.

section	Q (cfm)	D (in)	v (fpm)
fan–A	1500	13	1600
A–B	1200	12	1500
B–C	900	11	1400
C–D	600	9.5	1300
D–E	400	8	1150
E–F	200	6.3	975

These diameters are for round duct. The equivalent rectangular duct sides with an aspect ratio of 1.5 are found as follows.

$$a = \frac{D(1.5+1)^{0.25}}{(1.3)(1.5)^{0.625}} = 0.75D$$

$$b = Ra = (1.5)(0.75D) = 1.125D$$

Convert the diameters to sides a and b.

$$a_{fan-A} = (0.75)(13\text{ in}) = 9.75\text{ in}$$
$$b_{fan-A} = (1.125)(13\text{ in}) = 14.63\text{ in}$$

Use a 10×15 in duct.

The following table is prepared similarly, rounding up as appropriate.

section	D (in)	a (in)	b (in)
fan–A	13	10	15
A–B	12	9	14
B–C	11	9	13
C–D	9.5	8	11
D–E	8	6	9
E–F	6.3	5	8

(b) *step 4:* By inspection, the longest run is fan–F. From Table 20.4, the equivalent length of each bend is 12D. For two elbows,

$$L_{e,bend} = 12D = (12)\left(\frac{13\text{ in} + 9.5\text{ in}}{12\,\frac{in}{ft}}\right)$$

$$= 22.5\text{ ft}$$

The equivalent length of the entire run is

15 ft (fan to first bend)
45 ft (first bend to point A)
30 ft (section A–B)
30 ft (section B–C)
20 ft (point A to second bend)
22.5 ft (equivalent length of two bends)
10 ft (second bend to point D)
20 ft (section D–E)
20 ft (section E–F)

total: 212.5 ft

The straight-through friction loss in the longest run is

$$\left(\frac{212.5\ \text{ft}}{100\ \text{ft}}\right)\left(0.27\ \frac{\text{in wg}}{100\ \text{ft}}\right) = 0.57\ \text{in wg}$$

The fan must be able to supply a static pressure of

$$\text{SP}_{\text{fan}} = 0.57\ \text{in wg} + 0.25\ \text{in wg}$$

$$= \boxed{0.82\ \text{in wg}}$$

(c) The total pressure supplied by the fan is

$$\text{TP}_{\text{fan}} = 0.82\ \text{in wg} + \left(\frac{1600\ \text{fpm}}{4005}\right)^2$$

$$= \boxed{0.98\ \text{in wg}}$$

SI Solution

(a) *step 1:* From Table 20.7, choose the main duct velocity as 1600 cfm. From the table footnote (a), the SI velocity is

$$v_{\text{main}} = (1600\ \text{fpm})(0.00508) = 8.1\ \text{m/s}$$

step 2: The total air flow from the fan is 700 L/s. From Fig. 20.5, the main duct diameter is approximately 340 mm. The friction loss is 2.3 Pa/m.

step 3: After the first takeoff at A, the flow rate in section A–B is

$$700\ \frac{\text{L}}{\text{s}} - 150\ \frac{\text{L}}{\text{s}} = 550\ \text{L/s}$$

From Fig. 20.5 for 550 L/s and 2.3 Pa/m, the diameter is 300 mm and the velocity is 7.7 m/s. Similarly, the diameter and the velocity for other sections are obtained and listed in the following table.

section	Q (L/s)	D (mm)	v (m/s)
fan–A	700	340	8.1
A–B	550	300	7.7
B–C	400	275	7
C–D	250	225	6.3
D–E	150	180	5.5
E–F	50	125	4.4

These diameters are for round duct. The equivalent rectangular duct sides with an aspect ratio of 1.5 are found as follows.

$$a = \frac{D(1.5+1)^{0.25}}{(1.3)(1.5)^{0.625}} = 0.75D$$

$$b = Ra = (1.5)(0.75D) = 1.125D$$

Convert the diameters to sides a and b.

$$a_{\text{fan–A}} = (0.75)(340\ \text{mm}) = 255\ \text{mm}$$

$$b_{\text{fan–A}} = (1.125)(340\ \text{mm}) = 383\ \text{mm}$$

Use a 275 × 400 mm duct.

The following table is prepared similarly, rounding up as appropriate.

section	D (mm)	a (mm)	b (mm)
fan–A	340	275	400
A–B	300	225	350
B–C	275	225	325
C–D	225	175	275
D–E	180	150	225
E–F	125	100	150

(b) *step 4:* By inspection, the longest run is fan–F. From Table 20.4, the equivalent length of each bend is 12D. For two elbows,

$$L_{e,\text{bend}} = 12D$$

$$= (12)\left(\frac{340\ \text{mm} + 225\ \text{mm}}{1000\ \frac{\text{mm}}{\text{m}}}\right)$$

$$= 6.8\ \text{m}$$

The equivalent length of the entire run is

4.5 m (fan to first bend)
13.5 m (first bend to point A)
9 m (section A–B)
9 m (section B–C)
6 m (point C to second bend)
6.8 m (equivalent length of two bends)
3 m (second bend to point D)
6 m (section D–E)
6 m (section E–F)

total: 63.8 m

The straight-through friction loss in the longest run is

$$(63.8 \text{ m})\left(2.3 \ \frac{\text{Pa}}{\text{m}}\right) = 147 \text{ Pa}$$

The fan must be able to supply a static pressure of

$$\text{SP}_{\text{fan}} = 147 \text{ Pa} + 63 \text{ Pa} = \boxed{210 \text{ Pa}}$$

(c) The total pressure supplied by the fan is

$$\text{TP}_{\text{fan}} = 210 \text{ Pa} + \left(0.6 \ \frac{\text{Pa·s}^2}{\text{m}^2}\right)\left(8.1 \ \frac{\text{m}}{\text{s}}\right)^2$$

$$= \boxed{249 \text{ Pa}}$$

7. *Customary U.S. Solution*

(a) *step 1:* From Table 20.7, choose the main duct velocity as 1600 fpm.

step 2: The total air flow from the fan is

$$(12)(300 \text{ cfm}) = 3600 \text{ cfm}$$

From Fig. 20.4, the main duct diameter is 20 in. The friction loss is 0.16 in wg per 100 ft.

step 3: After the first takeoff, the flow rate between first and second is

$$3600 \text{ cfm} - (4)(300 \text{ cfm}) = 2400 \text{ cfm}$$

From Fig. 20.4, for 2400 cfm and 0.16 in wg per 100 ft, the diameter is 17.2 in and the velocity is 1440 fpm. Similarly, the diameter and the velocity for other sections are obtained and listed in the following table.

section	Q (cfm)	D (in)	v (fpm)
fan–first	3600	20	1600
first–second	2400	17.2	1440
second–third	1200	13.2	1210
first–A	1200	13.2	1210
A–B	900	12	1150
B–C	600	10.2	1030
C–D	300	7.9	860
second–E	1200	13.2	1210
E–F	900	12	1150
F–G	600	10.2	1030
G–H	300	7.9	860
I–J	900	12	1150
J–K	600	10.2	1030
K–L	300	7.9	860

(b) *step 4:* By inspection, the longest run is fan–L. From Table 20.4, the equivalent length of each bend is 14.5D (interpolated). For two elbows,

$$L_{e,\text{bend}} = 14.5D = (14.5)\left(\frac{20 \text{ in} + 13.2 \text{ in}}{12 \ \frac{\text{in}}{\text{ft}}}\right)$$

$$= 40.1 \text{ ft}$$

The equivalent length of the entire run is

25 ft	(fan to first bend)
35 ft	(first bend to first section)
20 ft	(first section to second section)
20 ft	(second section to third section)
10 ft	(third section to point I)
40.1 ft	(equivalent length of two bends)
20 ft	(point I to point J)
20 ft	(point J to point K)
20 ft	(point K to point L)

total: 210.1 ft

The straight-through friction loss in the longest run is

$$\left(\frac{210.1 \text{ ft}}{100 \text{ ft}}\right)\left(0.16 \ \frac{\text{in wg}}{100 \text{ ft}}\right) = 0.34 \text{ in wg}$$

The fan must be able to supply a static pressure of

$$\text{SP}_{\text{fan}} = 0.34 \text{ in wg} + 0.15 \text{ in wg}$$

$$= \boxed{0.49 \text{ in wg}}$$

(c) The total pressure supplied by the fan is

$$\text{TP}_{\text{fan}} = 0.49 \text{ in wg} + \left(\frac{1600 \text{ fpm}}{4005}\right)^2$$

$$= \boxed{0.65 \text{ in wg}}$$

SI Solution

(a) *step 1:* From Table 20.7, choose the main duct velocity as 1600 fpm. From the table footnote (*a*), the SI velocity is

$$v_{\text{main}} = (1600 \text{ fpm})(0.00508) = 8.1 \text{ m/s}$$

step 2: The total air flow rate from the fan is

$$(12)\left(140 \ \frac{\text{L}}{\text{s}}\right) = 1680 \text{ L/s}$$

From Fig. 20.5, the main duct diameter is 500 mm. The friction loss is 1.5 Pa/m.

step 3: After the first takeoff, the flow rate between first and second is

$$1680 \frac{\text{L}}{\text{s}} - (4)\left(140 \frac{\text{L}}{\text{s}}\right) = 1120 \text{ L/s}$$

From Fig. 20.5, for 1120 L/s and 1.5 Pa/m, the diameter is 440 mm and the velocity is 7.5 m/s. Similarly, the diameter and the velocity for other sections are obtained and listed in the following table.

section	Q (L/s)	D (mm)	v (m/s)
fan–first	1680	500	8.1
first–second	1120	440	7.5
second–third	560	335	6.4
first–A	560	335	6.4
A–B	420	305	5.9
B–C	280	260	5.4
C–D	140	195	4.5
second–E	560	335	6.4
E–F	420	305	5.9
F–G	280	260	5.4
G–H	140	195	4.5
I–J	420	305	5.9
J–K	280	260	5.4
K–L	140	195	4.5

(b) *step 4:* By inspection, the longest run is fan–L. From Table 20.4, the equivalent length of each bend is 14.5D (interpolated). For two elbows,

$$L_{e,\text{bend}} = 14.5D$$

$$= (14.5)\left(\frac{500 \text{ mm} + 335 \text{ mm}}{1000 \frac{\text{mm}}{\text{m}}}\right)$$

$$= 12.1 \text{ m}$$

The equivalent length of the entire run is

7.5 m (fan to first bend)
10.5 m (first bend to first section)
6 m (first section to second section)
6 m (second section to third section)
3 m (third section to point I)
12.1 m (equivalent length of two bends)
6 m (point I to point J)
6 m (point J to point K)
6 m (point K to point L)
total: 63.1 m

The straight-through friction loss in the longest run is

$$(63.1 \text{ m})\left(1.5 \frac{\text{Pa}}{\text{m}}\right) = 95 \text{ Pa}$$

The fan must be able to supply a static pressure of

$$SP_{\text{fan}} = 95 \text{ Pa} + 38 \text{ Pa} = \boxed{133 \text{ Pa}}$$

(c) The total pressure supplied by the fan is

$$TP_{\text{fan}} = 133 \text{ Pa} + (0.6)\left(8.1 \frac{\text{m}}{\text{s}}\right)^2$$

$$= \boxed{172 \text{ Pa}}$$

8. *step 1:* From Table 20.7, choose the main duct velocity as 1600 fpm.

step 2: The area and diameter of the main duct are

$$A = \frac{Q}{v} = \frac{3600 \text{ cfm}}{1600 \text{ fpm}} = 2.25 \text{ ft}^2$$

$$D = \sqrt{\frac{4A}{\pi}} = \sqrt{\frac{(4)(2.25 \text{ ft}^2)}{\pi}}\left(12 \frac{\text{in}}{\text{ft}}\right)$$

$$= 20.3 \text{ in}$$

step 3: From Table 20.4, the equivalent length of each bend is 14.5D (interpolated). For the first elbow,

$$L_{e,\text{bend}} = 14.5D = (14.5)\left(\frac{20.3 \text{ in}}{12 \frac{\text{in}}{\text{ft}}}\right) = 24.5 \text{ ft}$$

The equivalent length of the main duct from the fan to the first takeoff and bend is

$$L = 25 \text{ ft} + 24.5 \text{ ft} + 35 \text{ ft} = 84.5 \text{ ft}$$

step 4: From Fig. 20.4, the friction loss in the main run up to the branch takeoff is approximately 0.16 in wg per 100 ft. The actual friction loss is

$$FP_{\text{main}} = \left(0.16 \frac{\text{in wg}}{100 \text{ ft}}\right)\left(\frac{84.5 \text{ ft}}{100 \text{ ft}}\right)$$

$$= 0.135 \text{ in wg}$$

step 5: After the first takeoff,

$$Q = 3600 \text{ cfm} - 1200 \text{ cfm} = 2400 \text{ cfm}$$

$$L = 20 \text{ ft}$$

$$\frac{L}{Q^{0.61}} = \frac{20 \text{ ft}}{(2400 \text{ cfm})^{0.61}} = 0.173$$

From Fig. 20.9, the velocity, v_2, is 1390 fpm.

step 6: Solve for the duct size from $A = Q/v$.

$$D_2 = \sqrt{\frac{4A}{\pi}} = \sqrt{\frac{4Q}{\pi v_2}}$$

$$= \sqrt{\frac{(4)(2400 \text{ cfm})}{\pi(1390 \text{ fpm})}}\left(12 \frac{\text{in}}{\text{ft}}\right)$$

$$= 18 \text{ in}$$

step 7: After the second takeoff,

$$Q = 2400 \text{ cfm} - 1200 \text{ cfm} = 1200 \text{ cfm}$$

$$L = 20 \text{ ft} + 14.5D + 10 \text{ ft}$$

$$= 30 \text{ ft} + 14.5D$$

Since L contains diameter, D, as an unknown, this will require an iterative procedure. Using velocity $v_1 = 1390$ fpm before the takeoff and using an iterative procedure, $D = 15$ in and $v = 980$ fpm.

step 8: Proceeding similarly, the following table is developed for the remaining sizes.

section	L (ft)	Q (cfm)	$\frac{L}{Q^{0.61}}$	v (fpm)
I–J	20	900	0.32	830
J–K	20	600	0.40	660
K–L	20	300	0.62	500

step 9: Solve for the duct size from $A = Q/v$.

$$D = \sqrt{\frac{4A}{\pi}} = \sqrt{\frac{4Q}{\pi v}}$$

$$D_{\text{I–J}} = \sqrt{\frac{(4)(900 \text{ cfm})}{\pi(830 \text{ fpm})}}\left(12 \frac{\text{in}}{\text{ft}}\right)$$

$$= 14 \text{ in}$$

$$D_{\text{J–K}} = \sqrt{\frac{(4)(600 \text{ cfm})}{\pi(660 \text{ fpm})}}\left(12 \frac{\text{in}}{\text{ft}}\right)$$

$$= 13 \text{ in}$$

$$D_{\text{K–L}} = \sqrt{\frac{(4)(300 \text{ cfm})}{\pi(500 \text{ fpm})}}\left(12 \frac{\text{in}}{\text{ft}}\right)$$

$$= 11 \text{ in}$$

step 10: The total pressure supplied by the fan is

$$0.135 \text{ in wg} + 0.15 \text{ in wg} = \boxed{0.285 \text{ in wg}}$$

9. *Customary U.S. Solution*

((a) and (b)) No dampers are needed in duct A. The area of section A is

$$A = \frac{\pi}{4}D^2 = \left(\frac{\pi}{4}\right)\left(\frac{12 \text{ in}}{12 \frac{\text{in}}{\text{ft}}}\right)^2 = 0.7854 \text{ ft}^2$$

The velocity in section A is

$$v_{\text{A}} = \frac{Q}{A} = \frac{3000 \text{ cfm}}{(0.7854 \text{ ft}^2)\left(60 \frac{\text{sec}}{\text{min}}\right)}$$

$$= \frac{3820 \text{ fpm}}{60 \frac{\text{sec}}{\text{min}}} = 63.66 \text{ ft/sec}$$

For a four-piece elbow with a radius-to-diameter ratio of 1.5, $L_e \approx 14D$.

Assume $D = 10$ in. The total equivalent length of run C is

$$L_e = 50 \text{ ft} + 10 \text{ ft} + 10 \text{ ft} + (2)\left[(14)\left(\frac{10 \text{ in}}{12 \frac{\text{in}}{\text{ft}}}\right)\right]$$

$$= 93.3 \text{ ft}$$

For any diameter, D, in inches of section C, the velocity will be

$$v_{\text{C}} = \frac{Q}{A} = \frac{2000 \text{ cfm}}{\left(\frac{\pi}{4}\right)\left(\frac{D}{12 \frac{\text{in}}{\text{ft}}}\right)^2 \left(60 \frac{\text{sec}}{\text{min}}\right)}$$

$$= 6111.5/D^2$$

From Eq. 17.28, the friction loss in section C will be

$$h_{f,\text{C}} = \frac{fLv^2}{2Dg}$$

$$= \frac{(0.02)(93.3 \text{ ft})\left(\frac{6111.5}{D^2}\right)^2}{(2)\left(\frac{D}{12 \frac{\text{in}}{\text{ft}}}\right)\left(32.2 \frac{\text{ft}}{\text{sec}^2}\right)}$$

$$= \frac{1.3 \times 10^7}{D^5} \quad [\text{ft of air}]$$

The principle of static regain is that

$$h_{f,\text{C}} = h_{\text{regain}}$$

$$\frac{1.3 \times 10^7}{D^5} = 40.9 - \frac{3.77 \times 10^5}{D^4}$$

By trial and error, $D \approx 13.5$ in. Since the assumed value of D is different from the calculated value, this process should be repeated.

$$L_e = 50 \text{ ft} + 10 \text{ ft} + 10 \text{ ft} + (2)\left[(14)\left(\frac{13.5 \text{ in}}{12 \frac{\text{in}}{\text{ft}}}\right)\right]$$

$$= 101.5 \text{ ft}$$

From Eq. 17.28, the friction loss in section C will be

$$h_{f,\text{C}} = \frac{fLv^2}{2Dg}$$

$$= \frac{(0.02)(101.5 \text{ ft})\left(\frac{6111.5}{D^2}\right)^2}{(2)\left(\frac{D}{12 \frac{\text{in}}{\text{ft}}}\right)\left(32.2 \frac{\text{ft}}{\text{sec}^2}\right)}$$

$$= \frac{1.41 \times 10^7}{D^5} \quad [\text{ft of air}]$$

The principle of static regain is that

$$h_{f,\text{C}} = h_{\text{region}}$$

$$\frac{1.41 \times 10^7}{D^5} = 40.9 - \frac{3.77 \times 10^5}{D^4}$$

By trial and error,

$$D_{\text{C}} = \boxed{13.63 \text{ in} \quad [\text{say } 14 \text{ in}]}$$

This results in a friction loss of

$$h_{f,\text{C}} = \frac{1.41 \times 10^7}{(14 \text{ in})^5} = 26.2 \text{ ft of air}$$

Because the regain cancels friction loss, the pressure loss from A to C is zero. No dampers are needed in duct C.

For any diameter, D, in inches in section B, the velocity will be

$$v_{\text{B}} = \frac{Q}{A} = \frac{1000 \text{ cfm}}{\left(\frac{\pi}{4}\right)\left(\frac{D}{12 \frac{\text{in}}{\text{ft}}}\right)^2 \left(60 \frac{\text{sec}}{\text{min}}\right)}$$

$$= \frac{3055.8}{D^2} \quad [\text{ft/sec}]$$

The friction loss in section B for Eq. 17.28 will be

$$h_{f,\text{B}} = \frac{fLv^2}{2Dg}$$

$$= \frac{(0.02)(10 \text{ ft})\left(\frac{3055.8}{D^2}\right)^2}{(2)\left(\frac{D}{12 \frac{\text{in}}{\text{ft}}}\right)\left(32.2 \frac{\text{ft}}{\text{sec}^2}\right)}$$

$$= \frac{3.48 \times 10^5}{D^5} \quad [\text{ft of air}]$$

From Eq. 20.42, the friction loss in the branch takeoff between sections A and B will be

$$\Delta \text{TP}_{\text{A–B}} = K_{\text{br}}(\text{VP}_{\text{up}})$$

At this point, assume $v_{\text{B}}/v_{\text{A}} = 1.0$. Then from Table 20.6, for a 45° angle of takeoff, $K_{\text{br}} = 0.5$.

$$\Delta \text{TP}_{\text{A–B}} = (0.5)\left(\frac{3820 \text{ fpm}}{4005}\right)^2 = 0.455 \text{ in wg}$$

From Eq. 20.2,

$$p_{\text{psig}} = (0.455 \text{ in wg})\left(0.0361 \frac{\text{lbf}}{\text{in}^3}\right) = 0.01643 \text{ psig}$$

From Eq. 20.1,

$$h_f = \frac{p_{\text{psig}}}{\gamma} = \frac{\left(0.01643 \frac{\text{lbf}}{\text{in}^2}\right)\left(12 \frac{\text{in}}{\text{ft}}\right)^2}{0.075 \frac{\text{lbf}}{\text{ft}^3}}$$

$$= 31.5 \text{ ft of air}$$

The regain between A and B will be

$$h_{\text{regain}} = R\left(\frac{v_{\text{A}}^2 - v_{\text{B}}^2}{2g}\right)$$

$$= (0.65)\left[\frac{\left(63.66 \frac{\text{ft}}{\text{sec}}\right)^2 - \left(\frac{3055.8}{D^2}\right)^2}{(2)\left(32.2 \frac{\text{ft}}{\text{sec}^2}\right)}\right]$$

$$= 40.9 \text{ ft} - \frac{9.42 \times 10^4}{D^4} \quad [\text{ft of air}]$$

Set the regain equal to the loss.

$$40.9 \text{ ft} - \frac{9.42 \times 10^4}{D^4} = \frac{3.48 \times 10^5}{D^5} + 31.5 \text{ ft}$$

By trial and error,

$$D_B = \boxed{10.77 \text{ in} \quad [\text{say 11 in}]}$$

(c) No dampers are needed in duct B.

$$v_B = \frac{3055.8}{D^2}$$

$$= \frac{3055.8}{(11 \text{ in})^2} = 25.25 \text{ ft/sec}$$

$$\frac{v_B}{v_A} = \frac{25.25 \frac{\text{ft}}{\text{sec}}}{63.6 \frac{\text{ft}}{\text{sec}}} \approx 0.4$$

From Table 20.6, for a 45° angle of takeoff, $K_{br} = 0.5$. Since the value of K_{br} remains the same, there is no need to repeat the preceding procedure. For section B, the friction canceled by the regain is

$$h_{f,B} = 31.5 \text{ ft} + \frac{3.48 \times 10^5}{D^5}$$

$$= 31.5 \text{ ft} + \frac{3.48 \times 10^5}{(11 \text{ in})^5}$$

$$= \boxed{33.7 \text{ ft of air}}$$

SI Solution

((a) and (b)) No dampers are needed in duct A. The area of section A is

$$A = \frac{\pi}{4} D^2 = \left(\frac{\pi}{4}\right) \left(\frac{305 \text{ mm}}{1000 \frac{\text{mm}}{\text{m}}}\right)^2 = 0.0731 \text{ m}^2$$

The velocity in section A is

$$v_A = \frac{Q}{A} = \frac{\left(1400 \frac{\text{L}}{\text{s}}\right) \left(\frac{1 \text{ m}^3}{1000 \text{ L}}\right)}{0.0731 \text{ m}^2} = 19.15 \text{ m/s}$$

For a four-piece elbow with a radius-to-diameter ratio of 1.5, $L_e \approx 14D$.

Assume $D = 250$ mm. The total equivalent length of run C is

$$L_e = 15 \text{ m} + 3 \text{ m} + 3 \text{ m} + (2) \left[(14) \left(\frac{250 \text{ mm}}{1000 \frac{\text{mm}}{\text{m}}}\right)\right]$$

$$= 28 \text{ m}$$

For any diameter, D, in mm of section C, the velocity will be

$$v_C = \frac{Q}{A} = \frac{\left(900 \frac{\text{L}}{\text{s}}\right) \left(\frac{1 \text{ m}^3}{1000 \text{ L}}\right)}{\left(\frac{\pi}{4}\right) \left(\frac{D}{1000 \frac{\text{mm}}{\text{m}}}\right)^2}$$

$$= \frac{1.146 \times 10^6}{D^2} \quad [\text{m/s}]$$

From Eq. 17.28, the friction loss in section C will be

$$h_{f,C} = \frac{f L v^2}{2 D g}$$

$$= \frac{(0.02)(28 \text{ m}) \left(\frac{1.146 \times 10^6}{D^2}\right)^2}{(2) \left(\frac{D}{1000 \frac{\text{mm}}{\text{m}}}\right) \left(9.81 \frac{\text{m}}{\text{s}^2}\right)}$$

$$= \frac{3.75 \times 10^{13}}{D^5} \quad [\text{m of air}]$$

The regain between A and C will be

$$h_{\text{regain}} = R \left(\frac{v_A^2 - v_C^2}{2g}\right)$$

$$= (0.65) \left[\frac{\left(19.15 \frac{\text{m}}{\text{s}}\right)^2 - \left(\frac{1.146 \times 10^6}{D^2}\right)^2}{(2) \left(9.81 \frac{\text{m}}{\text{s}^2}\right)}\right]$$

$$= 12.15 \text{ m} - \frac{4.35 \times 10^{10}}{D^4} \quad [\text{m of air}]$$

The principle of static regain is that

$$h_{f,C} = h_{\text{regain}}$$

$$\frac{3.75 \times 10^{13}}{D^5} = 12.15 \text{ m} - \frac{4.35 \times 10^{10}}{D^4}$$

By trial and error, $D \approx 335$ mm. Since the assumed value of D is different from the calculated value, this process should be repeated.

$$L_e = 15 \text{ m} + 3 \text{ m} + 3 \text{ m} + (2) \left[(14) \left(\frac{335 \text{ mm}}{1000 \frac{\text{mm}}{\text{m}}}\right)\right]$$

$$= 30.4 \text{ m}$$

From Eq. 17.28, the friction loss in section C will be

$$h_{f,C} = \frac{fLv^2}{2Dg}$$

$$= \frac{(0.02)(30.4 \text{ m})\left(\dfrac{1.146 \times 10^6}{D^2}\right)^2}{(2)\left(\dfrac{D}{1000 \dfrac{\text{mm}}{\text{m}}}\right)\left(9.81 \dfrac{\text{m}}{\text{s}^2}\right)}$$

$$= \frac{4.07 \times 10^{13}}{D^5} \quad [\text{m of air}]$$

The principle of static regain is that

$$h_{f,C} = h_{\text{regain}}$$

$$\frac{4.07 \times 10^{13}}{D^5} = 12.15 - \frac{4.35 \times 10^{10}}{D^4}$$

By trial and error, $D = 340$ mm. This results in a friction loss of

$$h_{f,C} = \frac{4.07 \times 10^{13}}{(340 \text{ mm})^5} = 8.96 \text{ m of air}$$

Because the regain cancels this friction loss, the pressure loss from A to C is zero. No dampers are needed in duct C. A damper is needed at B, however.

For any diameter, D, in mm in section B, the velocity will be

$$v_B = \frac{Q}{A} = \frac{\left(500 \dfrac{\text{L}}{\text{s}}\right)\left(\dfrac{1 \text{ m}^3}{1000 \text{ L}}\right)}{\left(\dfrac{\pi}{4}\right)\left(\dfrac{D}{1000 \dfrac{\text{mm}}{\text{m}}}\right)^2}$$

$$= \frac{6.366 \times 10^5}{D^2} \quad [\text{m/s}]$$

From Eq. 17.28, the friction loss in section B will be

$$h_{f,B} = \frac{fLv^2}{2Dg}$$

$$= \frac{(0.02)(3 \text{ m})\left(\dfrac{6.366 \times 10^5}{D^2}\right)^2}{(2)\left(\dfrac{D}{1000 \dfrac{\text{mm}}{\text{m}}}\right)\left(9.81 \dfrac{\text{m}}{\text{s}^2}\right)}$$

$$= \frac{1.239 \times 10^{12}}{D^5} \quad [\text{m of air}]$$

From Eq. 20.42, the friction loss in the branch takeoff between sections A and B will be

$$\Delta \text{TP}_{A-B} = K_{\text{br}}(\text{VP}_{\text{up}})$$

At this point, assume $v_B/v_A = 1.0$. Then from Table 20.6, for a 45° angle of takeoff, $K_{\text{br}} = 0.5$.

$$\Delta \text{TP}_{A-B} = (0.5)(0.6)\left(19.15 \dfrac{\text{m}}{\text{s}}\right)^2$$

$$= 110 \text{ Pa}$$

From Eq. 20.1,

$$h_f = \frac{p}{\rho g} = \frac{110 \text{ Pa}}{\left(1.2 \dfrac{\text{kg}}{\text{m}^3}\right)\left(9.81 \dfrac{\text{m}}{\text{s}^2}\right)}$$

$$= 9.34 \text{ m of air}$$

The regain between A and B will be

$$h_{\text{regain}} = R\left(\frac{v_A^2 - v_B^2}{2g}\right)$$

$$= (0.65)\left[\frac{\left(19.15 \dfrac{\text{m}}{\text{s}}\right)^2 - \left(\dfrac{6.366 \times 10^5}{D^2}\right)^2}{(2)\left(9.81 \dfrac{\text{m}}{\text{s}^2}\right)}\right]$$

$$= \left(12.15 \text{ m} - \frac{1.343 \times 10^{10}}{D^4}\right) \quad [\text{m of air}]$$

Set the regain equal to the loss.

$$12.15 \text{ m} - \frac{1.343 \times 10^{10}}{D^4} = \frac{1.239 \times 10^{12}}{D^5} + 9.34 \text{ m}$$

By trial and error,

$$D_B = 280 \text{ mm}$$
$$v_B = 8.12 \text{ m/s}$$

No dampers are needed in duct B.

(c) $$\frac{v_B}{v_A} = \frac{8.12 \dfrac{\text{m}}{\text{s}}}{19.15 \dfrac{\text{m}}{\text{s}}} \approx 0.4$$

From Table 20.6, for a 45° angle of takeoff, $K_{\text{br}} = 0.5$. Since the value of K_{br} remains the same, there is no need to repeat the preceding procedure. For section B, the friction canceled by the regain is

$$h_{f,B} = 9.34 \text{ m} + \frac{1.239 \times 10^{12}}{D^5}$$

$$= 9.34 \text{ m} + \frac{1.239 \times 10^{12}}{(280 \text{ mm})^5}$$

$$= \boxed{10.06 \text{ m of air}}$$

Fluids

21 Inorganic Chemistry

1. Calculate the mole ratios of the atoms by assuming there are 100 g of sample.

For 100 g of sample,

substance	mass	$\dfrac{m}{AW}$ = no. moles	mole ratio
C	40 g	$\dfrac{40}{12} = 3.33$	1
H	6.7 g	$\dfrac{6.7}{1} = 6.7$	2
O	53.3 g	$\dfrac{53.3}{16} = 3.33$	1

The empirical formula is $\boxed{CH_2O.}$

2. Use App. 21.C to determine hardness for both carbonates and noncarbonates.

$$\text{total hardness} = \sum \text{carbonates} + \sum \text{noncarbonates}$$

(a) Al^{+3}: $\left(0.5 \dfrac{mg}{L}\right)(5.56) = 2.78$ mg/L as $CaCO_3$

Ca^{+2}: $\left(80.2 \dfrac{mg}{L}\right)(2.5) = 200.5$ mg/L as $CaCO_3$

Fe^{+2}: $\left(1.0 \dfrac{mg}{L}\right)(1.79) = 1.79$ mg/L as $CaCO_3$

Mg^{+2}: $\left(24.3 \dfrac{mg}{L}\right)(4.10) = 99.6$ mg/L as $CaCO_3$

total hardness = $\boxed{304.7 \text{ mg/L as } CaCO_3}$

(Singly charged ions are excluded.)

(b) To remove the carbonate hardness, first remove the carbon dioxide.

CO_2: $\left(19 \dfrac{mg}{L} CO_2\right)$
$\times \left(\dfrac{2.27 \text{ mg } CaCO_3}{L}\right)\left(\dfrac{1}{1.35}\right)$
$= 31.9$ mg/L $Ca(OH)_2$

HCO_3^{-1}: $\left(185 \dfrac{mg}{L} HCO_3^{-1}\right)$
$\times (0.82 \dfrac{mg}{L} CaCO_3)\left(\dfrac{1}{1.35}\right)$
$= 112.4$ mg/L $Ca(OH)_2$

total = $31.9 \dfrac{mg}{L} + 112.4 \dfrac{mg}{L}$

= $\boxed{144.3 \text{ mg/L of } Ca(OH)_2}$

Notice that it does not matter if the HCO_3^- carbonate hardness comes from the Ca^{++}, Mg^{++}, Fe^{++}, or Al^{+++}. Adding lime will remove it. (There might still be some of these ions left over in the form of noncarbonate hardness.)

No soda ash is required because it is used to remove noncarbonate hardness.

3. Initial hardness:

$Ca(HCO_3)_2$ = 137 mg/L $CaCO_3$
$MgSO_4$ = 72 mg/L $CaCO_3$
hardness = 209 mg/L $CaCO_3$

(a) Use lime to get the hardness down to 100 mg/L $CaCO_3$ knowing that an excess of 30 mg/L of $Ca(OH)_2$ is required.

The total hardness removed by $Ca(OH)_2$ is (209 mg/L $CaCO_3$ − 100 mg/L $CaCO_2$) 109 mg/L $CaCO_3$.

Use App. 21.C to convert from mg/L as $CaCO_3$ to mg/L as $Ca(OH)_2$.

$$\dfrac{mg}{L} Ca(OH)_2 = \left(109 \dfrac{mg}{L} CaCO_3\right)\left(\dfrac{1}{1.35}\right)$$
$$= 80.7 \text{ mg/L as } Ca(OH)_2$$

Add an additional 30 mg/L of $Ca(OH)_2$. Use the conversion factor 1 mg/L $= 8.345$ lbm/10^6 gal.

$$\text{lbm } Ca(OH)_2 = \left(80.7\ \frac{mg}{L} + 30\ \frac{mg}{L}\right)\left(\frac{\frac{8.345\ \text{lbm}}{10^6\ \text{gal}}}{1\ \frac{mg}{L}}\right)$$

$$= \boxed{924\ \text{lbm}/10^6\ \text{gal}}$$

(b) *Customary U.S. Solution*

Convert 109 mg/L as $CaCO_3$ to lbm/10^6 gal using the following conversion factor.

$$\left(109\ \frac{mg}{L}\right)\left(\frac{8.345\ \text{lbm}}{10^6\ \text{gal}}\right) = \frac{909.6\ \text{lbm hardness}}{10^6\ \text{gal}}$$

$$\left(\frac{909.6\ \text{lbm hardness}}{10^6\ \text{gal}}\right)\left(\frac{7000\ \text{grains}}{1\ \text{lbm}}\right)\left(\frac{0.5\ \text{lbm salt}}{1000\ \text{grains}}\right)$$

$$= \boxed{3184\ \text{lbm salt}/10^6\ \text{gal}}$$

SI Solution

$$\frac{\left(109\ \frac{mg}{L}\right)(4 \times 10^6 L)\left(3.5\ \frac{kg}{kg}\right)}{10^6\ \frac{mg}{kg}} = \boxed{1526\ \text{kg salt}/4\ \text{ML}}$$

22 Fuels and Combustion

1. *Customary U.S. Solution*

For standard conditions, from Table 14.3 for the gas industry,

$$T = 60°F + 460 = 520°R$$
$$p = 14.73 \text{ psia}$$

From Eq. 24.48,

$$R = \frac{R^*}{\text{MW}}$$

From Table 24.7, for methane, MW = 16.043 lbm/lbmol. From Table 24.6, $R^* = 1545.33$ ft-lbf/lbmol-°R.

$$R = \frac{1545.33 \dfrac{\text{ft-lbf}}{\text{lbmol-°R}}}{16.043 \dfrac{\text{lbm}}{\text{lbmol}}} = 96.32 \text{ ft-lbf/lbm-°R}$$

From Eq. 24.47,

$$m = \frac{pV}{RT}$$
$$= \frac{\left(14.73 \dfrac{\text{lbf}}{\text{in}^2}\right)\left(144 \dfrac{\text{in}^2}{\text{ft}^2}\right)(7 \text{ ft}^3)}{\left(96.32 \dfrac{\text{ft-lbf}}{\text{lbm-°R}}\right)(520°R)}$$
$$= 0.296 \text{ lbm}$$

The energy available from methane is

$$Q = m(\text{HV})\eta$$
$$= (0.296 \text{ lbm})\left(24{,}000 \dfrac{\text{Btu}}{\text{lbm}}\right)(0.5)$$
$$= 3552 \text{ Btu}$$

This energy is used by water to heat from 60°F to 200°F.

$$Q = m_{\text{water}}c_p(T_2 - T_1)$$

$$m_{\text{water}} = \frac{3552 \text{ Btu}}{\left(1 \dfrac{\text{Btu}}{\text{lbm-°F}}\right)(200°F - 60°F)} = \boxed{25.37 \text{ lbm}}$$

SI Solution

For standard conditions from Table 14.3 for the gas industry,

$$T = (60°F + 460)\left(\frac{1 \text{ K}}{1.8°R}\right) = 288.89 \text{K}$$
$$p = (14.73 \text{ psia})\left(\frac{101.325 \text{ kPa}}{14.696 \text{ psia}}\right) = 101.56 \text{ kPa}$$

From Eq. 24.48,

$$R = \frac{R^*}{\text{MW}}$$

From Table 24.7, for methane, MW = 16.043 kg/kmol. From Table 24.6, $R^* = 8314.3$ J/kmol·K.

$$R = \frac{8314.3 \dfrac{\text{J}}{\text{kmol·K}}}{16.043 \dfrac{\text{kg}}{\text{kmol}}} = 518.25 \text{ J/kg·K}$$

From Eq. 24.47,

$$m = \frac{pV}{RT}$$
$$= \frac{(101.56 \text{ kPa})\left(1000 \dfrac{\text{Pa}}{\text{kPa}}\right)(200 \text{ L})\left(\dfrac{1 \text{ m}^3}{1000 \text{ L}}\right)}{\left(518.25 \dfrac{\text{J}}{\text{kg·K}}\right)(288.89 \text{K})}$$
$$= 0.136 \text{ kg}$$

The energy available from methane is

$$Q = m(\text{HV})\eta$$
$$= (0.136 \text{ kg})\left(55.8 \dfrac{\text{MJ}}{\text{kg}}\right)\left(1000 \dfrac{\text{kJ}}{\text{MJ}}\right)(0.5)$$
$$= 3794 \text{ kJ}$$

This energy is used by water to heat it from 15°C to 95°C.

$$Q = m_{\text{water}}c_p(T_2 - T_1)$$

$$m_{\text{water}} = \frac{3794 \text{ kJ}}{\left(4.1868 \dfrac{\text{kJ}}{\text{kg·C}}\right)(95°C - 15°C)} = \boxed{11.33 \text{ kg}}$$

2. *Customary U.S. Solution*

From Table 22.7,

$$C_3H_8 \;+\; 5O_2 \;\longrightarrow\; 3CO_2 \;+\; 4H_2O$$

MW	44.097	(5)(32)	(3)(44.011)
	44.097	160	132.033

The amount of carbon dioxide produced is 132.033 lbm/ 44.097 lbm propane. For 15 lbm/hr of propane, the amount of carbon dioxide produced is

$$\left(\frac{132.033\ \text{lbm}}{44.097\ \text{lbm}}\right)\left(15\ \frac{\text{lbm}}{\text{hr}}\right) = 44.91\ \text{lbm/hr}$$

From Eq. 24.48,

$$R = \frac{R^*}{\text{MW}} = \frac{1545.33\ \dfrac{\text{ft-lbf}}{\text{lbmol-}^\circ\text{R}}}{44.097\ \dfrac{\text{lbm}}{\text{lbmol}}}$$

$$= 35.04\ \text{ft-lbf/lbm-}^\circ\text{R}$$

$$T = 70^\circ\text{F} + 460 = 530^\circ\text{R}$$

From Eq. 24.47,

$$V = \frac{mRT}{p}$$

$$= \frac{\left(44.91\ \dfrac{\text{lbm}}{\text{hr}}\right)\left(35.04\ \dfrac{\text{ft-lbf}}{\text{lbm-}^\circ\text{R}}\right)(530^\circ\text{R})}{\left(14.7\ \dfrac{\text{lbf}}{\text{in}^2}\right)\left(144\ \dfrac{\text{in}^2}{\text{ft}^2}\right)}$$

$$= \boxed{394\ \text{ft}^3/\text{hr}}$$

SI Solution

From Table 22.7,

$$C_3H_8 \;+\; 5O_2 \;\longrightarrow\; 3CO_2 \;+\; 4H_2O$$

MW	44.097	(5)(32)	(3)(44.011)
	44.097	160	132.033

The amount of carbon dioxide produced is 132.033 kg/ 44.097 kg propane. For 6.8 kg/h of propane, the amount of carbon dioxide produced is

$$\left(\frac{132.033\ \text{kg}}{44.097\ \text{kg}}\right)\left(6.8\ \frac{\text{kg}}{\text{h}}\right) = 20.36\ \text{kg/h}$$

From Eq. 24.48,

$$R = \frac{R^*}{\text{MW}} = \frac{8314.3\ \dfrac{\text{J}}{\text{kmol·K}}}{44.097\ \dfrac{\text{kg}}{\text{kmol}}}$$

$$= 188.55\ \text{J/kg·K}$$

$$T = 21^\circ\text{C} + 273 = 294\text{K}$$

From Eq. 24.47,

$$V = \frac{mRT}{p}$$

$$= \frac{\left(20.36\ \dfrac{\text{kg}}{\text{h}}\right)\left(188.55\ \dfrac{\text{J}}{\text{kg·K}}\right)(294\text{K})}{(101\ \text{kPa})\left(1000\ \dfrac{\text{Pa}}{\text{kPa}}\right)}$$

$$= \boxed{11.17\ \text{m}^3/\text{h}}$$

3. The balanced chemical reaction equation is from Table 22.7.

$$CH_4 + 2O_2 \longrightarrow CO_2 + 2H_2O$$

With 30% excess air and considering there are 3.773 volumes of nitrogen for every volume of oxygen (Table 22.6), the reaction equation is

$$CH_4 + (1.3)(2)O_2 + (1.3)(2)(3.773)N_2$$
$$\longrightarrow CO_2 + 2H_2O + (1.3)(2)(3.773)N_2 + 0.6O_2$$

$$CH_4 + 2.6O_2 + 9.81N_2$$
$$\longrightarrow CO_2 + 2H_2O + 9.81N_2 + 0.6O_2$$

Customary U.S. Solution

The volume of nitrogen that accompanies 4000 ft^3/hr of methane is

$$V_{N_2} = \left(\frac{9.81\ \text{ft}^3\ N_2}{1\ \text{ft}^3\ CH_4}\right)\left(4000\ \frac{\text{ft}^3}{\text{hr}}\ CH_4\right)$$
$$= 39{,}240\ \text{ft}^3\ N_2/\text{hr}$$

Since air is 79.05% nitrogen by volume (Table 22.6), the partial pressure of nitrogen from Dalton's law is

$$p_{N_2} = (15\ \text{psia})(0.7905) = 11.86\ \text{psia}$$

From Eq. 24.48, for nitrogen,

$$R = \frac{R^*}{\text{MW}} = \frac{1545.33\ \dfrac{\text{ft-lbf}}{\text{lbmol-}^\circ\text{R}}}{28.016\ \dfrac{\text{lbm}}{\text{lbmol}}}$$

$$= 55.16\ \text{ft-lbf/lbm-}^\circ\text{R}$$

The absolute temperature is

$$T = 100^\circ\text{F} + 460 = 560^\circ\text{R}$$

From Eq. 24.47,

$$m_{N_2} = \frac{p_{N_2} V_{N_2}}{RT}$$

$$= \frac{\left(11.86\ \dfrac{\text{lbf}}{\text{in}^2}\right)\left(144\ \dfrac{\text{in}^2}{\text{ft}^2}\right)\left(39{,}240\ \dfrac{\text{ft}^3}{\text{hr}}\right)}{\left(55.16\ \dfrac{\text{ft-lbf}}{\text{lbm-}^\circ\text{R}}\right)(560^\circ\text{R})}$$

$$= \boxed{2170\ \text{lbm/hr}}$$

SI Solution

The volume of nitrogen that accompanies 31 L/s of methane is

$$\left(\frac{9.81 \text{ m}^3 \text{ N}_2}{1 \text{ m}^3 \text{ CH}_4}\right)\left(31 \text{ }\frac{\text{L}}{\text{s}}\right)\left(\frac{1 \text{ m}^3}{1000 \text{ L}}\right) = 0.3041 \text{ m}^3/\text{s}$$

From Table 22.6, air is 79.05% nitrogen by volume. The partial pressure of nitrogen from Dalton's law is

$$p_{\text{N}_2} = (103 \text{ kPa})(0.7905) = 81.42 \text{ kPa}$$

From Eq. 24.48 for nitrogen,

$$R = \frac{R^*}{\text{MW}} = \frac{8314.3 \text{ }\frac{\text{J}}{\text{kmol·K}}}{28.016 \text{ }\frac{\text{kg}}{\text{kmol}}}$$

$$= 296.8 \text{ J/kg·K}$$

The absolute temperature is

$$T = 40°\text{C} + 273 = 313\text{K}$$

From Eq. 24.47,

$$m_{\text{N}_2} = \frac{p_{\text{N}_2} V_{\text{N}_2}}{RT}$$

$$= \frac{(81.42 \text{ kPa})\left(1000 \text{ }\frac{\text{Pa}}{\text{kPa}}\right)\left(0.3041 \text{ }\frac{\text{m}^3}{\text{s}}\right)}{\left(296.8 \text{ }\frac{\text{J}}{\text{kg·K}}\right)(313\text{K})}$$

$$= \boxed{0.267 \text{ kg/s}}$$

4. From Table 22.7, combustion reactions are

$$\begin{array}{cccc} \text{C} & + & \text{O}_2 & \longrightarrow & \text{CO}_2 \\ \text{MW} \quad 12 & & 32 & \end{array}$$

The mass of oxygen required per unit mass of carbon is

$$\frac{32}{12} = 2.67$$

$$\begin{array}{cccc} 2\text{H}_2 & + & \text{O}_2 & \longrightarrow & 2\text{H}_2\text{O} \\ \text{MW} \quad (2)(32) & & 32 & \end{array}$$

The mass of oxygen required per unit mass of hydrogen is

$$\frac{32}{4} = 8.0$$

$$\begin{array}{cccc} \text{S} & + & \text{O}_2 & \longrightarrow & \text{SO}_2 \\ \text{MW} \quad 32.1 & & 32 & \end{array}$$

The mass of oxygen required per unit mass of sulfur is

$$\frac{32}{32.1} = 1.0$$

Nitrogen does not burn.

The mass of oxygen required per unit mass of fuel is

$$(0.84)(2.67) + (0.153)(8) + (0.003)(1)$$
$$= 3.47 \text{ unit of mass of O}_2/\text{unit mass fuel}$$

From Table 22.6, air is 0.2315 O_2/unit mass, so the air required is

$$\frac{3.47}{0.2315} = \boxed{15.0 \text{ lbm air/lbm fuel}}$$
$$\text{[\textit{Customary U.S. Solution}]}$$

$$= \boxed{15.0 \text{ kg air/kg fuel}} \quad \text{[\textit{SI Solution}]}$$

5. The balanced chemical reaction equation is

$$\text{C}_3\text{H}_8 + 5\text{O}_2 \longrightarrow 3\text{CO}_2 + 4\text{H}_2\text{O}$$

With 20% excess air, the oxygen volume is $(1.2)(5) = 6$.

$$\text{C}_3\text{H}_8 + 6\text{O}_2 \longrightarrow 3\text{CO}_2 + 4\text{H}_2\text{O} + \text{O}_2$$

From Table 22.6, there are 3.773 volumes of nitrogen for every volume of oxygen.

$$(6)(3.773) = 22.6$$
$$\text{C}_3\text{H}_8 + 6\text{O}_2 + 22.6 \text{ N}_2 \longrightarrow 3\text{CO}_2 + 4\text{H}_2\text{O} + \text{O}_2 + 22.6 \text{ N}_2$$

The percentage of carbon dioxide by weight in flue gas is

$$\text{G}_{\text{CO}_2} = \frac{(3)(44.011)}{(3)(44.011) + (4)(18.016)} \\ + 32 + (22.6)(28.016)$$

$$= \boxed{0.152 \quad (15.2\%)}$$

6. The actual air/fuel ratio can be estimated from the flue gas analysis and the fraction of carbon in fuel.

From Eq. 22.9,

$$\frac{m_{\text{air}}}{m_{\text{fuel}}} = \frac{3.04 B_{\text{N}_2} G_{\text{C}}}{B_{\text{CO}_2} + B_{\text{CO}}}$$

$$= \frac{(3.04)(80\%)(0.80)}{12\% + 1\%}$$

$$= 14.97$$

The air required to burn 1 lbm of coal is $\boxed{14.97 \text{ lbm.}}$

(Customary U.S. Solution)

The air required to burn 1 kg of coal is $\boxed{14.97 \text{ kg.}}$

(SI Solution)

Alternate Solution

The use of Eq. 14.11 obscures the process of finding the air/fuel ratio. (The SI Solution is similar but is not presented here.)

step 1: Find the mass of oxygen in the stack gases.

$$R_{CO_2} = 35.11 \text{ ft-lbf/lbm-}°R$$

$$R_{CO} = 55.17 \text{ ft-lbf/lbm-}°R$$

$$R_{O_2} = 48.29 \text{ ft-lbf/lbm-}°R$$

The partial densities are

$$\rho_{CO_2} = \frac{p}{RT} = \frac{(0.12)\left(14.7 \dfrac{\text{lbf}}{\text{in}^2}\right)\left(144 \dfrac{\text{in}^2}{\text{ft}^2}\right)}{\left(35.11 \dfrac{\text{ft-lbf}}{\text{lbm-}°R}\right)(60°F + 460)}$$

$$= 1.391 \times 10^{-2} \text{ lbm/ft}^3$$

$$\rho_{CO} = \frac{(0.01)\left(14.7 \dfrac{\text{lbf}}{\text{in}^2}\right)\left(144 \dfrac{\text{in}^2}{\text{ft}^2}\right)}{\left(55.11 \dfrac{\text{ft-lbf}}{\text{lbm-}°R}\right)(60°F + 460)}$$

$$= 7.387 \times 10^{-4} \text{ lbm/ft}^3$$

$$\rho_{O_2} = \frac{(0.07)\left(14.7 \dfrac{\text{lbf}}{\text{in}^2}\right)\left(144 \dfrac{\text{in}^2}{\text{ft}^2}\right)}{\left(48.29 \dfrac{\text{ft-lbf}}{\text{lbm-}°R}\right)(60°F + 460)}$$

$$= 5.901 \times 10^{-3} \text{ lbm/ft}^3$$

The fraction of oxygen in the three components is

$$CO_2: \frac{32.0}{44} = 0.7273$$

$$CO: \frac{16}{28} = 0.5714$$

$$O_2: 1.00$$

In 100 ft^3 of stack gases, the total oxygen mass will be

$$(100 \text{ ft}^3)\left[(0.7273)\left(1.391 \times 10^{-2} \dfrac{\text{lbm}}{\text{ft}^3}\right)\right.$$

$$+ (0.5714)\left(7.387 \times 10^{-4} \dfrac{\text{lbm}}{\text{ft}^3}\right)$$

$$\left. + (1.00)\left(5.901 \times 10^{-3} \dfrac{\text{lbm}}{\text{ft}^3}\right)\right] = 1.644 \text{ lbm}$$

step 2: Since air is 23.15% oxygen by weight, the mass of air per 100 ft^3 of stack gases is

$$\frac{1.644 \text{ lbm}}{0.2315} = 7.102 \text{ lbm}$$

step 3: Find the mass of carbon in the stack gases by a similar process.

$$CO_2: \frac{12}{44} = 0.2727$$

$$CO: \frac{12}{28} = 0.4286$$

$$(100 \text{ ft}^3)\left[(0.2727)\left(1.391 \times 10^{-2} \dfrac{\text{lbm}}{\text{ft}^3}\right)\right.$$

$$\left. + (0.4286)\left(7.387 \times 10^{-4} \dfrac{\text{lbm}}{\text{ft}^3}\right)\right]$$

$$= 0.4110 \text{ lbm}$$

step 4: The coal is 80% carbon, so the air per lbm of coal for combustion of the carbon is

$$\left(\frac{0.80 \dfrac{\text{lbm carbon}}{\text{lbm coal}}}{0.4110 \dfrac{\text{lbm carbon}}{100 \text{ ft}^3}}\right)(7.102 \text{ lbm})$$

$$= 13.824 \text{ lbm air/lbm coal}$$

step 5: This does not include air to burn hydrogen, since Orsat is a dry analysis.

The theoretical air for the hydrogen is given by Eq. 22.6.

$$R_{a/f,H} = \left(34.5 \dfrac{\text{lbm}}{\text{lbm}}\right)\left(G_H - \frac{G_O}{8}\right)$$

$$= \left(34.05 \dfrac{\text{lbm}}{\text{lbm}}\right)\left(0.04 - \frac{0.02}{8}\right)$$

$$= 1.277 \text{ lbm air/lbm fuel}$$

Ignoring any excess air for the hydrogen, the total air per pound of coal is

$$13.824 \frac{\text{lbm air}}{\text{lbm coal}} + 1.277 \frac{\text{lbm air}}{\text{lbm coal}}$$

$$= \boxed{15.10 \text{ lbm air/lbm coal}}$$

7. From Eq. 14.11,

$$SG = \frac{141.5}{°API + 131.5}$$

$$= \frac{141.5}{40 + 131.5} = 0.825$$

Customary U.S. Solution

From Eq. 22.18(b),

$$HHV = 22{,}320 - (3780)(SG)^2$$
$$= 22{,}320 - (3780)(0.825)^2$$
$$= \boxed{19{,}747 \text{ Btu/lbm}}$$

SI Solution

From Eq. 22.18(a),

$$HHV = 51.92 - (8.792)(SG)^2$$
$$= 51.92 - (8.792)(0.825)^2$$
$$= \boxed{45.94 \text{ MJ/kg}}$$

8. *Customary U.S. Solution*

(a) *step 1:* From Eq. 22.16(b), the heating value of coal is

$$HHV = 14{,}093 G_C + (60{,}958)\left(G_H - \frac{G_O}{8}\right)$$
$$+ 3983 G_S$$
$$= (14{,}093)(0.75)$$
$$+ (60{,}958)\left(0.05 - \frac{0.03}{8}\right) + (3983)(0)$$
$$= 13{,}389 \text{ Btu/lbm}$$

step 2: The gravimetric analysis of 1 lbm of coal is

carbon: 0.75 lbm

free hydrogen: $\left(G_{H,total} - \dfrac{G_O}{8}\right) = 0.05 - \dfrac{0.03}{8} = 0.0463$

water: $(9)(0.05 - 0.0463) = 0.0333$

nitrogen: 0.02

step 3: From Table 22.8, the theoretical stack gases per lbm coal for 0.75 lbm of coal are

$$CO_2 = (0.75)(3.667 \text{ lbm}) = 2.750 \text{ lbm}$$
$$N_2 = (0.75)(8.883 \text{ lbm}) = 6.662 \text{ lbm}$$

All products are calculated similarly (as the following table summarizes).

	CO_2	N_2	H_2O
from C:	2.750 lbm	6.662 lbm	
from H_2:		1.217 lbm	0.414 lbm
from H_2O:			0.0333 lbm
from O_2:	shows up in	CO_2 and H_2	
from N_2:		0.02 lbm	
total:	2.750 lbm	7.899 lbm	0.4473 lbm

step 4: Assume the combustion gases leave at 1000°F.

$$T_{ave} = \left(\tfrac{1}{2}\right)(60°F + 1000°F) = 530°F$$
$$T_{ave} = 530°F + 460 = 990°R$$

The specific heat values are given in Table 22.1.

$$c_{p_{CO_3}} = 0.251 \text{ Btu/lbm-°F}$$
$$c_{p_{N_2}} = 0.255 \text{ Btu/lbm-°F}$$
$$c_{p_{H_2O}} = 0.475 \text{ Btu/lbm-°F}$$

The energy required to raise the combustion products for 1 lbm of coal 1°F is

$$m_{CO_2} c_{p_{CO_2}} + m_{N_2} c_{p_{N_2}} + m_{H_2O} c_{p_{H_2O}}$$
$$= (2.750 \text{ lbm})\left(0.251 \frac{\text{Btu}}{\text{lbm-°F}}\right)$$
$$+ (7.899 \text{ lbm})\left(0.255 \frac{\text{Btu}}{\text{lbm-°F}}\right)$$
$$+ (0.4473 \text{ lbm})\left(0.475 \frac{\text{Btu}}{\text{lbm-°F}}\right)$$
$$= 2.92 \text{ Btu/lbm-°F}$$

step 5: Assuming all combustion heat goes into the stack gases, the final temperature is given by Eq. 22.19.

$$T_{max} = T_i + \frac{\text{heat of combustion}}{\text{energy required}}$$

$$= 60°F + \frac{13{,}389 \dfrac{\text{Btu}}{\text{lbm}}}{2.92 \dfrac{\text{Btu}}{\text{lbm}}} = \boxed{4645°F}$$

[unreasonable]

(b) *step 6:* In reality, assuming 40% excess air and 75% of heat absorbed by the boiler, the excess air (based on 76.85% N_2 by weight) is

$$(0.40)\left(\frac{7.899 \text{ lbm}}{0.7685}\right) = 4.111 \text{ lbm}$$

From Table 22.1, $c_{p_{air}} = 0.249$ Btu/lbm-°R. Therefore,

$$T_{max} = 60°F + \frac{\left(13{,}389 \dfrac{\text{Btu}}{\text{lbm}}\right)(1 - 0.75)}{2.92 \dfrac{\text{Btu}}{\text{lbm-°F}} + (4.111 \text{ lbm})\left(0.249 \dfrac{\text{Btu}}{\text{lbm-°R}}\right)}$$

$$= \boxed{909°F}$$

SI Solution

(a) *step 1:* From Eq. 22.16(a), the heating value of coal is

$$\text{HHV} = 32.78 G_C + (141.8)\left(G_H - \frac{G_O}{8}\right) + 9.264\, G_S$$

$$= (32.78)(0.75) + (141.8)\left(0.05 - \frac{0.03}{8}\right)$$

$$+ (9.264)(0)$$

$$= 31.14 \text{ MJ/kg}$$

Steps 2 and 3 are the same as for the U.S. solution except that all masses are in kg.

step 4: Assume the combustion gases leave at 550°C.

$$T_{\text{ave}} = \left(\tfrac{1}{2}\right)(16°\text{C} + 550°\text{C}) + 273$$
$$= 283°\text{C} + 273 = 556\text{K}$$

Specific heat values are given in Table 22.1. Using the footnote for SI units,

$$c_{p\text{CO}_2} = 1.051 \text{ kJ/kg·K}$$
$$c_{p\text{N}_2} = 1.068 \text{ kJ/kg·K}$$
$$c_{p\text{H}_2\text{O}} = 1.989 \text{ kJ/kg·K}$$

The energy required to raise the combustion products for 1 kg of coal 1°C is

$$m_{\text{CO}_2} c_{p\text{CO}_2} + m_{\text{N}_2} c_{p\text{N}_2} + m_{\text{H}_2\text{O}} c_{p\text{H}_2\text{O}}$$

$$= (2.750 \text{ kg})\left(1.051 \frac{\text{kJ}}{\text{kg·K}}\right)$$

$$+ (7.899 \text{ kg})\left(1.068 \frac{\text{kJ}}{\text{kg·K}}\right)$$

$$+ (0.4473 \text{ kg})\left(1.989 \frac{\text{kJ}}{\text{kg·K}}\right)$$

$$= 12.22 \text{ kJ/kg}$$

step 5: Assuming all combustion heat goes into the stack gases, the final temperature is given by Eq. 22.19.

$$T_{\text{max}} = T_i + \frac{\text{heat of combustion}}{\text{energy required}}$$

$$= 16°\text{C} + \frac{\left(31.14 \frac{\text{MJ}}{\text{kg}}\right)\left(1000 \frac{\text{kJ}}{\text{MJ}}\right)}{12.22 \frac{\text{kJ}}{\text{kg}}}$$

$$= \boxed{2564°\text{C}} \quad \text{[unreasonable]}$$

(b) *step 6:* In reality, assuming 40% excess air and 75% of heat absorbed by the boiler, the excess air (based on 76.85% N_2 by weight) is

$$(0.40)\left(\frac{7.899 \text{ kg}}{0.7685}\right) = 4.111 \text{ kg}$$

From Table 22.1, using the table footnote, $c_{p\text{air}} = 10\,043 \text{ kJ/kg·K}$.

Therefore,

$$T_{\text{max}} = 16°\text{C} + \frac{\left(31.14 \frac{\text{MJ}}{\text{kg}}\right) \times \left(1000 \frac{\text{kJ}}{\text{MJ}}\right)(1 - 0.75)}{\left(12.22 \frac{\text{kJ}}{\text{kg·°C}}\right) + (4.111 \text{ kg})\left(1.043 \frac{\text{kJ}}{\text{kg·K}}\right)}$$

$$= \boxed{487.6°\text{C}}$$

9. Assume the oxygen is in the form of moisture in the fuel.

The available oxygen is

$$G_{\text{H,free}} = G_H - \frac{G_O}{8}$$

$$= 0.1131 - \frac{0.027}{8}$$

$$= 0.1097$$

Customary U.S. Solution

step 1: From Table 22.8, find the stoichiometric oxygen required per lbm of fuel oil.

$$\text{C} \longrightarrow \text{CO}_2: \text{ O}_2 \text{ required} = (0.8543)(2.667 \text{ lbm})$$
$$= 2.2784 \text{ lbm}$$

$$\text{H}_2 \longrightarrow \text{H}_2\text{O}: \text{ O}_2 \text{ required} = (0.1097)(7.936 \text{ lbm})$$
$$= 0.8706 \text{ lbm}$$

$$\text{S} \longrightarrow \text{SO}_2: \text{ O}_2 \text{ required} = (0.0034)(0.998 \text{ lbm})$$
$$= 0.0034 \text{ lbm}$$

The total amount of oxygen required per lbm of fuel oil is

$$2.2784 \text{ lbm} + 0.8706 \text{ lbm}$$
$$+ 0.0034 \text{ lbm} = 3.1524 \text{ lbm}$$

step 2: With 60% excess air, the excess oxygen is

$$(0.6)(3.1524 \text{ lbm}) = 1.8914 \text{ lbm O}_2/\text{lbm fuel}$$

From Eq. 24.47, this oxygen occupies a volume of

$$V = \frac{mRT}{p}$$

At standard conditions,

$$p = 14.7 \text{ psia}$$
$$T = 60°F + 460 = 520°R$$

From Table 24.7, for oxygen, $R = 48.29$ ft-lbf/lbm-°R.

$$V = \frac{(1.8914 \text{ lbm})\left(48.29 \dfrac{\text{ft-lbf}}{\text{lbm-°R}}\right)(520°R)}{\left(14.7 \dfrac{\text{lbf}}{\text{in}^2}\right)\left(144 \dfrac{\text{in}^2}{\text{ft}^2}\right)}$$
$$= 22.44 \text{ ft}^3$$

step 3: The theoretical nitrogen based on Table 22.6 is

$$\left(\frac{3.1524 \text{ lbm}}{0.2315}\right)(0.7685) = 10.465 \text{ lbm N}_2/\text{lbm fuel}$$

The actual nitrogen with 60% excess air and nitrogen in the fuel is

$$(10.465 \text{ lbm})(1.6) + 0.0022 \text{ lbm}$$
$$= 16.746 \text{ lbm N}_2/\text{lbm fuel}$$

From Eq. 24.47, this nitrogen occupies a volume of

$$V = \frac{mRT}{p}$$

From Table 24.7, R for nitrogen $= 55.16$ ft-lbf/lbm-°R.

$$V = \frac{(16.746 \text{ lbm})\left(55.16 \dfrac{\text{ft-lbf}}{\text{lbm-°R}}\right)(520°R)}{\left(14.7 \dfrac{\text{lbf}}{\text{in}^2}\right)\left(144 \dfrac{\text{in}^2}{\text{ft}^2}\right)}$$
$$= 226.91 \text{ ft}^3$$

step 4: From Table 22.8, the 60°F combustion product volumes per lbm of fuel will be

CO_2:	$(0.8543)(31.63 \text{ ft}^3)$	$=$	27.02 ft^3
H_2O:	$(0.1131)(188.25 \text{ ft}^3)$	$=$	21.29 ft^3
SO_2:	$(0.0034)(11.84 \text{ ft}^3)$	$=$	0.040 ft^3
N_2:	from step 3	$=$	226.91 ft^3
O_2:	from step 2	$=$	22.44 ft^3
		total $=$	297.7 ft^3

(a) At 60°F, the wet volume will be $\boxed{297.7 \text{ ft}^3.}$

At 600°F, the wet volume is

$$V_{\text{wet,600°F}} = (297.7 \text{ ft}^3)\left(\frac{600°F + 460}{60°F + 460}\right)$$
$$= \boxed{606.9 \text{ ft}^3}$$

(b) At 60°F, the dry volume will be

$$297.7 \text{ ft}^3 - 21.29 \text{ ft}^3 = \boxed{276.4 \text{ ft}^3}$$

At 600°F, the dry volume is

$$V_{\text{dry,600°F}} = (276.4 \text{ ft}^3)\left(\frac{600°F + 460}{60°F + 460}\right)$$
$$= \boxed{563.4 \text{ ft}^3}$$

(c) The volumetric fraction of dry carbon dioxide is

$$\frac{27.02 \text{ ft}^3}{276.41 \text{ ft}^3} = \boxed{0.098 \quad (9.8\%)}$$

SI Solution

step 1: From Table 22.8, find the stoichiometric oxygen required per lbm of fuel oil.

$$C \longrightarrow CO_2 : \ O_2 \text{ required} = (0.8543)(2.667 \text{ kg})$$
$$= 2.2784 \text{ kg}$$
$$H_2 \longrightarrow H_2O : \ O_2 \text{ required} = (0.1097)(7.936 \text{ kg})$$
$$= 0.8706 \text{ kg}$$
$$S \longrightarrow SO_2 : \ O_2 \text{ required} = (0.0034)(0.998 \text{ kg})$$
$$= 0.0034 \text{ kg}$$

The total amount of oxygen required per kg of fuel oil is

$$2.2784 \text{ kg} + 0.8706 \text{ kg}$$
$$+ 0.0034 \text{ kg} = 3.1524 \text{ kg}$$

step 2: With 60% excess air, the excess oxygen is

$$(0.6)(3.1524 \text{ kg}) = 1.8914 \text{ kg O}_2/\text{kg fuel}$$

From Eq. 24.47, this oxygen occupies a volume of

$$V = \frac{mRT}{p}$$

Thermodynamics

At standard conditions,

$$p = 101.3 \text{ kPa}$$
$$T = 16°C + 273 = 289K$$

From Table 24.7, for oxygen, $R = 259.82$ J/kg·K.

$$V = \frac{(1.8914 \text{ kg})\left(259.82 \frac{J}{kg \cdot K}\right)(289K)}{(101.3 \text{ kPa})(1000 \text{ kPa})}$$
$$= 1.402 \text{ m}^3$$

step 3: The theoretical nitrogen based on Table 22.6 is

$$\left(\frac{3.1524 \text{ kg}}{0.2315}\right)(0.7685) = 10.465 \text{ kg N}_2/\text{kg fuel}$$

The actual nitrogen with 60% excess air and nitrogen in the fuel is

$$(10.465 \text{ kg})(1.6) + 0.0022 \text{ kg}$$
$$= 16.746 \text{ kg N}_2/\text{kg fuel}$$

From Eq. 24.47, this nitrogen occupies a volume of
$$V = \frac{mRT}{p}$$

From Table 24.7, R for nitrogen = 296.77 J/kg·K.

$$V = \frac{(16.746 \text{ kg})\left(296.77 \frac{J}{kg \cdot K}\right)(289K)}{(101.3 \text{ kPa})\left(1000 \frac{Pa}{kPa}\right)}$$
$$= 14.178 \text{ m}^3$$

step 4: From Table 22.8, the 16°C combustion product volumes per kg of fuel will be

CO_2:	$(0.8543)(31.63 \text{ ft}^3)(0.06243)$	=	1.687 m³
H_2O:	$(0.1131)(188.25 \text{ ft}^3)(0.06243)$	=	1.329 m³
SO_2:	$(0.0034)(11.84 \text{ ft}^3)(0.06243)$	=	0.003 m³
N_2:	from step 3	=	14.178 m³
O_2:	from step 2	=	1.402 m³
		total =	18.599 m³

(a) At 16°C, the wet volume will be $\boxed{18.599 \text{ m}^3}$.

At 320°C, the wet volume is

$$V_{\text{wet},320°C} = (18.599 \text{ m}^3)\left(\frac{320°C + 273}{16°C + 273}\right)$$
$$= \boxed{38.16 \text{ m}^3}$$

(b) At 16°C, the dry volume will be

$$18.599 \text{ m}^3 - 1.329 \text{ m}^3 = \boxed{17.27 \text{ m}^3}$$

At 320°C, the dry volume is

$$V_{\text{dry},320°C} = (17.27 \text{ m}^3)\left(\frac{320°C + 273}{16°C + 273}\right)$$
$$= \boxed{35.44 \text{ m}^3}$$

(c) The volumetric fraction of dry carbon dioxide is
$$\frac{1.687 \text{ m}^3}{17.27 \text{ m}^3} = \boxed{0.098 \ (9.8\%)}$$

10. *Customary U.S. Solution*

step 1: Based on the 15,395 lbm of coal burned producing 2816 lbm of ash containing 20.9% carbon by weight, the usable percentage of carbon per lbm of fuel is

$$0.5145 - \frac{(2816 \text{ lbm})(0.209)}{15,395 \text{ lbm}} = 0.4763$$

step 2: Since moisture is reported separately, assume all of the oxygen and hydrogen are free. (This is not ordinarily the case.) From Table 22.8, find the stoichiometric oxygen required per lbm of fuel.

$$C \longrightarrow CO_2: \ O_2 \text{ required} = (0.4763)(2.667 \text{ lbm})$$
$$= 1.2703 \text{ lbm}$$
$$H_2 \longrightarrow H_2O: \ O_2 \text{ required} = (0.0402)(7.936 \text{ lbm})$$
$$= 0.3190 \text{ lbm}$$
$$S \longrightarrow SO_2: \ O_2 \text{ required} = (0.0392)(0.998 \text{ lbm})$$
$$= 0.0391 \text{ lbm}$$

The total amount of O_2 required per lbm of fuel is

$$1.2703 \text{ lbm} + 0.3190 \text{ lbm}$$
$$+ 0.0391 \text{ lbm} - 0.0728 \text{ lbm} = 1.5556 \text{ lbm}$$

step 3: The theoretical air based on Table 22.6 is

$$\frac{1.5556 \text{ lbm}}{0.2315} = 6.720 \text{ lbm air/lbm fuel}$$

step 4: Ignoring fly ash, the theoretical dry products are given from Table 22.8.

CO_2: $(0.4763)(3.667 \text{ lbm}) = 1.7466 \text{ lbm}$
SO_2: $(0.0392)(1.998 \text{ lbm}) = 0.0783 \text{ lbm}$
N_2: $\quad 0.0093 \text{ lbm}$
$\quad\quad + (6.720 \text{ lbm})$
$\quad\quad \times (0.7685 \text{ lbm}) \quad = 5.1736 \text{ lbm}$
$\quad\quad\quad\quad\quad\quad\quad\quad \text{total} = \overline{6.999 \text{ lbm}}$

step 5: The excess air is

$$13.3 \text{ lbm} - 6.999 \text{ lbm} = 6.301 \text{ lbm}$$

step 6: The total air supplied is

$$6.301 \text{ lbm} + 6.720 \text{ lbm} = \boxed{13.02 \text{ lbm}}$$

SI Solution

step 1: Based on the 6923 kg of coal burned producing 1267 kg of ash containing 20.9% carbon by weight, the usable percentage of carbon per kg of fuel is

$$0.5145 - \frac{(1267 \text{ kg})(0.209)}{6923 \text{ kg}} = 0.4763$$

step 2: From Table 22.8, find the stoichiometric oxygen required per kg of fuel.

$C \longrightarrow CO_2$: O_2 required $= (0.4763)(2.667 \text{ kg})$
$\quad\quad\quad\quad\quad\quad\quad\quad = 1.2703 \text{ kg}$

$H_2 \longrightarrow H_2O$: O_2 required $= (0.0402)(7.936 \text{ kg})$
$\quad\quad\quad\quad\quad\quad\quad\quad = 0.3190 \text{ kg}$

$S \longrightarrow SO_2$: O_2 required $= (0.0392)(0.998 \text{ kg})$
$\quad\quad\quad\quad\quad\quad\quad\quad = 0.0391 \text{ kg}$

The total amount of O_2 required per kg of fuel is

$1.2703 \text{ kg} + 0.3190 \text{ kg}$
$\quad + 0.0391 \text{ kg} - 0.0728 \text{ kg} = 1.5556 \text{ kg}$

step 3: The theoretical air based on Table 22.6 is

$$\frac{1.5556 \text{ kg}}{0.2315} = 6.720 \text{ kg air/kg fuel}$$

step 4: Ignoring fly ash, the theoretical dry products are given from Table 22.8.

CO_2: $(0.4763)(3.667 \text{ kg}) = 1.7466 \text{ kg}$
SO_2: $(0.0392)(1.998 \text{ kg}) = 0.0783 \text{ kg}$
N_2: $\quad 0.0093 \text{ kg}$
$\quad\quad + (6.720 \text{ kg})$
$\quad\quad \times (0.7685 \text{ kg}) \quad = 5.1736 \text{ kg}$
$\quad\quad\quad\quad\quad\quad\quad\quad \text{total} = \overline{6.999 \text{ kg}}$

step 5: The excess air is

$$13.3 \text{ kg} - 6.999 \text{ kg} = 6.301 \text{ kg}$$

step 6: The total air supplied is

$$6.301 \text{ kg} + 6.720 \text{ kg} = \boxed{13.02 \text{ kg}}$$

11. (The Customary U.S. and SI Solutions are essentially identical.)

From Eq. 22.9, the actual air-fuel ratio can be estimated as

$$R_{a/f,\text{actual}} = \frac{3.04 B_{N_2} G_C}{B_{CO_2} + B_{CO}}$$

A fraction of carbon is reduced due to the percentage of coal lost in the ash pit.

$$G_C = (1 - 0.03)(0.65) = 0.6305$$

$$R_{a/f,\text{actual}} = \frac{(3.04)(0.815)(0.6305)}{0.095 + 0}$$

$$= 16.44 \text{ lbm air/lbm fuel (kg air/kg fuel)}$$

Combustion uses 9.451 lbm of air/lbm of fuel.

$$= (9.451 \text{ lbm})(1 - 0.03)$$
$$= 9.167 \text{ lbm of air/lbm of fuel}$$

$$\% \text{ of excess air} = \left(\frac{16.44 \text{ lbm} - 9.167 \text{ lbm}}{9.167 \text{ lbm}} \right)(100\%)$$

$$= \boxed{79.3\%}$$

12. From Eq. 22.23, the heat loss due to the formation of carbon monoxide is

$$q = \frac{(HHV_C - HHV_{CO})G_C B_{CO}}{B_{CO_2} + B_{CO}}$$

From App. 22.A, the difference in the two heating values is

$$HHV_C - HHV_{CO} = 14{,}093 \frac{\text{Btu}}{\text{lbm}} - 4347 \frac{\text{Btu}}{\text{lbm}}$$

$$= 9746 \text{ Btu/lbm} \quad (22.67 \text{ MJ/kg})$$

$$G_C = (1 - 0.03)(0.6734) = 0.6532$$

Customary U.S. Solution

$$q = \frac{\left(9746\ \frac{Btu}{lbm}\right)(0.6532)(1.6\%)}{15.5\% + 1.6\%}$$

$$= \boxed{596\ Btu/lbm}$$

SI Solution

$$q = \frac{\left(22.67\ \frac{MJ}{kg}\right)(0.6532)(1.6\%)}{15.5\% + 1.6\%}$$

$$= \boxed{1.39\ MJ/kg}$$

13. (a) For methane, $B = 0.93$.

From ideal gas laws (from Table 24.7, R for methane = 96.32 ft-lbf/lbm-°R),

$$\rho = \frac{p}{RT}$$

$$= \frac{\left(14.7\ \frac{lbf}{in^2}\right)\left(144\ \frac{in^2}{ft^2}\right)}{\left(96.32\ \frac{ft\text{-}lbf}{lbm\text{-}°R}\right)(60°F + 460)}$$

$$= 0.0422\ lbm/ft^3$$

From Table 22.9, $K = 9.55$ ft³ air/ft³ fuel.

From Table 22.8,

products: 1 ft³ CO_2, 2 ft³ H_2O

From App. 22.A, HHV = 1013 Btu/lbm.

Similar results for all the other fuel components are tabulated in the following table.

From Eq. 24.78, the composite density is

$$\rho = \sum B_i \rho_i$$

$$= (0.93)\left(0.0422\ \frac{lbm}{ft^3}\right) + (0.0373)\left(0.0738\ \frac{lbm}{ft^3}\right)$$

$$+ (0.0045)\left(0.0738\ \frac{lbm}{ft^3}\right) + (0.0182)\left(0.0053\ \frac{lbm}{ft^3}\right)$$

$$+ (0.0025)\left(0.0739\ \frac{lbm}{ft^3}\right) + (0.0018)\left(0.0900\ \frac{lbm}{ft^3}\right)$$

$$+ (0.0035)\left(0.0843\ \frac{lbm}{ft^3}\right) + (0.0022)\left(0.1160\ \frac{lbm}{ft^3}\right)$$

$$= \boxed{0.0433\ lbm/ft^3}$$

(b) The air is 20.9% oxygen by volume. The theoretical air requirements are

$$\sum B_i - \frac{O_2\ \text{in fuel}}{0.209}$$

$$= (0.93)(9.55\ ft^3) + (0.0373)(0)$$

$$+ (0.0045)(2.392\ ft^3) + (0.0182)(2.392\ ft^3)$$

$$+ (0.0025)(14.25\ ft^3) + (0.0018)(7.176\ ft^3)$$

$$+ (0.0035)(0) + (0.0022)(0) - \frac{0.0035}{0.209}$$

$$= 8.984\ ft^3 - 0.01675\ ft^3$$

$$= \boxed{8.9676\ ft^3\ air/ft^3\ fuel}$$

((c) and (d)) The theoretical oxygen will be

$$(8.9676\ ft^3)(0.209) = 1.874\ ft^3/ft^3$$

The excess oxygen will be

$$(0.4)(1.874\ ft^3) = 0.7496\ ft^3/ft^3$$

gas	B	$\rho\left(\frac{lbm}{ft^3}\right)$	ft³ air	HHV $\left(\frac{Btu}{lbm}\right)$	volumes of products		
					CO_2	H_2O	other
CH_4	0.93	0.0422	9.55	1013	1	2	–
N_2	0.0373	0.0738	–	–	–	–	1 N_2
CO	0.0045	0.0738	2.392	322	1	–	–
H_2	0.0182	0.0053	2.392	325	–	1	–
C_2H_4	0.0025	0.0739	14.25	1614	2	2	–
H_2S	0.0018	0.0900	7.176	647	–	1	1 SO_2
O_2	0.0035	0.0843	–	–	–	–	–
CO_2	0.0022	0.1160	–	–	1	–	–

Similarly, the total nitrogen in the stack gases is

$$(1.4)(0.791)(8.9676 \text{ ft}^3) + 0.034 = 9.965 \text{ ft}^3/\text{ft}^3 \text{ fuel}$$

The stack gases per ft^3 of fuel are

excess O_2:	$= 0.7496 \text{ ft}^3$
excess N_2:	$= 9.965 \text{ ft}^3$
excess SO_2:	$= 0.0018 \text{ ft}^3$

excess CO_2: $(0.93)(1) + (0.0045)(1)$
$+ (0.0025)(2) + (0.0022)(1) = 0.942 \text{ ft}^3$

excess H_2O: $(0.93)(2) + (0.0182)(1)$
$+ (0.0025)(2) + (0.0018)(1) = 1.885 \text{ ft}^3$

$$\text{total} = \overline{13.55 \text{ ft}^3}$$

The total wet volume is $13.54 \text{ ft}^3/\text{ft}^3$ fuel.

The total dry volume is $11.66 \text{ ft}^3/\text{ft}^3$ fuel.

The volumetric analyses are

	O_2	N_2	SO_2	CO_2	H_2O
wet:	$\dfrac{0.7496 \text{ ft}^3}{13.54 \text{ ft}^3}$	$\dfrac{9.965 \text{ ft}^3}{13.54 \text{ ft}^3}$	$\dfrac{0.0018 \text{ ft}^3}{13.54 \text{ ft}^3}$	$\dfrac{0.942 \text{ ft}^3}{13.54 \text{ ft}^3}$	$\dfrac{1.885}{13.54}$
	$= 0.0554$	0.736	$-$	0.069	0.139
dry:	$\dfrac{0.7496 \text{ ft}^3}{11.66 \text{ ft}^3}$	$\dfrac{9.965 \text{ ft}^3}{11.66 \text{ ft}^3}$	$\dfrac{0.0018 \text{ ft}^3}{11.66 \text{ ft}^3}$	$\dfrac{0.942 \text{ ft}^3}{11.66 \text{ ft}^3}$	
	$= 0.0643$	0.855	$-$	0.081	$-$

14. *Customary U.S. Solution*

step 1: From App. 24.B, the heat of vaporization at $212°F$ is $h_{fg} = 970.3 \text{ Btu/lbm}$.

The heat absorbed in the boiler is

$$m_{H_2O}h_{fg} = (11.12 \text{ lbm } H_2O)\left(970.3 \frac{\text{Btu}}{\text{lbm}}\right)$$
$$= 10{,}789.7 \text{ Btu/lbm fuel}$$

step 2: The losses for heating stack gases can be found as follows.

The burned carbon per lbm of fuel is

$$0.7842 - (0.315)(0.0703) = 0.7621 \text{ lbm/lbm fuel}$$

The mass ratio of dry flue gases to solid fuel is given by Eq. 22.12.

$$\frac{\text{mass of}}{\text{flue gas}} \Big/ \frac{\text{mass of}}{\text{solid fuel}} = \frac{\begin{array}{c}(11B_{CO_2} + 8B_{O_2} \\ + (7)(B_{CO} + B_{N_2}))\end{array}\left(G_C + \dfrac{G_S}{1.833}\right)}{(3)(B_{CO_2} + B_{CO})}$$

$$= \frac{\begin{array}{c}((11)(14.0) + (8)(5.5) \\ + (7)(0.42 + 80.08))\end{array}\left(0.7621 + \dfrac{0.01}{1.833}\right)}{(3)(14.0 + 0.42)}$$

$$= 13.51 \text{ lbm stack gases/lbm fuel}$$

Properties of nitrogen frequently are assumed for dry flue gas. From Table 22.1, for nitrogen at an average temperature of $(575°F + 67°F)/2 = 781°R$, $c_p \approx 0.252 \text{ Btu/lbm-}°F$.

The losses for heating stack gases are given by Eq. 22.20.

$$q_1 = m_{\text{flue gas}}c_p(T_{\text{flue gas}} - T_{\text{incoming air}})$$
$$= (13.51 \text{ lbm})\left(0.252 \frac{\text{Btu}}{\text{lbm-}°F}\right)(575°F - 67°F)$$
$$= 1729.5 \text{ Btu/lbm fuel}$$

The heat loss in the vapor formed during the combustion of hydrogen is given by Eq. 22.21.

$$q_2 = 8.94G_H(h_g - h_f)$$

h_g at $575°F$ can be found from App. 24.A.

$$h_g = 1193.8 \text{ Btu/lbm}$$

h_f at $67°F$ can be found from App. 24.A.

$$h_f = 35.09 \text{ Btu/lbm}$$

$$q_2 = (8.94)(0.0556)\left(1193.8 \frac{\text{Btu}}{\text{lbm}} - 35.09 \frac{\text{Btu}}{\text{lbm}}\right)$$
$$= 576.0 \text{ Btu/lbm fuel}$$

Heat is also lost when it is absorbed by the moisture originally in the combustion air.

$$q_3 = \omega m_{\text{combustion air}}(h_g - h'_g)$$

From App. 24.A, $h_g = 1090.8 \text{ Btu/lbm}$. From the psychrometric chart,

$$\omega = 90 \text{ grains/lbm air}$$
$$= 0.0129 \text{ lbm water/lbm air}$$

After modifying for sulfur content, find the air/fuel ratio.

$$\frac{\text{lbm air}}{\text{lbm fuel}} = \frac{3.04B_{N_2}\left(G_C - \dfrac{G_S}{1.833}\right)}{B_{CO_2} + B_{CO}}$$

$$= \frac{(3.04)(80.08\%)\left(0.7621 + \dfrac{0.01}{1.833}\right)}{14\% + 0.42\%}$$

$$= 12.96 \text{ lbm air/lbm fuel}$$

$$q_3 = \left(0.0129 \frac{\text{lbm water}}{\text{lbm air}}\right)\left(12.96 \frac{\text{lbm air}}{\text{lbm fuel}}\right)$$
$$\times \left(1193.8 \frac{\text{Btu}}{\text{lbm}} - 1090.8 \frac{\text{Btu}}{\text{lbm}}\right)$$
$$= 17.2 \text{ Btu/lbm fuel}$$

The energy lost in incomplete combustion is given by Eq. 22.23.

$$q_4 = \frac{(\text{HHV}_\text{C} - \text{HHV}_\text{CO}) G_\text{C} B_\text{CO}}{B_{\text{CO}_2} + B_\text{CO}}$$

$$= \frac{\left(9746 \dfrac{\text{Btu}}{\text{lbm}}\right)(0.7621)(0.42\%)}{14\% + 0.42\%}$$

$$= 216.3 \text{ Btu/lbm fuel}$$

The energy lost in unburned carbon is given by Eq. 22.24.

$$q_5 = \left(14{,}093 \frac{\text{Btu}}{\text{lbm}}\right) m_\text{ash} G_\text{C,ash}$$

$$= \left(14{,}093 \frac{\text{Btu}}{\text{lbm}}\right)(0.0703)(0.315)$$

$$= 312.1 \text{ Btu/lbm fuel}$$

The energy lost in radiation and unaccounted for is

$$14{,}000 \frac{\text{Btu}}{\text{lbm}} - 10{,}789.7 \frac{\text{Btu}}{\text{lbm}} - 1729.5 \frac{\text{Btu}}{\text{lbm}}$$

$$- 576.0 \frac{\text{Btu}}{\text{lbm}} - 17.2 \frac{\text{Btu}}{\text{lbm}} - 216.3 \frac{\text{Btu}}{\text{lbm}}$$

$$- 312.1 \frac{\text{Btu}}{\text{lbm}}$$

$$= \boxed{359.2 \text{ Btu/lbm fuel}}$$

SI Solution

step 1: From App. 24.N, the heat of vaporization at 100°C is $h_{fg} = 2257.0$ kJ/kg.

The heat absorbed in the boiler is

$$m_{\text{H}_2\text{O}} h_{fg} = (11.12 \text{ kg})\left(2257.0 \frac{\text{kJ}}{\text{kg}}\right)$$

$$= 25\,098 \text{ kJ/kg fuel}$$

step 2: From step 2 of the U.S. solution,

$$\frac{\text{mass of flue gas}}{\text{mass of solid fuel}} = 13.51 \text{ kg stack gases/kg fuel}$$

Properties of nitrogen frequently are assumed for dry flue gas. For an average nitrogen temperature of $(\frac{1}{2})(300°\text{C} + 23°\text{C}) + 273 = 434.5 \text{ K } (782°\text{R})$, $c_p \approx 0.252$ Btu/lbm-°R.

c_p from Table 22.1 can be found (using the table footnote) as

$$c_p = \left(0.252 \frac{\text{Btu}}{\text{lbm-}°\text{R}}\right)\left(4.187 \frac{\dfrac{\text{kJ}}{\text{kg·K}}}{\dfrac{\text{Btu}}{\text{lbm-}°\text{R}}}\right)$$

$$= 1.055 \text{ kJ/kg·K}$$

The losses for heating stack gases are given by Eq. 22.20.

$$q_1 = m_\text{flue gas} c_p (T_\text{flue gas} - T_\text{incoming air})$$

$$= (13.51 \text{ kg})\left(1.055 \frac{\text{kJ}}{\text{kg·K}}\right)(300°\text{C} - 23°\text{C})$$

$$= 3948.1 \text{ kJ/kg fuel}$$

The heat loss in the vapor formed during the combustion of hydrogen is given by Eq. 22.21.

$$q_2 = 8.94 G_\text{H}(h_g - h_f)$$

h_g at 300°C can be found from App. 24.N.

$$h_g = 2749 \text{ kJ/kg}$$

h_f at 23°C can be found from App. 24.N.

$h_f = 96.52$ kJ/kg

$$q_2 = (8.94)(0.0556)\left(2749 \frac{\text{kJ}}{\text{kg}} - 96.52 \frac{\text{kJ}}{\text{kg}}\right)$$

$$= 1318.5 \text{ kJ/kg fuel}$$

Heat is also lost when it is absorbed by the moisture originally in the combustion air.

$$q_3 = \omega m_\text{combustion air}(h_g - h'_g)$$

From App. 24.N, $h'_g = 2453.5$ kJ/kg.

From the psychrometric chart for 19°C wet bulb and 23°C dry bulb, $\omega = 12.2$ g/kg dry air.

The air-fuel ratio from the Customary U.S. Solution is

$$\frac{\text{kg air}}{\text{kg fuel}} = 12.96 \text{ kg air/kg fuel}$$

$$q_3 = \left(12.2 \frac{\text{g}}{\text{kg}}\right)\left(\frac{1 \text{ kg}}{1000 \text{ g}}\right)\left(12.96 \frac{\text{kg}}{\text{kg}}\right)$$

$$\times \left(2749 \frac{\text{kJ}}{\text{kg}} - 2453.5 \frac{\text{kJ}}{\text{kg}}\right)$$

$$= 46.72 \text{ kJ/kg}$$

Energy lost in incomplete combustion is given by Eq. 22.23.

$$q_4 = \frac{(\text{HHV}_\text{C} - \text{HHV}_\text{CO}) G_\text{C} B_\text{CO}}{B_{\text{CO}_2} + B_\text{CO}}$$

$$= \left(\frac{\left(22.67 \, \dfrac{\text{MJ}}{\text{kg}} \right) (0.7621)(0.42)}{14 + 0.42} \right) \left(1000 \, \frac{\text{kJ}}{\text{MJ}} \right)$$

$$= \left(0.5032 \, \frac{\text{MJ}}{\text{kg}} \right) \left(1000 \, \frac{\text{kJ}}{\text{MJ}} \right)$$

$$= 503.2 \text{ kJ/kg fuel}$$

The energy lost in unburned carbon is given by Eq. 22.24.

$$q_5 = \left(32.8 \, \frac{\text{MJ}}{\text{kg}} \right) m_\text{ash} G_\text{C,ash}$$

$$= \left(32.8 \, \frac{\text{MJ}}{\text{kg}} \right) \left(1000 \, \frac{\text{kJ}}{\text{MJ}} \right) (0.0703)(0.315)$$

$$= 726.3 \text{ kJ/kg fuel}$$

Energy lost in radiation and unaccounted for is

$$\left(32.6 \, \frac{\text{MJ}}{\text{kg}} \right) \left(1000 \, \frac{\text{kJ}}{\text{MJ}} \right) - 25\,098 \, \frac{\text{kJ}}{\text{kg}}$$

$$- 3948.1 \, \frac{\text{kJ}}{\text{kg}} - 1318.5 \, \frac{\text{kJ}}{\text{kg}} - 46.72 \, \frac{\text{kJ}}{\text{kg}}$$

$$- 503.2 \, \frac{\text{kJ}}{\text{kg}} - 726.3 \, \frac{\text{kJ}}{\text{kg}} = \boxed{959.2 \text{ kJ/kg}}$$

15. *Customary U.S. Solution*

step 1: The incoming reactants on a per-pound basis are

> 0.07 lbm ash
> 0.05 lbm hydrogen
> 0.05 lbm oxygen
> 0.83 lbm carbon

This is an ultimate analysis. Assume that only the hydrogen that is not locked up with oxygen in the form of water is combustible. From Eq. 22.15, the available hydrogen is

$$G_\text{H,available} = G_\text{H,total} - \frac{G_\text{O}}{8}$$

$$= 0.05 \text{ lbm} - \frac{0.05 \text{ lbm}}{8}$$

$$= 0.04375 \text{ lbm}$$

The mass of water produced is the hydrogen mass plus eight times as much oxygen. The locked hydrogen is

$$0.05 \text{ lbm} - 0.04375 \text{ lbm} = 0.00625 \text{ lbm}$$

$$\begin{aligned} \text{lbm of} \atop \text{moisture} &= G_\text{H} + G_\text{O} \\ &= G_\text{H} + 8 G_\text{H} \\ &= 0.00625 \text{ lbm} + (8)(0.00625 \text{ lbm}) \\ &= 0.05625 \text{ lbm} \end{aligned}$$

The air is 23.15% oxygen by weight (Table 22.6), so other reactants for 26 lbm of air are

$$(0.2315)(26 \text{ lbm}) = 6.019 \text{ lbm O}_2$$

$$(0.7685)(26 \text{ lbm}) = 19.981 \text{ lbm N}_2$$

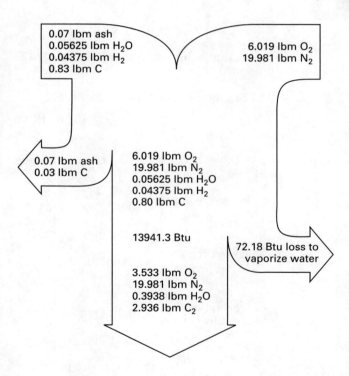

step 2: Ash pit material losses are 10% or 0.1 lbm, which includes all of the ash.

> 0.07 lbm ash (noncombustible matter)
> 0.03 lbm unburned carbon

step 3: Determine what remains.

> 6.019 lbm oxygen
> 19.981 lbm nitrogen
> 0.05625 lbm water
> 0.04375 lbm hydrogen
> 0.080 lbm carbon

step 4: Determine the energy loss in vaporizing the moisture.

$$q = (\text{moisture})(h_g - h_f)$$

From App. 24.C, h_g at 550°F and 14.7 psia is 1311.3 Btu/lbm.

From App. 24.A, h_f at 60°F is 28.08 Btu/lbm.

$$q = (0.05625 \text{ lbm}) \left(1311.3 \frac{\text{Btu}}{\text{lbm}} - 28.08 \frac{\text{Btu}}{\text{lbm}} \right)$$

$$= 72.18 \text{ Btu}$$

step 5: Calculate the heating value of the remaining fuel components using App. 22.A.

$$HV_C = (0.80 \text{ lbm}) \left(14,093 \frac{\text{Btu}}{\text{lbm}} \right)$$

$$= 11274.4 \text{ Btu}$$

$$HV_H = (0.04375 \text{ lbm}) \left(60,958 \frac{\text{Btu}}{\text{lbm}} \right)$$

$$= 2666.9 \text{ Btu}$$

The heating value after the coal moisture is evaporated is

$$11,274.4 \text{ Btu} + 2666.9 \text{ Btu} - 72.18 \text{ Btu}$$

$$= 13,869 \text{ Btu}$$

step 6: Using Table 22.8, determine the combustion products.

$$\begin{aligned}\text{oxygen required} \\ \text{by carbon}\end{aligned} = (0.80)(2.667 \text{ lbm})$$

$$= 2.134 \text{ lbm}$$

$$\begin{aligned}\text{oxygen required} \\ \text{by hydrogen}\end{aligned} = (0.04375)(7.936 \text{ lbm})$$

$$= 0.3472 \text{ lbm}$$

$$\begin{aligned}\text{carbon dioxide} \\ \text{produced by carbon}\end{aligned} = (0.8)(3.667 \text{ lbm})$$

$$= 2.934 \text{ lbm}$$

$$\begin{aligned}\text{water produced} \\ \text{by hydrogen}\end{aligned} = (0.04375)(8.936 \text{ lbm})$$

$$= 0.3910 \text{ lbm}$$

The remaining oxygen is

$$6.019 \text{ lbm} - 2.134 \text{ lbm} - 0.3472 \text{ lbm} = 3.538 \text{ lbm}$$

step 7: The gaseous products must be heated from 70°F to 550°F. The average temperature is

$$\left(\tfrac{1}{2} \right) (70°F + 550°F) = 310°F \; (770°R)$$

From Table 22.1, the specific heat of gaseous products is

gas	c_p $\left(\dfrac{\text{Btu}}{\text{lbm-°R}} \right)$
oxygen	0.228
nitrogen	0.252
water	0.460
carbon dioxide	0.225

$$\begin{aligned}
Q_{\text{heating}} = &\left((3.538 \text{ lbm}) \left(0.228 \frac{\text{Btu}}{\text{lbm-°R}} \right) \right. \\
&+ (19.981 \text{ lbm}) \left(0.252 \frac{\text{Btu}}{\text{lbm-°R}} \right) \\
&+ (0.3910 \text{ lbm}) \left(0.460 \frac{\text{Btu}}{\text{lbm-°R}} \right) \\
&\left. + (2.934 \text{ lbm}) \left(0.225 \frac{\text{Btu}}{\text{lbm-°R}} \right) \right) \\
&\times (550°F - 70°F) \\
= &\; 3207.3 \text{ Btu}
\end{aligned}$$

step 8: The percent loss is

$$\frac{3207.3 \text{ Btu} + 72.18 \text{ Btu}}{13,869 \text{ Btu}} = \boxed{0.236 \; (23.6\%)}$$

SI Solution

Steps 1 through 3 are the same as for the Customary U.S. Solution except that everything is based on kg.

step 4: Determine the energy loss in the vaporizing moisture.

$$q = (\text{moisture})(h_g - h_f)$$

From App. 24.P, h_g at 290°C and 101.3 kPa is 3054.3 kJ/kg.

h_f at 15.6°C from App. 24.N is 65.51 kJ/kg.

$$q = (0.05625 \text{ kg}) \left(3054.3 \frac{\text{kJ}}{\text{kg}} - 65.51 \frac{\text{kJ}}{\text{kg}} \right)$$

$$= 168.1 \text{ kJ}$$

step 5: Calculate the heating value of the remaining fuel components using App. 22.A and the table footnote.

$$HV_C = (0.80\ \text{kg})\left(14\,093\ \frac{\text{Btu}}{\text{lbm}}\right)\left(2.326\ \frac{\frac{\text{kJ}}{\text{kg}}}{\frac{\text{Btu}}{\text{lbm}}}\right)$$

$$= 26\,224\ \text{kJ}$$

$$HV_H = (0.04375\ \text{kg})\left(60\,958\ \frac{\text{Btu}}{\text{lbm}}\right)\left(2.326\ \frac{\frac{\text{kJ}}{\text{kg}}}{\frac{\text{Btu}}{\text{lbm}}}\right)$$

$$= 6203\ \text{kJ}$$

The heating value after the coal moisture is evaporated is

$$26\,224\ \text{kJ} + 6203\ \text{kJ} - 168.1\ \text{kJ} = 32\,259\ \text{kJ}$$

step 6: This step is the same as for the Customary U.S. Solution except that all quantities are in kg.

step 7: The gaseous products must be heated from 21°C to 290°C. The average temperature is

$$\left(\tfrac{1}{2}\right)(21°\text{C} + 290°\text{C}) = 156°\text{C}\ (429°\text{K})$$

$$(429\text{K})\left(1.8\ \frac{°\text{R}}{\text{K}}\right) = 771°\text{R}$$

From Table 22.1, the specific heat of gaseous products is calculated using the table footnote.

gas	c_p $\left(\frac{\text{kJ}}{\text{kg·K}}\right)$
oxygen	0.955
nitrogen	1.055
water	1.926
carbon dioxide	0.942

$$Q_{\text{heating}} = \left((3.538\ \text{kg})\left(0.955\ \frac{\text{kJ}}{\text{kg·K}}\right)\right.$$
$$+ (19.981\ \text{lbm})\left(1.055\ \frac{\text{kJ}}{\text{kg·K}}\right)$$
$$+ (0.3910\ \text{kg})\left(1.926\ \frac{\text{kJ}}{\text{kg·K}}\right)$$
$$\left.+ (2.934\ \text{kg})\left(0.942\ \frac{\text{kJ}}{\text{kg·K}}\right)\right)$$
$$\times (290°\text{C} - 21°\text{C})$$
$$= \boxed{7525.4\ \text{kJ}}$$

step 8: The percentage loss is

$$\frac{7525.4\ \text{kJ} + 168.1\ \text{kJ}}{32\,259\ \text{kJ}} = \boxed{0.238\ \ (23.8\%)}$$

16. (a) Silicon in ash is SiO_2 with a molecular weight of

$$28.09\ \frac{\text{lbm}}{\text{lbmol}} + (2)\left(16\ \frac{\text{lbm}}{\text{lbmol}}\right) = 60.09\ \text{lbm/lbmol}$$

The oxygen used with 6.1% by mass silicon is

$$\left(\frac{(2)(16\ \text{lbm})}{28.09\ \text{lbm}}\right)\left(0.061\ \frac{\text{lbm}}{\text{lbm coal}}\right)$$
$$= 0.0695\ \text{lbm/lbm coal}$$

Silicon ash produced per lbm of coal is

$$0.061\ \frac{\text{lbm}}{\text{lbm coal}} + 0.0695\ \frac{\text{lbm}}{\text{lbm coal}}$$
$$= 0.1305\ \text{lbm/lbm coal}$$

Silicon ash produced per hour is

$$\left(0.1305\ \frac{\text{lbm}}{\text{lbm coal}}\right)\left(15,300\ \frac{\text{lbm coal}}{\text{hr}}\right)$$
$$= 1996.7\ \text{lbm/hr}$$

The silicon in 410 lbm/hr refuse is

$$\left(410\ \frac{\text{lbm}}{\text{hr}}\right)(1 - 0.3) = 287\ \text{lbm/hr}$$

The emission rate is

$$1996.7\ \text{lbm/hr} - 287\ \text{lbm/hr} = \boxed{1709.7\ \text{lbm/hr}}$$

(b) From Table 22.7, the stoichiometric reaction for sulfur is

$$\text{S} + \text{O}_2 \longrightarrow \text{SO}_2$$
$$\text{MW}\quad 32\quad 32\quad\quad 64$$

Sulfur dioxide produced for 15,300 lbm/hr of coal feed is

$$\left(15,300\ \frac{\text{lbm}}{\text{hr}}\right)(0.0244\ \text{lbm S})\left(\frac{64\ \text{lbm SO}_2}{32\ \text{lbm S}}\right)$$
$$= \boxed{746.6\ \text{lbm/hr}}$$

(c) From Eq. 22.16(b), the heating value of the fuel is

$$\text{HHV} = 14{,}093 G_\text{C} + (60{,}958)\left(G_\text{H} - \frac{G_\text{O}}{8}\right) + 3983 G_\text{S}$$

$$= \left(14{,}093\ \frac{\text{Btu}}{\text{lbm}}\right)(0.7656)$$

$$+ \left(60{,}958\ \frac{\text{Btu}}{\text{lbm}}\right)\left(0.055 - \frac{0.077}{8}\right)$$

$$+ \left(3983\ \frac{\text{Btu}}{\text{lbm}}\right)(0.0244)$$

$$= 13{,}653\ \text{Btu/lbm}$$

The gross available combustion power is

$$\dot{m}_f(\text{HV}) = \left(15{,}300\ \frac{\text{lbm}}{\text{hr}}\right)\left(13{,}653\ \frac{\text{Btu}}{\text{lbm}}\right)$$

$$= 2.089 \times 10^8\ \text{Btu/hr}$$

The carbon in 410 lbm/hr refuse is

$$\left(410\ \frac{\text{lbm}}{\text{hr}}\right)(0.3) = 123\ \text{lbm/hr}$$

Power lost in unburned carbon in refuse is $\dot{m}_\text{C}(\text{HV})$.

From App. 22.A, the gross heat of combustion for C is 14,093 Btu/lbm.

$$\left(123\ \frac{\text{lbm}}{\text{hr}}\right)\left(14{,}093\ \frac{\text{Btu}}{\text{lbm}}\right) = 1.733 \times 10^6\ \text{Btu/hr}$$

The remaining combustion power is

$$2.089 \times 10^8\ \frac{\text{Btu}}{\text{hr}} - 1.733 \times 10^6\ \frac{\text{Btu}}{\text{hr}}$$
$$= 2.072 \times 10^8\ \text{Btu/hr}$$

Losses in the steam generator and electrical generator will further reduce this to

$$(0.86)\left(2.072 \times 10^8\ \frac{\text{Btu}}{\text{hr}}\right) = 1.782 \times 10^8\ \text{Btu/hr}$$

With an electrical output of 17 MW, thermal energy removed by cooling water is

$$Q = 1.782 \times 10^8\ \frac{\text{Btu}}{\text{hr}} - (17\ \text{MW})\left(1000\ \frac{\text{kW}}{\text{MW}}\right)$$

$$\times \left(3413\ \frac{\frac{\text{Btu}}{\text{hr}}}{\text{kW}}\right)$$

$$= 1.202 \times 10^8\ \text{Btu/hr}$$

The temperature rise of the cooling water is

$$\Delta T = \frac{Q}{\dot{m} c_p}$$

At 60°F, the specific heat of water is $c_p = 1$ Btu/lbm-°F.

$$\Delta T = \frac{1.202 \times 10^8\ \dfrac{\text{Btu}}{\text{hr}}}{\left(225\ \dfrac{\text{ft}^3}{\text{sec}}\right)\left(62.4\ \dfrac{\text{lbm}}{\text{ft}^3}\right)\left(3600\ \dfrac{\text{sec}}{\text{hr}}\right)\left(1\ \dfrac{\text{Btu}}{\text{lbm-}°\text{F}}\right)}$$

$$= \boxed{2.38°\text{F}}$$

The electrical generation is not cooled by the cooling water. Therefore, it is not correct to include the generation efficiency in the calculation of losses.

(d) Limiting 0.1 lbm of particulates per million Btu per hour, the allowable emission rate is

$$\left(0.1\ \frac{\text{lbm}}{\text{MBtu}}\right)\left(15{,}300\ \frac{\text{lbm}}{\text{hr}}\right)$$

$$\times \left(13{,}653\ \frac{\text{Btu}}{\text{lbm}}\right)\left(\frac{1\ \text{MBtu}}{10^6\ \text{Btu}}\right) = 20.89\ \text{lbm/hr}$$

The efficiency of the flue gas particulate collectors is

$$\eta = \frac{\text{actual emission rate} - \text{allowable emission rate}}{\text{actual emission rate}}$$

$$= \frac{1709.7\ \dfrac{\text{lbm}}{\text{hr}} - 20.89\ \dfrac{\text{lbm}}{\text{hr}}}{1709.7\ \dfrac{\text{lbm}}{\text{hr}}}$$

$$= \boxed{0.988\ (98.8\%)}$$

17. *Customary U.S. Solution*

(c) The stoichiometric reaction for propane is given in Table 22.7.

$$\begin{array}{cccccc} & \text{C}_3\text{H}_8 + & 5\text{O}_2 & \longrightarrow & 3\text{CO}_2 & + & 4\text{H}_2\text{O} \\ \text{MW} & 44.097 & (5)(32.000) & & (3)(44.011) & & (4)(18.016) \end{array}$$

With 40% excess O_2 by weight,

$$\begin{array}{ccc} \text{C}_3\text{H}_8 & (1.4)(5)\text{O}_2 \\ \text{MW } 44.097 + & (7)(32.000) \\ 44.097 & 224 \end{array}$$

$$\begin{array}{cccc} & 3\text{CO}_2 & 4\text{H}_2\text{O} & 2\text{O}_2 \\ \longrightarrow & (3)(44.011) + & (4)(18.016) + & (2)(32.000) \\ & 132.033 & 72.064 & 64 \end{array}$$

FUELS AND COMBUSTION 111

The excess oxygen is

$$(2)(32) = 64 \text{ lbm/lbmol } C_3H_8$$

The mass ratio of nitrogen to oxygen is

$$\frac{G_N}{G_O} = \left(\frac{B_N}{R_N}\right)\left(\frac{R_O}{B_O}\right)$$

$$= \left(\frac{0.40}{55.16 \frac{\text{ft-lbf}}{\text{lbm-}°R}}\right)\left(\frac{48.29 \frac{\text{ft-lbf}}{\text{lbm-}°R}}{0.60}\right)$$

$$= 0.584$$

(Values of R_N and R_O are taken from Table 24.7.)

The nitrogen accompanying the oxygen is

$$(7)(32)(0.584) = 130.8 \text{ lbm}$$

The mass balance per mole of propane is

$$C_3H_8 + O_2 + N_2 \longrightarrow CO_2 + H_2O + O_2 + N_2$$

mass per mole: $44.097 + 224 + 130.8 \longrightarrow 132.033 + 72.064 + 64 + 130.8$

At standard conditions (60°F, 1 atm), the propane density is given by Eq. 24.50.

$$\rho = \frac{p}{RT}$$

The absolute temperature, T, is

$$60°F + 460 = 520°R$$

R for propane from Table 24.7 is 35.04 ft-lbf/lbm-°R.

$$\rho = \frac{\left(14.7 \frac{\text{lbf}}{\text{in}^2}\right)\left(144 \frac{\text{in}^2}{\text{ft}^2}\right)}{\left(35.04 \frac{\text{ft-lbf}}{\text{lbm-}°R}\right)(520°R)}$$

$$= 0.1162 \text{ lbm/ft}^3$$

The mass flow rate of propane based on 250 SCFM of propane is

$$\left(250 \frac{\text{ft}^3}{\text{min}}\right)\left(0.1162 \frac{\text{lbm}}{\text{ft}^3}\right) = 29.05 \text{ lbm/min}$$

Scaling the other mass balance factors down by

$$\frac{29.05 \frac{\text{lbm}}{\text{min}}}{44.097 \frac{\text{lbm}}{\text{lbmol}}} = 0.6588 \text{ lbmol/min}$$

$$\frac{\text{lbm}}{\text{min}} \quad \begin{array}{ccc} C_3H_8 + & O_2 & + N_2 \\ 29.05 + & 147.57 + & 86.17 \end{array}$$

$$\longrightarrow \begin{array}{cccc} CO_2 + & H_2O + & O_2 + & N_2 \\ 86.98 + & 47.48 + & 42.16 + & 86.17 \end{array}$$

The oxygen flow rate is $\boxed{14.76 \text{ lbm/min}}$ [part (c)].

(a) Using R from Table 24.7, the specific volumes of the reactants are given by Eq. 24.50.

$$v_{C_3H_8} = \frac{RT}{p}$$

$$= \frac{\left(35.04 \frac{\text{ft-lbf}}{\text{lbm-}°R}\right)(80°F + 460)}{\left(14.7 \frac{\text{lbf}}{\text{in}^2}\right)\left(144 \frac{\text{in}^2}{\text{ft}^2}\right)}$$

$$= 8.939 \text{ ft}^3/\text{lbm}$$

$$v_{O_2} = \frac{\left(48.29 \frac{\text{ft-lbf}}{\text{lbm-}°R}\right)(80°F + 460)}{\left(14.7 \frac{\text{lbf}}{\text{in}^2}\right)\left(144 \frac{\text{in}^2}{\text{ft}^2}\right)}$$

$$= 12.319 \text{ ft}^3/\text{lbm}$$

$$v_{N_2} = \frac{\left(55.16 \frac{\text{ft-lbf}}{\text{lbm-}°R}\right)(80°F + 460)°R}{\left(14.7 \frac{\text{lbf}}{\text{in}^2}\right)\left(144 \frac{\text{in}^2}{\text{ft}^2}\right)}$$

$$= 14.071 \text{ ft}^3/\text{lbm}$$

The total incoming volume is

$$\dot{V} = \left(29.05 \frac{\text{lbm}}{\text{min}}\right)\left(8.939 \frac{\text{ft}^3}{\text{lbm}}\right)$$
$$+ \left(147.57 \frac{\text{lbm}}{\text{min}}\right)\left(12.319 \frac{\text{ft}^3}{\text{lbm}}\right)$$
$$+ \left(86.17 \frac{\text{lbm}}{\text{min}}\right)\left(14.071 \frac{\text{ft}^3}{\text{lbm}}\right)$$
$$= 3290 \text{ ft}^3/\text{min}$$

Since the velocity must be kept below 400 ft/min, the area of inlet pipe is

$$A_{in} = \frac{\dot{V}}{v} = \frac{3290 \frac{\text{ft}^3}{\text{min}}}{400 \frac{\text{ft}}{\text{min}}} = \boxed{8.23 \text{ ft}^2}$$

PROFESSIONAL PUBLICATIONS, INC. BELMONT, CA

(d) Similarly, the specific volumes of the products are

$$v_{CO_2} = \frac{\left(35.11 \ \frac{\text{ft-lbf}}{\text{lbm-}°\text{R}}\right)(460°\text{F} + 460)}{\left(8 \ \frac{\text{lbf}}{\text{in}^2}\right)\left(144 \ \frac{\text{in}^2}{\text{ft}^2}\right)}$$
$$= 28.04 \ \text{ft}^3/\text{lbm}$$

$$v_{H_2O} = \frac{\left(85.78 \ \frac{\text{ft-lbf}}{\text{lbm-}°\text{R}}\right)(460°\text{F} + 460)}{\left(8 \ \frac{\text{lbf}}{\text{in}^2}\right)\left(144 \ \frac{\text{in}^2}{\text{ft}^2}\right)}$$
$$= 68.50 \ \text{ft}^3/\text{lbm}$$

$$v_{O_2} = \frac{\left(48.29 \ \frac{\text{ft-lbf}}{\text{lbm-}°\text{R}}\right)(460°\text{F} + 460)}{\left(8 \ \frac{\text{lbf}}{\text{in}^2}\right)\left(144 \ \frac{\text{in}^2}{\text{ft}^2}\right)}$$
$$= 38.56 \ \text{ft}^3/\text{lbm}$$

$$v_{N_2} = \frac{\left(55.16 \ \frac{\text{ft-lbf}}{\text{lbm-}°\text{R}}\right)(460°\text{F} + 460)}{\left(8 \ \frac{\text{lbf}}{\text{in}^2}\right)\left(144 \ \frac{\text{in}^2}{\text{ft}^2}\right)}$$
$$= 44.05 \ \text{ft}^3/\text{lbm}$$

The total exhaust volume is

$$\dot{V} = \left(86.98 \ \frac{\text{lbm}}{\text{min}}\right)\left(28.04 \ \frac{\text{ft}^3}{\text{lbm}}\right)$$
$$+ \left(47.48 \ \frac{\text{lbm}}{\text{min}}\right)\left(68.50 \ \frac{\text{ft}^3}{\text{lbm}}\right)$$
$$+ \left(42.16 \ \frac{\text{lbm}}{\text{min}}\right)\left(38.56 \ \frac{\text{ft}^3}{\text{lbm}}\right)$$
$$+ \left(86.98 \ \frac{\text{lbm}}{\text{min}}\right)\left(44.05 \ \frac{\text{ft}^3}{\text{min}}\right)$$
$$= \boxed{11,148 \ \text{ft}^3/\text{min}} \quad [\text{part (d)}]$$

(b)   Since the velocity of the products must be kept below 800 ft/min, the area of the stack is

$$A_{\text{stack}} = \frac{Q}{v} = \frac{11,148 \ \frac{\text{ft}^3}{\text{min}}}{800 \ \frac{\text{ft}}{\text{min}}}$$
$$= \boxed{13.94 \ \text{ft}^2} \quad [\text{part (b)}]$$

(e) For ideal gases, the partial pressure is volumetrically weighted. The water vapor partial pressure in the stack is

$$(8 \ \text{psia})\left(\frac{\left(47.48 \ \frac{\text{lbm}}{\text{min}}\right)\left(68.50 \ \frac{\text{ft}^3}{\text{lbm}}\right)}{11,148 \ \frac{\text{ft}^3}{\text{lbm}}}\right) = 2.33 \ \text{psia}$$

The saturation temperature corresponding to 2.33 psia is $T_{\text{dp}} = \boxed{132°\text{F}.}$

SI Solution

(c) Following the procedure for the Customary U.S. Solution, the mass balance per mole of propane is

$$C_3H_8 + O_2 + N_2 \longrightarrow CO_2 + H_2O + O_2 + N_2$$

kg per mole $44.097 + 224 + 130.8 \longrightarrow 132.033 + 72.064 + 64 + 130.8$

At standard conditions (16°C, 101.3 kPa), the propane density is given by Eq. 24.50.

$$\rho = \frac{p}{RT}$$

The absolute temperature is

$$T = 16°\text{C} + 273 = 289\text{K}$$

From Table 24.7, R for propane is 188.55 J/kg·K.

$$\rho = \frac{(101.3 \ \text{kPa})\left(1000 \ \frac{\text{Pa}}{\text{kPa}}\right)}{\left(188.55 \ \frac{\text{J}}{\text{kg·K}}\right)(289\text{K})}$$
$$= 1.86 \ \text{kg/m}^3$$

The mass flow rate of propane based on 118 L/s of propane is

$$\left(118 \ \frac{\text{L}}{\text{s}}\right)\left(\frac{1 \ \text{m}^3}{1000 \ \text{L}}\right)\left(1.86 \ \frac{\text{kg}}{\text{m}^3}\right) = 0.2195 \ \text{kg/s}$$

Scale the other mass balance factors down.

$$\frac{0.2195 \ \frac{\text{kg}}{\text{s}}}{44.097 \ \frac{\text{kg}}{\text{kmol}}} = 0.004978 \ \text{kmol/s}$$

$$C_3H_8 + O_2 + N_2 \longrightarrow CO_2 + H_2O$$

$\frac{\text{kg}}{\text{s}}$ 0.2195   1.115   0.6511   0.6572   0.3587

$$+ \ O_2 + N_2$$
                    0.3186   0.6511

The oxygen flow rate is $\boxed{1.115 \ \text{kg/s.}}$

(a) Using R from Table 24.7, the specific volumes of the reactants are given by Eq. 24.50.

$$v_{C_3H_8} = \frac{RT}{p} = \frac{\left(188.55 \dfrac{J}{kg\cdot K}\right)(27°C + 273)}{(101 \text{ kPa})\left(1000 \dfrac{Pa}{kPa}\right)}$$

$$= 0.5600 \text{ m}^3/\text{kg}$$

$$v_{O_2} = \frac{\left(259.82 \dfrac{J}{kg\cdot K}\right)(27°C + 273)}{(101 \text{ kPa})\left(1000 \dfrac{Pa}{kPa}\right)}$$

$$= 0.7717 \text{ m}^3/\text{kg}$$

$$v_{N_2} = \frac{\left(296.77 \dfrac{J}{kg\cdot K}\right)(27°C + 273)}{(101 \text{ kPa})\left(1000 \dfrac{Pa}{kPa}\right)}$$

$$= 0.8815 \text{ m}^3/\text{kg}$$

The total incoming volume, $\dot{V}$, is

$$\dot{V} = \left(0.2195 \frac{kg}{s}\right)\left(0.5600 \frac{m^3}{kg}\right)$$

$$+ \left(1.115 \frac{kg}{s}\right)\left(0.7717 \frac{m^3}{kg}\right)$$

$$+ \left(0.6511 \frac{kg}{s}\right)\left(0.8815 \frac{m^3}{kg}\right)$$

$$= 1.557 \text{ m}^3/\text{s}$$

Since the velocity for the reactants must be kept below 2 m/s, the area of inlet pipe is

$$A_{in} = \frac{\dot{V}}{v} = \frac{1.557 \dfrac{m^3}{s}}{2 \dfrac{m}{s}} = \boxed{0.779 \text{ m}^2}$$

(d) Similarly, the specific volumes of the products are

$$v_{CO_2} = \frac{\left(188.92 \dfrac{J}{kg}\right)(240°C + 273)}{(55 \text{ kPa})\left(1000 \dfrac{Pa}{kPa}\right)}$$

$$= 1.762 \text{ m}^3/\text{kg}$$

$$v_{H_2O} = \frac{\left(461.5 \dfrac{J}{kg}\right)(240°C + 273)}{(55 \text{ kPa})\left(1000 \dfrac{Pa}{kPa}\right)}$$

$$= 4.305 \text{ m}^3/\text{kg}$$

$$v_{O_2} = \frac{\left(259.82 \dfrac{J}{kg\cdot K}\right)(240°C + 273)}{(55 \text{ kPa})\left(1000 \dfrac{Pa}{kPa}\right)}$$

$$= 2.423 \text{ m}^3/\text{kg}$$

$$v_{N_2} = \frac{\left(296.77 \dfrac{J}{kg\cdot K}\right)(240°C + 273)}{(55 \text{ kPa})\left(1000 \dfrac{Pa}{kPa}\right)}$$

$$= 2.768 \text{ m}^3/\text{kg}$$

The total exhaust volume is

$$\dot{V} = \left(0.6572 \frac{kg}{s}\right)\left(1.762 \frac{m^3}{kg}\right)$$

$$+ \left(0.3587 \frac{kg}{s}\right)\left(4.305 \frac{m^3}{kg}\right)$$

$$+ \left(0.3186 \frac{kg}{s}\right)\left(2.423 \frac{m^3}{kg}\right)$$

$$+ \left(0.6511 \frac{kg}{s}\right)\left(2.768 \frac{m^3}{kg}\right)$$

$$= \boxed{5.276 \text{ m}^3/\text{s}}$$

(b) Since the velocity of products must be kept below 4 m/s, the area of stack is

$$A_{stack} = \frac{\dot{V}}{v} = \frac{5.276 \dfrac{m^3}{s}}{4 \dfrac{m}{s}}$$

$$= \boxed{1.319 \text{ m}^2}$$

(e) For ideal gases, the partial pressure is volumetrically weighted. The water vapor partial pressure in the stack is

$$(55 \text{ kPa})\left(\frac{\left(0.3584 \dfrac{kg}{s}\right)\left(4.305 \dfrac{m^3}{kg}\right)}{5.273 \dfrac{m^3}{s}}\right)$$

$$= 16.093 \text{ kPa}$$

The saturation temperature corresponding to 16.093 kPa is found from App. 24.O to be $T_{dp} = \boxed{54.5°C}$.

18. *Customary U.S. Solution*

(a) Since atmospheric air is not used, the nitrogen and oxygen can be varied independently. Furthermore, since enthalpy increase information is not given for oxygen, a 0% excess oxygen can be assumed.

Thermodynamics

From Table 22.7,

$$C_3H_8 + 5O_2 \longrightarrow 3CO_2 + 4H_2O$$
$$\text{moles} \quad (1) \qquad (5) \qquad (3) \qquad (4)$$

Subtract the reactant enthalpies from the product enthalpies to calculate the heat of reaction. The enthalpy of formation of oxygen is zero, since it is an element in its natural state.

$$n_{CO_2}(\Delta H_f)_{CO_2} + n_{H_2O}(\Delta H_f)_{H_2O}$$
$$- n_{C_3H_8}(\Delta H_f)_{C_3H_8} - n_{O_2}(\Delta H_f)_{O_2}$$
$$= (3 \text{ lbmol}) \left(-169,300 \frac{\text{Btu}}{\text{lbmol}}\right)$$
$$+ (4 \text{ lbmol}) \left(-104,040 \frac{\text{Btu}}{\text{lbmol}}\right)$$
$$- (1 \text{ lbmol}) \left(28,800 \frac{\text{Btu}}{\text{lbmol}}\right)$$
$$- (5 \text{ lbmol})(0)$$
$$= -952,860 \text{ Btu/lbmol of fuel}$$

The negative sign indicates an exothermal reaction.

Let x be the number of moles of nitrogen per mole of propane. Use the nitrogen to cool the combustion. The above heat of reaction will increase the enthalpy of products from the standard reference temperature to 3600°R. Therefore,

$$952,860 \frac{\text{Btu}}{\text{lbmol}} = (3 \text{ lbmol}) \left(39,791 \frac{\text{Btu}}{\text{lbmol}}\right)$$
$$+ (4 \text{ lbmol}) \left(31,658 \frac{\text{Btu}}{\text{lbmol}}\right)$$
$$+ x \left(24,471 \frac{\text{Btu}}{\text{lbmol}}\right)$$
$$x = 28.89 \text{ lbmol/lbmol fuel}$$

The mass of nitrogen per lbmole of propane is

$$M_{N_2} = \left(28.89 \frac{\text{lbmol}}{\text{lbmol fuel}}\right) \left(28.016 \frac{\text{lbm}}{\text{lbmol}}\right)$$
$$= \boxed{809.4 \text{ lbm/lbmol propane}}$$

The mass of oxygen per lbmole of propane is

$$M_{O_2} = (5 \text{ lbmol}) \left(32 \frac{\text{lbm}}{\text{lbmol}}\right)$$
$$= \boxed{160 \text{ lbm/lbmol fuel}}$$

(b) The partial pressure is volumetrically weighted. This is the same as molar weighting.

product	lbmol	volumetric fraction
CO_2	3	$3/35.89 = 0.0836$
H_2O	4	$4/35.89 = 0.1115$
N_2	28.89	$28.89/35.89 = 0.8049$
O_2	0	$0/35.89 = 0$
	35.89 lbmol	1.000

The partial pressure of water vapor is

$$p_{H_2O} = \left(\frac{n_{H_2O}}{n}\right) p = (0.1115)(14.7 \text{ psia})$$
$$= 1.64 \text{ psia}$$

From App. 24.B, this corresponds to approximately 118°F. Since the stack temperature is 100°F, some of the water will condense. From App. 24.A, the maximum vapor pressure of water is 0.9503 psia. Let n be the number of moles of water in the stack gas.

$$n_{H_2O} = \left(\frac{p_{H_2O}}{p}\right) n = \left(\frac{0.9503 \text{ psia}}{14.7 \text{ psia}}\right) (35.89 \text{ lbmol})$$
$$= \boxed{2.320 \text{ lbmol/lbmol } C_3H_8}$$

(c) The water removed is

$$4 - n_{H_2O} = 4 \text{ lbmol} - 2.320 \text{ lbmol}$$
$$= 1.680 \text{ lbmol of } H_2O/\text{lbmol of } C_3H_8$$
$$m = (1.680 \text{ lbmol}) \left(18.016 \frac{\text{lbm}}{\text{lbmol}}\right)$$
$$= \boxed{30.27 \text{ lbm } H_2O/\text{lbmol } C_3H_8}$$

SI Solution

(a) From the Customary U.S. Solution, the heat of reaction is

$$n_{CO_2}(\Delta H_f)_{CO_2} + n_{H_2O}(\Delta H_f)_{H_2O}$$
$$- n_{C_3H_8}(\Delta H_f)_{C_3H_8} - n_{O_2}(\Delta H_f)_{O_2}$$
$$= (3 \text{ kmol}) \left(-393.8 \frac{\text{GJ}}{\text{kmol}}\right)$$
$$+ (4 \text{ kmol}) \left(-242 \frac{\text{GJ}}{\text{kmol}}\right)$$
$$- (1 \text{ kmol}) \left(67.0 \frac{\text{GJ}}{\text{kmol}}\right) - (5 \text{ kmol})(0)$$
$$= -2216.4 \text{ GJ/kmol fuel}$$

The negative sign indicates an exothermal reaction.

Let x be the number of moles of nitrogen per mole of propane. Use the nitrogen to cool the combustion. The above heat of reaction will increase the enthalpy of products from the standard reference temperature to 1980°C. Therefore,

$$2216.4 \frac{\text{GJ}}{\text{mol}} = (3 \text{ kmol}) \left(92.6 \frac{\text{GJ}}{\text{kmol}} \right)$$
$$+ (4 \text{ kmol}) \left(73.6 \frac{\text{GJ}}{\text{kmol}} \right)$$
$$+ x \left(56.9 \frac{\text{GJ}}{\text{kmol}} \right)$$
$$x = 28.90 \text{ kmol/kmol fuel}$$

The mass of nitrogen per mole of propane is

$$M_{N_2} = (28.90 \text{ kmol}) \left(28.016 \frac{\text{kg}}{\text{kmol}} \right)$$
$$= \boxed{809.7 \text{ kg/kg fuel}}$$

The mass of oxygen per kmol of propane is

$$M_{O_2} = (5 \text{ kmol}) \left(32 \frac{\text{kg}}{\text{kmol}} \right)$$
$$= \boxed{160 \text{ kg/kmol propane}}$$

(b) The partial pressure is volumetrically weighted. This is the same as molar weighting.

product	kmol	volumetric fraction
CO_2	3	$3/35.90 = 0.0836$
H_2O	4	$4/35.90 = 0.1114$
N_2	28.90	$28.90/35.90 = 0.8050$
O_2	0	$0/35.90 = 0$
	35.90 kmol	1.000

The partial pressure of water vapor is

$$p_{H_2O} = \left(\frac{n_{H_2O}}{n} \right) p = (0.1114)(101 \text{ kPa})$$
$$= 11.25 \text{ kPa}$$

From App. 24.0, this corresponds to approximately 47.6°C. Since the stack temperature is 38°C, some of the water will condense. From App. 24.N, the maximum vapor pressure of water at the stack temperature is 6.632 kPa. Let n be the number of moles of water in the stack gas.

$$n_{H_2O} = \left(\frac{p_{H_2O}}{p} \right) n = \left(\frac{6.632 \text{ kPa}}{101 \text{ kPa}} \right) (35.90 \text{ kmol})$$
$$= \boxed{2.357 \text{ kmol } H_2O/\text{kmol } C_3H_8}$$

(c) The liquid water removed is

$$4 - n_{H_2O} = 4 \text{ kmol} - 2.357 \text{ kmol}$$
$$= 1.643 \text{ kmol of } H_2O/\text{kmol propane}$$
$$m = (1.643 \text{ lbmol}) \left(18.016 \frac{\text{kg}}{\text{kmol}} \right)$$
$$= \boxed{29.6 \text{ kg } H_2O/\text{kmol } C_3H_8}$$

19. *Customary U.S. Solution*

(a) If the power output is to be unchanged,

$$BHP_1 = BHP_2$$
$$(\dot{m}_{F,1})(LHV_1) = (\dot{m}_{F,2})(LHV_2)$$

From Eq. 29.8,

$$\dot{m}_F = (BSFC)(BHP)$$
$$(BSFC_1)(LHV_1) = (BSFC_2)(LHV_2)$$
$$\frac{BSFC_2}{BSFC_1} = \frac{LHV_1}{LHV_2} = \frac{23{,}200 \frac{\text{Btu}}{\text{lbm}}}{11{,}930 \frac{\text{Btu}}{\text{lbm}}}$$
$$= 1.945$$
$$\frac{BSFC_2 - BSFC_1}{BSFC_1} = \frac{BSFC_2}{BSFC_1} - 1 = 1.945 - 1$$
$$= \boxed{0.945 \quad [94.5\% \text{ increase}]}$$

(b) If the fuel injection velocity is to be unchanged ($v_2 = v_1$),

$$\dot{m} = \rho A v$$
$$A = \frac{\dot{m}}{\rho v}$$
$$\dot{m}_2 = 1.945 \dot{m}_1 \quad [\text{part (a)}]$$
$$\frac{A_2 - A_1}{A_1} = \frac{\dfrac{\dot{m}_2}{\rho_2 v_2} - \dfrac{\dot{m}_1}{\rho_1 v_1}}{\dfrac{\dot{m}_1}{\rho_1 v_1}} = \frac{\dfrac{\dot{m}_2}{\rho_2} - \dfrac{\dot{m}_1}{\rho_1}}{\dfrac{\dot{m}_1}{\rho_1}}$$
$$= \frac{\dfrac{1.945 m_1}{\rho_2} - \dfrac{\dot{m}_1}{\rho_1}}{\dfrac{\dot{m}_1}{\rho_1}} = \frac{\dfrac{1.945}{\rho_2} - \dfrac{1}{\rho_1}}{\dfrac{1}{\rho_1}}$$
$$\frac{A_2 - A_1}{A_1} = (1.945) \left(\frac{\rho_1}{\rho_2} \right) - 1$$

From Table 22.3, for gasoline, $SG_1 = 0.74$. For ethanol, $SG_2 = 0.794$.

$$\frac{\rho_1}{\rho_2} = \frac{SG_1}{SG_2} = \frac{0.74}{0.794}$$

$$\frac{A_2 - A_1}{A_1} = (1.945)\left(\frac{0.74}{0.794}\right) - 1$$

$$= \boxed{0.810 \quad [81\% \text{ increase}]}$$

(c) If no changes are made to the engine, power output is proportional to the weight flow and heating value.

$$\frac{P_2 - P_1}{P_1} = \frac{\dot{m}_{F2}(LHV_2) - \dot{m}_{F1}(LHV_1)}{\dot{m}_{F1}(LHV_1)}$$

$$\dot{m}_F = \rho A v$$

$$\frac{P_2 - P_1}{P_1} = \frac{(\rho_2 A_2 v_2)(LHV_2) - (\rho_1 A_1 v_1)(LHV_1)}{(\rho_1 A_1 v_1)(LHV_1)}$$

Since no changes are made to the engine, $A_2 = A_1$ and $v_2 = v_1$.

$$\frac{P_2 - P_1}{P_1} = \frac{\rho_2(LHV_2) - \rho_1(LHV_1)}{\rho_1(LHV_1)}$$

$$= \frac{LHV_2 - \left(\dfrac{\rho_1}{\rho_2}\right)(LHV_1)}{\left(\dfrac{\rho_1}{\rho_2}\right)(LHV_2)}$$

From part (b),

$$\frac{\rho_1}{\rho_2} = \frac{0.74}{0.794}$$

$$\frac{P_2 - P_1}{P_1} = \frac{11{,}930 \dfrac{Btu}{lbm} - \left(\dfrac{0.74}{0.794}\right)\left(23{,}200 \dfrac{Btu}{lbm}\right)}{\left(\dfrac{0.74}{0.794}\right)\left(23{,}200 \dfrac{Btu}{lbm}\right)}$$

$$= \boxed{-0.45 \quad [45\% \text{ decrease}]}$$

SI Solution

(a) From part (a) of the Customary U.S. Solution,

$$\frac{BSFC_2}{BSFC_1} = \frac{LHV_1}{LHV_2} = \frac{54 \dfrac{MJ}{kg}}{27.7 \dfrac{MJ}{kg}} = 1.949$$

$$\frac{BSFC_2 - BSFC_1}{BSFC_1} = \frac{BSFC_2}{BSFC_1} - 1 = 1.949 - 1$$

$$= \boxed{0.949 \quad [94.9\% \text{ increase}]}$$

(b) From part (b) of the Customary U.S. Solution,

$$\frac{A_2 - A_1}{A_1} = \frac{\dfrac{\dot{m}_2}{\rho_2} - \dfrac{\dot{m}_1}{\rho_1}}{\dfrac{\dot{m}_1}{\rho_1}}$$

$$\dot{m}_2 = 1.949\dot{m}_1 \quad [\text{part (a)}]$$

$$\frac{A_2 - A_1}{A_1} = \frac{\dfrac{1.949\dot{m}_1}{\rho_2} - \dfrac{\dot{m}_1}{\rho_1}}{\dfrac{\dot{m}_1}{\rho_1}}$$

$$= (1.949)\left(\frac{\rho_1}{\rho_2}\right) - 1$$

$$= (1.949)\left(\frac{0.74}{0.794}\right) - 1$$

$$= \boxed{0.816 \quad [81.6\% \text{ increase}]}$$

(c) From part (c) of the Customary U.S. Solution,

$$\frac{P_2 - P_1}{P_1} = \frac{LHV_2 - \left(\dfrac{\rho_1}{\rho_2}\right)(LHV_1)}{\left(\dfrac{\rho_1}{\rho_2}\right)(LHV_1)}$$

$$= \frac{27.7 \dfrac{MJ}{kg} - \left(\dfrac{0.74}{0.794}\right)\left(54 \dfrac{MJ}{kg}\right)}{\left(\dfrac{0.74}{0.795}\right)\left(54 \dfrac{MJ}{kg}\right)}$$

$$= \boxed{-0.45 \quad [45\% \text{ decrease}]}$$

24 Thermodynamic Properties of Substances

1. *Customary U.S. Solution*

From App. 24.A, for 250°F steam, the enthalpy of saturated liquid, h_f, is 218.6 Btu/lbm. The heat of vaporization, h_{fg}, is 945.6 Btu/lbm. The enthalpy is given by Eq. 24.40.

$$h = h_f + xh_{fg}$$
$$= 218.6 \; \frac{\text{Btu}}{\text{lbm}} + (0.92)\left(945.6 \; \frac{\text{Btu}}{\text{lbm}}\right)$$
$$= 1088.6 \; \text{Btu/lbm}$$

The molecular weight of water is 18 lbm/lbmol. The molar enthalpy is given by Eq. 24.14.

$$H = (\text{MW})h$$
$$= \left(18 \; \frac{\text{lbm}}{\text{lbmol}}\right)\left(1088.6 \; \frac{\text{Btu}}{\text{lbm}}\right)$$
$$= \boxed{19{,}595 \; \text{Btu/lbmol}}$$

SI Solution

From App. 24.N, for 120°C steam, the enthalpy of saturated liquid, h_f, is 503.71 kJ/kg. The heat of vaporization, h_{fg}, is 2202.6 kJ/kg. The enthalpy is given by Eq. 24.40.

$$h = h_f + xh_{fg}$$
$$= 503.71 \; \frac{\text{kJ}}{\text{kg}} + (0.92)\left(2202.6 \; \frac{\text{kJ}}{\text{kg}}\right)$$
$$= 2530.1 \; \text{kJ/kg}$$

The molecular weight of water is 18 kg/kmol. Molar enthalpy is given by Eq. 24.14.

$$H = (\text{MW})h$$
$$= \left(18 \; \frac{\text{kg}}{\text{kmol}}\right)\left(2530.1 \; \frac{\text{kJ}}{\text{kg}}\right)$$
$$= \boxed{45\,542 \; \text{kJ/kmol}}$$

2. *Customary U.S. Solution*

The absolute temperature is

$$600°\text{F} + 460 = 1060°\text{R}$$

From Table 22.1, the specific heat at constant pressure for air at 1060°R is $c_p = 0.250$ Btu/lbm-°R.

From Eq. 24.48, the specific gas constant is

$$R = \frac{R^*}{\text{MW}} = \frac{1545.33 \; \dfrac{\text{ft-lbf}}{\text{lbmol-°R}}}{28.967 \; \dfrac{\text{lbm}}{\text{lbmol}}}$$
$$= 53.35 \; \text{ft-lbf/lbm-°R}$$

From Eq. 24.95(b),

$$c_{\text{v}} = c_p - \frac{R}{J}$$
$$= 0.250 \; \frac{\text{Btu}}{\text{lbm-°R}} - \frac{53.35 \; \dfrac{\text{ft-lbf}}{\text{lbm-°R}}}{778 \; \dfrac{\text{ft-lbf}}{\text{Btu}}}$$
$$= 0.1814 \; \text{Btu/lbm-°R}$$

The ratio of specific heats is given by Eq. 24.28.

$$k = \frac{c_p}{c_{\text{v}}} = \frac{0.250 \; \dfrac{\text{Btu}}{\text{lbm-°R}}}{0.1814 \; \dfrac{\text{Btu}}{\text{lbm-°R}}}$$
$$= \boxed{1.378}$$

SI Solution

From Table 22.1, specific heat at constant pressure for air is 0.250 Btu/lbm-°R. From the table footnote, the SI specific heat at constant pressure for air is

$$c_p = \left(0.250 \; \frac{\text{Btu}}{\text{lbm·°R}}\right)\left(4.187 \; \frac{\dfrac{\text{kJ}}{\text{kg·K}}}{\dfrac{\text{Btu}}{\text{lbm-°R}}}\right)$$
$$= 1.047 \; \text{kJ/kg·K}$$

From Eq. 24.48, the specific gas constant is

$$R = \frac{R^*}{MW} = \frac{8314.3 \frac{J}{kmol \cdot K}}{28.967 \frac{kg}{kmol}}$$
$$= 287.0 \text{ J/kg·K}$$

From Eq. 24.95(a),

$$c_v = c_p - R$$
$$= \left(1.047 \frac{kJ}{kg \cdot K}\right)\left(1000 \frac{J}{kJ}\right) - 287.0 \frac{J}{kg \cdot K}$$
$$= 760 \text{ J/kg·K}$$

The ratio of specific heats is given by Eq. 24.28.

$$k = \frac{c_p}{c_v} = \frac{\left(1.047 \frac{kJ}{kg \cdot K}\right)\left(1000 \frac{J}{kJ}\right)}{760 \frac{J}{kg \cdot K}}$$
$$= \boxed{1.377}$$

3. *Customary U.S. Solution*

From Eq. 24.48, the specific gas constant is

$$R = \frac{R^*}{MW} = \frac{1545.33 \frac{ft\text{-}lbf}{lbmol \text{-} °R}}{4 \frac{lbm}{lbmol}}$$
$$= 386.3 \text{ ft-lbf/lbm-°R}$$

The absolute temperature is

$$600°F + 460 = 1060°R$$

From Eq. 24.50, the density of helium is

$$\rho = \frac{p}{RT}$$
$$= \frac{\left(14.7 \frac{lbf}{in^2}\right)\left(144 \frac{in^2}{ft^2}\right)}{\left(386.3 \frac{ft\text{-}lbf}{lbm\text{-}°R}\right)(1060°R)}$$
$$= \boxed{0.00517 \text{ lbm/ft}^3}$$

SI Solution

From Eq. 24.48, the specific gas constant is

$$R = \frac{R^*}{MW} = \frac{8314.3 \frac{J}{kmol \cdot K}}{4 \frac{kg}{kmol}}$$
$$= 2079 \text{ J/kg·K}$$

The absolute temperature is

$$300°C + 273 = 573K$$

From Eq. 24.50, the density of helium is

$$\rho = \frac{p}{RT}$$
$$= \frac{1.013 \times 10^5 \text{ Pa}}{\left(2079 \frac{J}{kg \cdot K}\right)(573K)}$$
$$= \boxed{0.0850 \text{ kg/m}^3}$$

25 Changes in Thermodynamic Properties

1. Customary U.S. Solution

From Table 24.2, the approximate value of specific heat for cast iron is $c_p = 0.10$ Btu/lbm-°F.

The heat required per unit mass is

$$q = c_p(T_2 - T_1)$$
$$= \left(0.10 \; \frac{\text{Btu}}{\text{lbm-°F}}\right)(780°\text{F} - 80°\text{F})$$
$$= \boxed{70 \; \text{Btu/lbm}}$$

SI Solution

From Table 24.2, the approximate value of specific heat of cast iron is $c_p = 0.42$ kJ/kg·K.

The heat required per unit mass is

$$q = c_p(T_2 - T_1)$$
$$= \left(0.42 \; \frac{\text{kJ}}{\text{kg·K}}\right)(416°\text{C} - 27°\text{C})$$
$$= \boxed{163.4 \; \text{kJ/kg}}$$

2. Customary U.S. Solution

First calculate the mass flow rate of air to be heated by using the ideal gas law.

$$\dot{m}_{\text{air}} = \frac{p\dot{V}}{RT}$$

The absolute temperature is

$$T = 75°\text{F} + 460 = 535°\text{R}$$
$$\dot{m}_{\text{air}} = \frac{\left(14.7 \; \frac{\text{lbf}}{\text{in}^2}\right)\left(144 \; \frac{\text{in}^2}{\text{ft}^2}\right)\left(3 \times 10^5 \; \frac{\text{ft}^3}{\text{hr}}\right)}{\left(53.3 \; \frac{\text{ft-lbf}}{\text{lbm-°R}}\right)(535°\text{R})}$$
$$= 2.227 \times 10^4 \; \text{lbm/hr}$$

The heat lost by the water is equal to the heat gained by the air.

$$\dot{m}_w c_{p,w}(T_{1,w} - T_{2,w}) = \dot{m}_{\text{air}} c_{p,\text{air}}(T_{2,\text{air}} - T_{1,\text{air}})$$

$$\dot{m}_w \left(1 \; \frac{\text{Btu}}{\text{lbm-°F}}\right)(180°\text{F} - 150°\text{F})$$
$$= \left(2.227 \times 10^4 \; \frac{\text{lbm}}{\text{hr}}\right)\left(0.241 \; \frac{\text{Btu}}{\text{lbm-°F}}\right)(75°\text{F} - 35°\text{F})$$
$$\dot{m}_w = 7156.1 \; \text{lbm/hr}$$

From App. 35.A, the density of water at 165°F is approximately 61 lbm/ft³. The water volume flow rate is

$$\dot{V}_w = \frac{\dot{m}}{\rho} = \frac{\left(7156.1 \; \frac{\text{lbm}}{\text{hr}}\right)\left(\frac{1 \; \text{hr}}{3600 \; \text{sec}}\right)}{\left(61 \; \frac{\text{lbm}}{\text{ft}^3}\right)\left(0.002228 \; \frac{\text{ft}^3\text{-min}}{\text{sec-gal}}\right)}$$
$$= \boxed{14.63 \; \text{gal/min}}$$

SI Solution

First calculate the mass flow rate of air to be heated by using the ideal gas law.

$$\dot{m}_{\text{air}} = \frac{p\dot{V}}{RT}$$

The absolute temperature is

$$T = 24°\text{C} + 273 = 297\text{K}$$

$$\dot{m}_{\text{air}} = \frac{(1.013 \times 10^5 \; \text{Pa})\left(2.4 \; \frac{\text{m}^3}{\text{s}}\right)}{\left(287 \; \frac{\text{J}}{\text{kg·K}}\right)(297\text{K})}$$
$$= 2.85 \; \text{kg/s}$$

The heat lost by the water is equal to the heat gained by the air.

$$\dot{m}_w c_{p,w}(T_{1,w} - T_{2,w}) = \dot{m}_{\text{air}} c_{p,\text{air}}(T_{2,\text{air}} - T_{1,\text{air}})$$

$$\dot{m}_w \left(4.190 \; \frac{\text{kJ}}{\text{kg·K}}\right)(82°\text{C} - 66°\text{C})$$
$$= \left(2.85 \; \frac{\text{kg}}{\text{s}}\right)\left(1.005 \; \frac{\text{kJ}}{\text{kg·K}}\right)(24°\text{C} - 2°\text{C})$$
$$\dot{m}_w = 0.940 \; \text{kg/s}$$

From App. 35.B, the density of water at 74°C is approximately 976 kg/m³. The water volume flow rate is

$$\dot{V}_w = \left(\frac{\dot{m}}{\rho}\right) = \left(0.940 \ \frac{\text{kg}}{\text{s}}\right)\left(976 \ \frac{\text{kg}}{\text{m}^3}\right)\left(1000 \ \frac{\text{L}}{\text{m}^3}\right)$$

$$= \boxed{0.963 \ \text{L/s}}$$

3. *Customary U.S. Solution*

The mass of air is

$$m = \frac{p_1 V_1}{R T_1}$$

$$= \frac{\left(14.7 \ \frac{\text{lbf}}{\text{in}^2}\right)\left(144 \ \frac{\text{in}^2}{\text{ft}^2}\right)(8.0 \ \text{ft}^3)}{\left(53.3 \ \frac{\text{ft-lbf}}{\text{lbm-}^\circ\text{R}}\right)(180^\circ\text{F} + 460)}$$

$$= 0.4964 \ \text{lbm}$$

For a constant pressure process from Eq. 25.51, on a per unit mass basis,

$$W = R(T_2 - T_1)$$

The total work for m in lbm is

$$W = mR(T_2 - T_1)$$

$$= (0.4964 \ \text{lbm})\left(53.3 \ \frac{\text{ft-lbf}}{\text{lbm-}^\circ\text{R}}\right)(100^\circ\text{F} - 180^\circ\text{F})$$

$$= \boxed{-2116.6 \ \text{ft-lbf}}$$

This is negative because work is done by the system.

SI Solution

The mass of air is

$$m = \frac{p_1 V_1}{R T_1}$$

$$= \frac{(101.3 \ \text{kPa})\left(1000 \ \frac{\text{Pa}}{\text{kPa}}\right)(0.25 \ \text{m}^3)}{\left(287 \ \frac{\text{J}}{\text{kg·K}}\right)(82^\circ\text{C} + 273)}$$

$$= 0.2486 \ \text{kg}$$

For a constant pressure process from Eq. 25.51, on a per unit mass basis,

$$W = R(T_2 - T_1)$$

The total work for m in kg is

$$W = mR(T_2 - T_1)$$

$$= (0.2486 \ \text{kg})\left(287 \ \frac{\text{J}}{\text{kg·K}}\right)(38^\circ\text{C} - 82^\circ\text{C})$$

$$= \boxed{-3139.3 \ \text{J}}$$

4. *Customary U.S. Solution*

From App. 24.B, for 300 psia, the enthalpy of saturated liquid, h_f, is 394.1 Btu/lbm. The heat of vaporization, h_{fg}, is 809.8 Btu/lbm. The enthalpy is given by Eq. 24.40.

$$h_1 = h_f + x h_{fg}$$

$$= 394.1 \ \frac{\text{Btu}}{\text{lbm}} + (0.95)\left(809.8 \ \frac{\text{Btu}}{\text{lbm}}\right)$$

$$= 1163.4 \ \text{Btu/lbm}$$

From the Mollier diagram, for an isentropic process from 300 psia to 50 psia, $h_2 = 1031$ Btu/lbm.

The availability is calculated from Eq. 25.164 using an isentropic process ($s_1 = s_2$) for unit mass.

$$\text{availability} = h_1 - h_2$$

$$= 1163.4 \ \frac{\text{Btu}}{\text{lbm}} - 1031 \ \frac{\text{Btu}}{\text{lbm}}$$

$$= \boxed{132.4 \ \text{Btu/lbm}}$$

SI Solution

From App. 24.0, for 2 MPa, the enthalpy of saturated liquid, h_f, is 908.79 kJ/kg. The heat of vaporization, h_{fg}, is 1890.7 kJ/kg. The enthalpy is given by Eq. 24.40.

$$h_1 = h_f + x h_{fg}$$

$$= 908.79 \ \frac{\text{kJ}}{\text{kg}} + (0.95)\left(1890.7 \ \frac{\text{kJ}}{\text{kg}}\right)$$

$$= 2705.0 \ \text{kJ/kg}$$

From the Mollier diagram, for an isentropic process from 2 MPa to 0.35 MPa, $h_2 = 2405$ kJ/kg.

The availability is calculated from Eq. 25.164 using an isentropic process ($s_1 = s_2$) for unit mass.

$$\text{availability} = h_1 - h_2$$

$$= 2705 \ \frac{\text{kJ}}{\text{kg}} - 2405 \ \frac{\text{kJ}}{\text{kg}}$$

$$= \boxed{300 \ \text{kJ/kg}}$$

5. *Customary U.S. Solution*

The absolute temperature at the inlet of the air heater is

$$T_1 = 540°F + 460 = 1000°R$$

The absolute temperature at the outlet of the air heater is

$$T_2 = 1540°F + 460 = 2000°R$$

Since pressures are low and temperatures are high, use an air table.

From App. 24.F at 1000°R,

$$h_1 = 240.98 \text{ Btu/lbm}$$
$$\phi_1 = 0.75042 \text{ Btu/lbm-°R}$$

From App. 24.F at 2000°R,

$$h_2 = 504.71 \text{ Btu/lbm}$$
$$\phi_2 = 0.93205 \text{ Btu/lbm-°R}$$

The availability per unit mass is calculated from Eq. 25.164 using $T_L = 100°F + 460 = 560°R$.

$$W_{\max} = h_1 - h_2 + T_L(s_2 - s_1)$$

For no pressure drop,

$$s_2 - s_1 = \phi_2 - \phi_1$$
$$W_{\max} = h_1 - h_2 + T_L(\phi_2 - \phi_1)$$
$$= 240.98 \frac{\text{Btu}}{\text{lbm}} - 504.71 \frac{\text{Btu}}{\text{lbm}}$$
$$+ (560°R) \left(0.93205 \frac{\text{Btu}}{\text{lbm-°R}} \right.$$
$$\left. -0.75042 \frac{\text{Btu}}{\text{lbm-°R}} \right)$$
$$= -162.02 \text{ Btu/lbm}$$

With a pressure drop from 100 psia to 80 psia,

$$s_2 - s_1 = \phi_2 - \phi_1 - \left(\frac{R}{J}\right) \ln\left(\frac{p_2}{p_1}\right)$$

$$W_{\max,p \text{ loss}} = h_1 - h_2 + T_L \left[\phi_2 - \phi_1 \right.$$
$$\left. -\left(\frac{R}{J}\right) \ln\left(\frac{p_2}{p_1}\right) \right]$$
$$= 240.98 \frac{\text{Btu}}{\text{lbm}} - 504.71 \frac{\text{Btu}}{\text{lbm}} + (560°R)$$

$$\times \left[0.93205 \frac{\text{Btu}}{\text{lbm-°R}} - 0.75042 \frac{\text{Btu}}{\text{lbm-°R}} \right.$$
$$\left. - \left(\frac{53.3 \frac{\text{ft-lbf}}{\text{lbm-°R}}}{778 \frac{\text{ft-lbf}}{\text{Btu}}} \right) \ln\left(\frac{80 \text{ psia}}{100 \text{ psia}} \right) \right]$$
$$= -153.46 \text{ Btu/lbm}$$

The percentage loss in available energy is

$$\frac{W_{\max} - W_{\max,p \text{ loss}}}{W_{\max}} \times 100\%$$

$$= \frac{-162.02 \frac{\text{Btu}}{\text{lbm}} - \left(-153.46 \frac{\text{Btu}}{\text{lbm}} \right)}{-162.02 \frac{\text{Btu}}{\text{lbm}}} \times 100\%$$

$$= \boxed{5.28\%}$$

SI Solution

The absolute temerature at the inlet of the air heater is

$$T_1 = 280°C + 273 = 553K$$

The absolute temperature at the outlet of the air heater is

$$T_2 = 840°C + 273 = 1113K$$

Since pressures are low and temperatures are high, use an air table.

From App. 24.S at 553K,

$$h_1 = 557.9 \text{ kJ/kg}$$
$$\phi_1 = 2.32372 \text{ kJ/kg·K}$$

From App. 24.S at 1113K,

$$h_2 = 1176.2 \text{ kJ/kg}$$
$$\phi_2 = 3.09092 \text{ kJ/kg·K}$$

The availability per unit mass is calculated from Eq. 25.164 using $T_L = 40°C + 273 = 313K$.

$$W_{\max} = h_1 - h_2 + T_L(s_2 - s_1)$$

For no pressure drop,

$$s_2 - s_1 = \phi_2 - \phi_1$$
$$W_{\max} = h_1 - h_2 + T_L(\phi_2 - \phi_1)$$
$$= 557.9 \frac{\text{kJ}}{\text{kg}} - 1176.2 \frac{\text{kJ}}{\text{kg}}$$
$$+ (313K) \left(3.09092 \frac{\text{kJ}}{\text{kg·K}} - 2.32372 \frac{\text{kJ}}{\text{kg·K}} \right)$$
$$= -378.17 \text{ kJ/kg}$$

With a pressure drop from 700 kPa to 550 kPa,

$$s_2 - s_1 = \phi_2 - \phi_1 - R \ln \left(\frac{p_2}{p_1} \right)$$

$$W_{\text{max},p \text{ loss}} = h_1 - h_2$$
$$+ T_L \left[\phi_2 - \phi_1 - R \ln \left(\frac{p_2}{p_1} \right) \right]$$
$$= 557.9 \ \frac{\text{kJ}}{\text{kg}} - 1176.2 \ \frac{\text{kJ}}{\text{kg}}$$
$$+ (313\text{K}) \left[3.09092 \ \frac{\text{kJ}}{\text{kg·K}} - 2.32372 \ \frac{\text{kJ}}{\text{kg·K}} \right.$$
$$\left. - \left(\frac{287 \ \frac{\text{J}}{\text{kg·K}}}{1000 \ \frac{\text{J}}{\text{kJ}}} \right) \ln \left(\frac{550 \ \text{kPa}}{700 \ \text{kPa}} \right) \right]$$
$$= -356.50 \ \text{kJ/kg}$$

The percentage loss in available energy is

$$\frac{W_{\text{max}} - W_{\text{max},p \text{ loss}}}{W_{\text{max}}} \times 100\%$$

$$= \frac{-378.17 \ \frac{\text{kJ}}{\text{kg}} - \left(-356.50 \ \frac{\text{kJ}}{\text{kg}} \right)}{-378.17 \ \frac{\text{kJ}}{\text{kg}}} \times 100\%$$

$$= \boxed{5.73\%}$$

6. *Customary U.S. Solution*

(a) Assume the tank is originally at 70°F. The absolute temperature is

$$T = 70°\text{F} + 460 = 530°\text{R}$$

From Table 24.7, $R = 11.77$ ft-lbf/lbm-°R. From Eq. 24.47,

$$m = \frac{pV}{RT}$$
$$= \frac{\left(20 \ \frac{\text{lbf}}{\text{in}^2} \right) \left(144 \ \frac{\text{in}^2}{\text{ft}^2} \right) (100 \ \text{ft}^3)}{\left(11.77 \ \frac{\text{ft-lbf}}{\text{lbm-°R}} \right) (530°\text{R})}$$
$$= \boxed{46.17 \ \text{lbm}}$$

(b) From Table 24.4, the critical temperature and pressure of xenon are 521.9°R and 58.2 atm, respectively.

The reduced variables are

$$T_r = \frac{T}{T_c} = \frac{530°\text{R}}{521.9°\text{R}} = 1.02$$

$$p_r = \frac{p}{p_c} = \frac{3800 \ \text{psia}}{(58.2 \ \text{atm}) \left(14.7 \ \frac{\text{psia}}{\text{atm}} \right)} = 4.44$$

From App. 24.Z, z is read as 0.61. Using Eq. 24.93,

$$m = \frac{pV}{zRT} = \frac{\left(3800 \ \frac{\text{lbf}}{\text{in}^2} \right) \left(144 \ \frac{\text{in}^2}{\text{ft}^2} \right) (100 \ \text{ft}^3)}{(0.61) \left(11.77 \ \frac{\text{ft-lbf}}{\text{lbm-°R}} \right) (530°\text{R})}$$
$$= 14{,}380 \ \text{lbm}$$

The average mass flow rate of xenon is

$$\dot{m} = \frac{14{,}380 \ \text{lbm} - 46.17 \ \text{lbm}}{1 \ \text{hr}}$$
$$= \boxed{14{,}334 \ \text{lbm/hr}}$$

(c) For isothermal compression, the work per unit mass is calculated from Eq. 25.79.

$$W = mRT \ln \left(\frac{p_1}{p_2} \right)$$

$$= \frac{(14{,}334 \ \text{lbm}) \left(11.77 \ \frac{\text{ft-lbf}}{\text{lbm-°R}} \right)}{\left(778 \ \frac{\text{ft-lbf}}{\text{Btu}} \right) \left(3413 \ \frac{\text{Btu}}{\text{kW}} \right)}$$
$$\quad \times (530°\text{R}) \ln \left(\frac{20 \ \text{psia}}{3800 \ \text{psia}} \right)$$

$$= -176.7 \ \text{kW-hr} \quad \text{(for 1 hr)}$$

The cost of electricity is

$$\left(\frac{\$0.045}{\text{kW-hr}} \right) (176.7 \ \text{kW-hr}) = \boxed{\$7.95}$$

SI Solution

(a) Assume the tank is originally at 21°C. The absolute temperature is

$$T = 21°\text{C} + 273 = 294\text{K}$$

From Table 24.7, $R = 63.32$ J/kg·K. From Eq. 24.47,

$$m = \frac{pV}{RT}$$

$$= \frac{(150 \ \text{kPa}) \left(1000 \ \frac{\text{Pa}}{\text{kPa}} \right) (3 \ \text{m}^3)}{\left(63.32 \ \frac{\text{J}}{\text{kg·K}} \right) (294\text{K})}$$

$$= \boxed{24.17 \ \text{kg}}$$

(b) From Table 24.4, the critical temperature and pressure of xenon are 289.9K and 58.2 atm, respectively. The reduced variables are

$$T_r = \frac{T}{T_c} = \frac{294K}{289.9K} = 1.01$$

$$p_r = \frac{p}{p_c} = \frac{25 \text{ MPa}}{(58.2 \text{ atm})\left(0.1013 \dfrac{\text{MPa}}{\text{atm}}\right)} = 4.24$$

From App. 24.Z, z is read as 0.59. Using Eq. 24.93,

$$m = \frac{pV}{zRT}$$

$$= \frac{(25 \text{ MPa})\left(10^6 \dfrac{\text{Pa}}{\text{MPa}}\right)(3 \text{ m}^3)}{(0.59)\left(63.32 \dfrac{\text{J}}{\text{kg·K}}\right)(294K)}$$

$$= 6.828 \text{ kg}$$

The average mass flow rate of xenon is

$$\dot{m} = \frac{6828 \text{ kg} - 24.17 \text{ kg}}{(1 \text{ h})\left(3600 \dfrac{\text{s}}{\text{h}}\right)}$$

$$= \boxed{1.89 \text{ kg/s}}$$

(c) For isothermal compression, the work per unit mass is calculated from Eq. 25.79.

$$W = mRT \ln\left(\frac{p_1}{p_2}\right)$$

$$= (6828 \text{ kg} - 24.17 \text{ kg})\left(63.32 \dfrac{\text{J}}{\text{kg·K}}\right)(294K)$$

$$\times \ln\left(\frac{150 \text{ kPa}}{(25 \text{ MPa})\left(1000 \dfrac{\text{kPa}}{\text{MPa}}\right)}\right)$$

$$\times \left(\frac{1 \text{ kJ}}{1000 \text{ J}}\right)\left(\frac{1 \text{ h}}{3600 \text{ s}}\right)$$

$$= -180 \text{ kW·h}$$

The cost of electricity is

$$\left(\frac{\$0.045}{\text{kW·h}}\right)(180 \text{ kW·h}) = \boxed{\$8.10}$$

7. Choose the control volume to include the air outside the tank that is pushed into the tank (subscript "e" for "entering"), as well as the tank volume.

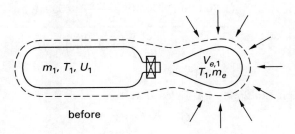

before

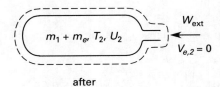

after

Customary U.S. Solution

The absolute temperature of the air in the tank when evacuated is

$$T_1 = 70°\text{F} + 460 = 530°\text{R}$$

From Table 24.7, $R = 53.3$ ft-lbf/lbm-°R. From Eq. 24.47,

$$m = \frac{p_1 V_1}{RT_1}$$

$$= \frac{\left(1 \dfrac{\text{lbf}}{\text{in}^2}\right)\left(144 \dfrac{\text{in}^2}{\text{ft}^2}\right)(20 \text{ ft}^3)}{\left(53.3 \dfrac{\text{ft-lbf}}{\text{lbm-°R}}\right)(530°\text{R})}$$

$$= 0.102 \text{ lbm}$$

Assume $T_2 = 80°$F. The absolute temperature is

$$T_2 = 80°\text{F} + 460 = 540°\text{R}$$

From Eq. 24.47,

$$m_2 = m_1 + m_e$$

$$= \frac{p_2 V_2}{RT_2}$$

$$= \frac{\left(14.7 \dfrac{\text{lbf}}{\text{in}^2}\right)\left(144 \dfrac{\text{in}^2}{\text{ft}^2}\right)(20 \text{ ft}^3)}{\left(53.3 \dfrac{\text{ft-lbf}}{\text{lbm-°R}}\right)(540°\text{R})}$$

$$m_1 + m_e \approx 1.471 \text{ lbm}$$

$$m_e \approx 1.471 \text{ lbm} - m_1$$

$$= 1.471 \text{ lbm} - 0.102 \text{ lbm}$$

$$= 1.369 \text{ lbm}$$

From Eq. 24.47, the initial volume of the external air is

$$V_{e,1} = \frac{mRT}{p}$$

$$= \frac{(1.369 \text{ lbm})\left(53.3 \frac{\text{ft-lbf}}{\text{lbm-}°\text{R}}\right)(530°\text{R})}{\left(14.7 \frac{\text{lbf}}{\text{in}^2}\right)\left(144 \frac{\text{in}^2}{\text{ft}^2}\right)}$$

$$= 18.27 \text{ ft}^3$$

From Eq. 25.23, for a closed system,

$$Q = \Delta U + W$$

For an adiabatic system, $Q = 0$.

$$W_{\text{ext}} = \Delta U$$

For a constant pressure, closed system, from Eq. 25.50,

$$W_{\text{ext}} = p(v_{e,2} - v_{e,1})$$

$$= \frac{\left(14.7 \frac{\text{lbf}}{\text{in}^2}\right)\left(144 \frac{\text{in}^2}{\text{ft}^2}\right)(0 - 18.27 \text{ ft}^3)}{778 \frac{\text{ft-lbf}}{\text{Btu}}}$$

$$= -49.71 \text{ Btu} \quad \begin{bmatrix} \text{surroundings do work} \\ \text{on the system} \end{bmatrix}$$

This energy is used to raise the temperature of air and the tank material. Consider air as an ideal gas.

$$W_{\text{ext}} = ((m_1 + m_e)c_v + m_{\text{tank}}c_p)(T_1 - T_2)$$

$$-49.71 \text{ Btu} = \left((1.471 \text{ lbm})\left(0.171 \frac{\text{Btu}}{\text{lbm-}°\text{F}}\right)\right.$$

$$\left. + (40 \text{ lbm})\left(0.11 \frac{\text{Btu}}{\text{lbm-}°\text{F}}\right)\right)$$

$$\times (70°\text{F} - T_2)$$

$$T_2 = \boxed{80.7°\text{F}}$$

This is close enough to the assumed value of T_2 that a second iteration is not required.

SI Solution

The absolute temperature of the air in the tank when evacuated is

$$T_1 = 21°\text{C} + 273 = 294\text{K}$$

From Table 24.7, $R = 287$ J/kg·K. From Eq. 24.47,

$$m = \frac{p_1 V_1}{RT_1}$$

$$= \frac{(7 \text{ kPa})\left(1000 \frac{\text{Pa}}{\text{kPa}}\right)(0.6 \text{ m}^3)}{\left(287 \frac{\text{J}}{\text{kg·K}}\right)(294\text{K})}$$

$$= 0.0498 \text{ kg}$$

Assume $T_2 = 27°\text{C}$. The absolute temperature is

$$T_2 = 27°\text{C} + 273 = 300\text{K}$$

From Eq. 24.47,

$$m_2 = m_1 + m_e = \frac{p_2 V_2}{RT_2}$$

$$= \frac{(101.3 \text{ kPa})\left(1000 \frac{\text{Pa}}{\text{kPa}}\right)(0.6 \text{ m}^3)}{\left(287 \frac{\text{J}}{\text{kg·K}}\right)(300\text{K})}$$

$$= 0.7059 \text{ kg}$$

$$m_e \approx 0.7059 \text{ kg} - m_1$$

$$= 0.7059 \text{ kg} - 0.0498 \text{ kg}$$

$$= 0.6561 \text{ kg}$$

From Eq. 24.47, the initial volume of the external air is

$$V_{e,1} = \frac{mRT}{p}$$

$$= \frac{(0.6561 \text{ kg})\left(287 \frac{\text{J}}{\text{kg·K}}\right)(294\text{K})}{(101.3 \text{ kPa})\left(1000 \frac{\text{Pa}}{\text{kPa}}\right)}$$

$$= 0.5465 \text{ m}^3$$

From Eq. 25.23, for a closed system,

$$Q = \Delta U + W$$

For an adiabatic system, $Q = 0$.

$$W_{\text{ext}} = \Delta U$$

For a constant pressure, closed system, from Eq. 25.50,

$$W_{\text{ext}} = p(v_{e,2} - v_{e,1})$$

$$= (101.3 \text{ kPa})\left(1000 \frac{\text{Pa}}{\text{kPa}}\right)(0 - 0.5465 \text{ m}^3)$$

$$= -55\,360 \text{ J} \quad \begin{bmatrix} \text{surroundings do work} \\ \text{on the system} \end{bmatrix}$$

This energy is used to raise the temperature of air and the tank material. Consider air as an ideal gas.

$$W_{\text{ext}} = ((m_1 + m_e)c_v + m_{\text{tank}}c_p)(T_1 - T_2)$$

$$-55\,360 \text{ J} = \left((0.7059 \text{ kg})\left(718 \frac{\text{J}}{\text{kg·K}}\right)\right.$$

$$+ (20 \text{ kg})\left(0.46 \frac{\text{kJ}}{\text{kg·K}}\right)$$

$$\left. \times \left(1000 \frac{\text{J}}{\text{kJ}}\right)(21°\text{C} - T_2)\right)$$

$$T_2 = \boxed{26.7°\text{C}}$$

This is close enough to the assumed value of T_2 that a second iteration is not necessary.

26 Compressible Fluid Dynamics

1. *Customary U.S. Solution*

(a)

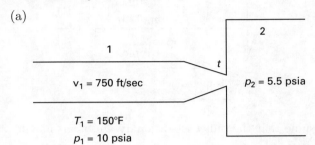

$$T_1 = 150°F + 460$$
$$= 610°R$$

The entrance Mach number is given by Eq. 26.4(b) as

$$M_1 = \frac{v_1}{a_1} = \frac{v_1}{\sqrt{\dfrac{kg_c R^* T_1}{(MW)}}}$$

$$= \frac{750 \; \dfrac{ft}{sec}}{\sqrt{\dfrac{(1.4)\left(32.2 \; \dfrac{lbm\text{-}ft}{lbf\text{-}sec^2}\right) \times \left(1545 \; \dfrac{ft\text{-}lbf}{lbmol\text{-}°R}\right)(610°R)}{29.0 \; \dfrac{lbm}{lbmol}}}}$$

$$= \boxed{0.62}$$

(b) From the M = 0.62 line in App. 26.A, the following factors can be read.

$$\frac{T_1}{T_0} = 0.9286$$

$$\frac{p_1}{p_0} = 0.7716$$

$$T_0 = \frac{T_1}{0.9286} = \frac{610°R}{0.9286} = 656.9°R$$

$$p_0 = \frac{p_1}{0.7716} = \frac{10 \; psia}{0.7716} = 12.96 \; psia$$

$$\frac{p_2}{p_0} = \frac{5.5 \; psia}{12.96 \; psia} = 0.424$$

The critical pressure ratio for air is 0.5283. Since $p_2/p_0 < 0.5283$, the flow is choked and the Mach number at the throat is $M_t = 1$. From App. 26.A, for M = 1,

$$\frac{p}{p_0} = 0.5283$$

$$\frac{T}{T_0} = 0.8333$$

$$p = (0.5283)p_0 = (0.5283)(12.96 \; psia)$$

$$= \boxed{6.85 \; psia}$$

(c) $\qquad T = (0.8333)T_0 = (0.8333)(656.9°R)$

$$= \boxed{547.4°R}$$

SI Solution

(a)

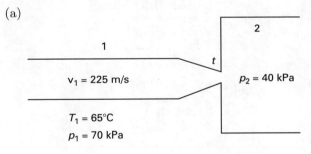

$$T_1 = 65°C + 273 = 338K$$

The entrance Mach number is given by Eq. 26.4(a) as

$$M_1 = \frac{v_1}{\sqrt{\dfrac{kR^* T}{(MW)}}}$$

$$= \frac{225 \; \dfrac{m}{s}}{\sqrt{\dfrac{(1.4)\left(8314 \; \dfrac{J}{kmol\cdot k}\right)(338K)}{29.0 \; \dfrac{kg}{kmol}}}}$$

$$= \boxed{0.61}$$

Thermodynamics

(b) From the M = 0.61 line in App. 26.A, the following factors can be read.

$$\frac{T_1}{T_0} = 0.9307$$

$$\frac{p_1}{p_0} = 0.7778$$

$$T_0 = \frac{T_1}{0.9307} = \frac{338.2\text{K}}{0.9307}$$

$$= 363.4\text{K}$$

$$p_0 = \frac{p_1}{0.7778} = \frac{70 \text{ kPa}}{0.7778}$$

$$= 90.0 \text{ kPa}$$

$$\frac{p_2}{p_0} = \frac{40 \text{ kPa}}{90.0 \text{ kPa}} = 0.444$$

The critical pressure ratio for air is 0.5283. Since $p_2/p_0 < 0.5283$, the flow is choked and the Mach number at the throat is $M_t = 1$. From App. 26.A, for M = 1,

$$\frac{p}{p_0} = 0.5283$$

$$\frac{T}{T_0} = 0.8333$$

$$p = (0.5283)p_0$$

$$= (0.5283)(90.0 \text{ kPa})$$

$$= \boxed{47.5 \text{ kPa}}$$

$$T = (0.8333)T_0$$

(c)
$$= (0.8333)(363.4\text{K})$$

$$= \boxed{302.8\text{K}}$$

2. *Customary U.S. Solution*

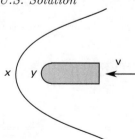

$$T_x = 32°\text{F} + 460$$

$$= 492°\text{R}$$

$$p_x = 14.7 \text{ psia}$$

(a) Using Eq. 26.4(b), the Mach number at y is

$$M = \frac{v}{\sqrt{\dfrac{kg_cR^*T}{(\text{MW})}}}$$

$$= \frac{2000 \dfrac{\text{ft}}{\text{sec}}}{\sqrt{\dfrac{(1.4)\left(32.2 \dfrac{\text{lbm-ft}}{\text{lbf-sec}^2}\right) \times \left(1545 \dfrac{\text{ft-lbf}}{\text{lbmol-°R}}\right)(492°\text{R})}{29.0 \dfrac{\text{lbm}}{\text{lbmol}}}}}$$

$$= 1.84 \quad \boxed{[\text{supersonic}]}$$

Assume that the bullet is stationary and air is moving at M = 1.84.

(b) The ratio of static pressure before the shock to the total pressure after the shock is read from the normal shock table (App. 26.B) for $M_x = 1.84$ (interpolation).

$$\frac{p_x}{p_{0,y}} = 0.2060$$

Therefore, the stagnation pressure is

$$p_{0,y} = \frac{p_x}{0.2060} = \frac{14.7 \text{ psia}}{0.2060}$$

$$= \boxed{71.36 \text{ psia}}$$

(c) The ratio of static temperature before the shock to the total temperature after the shock is read from the normal shock table (App. 26.B) for $M_x = 1.84$ (interpolation).

$$\frac{T_x}{T_0} = 0.5963$$

Therefore, the stagnation temperature is

$$T_0 = \frac{T_x}{0.5963} = \frac{492°\text{R}}{0.5963}$$

$$= \boxed{825.1°\text{R}}$$

Since the shock wave is adiabatic, T_0 remains constant.

(d) The enthalpy at the bullet face from the air tables is $h \approx \boxed{197.9 \text{ Btu/lbm.}}$

SI Solution

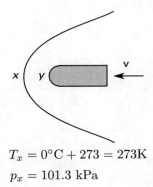

$$T_x = 0°C + 273 = 273K$$
$$p_x = 101.3 \text{ kPa}$$

(a) Using Eq. 26.4(a), the Mach number at y is

$$M = \frac{v}{\sqrt{\frac{kR^*T}{(MW)}}}$$

$$= \frac{600 \ \frac{m}{s}}{\sqrt{\frac{(1.4)\left(8314 \ \frac{J}{\text{kmol·K}}\right)(273K)}{29.0 \ \frac{\text{kg}}{\text{kmol}}}}}$$

$$= 1.81 \ \boxed{[\text{supersonic}]}$$

Assume that the bullet is stationary and air is moving at M = 1.81.

(b) The ratio of static pressure before the shock to the total pressure after the shock is read from the normal shock table (App. 26.B) for $M_x = 1.81$ (interpolation).

$$\frac{p_x}{p_{0,y}} = 0.2122$$

Therefore, the stagnation pressure is

$$p_{0,y} = \frac{p_x}{0.2122} = \frac{101.3 \text{ kPa}}{0.2122} = \boxed{477.4 \text{ kPa}}$$

(c) The ratio of static temperature before the shock to the total temperature after the shock is read from the normal shock table (App. 26.B) for $M_x = 1.81$ (interpolation).

$$\frac{T_x}{T_0} = 0.6042$$

Therefore, the stagnation temperature is

$$T_0 = \frac{T_x}{0.6042} = \frac{273K}{0.6042} = \boxed{451.8K}$$

Since the shock wave is adiabatic, T_0 remains constant.

(d) Enthalpy at the bullet face from air tables is $h \approx$

$$\boxed{454.0 \text{ kJ/kg.}}$$

3. *Customary U.S. Solution*

(a) The absolute total temperature is

$$T_0 = 240°F + 460 = 700°R$$

The total density of the air is

$$\rho_0 = \frac{p_0}{RT_0}$$

$$= \frac{\left(160 \ \frac{\text{lbf}}{\text{in}^2}\right)\left(144 \ \frac{\text{in}^2}{\text{ft}^2}\right)}{\left(53.3 \ \frac{\text{ft-lbf}}{\text{lbm-°R}}\right)(700°R)}$$

$$= 0.6175 \text{ lbm/ft}^3$$

$$\frac{p_{\text{back}}}{p_0} = \frac{20 \text{ psia}}{160 \text{ psia}}$$

$$= 0.125$$

Since $p_{\text{back}}/p_0 < 0.5283$, the nozzle is supersonic and the throat flow is sonic. So, $\boxed{M = 1}$ at throat.

(b) Read the property ratios for Mach 1 from the isentropic flow table: $[T/T_0] = 0.8333$ and $[\rho/\rho_0] = 0.6339$. The sonic properties at the throat are

$$T^* = \left[\frac{T}{T_0}\right] T_0 = (0.8333)(700°R)$$

$$= 583.3°R$$

$$\rho^* = \left[\frac{\rho}{\rho_0}\right] \rho_0 = (0.6339)\left(0.6175 \ \frac{\text{lbm}}{\text{ft}^3}\right)$$

$$= 0.3914 \text{ lbm/ft}^3$$

The sonic velocity at the throat is

$$a^* = \sqrt{kg_cRT^*}$$

$$= \sqrt{\frac{(1.4)\left(32.2 \ \frac{\text{ft-lbm}}{\text{lbf-sec}^2}\right)}{\times \left(53.3 \ \frac{\text{ft-lbf}}{\text{lbm-°R}}\right)(583.3°R)}}$$

$$= 1183.9 \text{ ft/sec}$$

The throat area is

$$A^* = \frac{\dot{m}}{\rho^* a^*}$$

$$= \frac{4.5 \ \frac{\text{lbm}}{\text{sec}}}{\left(0.3914 \ \frac{\text{lbm}}{\text{ft}^3}\right)\left(1183.9 \ \frac{\text{ft}}{\text{sec}}\right)}$$

$$= \boxed{0.00971 \text{ ft}^2}$$

Thermodynamics

(c) At the exit,

$$\frac{p_e}{p_0} = \frac{20 \text{ psia}}{160 \text{ psia}} = 0.125$$

Searching the $[p/p_0]$ column of the isentropic flow tables for this value gives $\boxed{\text{M} \approx 2.01.}$

(d) The corresponding ratio is $[A/A^*] = 1.7024$.

$$A_e = \left[\frac{A_e}{A^*}\right] A^*$$
$$= (1.7024)(0.00971 \text{ ft}^2)$$
$$= \boxed{0.01653 \text{ ft}^2}$$

SI Solution

(a) The absolute total temperature is

$$T_0 = 120°C + 273 = 393K$$

The total density of the air is

$$\rho_0 = \frac{p_0}{RT_0}$$
$$= \frac{(1.1 \text{ MPa})\left(10^6 \frac{\text{Pa}}{\text{MPa}}\right)}{\left(287 \frac{\text{J}}{\text{kg·K}}\right)(393K)}$$
$$= 9.753 \text{ kg/m}^3$$

$$\frac{p_{\text{back}}}{p_0} = \frac{140 \text{ kPa}}{(1.1 \text{ MPa})\left(10^3 \frac{\text{kPa}}{\text{MPa}}\right)} = 0.127$$

Since $p_{\text{back}}/p_0 < 0.5283$, the nozzle is supersonic and the throat flow is sonic. So, $\boxed{\text{M} = 1}$ at throat.

(b) Read the property ratios for Mach 1 from the isentropic flow table: $[T/T_0] = 0.8333$ and $[\rho/\rho_0] = 0.6339$. The sonic properties at the throat are

$$T^* = \left[\frac{T}{T_0}\right] T_0 = (0.8333)(393K) = 327.5K$$
$$\rho^* = \left[\frac{\rho}{\rho_0}\right] \rho_0 = (0.6339)\left(9.753 \frac{\text{kg}}{\text{m}^3}\right)$$
$$= 6.182 \text{ kg/m}^3$$

The sonic velocity at the throat is

$$a^* = \sqrt{kRT^*}$$
$$= \sqrt{(1.4)\left(287 \frac{\text{J}}{\text{kg·K}}\right)(327.5K)}$$
$$= 362.8 \text{ m/sec}$$

The throat area is

$$A^* = \frac{\dot{m}}{\rho^* a^*}$$
$$= \frac{2 \frac{\text{kg}}{\text{s}}}{\left(6.182 \frac{\text{kg}}{\text{m}^3}\right)\left(362.8 \frac{\text{m}}{\text{s}}\right)}$$
$$= \boxed{8.92 \times 10^{-4} \text{ m}^2}$$

(c) At the exit,

$$\frac{p_e}{p_0} = \frac{140 \text{ kPa}}{(1.1 \text{ MPa})\left(10^3 \frac{\text{kPa}}{\text{MPa}}\right)} = 0.127$$

Searching the $[p/p_0]$ column of the isentropic flow tables for this value gives $\boxed{\text{M} \approx 2.00.}$

(d) The corresponding ratio is $[A/A^*] = 1.6875$.

$$A_e = \left[\frac{A_e}{A^*}\right] A^*$$
$$= (1.6875)(8.92 \times 10^{-4} \text{ m}^2)$$
$$= \boxed{1.505 \times 10^{-3} \text{ m}^2}$$

4. *Customary U.S. Solution*

(This solution is for a wedge with a 20° semivertex angle.)

The absolute total temperature is

$$T_0 = 60°F + 460 = 520°R$$

The sonic velocity is

$$a = \sqrt{kg_c RT_0}$$
$$= \sqrt{\begin{array}{c}(1.4)\left(32.2 \frac{\text{ft-lbm}}{\text{lbf-sec}^2}\right)\\ \times \left(53.3 \frac{\text{ft-lbf}}{\text{lbm-°R}}\right)(520°R)\end{array}}$$
$$= 1117.8 \text{ ft/sec}$$

The Mach number is

$$\text{M} = \frac{\text{v}}{a} = \frac{2700 \frac{\text{ft}}{\text{sec}}}{1117.8 \frac{\text{ft}}{\text{sec}}} = 2.42$$

From Fig. 26.3, $\boxed{\theta \approx 46°.}$

SI Solution

(This solution is for a wedge with a 20° semivertex angle.)

The absolute total temperature is

$$T_0 = 16°C + 273 = 289K$$

The sonic velocity is

$$a = \sqrt{kRT_0}$$

$$= \sqrt{(1.4)\left(287\ \frac{J}{kg\cdot K}\right)(289K)}$$

$$= 340.8\ m/s$$

The Mach number is

$$M = \frac{v}{a} = \frac{800\ \frac{m}{s}}{340.8\ \frac{m}{s}} = 2.35$$

From Fig. 26.3, $\boxed{\theta \approx 46°.}$

5. *Customary U.S. Solution*

(a) The absolute total temperature is

$$T_0 = 80°F + 460 = 540°R$$

The total pressure is $p_0 = 100$ psia.

From the isentropic flow tables at M = 2, $[p/p_0] = 0.1278$, $[T/T_0] = 0.5556$, and $[A/A^*] = 1.6875$.

The properties at Mach 2 are

$$T = \left[\frac{T}{T_0}\right]T_0 = (0.5556)(540°R) = \boxed{300°R}$$

$$p = \left[\frac{p}{p_0}\right]p_0 = (0.1278)(100\ \text{psia}) = 12.78\ \text{psia}$$

(b) $A = \left[\dfrac{A}{A^*}\right]A^* = (1.6875)(1\ \text{in}^2) = \boxed{1.6875\ \text{in}^2}$

(c) $a = \sqrt{kg_cRT}$

$$= \sqrt{\begin{array}{l}(1.4)\left(32.2\ \dfrac{\text{ft-lbm}}{\text{lbf-sec}^2}\right) \\ \times \left(53.3\ \dfrac{\text{ft-lbf}}{\text{lbm-°R}}\right)(300°R)\end{array}}$$

$$= 849\ \text{ft/sec}$$

$$v = Ma = (2)\left(849\ \frac{ft}{sec}\right)$$

$$= 1698\ ft/sec$$

$$\rho = \frac{p}{RT}$$

$$= \frac{\left(12.78\ \dfrac{lbf}{in^2}\right)\left(144\ \dfrac{in^2}{ft^2}\right)}{\left(53.3\ \dfrac{ft\text{-}lbf}{lbm\text{-}°R}\right)(300°R)}$$

$$= 0.1151\ lbm/ft^3$$

$$\dot{m} = \rho A v$$

$$= \left(0.1151\ \frac{lbm}{ft^3}\right)(1.6875\ in^2)\left(\frac{1\ ft^2}{144\ in^2}\right)$$

$$\times \left(1698\ \frac{ft}{sec}\right)$$

$$= \boxed{2.29\ lbm/sec}$$

SI Solution

(a) The absolute total temperature is

$$T_0 = 27°C + 273 = 300K$$

The total pressure is

$$p_0 = (0.7\ \text{MPa})\left(10^6\ \frac{Pa}{MPa}\right) = 7 \times 10^5\ Pa$$

From the isentropic flow table at M = 2, $[p/p_0] = 0.1278$, $[T/T_0] = 0.5556$, and $[A/A^*] = 1.6875$.

The properties at Mach 2 are

$$T = \left[\frac{T}{T_0}\right]T_0 = (0.5556)(300K) = \boxed{166.7K}$$

$$p = \left[\frac{p}{p_0}\right]p_0 = (0.1278)(7 \times 10^5\ Pa) = 89\,460\ Pa$$

(b) $A = \left[\dfrac{A}{A^*}\right]A^* = (1.6875)(6.45 \times 10^{-4}\ m^2)$

$$= \boxed{0.00109\ m^2}$$

(c) $a = \sqrt{kRT}$

$$= \sqrt{(1.4)\left(287\ \frac{J}{kg\cdot K}\right)(166.7K)}$$

$$= 258.8\ m/s$$

$$v = Ma = (2)\left(258.8\ \frac{m}{s}\right)$$

$$= 517.6\ m/s$$

$$\rho = \frac{p}{RT}$$

$$= \frac{89\,460 \text{ Pa}}{\left(287 \ \frac{\text{J}}{\text{kg·K}}\right)(166.7\text{K})}$$

$$= 1.870 \text{ kg/m}^3$$

$$\dot{m} = \rho A v$$

$$= \left(1.870 \ \frac{\text{kg}}{\text{m}^3}\right)(0.00109 \text{ m}^2)\left(517.6 \ \frac{\text{m}}{\text{s}}\right)$$

$$= \boxed{1.055 \text{ kg/s}}$$

6. *Customary U.S. Solution*

From the normal shock table at $M_x = 2$,

$$M_y = 0.5744$$

$$\frac{T_y}{T_x} = 1.687$$

The properties behind the shock wave are

$$T_y = \left[\frac{T_y}{T_x}\right]T_x$$

$$= (1.687)(500°\text{R})$$

$$= 843.5°\text{R}$$

$$a_y = \sqrt{kg_cRT_y}$$

$$= \sqrt{\begin{array}{c}(1.4)\left(32.2 \ \frac{\text{ft-lbm}}{\text{lbf-sec}^2}\right) \\ \times \left(53.3 \ \frac{\text{ft-lbf}}{\text{lbm-°R}}\right)(843.5°\text{R})\end{array}}$$

$$= 1423.6 \text{ ft/sec}$$

$$v_y = M_y a_y$$

$$= (0.5744)\left(1423.6 \ \frac{\text{ft}}{\text{sec}}\right)$$

$$= \boxed{817.7 \text{ ft/sec}}$$

SI Solution

From the normal shock table at $M_x = 2$,

$$M_y = 0.5744$$

$$\frac{T_y}{T_x} = 1.687$$

The properties behind the shock wave are

$$T_y = \left(\frac{T_y}{T_x}\right)T_x = (1.687)(280\text{K}) = 472.4\text{K}$$

$$a_y = \sqrt{kRT_y}$$

$$= \sqrt{(1.4)\left(287 \ \frac{\text{J}}{\text{kg·K}}\right)(472.4\text{K})}$$

$$= 435.7 \text{ m/s}$$

$$v_y = M_y a_y = (0.5744)\left(435.7 \ \frac{\text{m}}{\text{s}}\right)$$

$$= \boxed{250.3 \text{ m/s}}$$

7. *Customary U.S. Solution*

(a) The absolute total temperature is

$$T_0 = 70°\text{F} + 460 = 530°\text{R}$$

The total pressure is $p_0 = 100$ psia.

The ratio of flow area to the critical throat area is

$$\frac{A}{A^*} = 1.555$$

From the isentropic flow tables at $A/A^* = 1.555$, $[p/p_0] = 0.1492$, $[T/T_0] = 0.5807$, and $\boxed{M = 1.90.}$

(b) The properties at $A/A^* = 1.555$ are

$$T = \left[\frac{T}{T_0}\right]T_0 = (0.5807)(530°\text{R}) = \boxed{307.8°\text{R}}$$

(c) $p = \left[\dfrac{p}{p_0}\right]p_0 = (0.1492)(100 \text{ psia}) = \boxed{14.92 \text{ psia}}$

SI Solution

(a) The absolute total temperature is

$$T_0 = 21°\text{C} + 273 = 294\text{K}$$

The total pressure is $p_0 = 0.7$ MPa.

The ratio of flow area to the critical throat area is

$$\frac{A}{A^*} = 1.555$$

From the isentropic flow tables at $A/A^* = 1.555$, $[p/p_0] = 0.1492$, $[T/T_0] = 0.5807$, and $\boxed{M = 1.90.}$

(b) The properties at $A/A^* = 1.555$ are

$$T = \left[\frac{T}{T_0}\right]T_0 = (0.5807)(294\text{K}) = \boxed{170.7\text{K}}$$

(c) $p = \left[\dfrac{p}{p_0}\right]p_0 = (0.1492)(0.7 \text{ MPa}) = \boxed{0.104 \text{ MPa}}$

8. *Customary U.S. Solution*

The absolute total temperature is

$$T_0 = 40°F + 460 = 500°R$$

Since v is unknown, assume that static temperature is 500°R. An iterative process may be required for this problem.

The density of air is

$$\rho = \frac{p}{RT}$$

$$= \frac{\left(10 \ \frac{lbf}{in^2}\right)\left(144 \ \frac{in^2}{ft^2}\right)}{\left(53.3 \ \frac{ft\text{-}lbf}{lbm\text{-}°R}\right)(500°R)}$$

$$= 0.054 \ lbm/ft^3$$

The velocity of air is

$$v = \frac{\dot{m}}{A\rho}$$

$$= \frac{20 \ \frac{lbm}{sec}}{(1 \ ft^2)\left(0.054 \ \frac{lbm}{ft^3}\right)}$$

$$= 370.4 \ ft/sec$$

The sonic velocity is

$$a = \sqrt{kg_c RT}$$

$$= \sqrt{\begin{array}{c}(1.4)\left(32.2 \ \frac{ft\text{-}lbm}{lbf\text{-}sec^2}\right) \\ \times \left(53.3 \ \frac{ft\text{-}lbf}{lbm\text{-}°R}\right)(500°R)\end{array}}$$

$$= 1096.1 \ ft/sec$$

The Mach number is

$$M = \frac{v}{a}$$

$$= \frac{370.4 \ \frac{ft}{sec}}{1096.1 \ \frac{ft}{sec}}$$

$$= 0.338$$

From the isentropic flow tables at M = 0.338, $[T/T_0] =$ 0.9777. A closer approximation to static temperature is

$$T = \left[\frac{T}{T_0}\right]T_0 = (0.9777)(500°R)$$

$$= 488.9°R$$

Recalculate all the properties at $T = 488.9°R$.

$$\rho = \frac{p}{RT}$$

$$= \frac{\left(10 \ \frac{lbf}{in^2}\right)\left(144 \ \frac{in^2}{ft^2}\right)}{\left(53.3 \ \frac{ft\text{-}lbf}{lbm\text{-}°R}\right)(488.9°R)}$$

$$= 0.0553 \ lbm/ft^3$$

$$v = \frac{\dot{m}}{A\rho} = \frac{20 \ \frac{lbm}{sec}}{(1 \ ft^2)\left(0.0553 \ \frac{lbm}{ft^3}\right)}$$

$$= 361.7 \ ft/sec$$

$$a = \sqrt{kg_c RT}$$

$$= \sqrt{\begin{array}{c}(1.4)\left(32.2 \ \frac{ft\text{-}lbm}{lbf\text{-}sec^2}\right) \\ \times \left(53.3 \ \frac{ft\text{-}lbf}{lbm\text{-}°R}\right)(488.9°R)\end{array}}$$

$$= 1083.8 \ ft/sec$$

$$M = \frac{v}{a} = \frac{361.7 \ \frac{ft}{sec}}{1083.8 \ \frac{ft}{sec}} = 0.334$$

From the isentropic flow tables at M = 0.334, $[A/A^*] =$ 1.8516.

$$A_{smallest} = \left[\frac{A^*}{A}\right]A$$

$$= \left(\frac{1}{1.8516}\right)(1 \ ft^2)$$

$$= \boxed{0.540 \ ft^2}$$

SI Solution

The absolute total temperature is

$$T_0 = 4°C + 273 = 277K$$

Since v is unknown, assume that static temperature is 277K. An iterative process may be required for this problem.

The density of air is

$$\rho = \frac{p}{RT}$$

$$= \frac{(70 \ kPa)\left(1000 \ \frac{Pa}{kPa}\right)}{\left(287 \ \frac{J}{kg\cdot K}\right)(277K)}$$

$$= 0.8805 \ kg/m^3$$

The velocity of air is

$$v = \frac{\dot{m}}{A\rho} = \frac{9 \, \frac{\text{kg}}{\text{s}}}{(0.09 \, \text{m}^2) \left(0.8805 \, \frac{\text{kg}}{\text{m}^3}\right)}$$

$$= 113.6 \, \text{m/s}$$

The sonic velocity is

$$a = \sqrt{kRT}$$

$$= \sqrt{(1.4) \left(287 \, \frac{\text{J}}{\text{kg·K}}\right)(277\text{K})}$$

$$= 333.6 \, \text{m/s}$$

The Mach number is

$$M = \frac{v}{a} = \frac{113.6 \, \frac{\text{m}}{\text{s}}}{333.6 \, \frac{\text{m}}{\text{s}}} = 0.34$$

From the isentropic flow tables at M = 0.34, $[T/T_0] = 0.9774$. A closer approximation to the static temperature is

$$T = \left[\frac{T}{T_0}\right] T_0 = (0.9774)(277\text{K})$$

$$= 270.7\text{K}$$

Recalculate all the properties at $T = 270.7\text{K}$.

$$\rho = \frac{p}{RT}$$

$$= \frac{(70 \, \text{kPa}) \left(1000 \, \frac{\text{Pa}}{\text{kPa}}\right)}{\left(287 \, \frac{\text{J}}{\text{kg·K}}\right)(270.7\text{K})}$$

$$= 0.901 \, \text{kg/m}^3$$

$$v = \frac{\dot{m}}{A\rho} = \frac{9 \, \frac{\text{kg}}{\text{s}}}{(0.09 \, \text{m}^2) \left(0.901 \, \frac{\text{kg}}{\text{m}^3}\right)}$$

$$= 111.0 \, \text{m/s}$$

$$a = \sqrt{kRT}$$

$$= \sqrt{(1.4) \left(287 \, \frac{\text{J}}{\text{kg·K}}\right)(270.7\text{K})}$$

$$= 329.8 \, \text{m/s}$$

$$M = \frac{v}{a} = \frac{111.0 \, \frac{\text{m}}{\text{s}}}{329.8 \, \frac{\text{m}}{\text{s}}} = 0.337$$

From the isentropic flow tables at M = 0.337, $[A/A^*] = 1.8372$.

$$A_{\text{smallest}} = \left[\frac{A^*}{A}\right] A$$

$$= \left(\frac{1}{1.8372}\right)(0.09 \, \text{m}^2) = \boxed{0.0490 \, \text{m}^2}$$

9. *Customary U.S. Solution*

The ratio of static pressure before the shock to total pressure after the shock is

$$\frac{p_x}{p_{0,y}} = \frac{1.38 \, \text{psia}}{20 \, \text{psia}} = 0.069$$

From the normal shock table (App. 26.B) for $p_x/p_{0,y} = 0.069$, the Mach number in the tunnel is read directly as $\boxed{M_x = 3.3.}$

SI Solution

The ratio of static pressure before the shock to total pressure after the shock is

$$\frac{p_x}{p_{0,y}} = \frac{9.51 \, \text{kPa}}{140 \, \text{kPa}} = 0.068$$

From the normal shock table (App. 26.B) for $p_x/p_{0,y} = 0.068$, the Mach number in the tunnel is interpolated as

$$\boxed{M_x = 3.32.}$$

10. *Customary U.S. Solution*

The initial enthalpy is found from the superheat tables at 100 psia and 800°F.

$$h_1 = 1428.9 \, \text{Btu/lbm}$$

Using the Mollier diagram and assuming isentropic expansion, the final enthalpy at 60 psia is $h_2 = 1362 \, \text{Btu/lbm}$.

From Eq. 26.2, the steam exit velocity is

$$v_2 = \sqrt{2g_c J(h_1 - h_2)}$$

$$= \left[\begin{array}{c} (2) \left(32.2 \, \frac{\text{lbm-ft}}{\text{lbf-sec}^2}\right) \left(778 \, \frac{\text{ft-lbf}}{\text{Btu}}\right) \\ \times \left(1428.9 \, \frac{\text{Btu}}{\text{lbm}} - 1362 \, \frac{\text{Btu}}{\text{lbm}}\right) \end{array} \right]^{1/2}$$

$$= \boxed{1830.8 \, \text{ft/sec}}$$

SI Solution

The initial enthalpy is found from the superheat tables at 0.7 MPa and 425°C.

$$h_1 = 3321.5 \, \text{kJ/kg}$$

Using the Mollier diagram and assuming isentropic expansion, the final enthalpy at 400 kPa is $h_2 = 3154 \, \text{kJ/kg}$.

The steam exit velocity is

$$v_2 = \sqrt{(2)(h_1 - h_2)}$$

$$= \sqrt{(2)\left(3321.5 \ \frac{\text{kJ}}{\text{kg}} - 3154 \ \frac{\text{kJ}}{\text{kg}}\right)\left(1000 \ \frac{\text{J}}{\text{kJ}}\right)}$$

$$= \boxed{578.8 \ \text{m/s}}$$

11. *Customary U.S. Solution*

(a) At the particular point, the sonic velocity is

$$a = \sqrt{kg_cRT}$$

$$= \sqrt{\begin{array}{c}(1.4)\left(32.2 \ \dfrac{\text{ft-lbm}}{\text{lbf-sec}^2}\right) \\ \times \left(53.3 \ \dfrac{\text{ft-lbf}}{\text{lbm-}^\circ\text{R}}\right)(1000^\circ\text{R})\end{array}}$$

$$= 1550.1 \ \text{ft/sec}$$

The Mach number is

$$M = \frac{v}{a} = \frac{600 \ \dfrac{\text{ft}}{\text{sec}}}{1550.1 \ \dfrac{\text{ft}}{\text{sec}}} = \boxed{0.387} \quad [\text{say } 0.39]$$

(b) From the isentropic flow tables at M = 0.39, $[p/p_0] = 0.9004$, $[T/T_0] = 0.9705$, and $[A/A^*] = 1.6243$.

The total properties at Mach 0.39 are

$$T_0 = \left[\frac{T_0}{T}\right]T = \left(\frac{1}{0.9705}\right)(1000^\circ\text{R})$$

$$= \boxed{1030.4^\circ\text{R}}$$

(c) $\quad p_0 = \left[\dfrac{p_0}{p}\right]p = \left(\dfrac{1}{0.9004}\right)(50 \ \text{psia})$

$$= \boxed{55.5 \ \text{psia}}$$

(d) $\quad A^* = \left[\dfrac{A^*}{A}\right]A = \left(\dfrac{1}{1.6243}\right)(0.1 \ \text{ft}^2)$

$$= \boxed{0.0616 \ \text{ft}^2}$$

From the isentropic flow tables at M = 1 (critical conditions), $[p^*/p] = 0.5283$ and $[T^*/T_0] = 0.8333$.

Critical properties at Mach 1 are

(e) $\quad p^* = \left[\dfrac{p^*}{p_0}\right]p_0 = (0.5283)(55.5 \ \text{psia})$

$$= \boxed{29.32 \ \text{psia}}$$

(f) $\quad T^* = \left[\dfrac{T^*}{T_0}\right]T_0 = (0.8333)(1030.4^\circ\text{R})$

$$= \boxed{858.6^\circ\text{R}}$$

SI Solution

(a) At the particular point, the sonic velocity is

$$a = \sqrt{kRT}$$

$$= \sqrt{(1.4)\left(287 \ \frac{\text{J}}{\text{kg·K}}\right)(560\text{K})}$$

$$= 474.4 \ \text{m/s}$$

The Mach number is

$$M = \frac{v}{a} = \frac{180 \ \dfrac{\text{m}}{\text{s}}}{474.4 \ \dfrac{\text{m}}{\text{s}}} = \boxed{0.38}$$

(b) From the isentropic flow tables at M = 0.38, $[p/p_0] = 0.9052$, $[T/T_0] = 0.9719$, and $[A/A^*] = 1.6587$.

The total properties are

$$T_0 = \left[\frac{T_0}{T}\right]T = \left(\frac{1}{0.9719}\right)(560\text{K}) = \boxed{576.2\text{K}}$$

(c) $\quad p_0 = \left[\dfrac{p_0}{p}\right]p = \left(\dfrac{1}{0.9052}\right)(350 \ \text{kPa}) = \boxed{386.7 \ \text{kPa}}$

(d) $A^* = \left[\dfrac{A^*}{A}\right]A = \left(\dfrac{1}{1.6587}\right)(0.0009 \ \text{m}^2)$

$$= \boxed{5.43 \times 10^{-4} \ \text{m}^2}$$

From the isentropic flow tables at M = 1 (critical conditions), $[p^*/p_0] = 0.5283$ and $[T^*/T_0] = 0.8333$.

The critical properties are

(e) $p^* = \left[\dfrac{p^*}{p_0}\right]p_0 = (0.5283)(386.7 \ \text{kPa}) = \boxed{204.3 \ \text{kPa}}$

(f) $T^* = \left[\dfrac{T^*}{T_0}\right]T_0 = (0.8333)(576.2\text{K}) = \boxed{480.1\text{K}}$

12. *Customary U.S. Solution*

The initial enthalpy is found from the superheat tables at 200 psia and 600°F.

$$h_1 = 1322.1 \ \text{Btu/lbm}$$

If the expansion through the nozzle had been isentropic, the exit enthalpy would have been approximately 1228 Btu/lbm. The nozzle efficiency is defined by Eq. 26.18.

$$\eta_{\text{nozzle}} = \frac{h_1 - h_2'}{h_1 - h_2}$$

$$h_2' = h_1 - \eta_{\text{nozzle}}(h_1 - h_2)$$

$$= 1322.1 \ \frac{\text{Btu}}{\text{lbm}}$$

$$\quad - (0.85)\left(1322.1 \ \frac{\text{Btu}}{\text{lbm}} - 1228 \ \frac{\text{Btu}}{\text{lbm}}\right)$$

$$= 1242.1 \ \text{Btu/lbm}$$

Thermodynamics

Knowing $h = 1242.1$ Btu/lbm and $p = 80$ psia establishes (from superheat tables) that

$$T_2' = 422.6°F$$
$$v_2' = 6.401 \text{ ft}^3/\text{lbm}$$
$$\rho_2' = \frac{1}{v_2'} = \frac{1}{6.401 \dfrac{\text{ft}^3}{\text{lbm}}} = 0.1562 \text{ lbm/ft}^3$$

The nozzle exit velocity can be calculated as

$$v_2' = \sqrt{2g_c J(h_1 - h_2') + v_1^2}$$
$$= \sqrt{\begin{array}{c}(2)\left(32.2 \dfrac{\text{lbm-ft}}{\text{lbf-sec}^2}\right)\left(778 \dfrac{\text{ft-lbf}}{\text{Btu}}\right) \\ \times \left(1322.1 \dfrac{\text{Btu}}{\text{lbm}} - 1242.1 \dfrac{\text{Btu}}{\text{lbm}}\right) + \left(300 \dfrac{\text{ft}}{\text{sec}}\right)^2\end{array}}$$
$$= 2024.4 \text{ ft/sec}$$

The exit area of the nozzle is

$$A_e = \frac{\dot{m}}{\rho_2' v_2'} = \frac{3 \dfrac{\text{lbm}}{\text{sec}}}{\left(0.1562 \dfrac{\text{lbm}}{\text{ft}^3}\right)\left(2024.4 \dfrac{\text{ft}}{\text{sec}}\right)}$$
$$= 0.009487 \text{ ft}^2$$

The absolute temperature at the nozzle exit is

$$T_1 = 422.6°F + 460 = 882.6°R$$
$$k_{\text{steam}} = 1.31$$
$$R_{\text{steam}} = 85.8 \text{ ft-lbf/lbm-}°R$$

The sonic velocity is

$$a = \sqrt{kg_c RT}$$
$$= \sqrt{\begin{array}{c}(1.31)\left(32.2 \dfrac{\text{ft-lbm}}{\text{lbf-sec}^2}\right) \\ \times \left(85.8 \dfrac{\text{ft-lbf}}{\text{lbm-}°R}\right)(882.6°R)\end{array}}$$
$$= 1787.3 \text{ ft/sec}$$

The Mach number is

$$M = \frac{v_2'}{a} = \frac{2024.4 \dfrac{\text{ft}}{\text{sec}}}{1787.3 \dfrac{\text{ft}}{\text{sec}}} = 1.13$$

Calculate the throat area. Since tables for $k = 1.31$ are not available,

$$\frac{A}{A^*} = \left(\frac{1}{M}\right)\left[\frac{\left(\frac{1}{2}\right)(k-1)M^2 + 1}{\left(\frac{1}{2}\right)(k-1) + 1}\right]^{\frac{k+1}{(2)(k-1)}}$$
$$\frac{A_e}{A^*} = \left(\frac{1}{1.13}\right)\left[\frac{\left(\frac{1}{2}\right)(1.31-1)(1.13)^2 + 1}{\left(\frac{1}{2}\right)(1.31-1) + 1}\right]^{\frac{1.31+1}{(2)(1.31-1)}}$$
$$= 1.0138$$
$$A^* = \left[\frac{A^*}{A_e}\right]A_e = \left(\frac{1}{1.0138}\right)(0.009487 \text{ ft}^2)$$
$$= \boxed{0.00936 \text{ ft}^2}$$

SI Solution

The initial enthalpy is found from the superheat tables at 1.5 MPa and 300°C.

$$h_1 = 3037.6 \text{ kJ/kg}$$

If the expansion through the nozzle had been isentropic, the exit enthalpy would have been approximately 2790 kJ/kg. The nozzle efficiency is defined by Eq. 26.18.

$$\eta_{\text{nozzle}} = \frac{h_1 - h_2'}{h_1 - h_2}$$
$$h_2' = h_1 - \eta_{\text{nozzle}}(h_1 - h_2)$$
$$= 3037.6 \frac{\text{kJ}}{\text{kg}}$$
$$- (0.85)\left(3037.6 \frac{\text{kJ}}{\text{kg}} - 2790 \frac{\text{kJ}}{\text{kg}}\right)$$
$$= 2827 \text{ kJ/kg}$$

Knowing $h = 2827$ kJ/kg and $p = 500$ kPa establishes (from superheat tables) that

$$T_2' = 187.1°C$$
$$v_2' = 0.4118 \text{ m}^3/\text{kg}$$
$$\rho_2' = \frac{1}{v_2'} = \frac{1}{0.4118 \dfrac{\text{m}^3}{\text{kg}}} = 2.428 \text{ kg/m}^3$$

The nozzle exit velocity can be calculated as

$$v_2' = \sqrt{(2)(h_1 - h_2') + v_1^2}$$
$$= \sqrt{\begin{array}{c}(2)\left(3037.6 \dfrac{\text{kJ}}{\text{kg}} - 2827 \dfrac{\text{kJ}}{\text{kg}}\right) \\ \times \left(1000 \dfrac{\text{J}}{\text{kJ}}\right) + \left(90 \dfrac{\text{m}}{\text{s}}\right)^2\end{array}}$$
$$= 655.2 \text{ m/s}$$

The exit area of the nozzle is

$$A_e = \frac{\dot{m}}{\rho_2' \mathrm{v}_2'} = \frac{1.4 \, \frac{\text{kg}}{\text{s}}}{\left(2.428 \, \frac{\text{kg}}{\text{m}^3}\right)\left(655.2 \, \frac{\text{m}}{\text{s}}\right)}$$

$$= 8.800 \times 10^{-4} \text{ m}^2$$

The absolute temperature at the nozzle exit is

$$T_1 = 187.1°\text{C} + 273 = 460.1\text{K}$$

$$k_{\text{steam}} = 1.31$$

$$R_{\text{steam}} = 461.50 \text{ J/kg·K}$$

The sonic velocity is

$$a = \sqrt{kRT}$$

$$= \sqrt{(1.31)\left(461.50 \, \frac{\text{J}}{\text{kg·K}}\right)(460.1\text{K})}$$

$$= 527.4 \text{ m/s}$$

The Mach number is

$$\text{M} = \frac{\mathrm{v}_2'}{a} = \frac{655.2 \, \frac{\text{m}}{\text{s}}}{527.4 \, \frac{\text{m}}{\text{s}}} = 1.24$$

Calculate the throat area. Since tables for $k = 1.31$ are not available,

$$\frac{A}{A^*} = \left(\frac{1}{\text{M}}\right)\left[\frac{\left(\frac{1}{2}\right)(k-1)\text{M}^2 + 1}{\left(\frac{1}{2}\right)(k-1) + 1}\right]^{\frac{k+1}{(2)(k-1)}}$$

$$\frac{A_e}{A^*} = \left(\frac{1}{1.24}\right)\left[\frac{\left(\frac{1}{2}\right)(1.31-1)(1.24)^2 + 1}{\left(\frac{1}{2}\right)(1.31-1) + 1}\right]^{\frac{1.31+1}{(2)(1.31-1)}}$$

$$= 1.0454$$

$$A^* = \left[\frac{A^*}{A_e}\right]A_e = \left(\frac{1}{1.0454}\right)(8.800 \times 10^{-4} \text{ m}^2)$$

$$= \boxed{8.418 \times 10^{-4} \text{ m}^2}$$

13. *Customary U.S. Solution*

This is a Fanno flow problem. Check for choked flow.

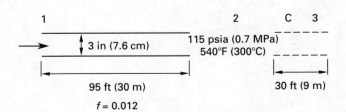

$f = 0.012$

At point 2, from superheat tables at 115 psia and 540°F, $v_2 = 5.066 \text{ ft}^3/\text{lbm}$.

The velocity at point 2 can be calculated as

$$\mathrm{v}_2 = \frac{\dot{m}}{A\rho_2} = \frac{\dot{m}v_2}{A}$$

$$= \frac{\left(35{,}200 \, \frac{\text{lbm}}{\text{hr}}\right)\left(\frac{1 \text{ hr}}{3600 \text{ sec}}\right)\left(5.066 \, \frac{\text{ft}^3}{\text{lbm}}\right)}{\left(\frac{\pi}{4}\right)(3 \text{ in})^2\left(\frac{1 \text{ ft}}{12 \text{ in}}\right)^2}$$

$$= 1009 \text{ ft/sec}$$

The absolute temperature at point 2 is

$$T_2 = 540°\text{F} + 460 = 1000°\text{R}$$

For 1000°R steam, $k = 1.29$ and $R = 85.8$ ft-lbf/lbm-°R.

The sonic velocity at point 2 is

$$a_2 = \sqrt{kg_c RT}$$

$$= \sqrt{\begin{aligned}&(1.29)\left(32.2 \, \frac{\text{ft-lbm}}{\text{lbf-sec}^2}\right)\\&\times\left(85.8 \, \frac{\text{ft-lbf}}{\text{lbm-}°\text{R}}\right)(1000°\text{R})\end{aligned}}$$

$$= 1888 \text{ ft/sec}$$

The Mach number at point 2 is

$$\text{M}_2 = \frac{\mathrm{v}_2}{a_2} = \frac{1009 \, \frac{\text{ft}}{\text{sec}}}{1888 \, \frac{\text{ft}}{\text{sec}}} = 0.534$$

The distance from point 2 to where the flow becomes choked is calculated from Eq. 26.34.

$$\frac{4fL_{\max}}{D} = \frac{1 - \text{M}^2}{k\text{M}^2} + \left(\frac{1+k}{2k}\right)\ln\left(\frac{(1+k)\text{M}^2}{(2)\left[1 + \left(\frac{1}{2}\right)(k-1)\text{M}^2\right]}\right)$$

$$L_{\max} = \left[\frac{(3 \text{ in})\left(\frac{1 \text{ ft}}{12 \text{ in}}\right)}{(4)(0.012)}\right]$$

$$\times\left[\frac{1 - (0.534)^2}{(1.29)(0.534)^2} + \frac{1 + 1.29}{(2)(1.29)}\right.$$

$$\left.\times\ln\left(\frac{(1 + 1.29)(0.534)^2}{(2)\left[1 + \left(\frac{1}{2}\right)(1.29 - 1)(0.534)^2\right]}\right)\right]$$

$$= 4.76 \text{ ft}$$

The flow will be choked in less than 30 ft; steam flow is not maintained.

SI Solution

At point 2, from the superheat tables at 0.7 MPa and 300°C, $v_2 = 0.3714 \text{ m}^3/\text{kg}$.

The velocity at point 2 can be calculated as

$$v_2 = \frac{\dot{m}}{\rho_2 A} = \frac{\dot{m} v_2}{A}$$

$$= \frac{\left(4.4 \ \dfrac{\text{kg}}{\text{s}}\right)\left(0.3714 \ \dfrac{\text{m}^3}{\text{kg}}\right)}{\left(\dfrac{\pi}{4}\right)(7.6 \text{ cm})^2 \left(\dfrac{1 \text{ m}}{100 \text{ cm}}\right)^2}$$

$$= 360.2 \text{ m/s}$$

The absolute temperature at point 2 is

$$T_2 = 300°\text{C} + 273 = 573\text{K}$$

For 573K steam, $k = 1.29$ and $R = 461.5 \text{ J/kg·K}$. The sonic velocity at point 2 is

$$a_2 = \sqrt{kRT}$$

$$= \sqrt{(1.29)\left(461.5 \ \frac{\text{J}}{\text{kg·K}}\right)(573\text{K})}$$

$$= 584.1 \text{ m/s}$$

The Mach number at point 2 is

$$M_2 = \frac{v_2}{a_2} = \frac{360.2 \ \dfrac{\text{m}}{\text{s}}}{584.1 \ \dfrac{\text{m}}{\text{s}}} = 0.617$$

The distance from point 2 to where the flow becomes choked is calculated from Eq. 26.34.

$$\frac{4fL_{\max}}{D} = \frac{1-M^2}{kM^2}$$
$$+ \left(\frac{1+k}{2k}\right) \ln\left(\frac{(1+k)M^2}{(2)\left[1+\left(\frac{1}{2}\right)(k-1)M^2\right]}\right)$$

$$L_{\max} = \left[\frac{(7.6 \text{ cm})\left(\dfrac{1 \text{ m}}{100 \text{ cm}}\right)}{(4)(0.012)}\right]$$

$$\times \left[\frac{1-(0.617)^2}{(1.29)(0.617)^2} + \frac{1+1.29}{(2)(1.29)}\right.$$

$$\left. \times \ln\left(\frac{(1+1.29)(0.617)^2}{(2)\left[1+\left(\frac{1}{2}\right)(1.29-1)(0.617)^2\right]}\right)\right]$$

$$= 0.75 \text{ m}$$

The flow will be choked in less than 9 m; steam flow is not maintained.

14. *Customary U.S. Solution*

Since $p_e/p_0 < 0.5283$, the flow must be supersonic.

The throat flow is sonic. Read the property ratios for Mach 1 from the isentropic flow table: $[T/T_0] = 0.8333$ and $[p/p_0] = 0.5283$.

The sonic properties at the throat are

$$T^* = \left[\frac{T}{T_0}\right] T_0 = (0.8333)(660°\text{R}) = 550°\text{R}$$

$$p^* = \left[\frac{p}{p_0}\right] p_0 = (0.5283)(160 \text{ psia}) = 84.53 \text{ psia}$$

$$a^* = \sqrt{kg_c RT^*}$$

$$= \sqrt{\begin{array}{c}(1.4)\left(32.2 \ \dfrac{\text{ft-lbm}}{\text{lbf-sec}^2}\right) \\ \times \left(53.3 \ \dfrac{\text{ft-lbf}}{\text{lbm-°R}}\right)(550°\text{R})\end{array}}$$

$$= 1150 \text{ ft/sec}$$

$$\rho^* = \frac{p^*}{RT^*} = \frac{\left(84.53 \ \dfrac{\text{lbf}}{\text{in}^2}\right)\left(144 \ \dfrac{\text{in}^2}{\text{ft}^2}\right)}{\left(53.3 \ \dfrac{\text{ft-lbf}}{\text{lbm-°R}}\right)(550°\text{R})}$$

$$= 0.415 \text{ lbm/ft}^3$$

The overall nozzle efficiency is $C_D = 0.90$. From $\dot{m} = C_D A v \rho$, the throat area is

$$A^* = \frac{\dot{m}}{C_D v \rho} = \frac{\left(3600 \ \dfrac{\text{lbm}}{\text{hr}}\right)\left(\dfrac{1 \text{ hr}}{3600 \text{ sec}}\right)}{(0.90)\left(1150 \ \dfrac{\text{ft}}{\text{sec}}\right)\left(0.415 \ \dfrac{\text{lbm}}{\text{ft}^3}\right)}$$

$$= \boxed{0.002328 \text{ ft}^2}$$

$$D^* = \sqrt{\frac{4A^*}{\pi}}$$

$$= \sqrt{\frac{(4)(0.002328 \text{ ft}^2)}{\pi}}$$

$$= 0.0544 \text{ ft}$$

At the exit,

$$p_3 = 14.7 \text{ psia}$$

$$\frac{p_e}{p_0} = \frac{14.7 \text{ psia}}{160 \text{ psia}} = 0.0919$$

From the isentropic flow tables at $p/p_0 = 0.0919$, M $= 2.22$ and $[A/A^*] = 2.041$.

$$A_e = \left[\frac{A}{A^*}\right] A^* = (2.041)(0.002328 \text{ ft}^2) = 0.004751 \text{ ft}^2$$

$$D_e = \sqrt{\frac{4A}{\pi}} = \sqrt{\frac{(4)(0.004751 \text{ ft}^2)}{\pi}}$$
$$= 0.0778 \text{ ft}$$

The longitudinal distance from the throat to the exit is

$$x = \frac{0.0778 \text{ ft} - 0.0544 \text{ ft}}{(2)(\tan 3^\circ)} = 0.223 \text{ ft}$$

The entrance velocity is not known, so the entrance area cannot be found. However, the longitudinal distance from the entrance to the throat is

$$(0.05)(0.223 \text{ ft}) = 0.0112 \text{ ft}$$

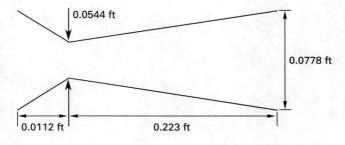

SI Solution

Since $p_e/p_0 < 0.5283$, the flow must be supersonic. The throat flow is sonic. Read the property ratio for Mach 1 from the isentropic flow table: $[T/T_0] = 0.8333$ and $[p/p_0] = 0.5283$.

The sonic properties at the throat are

$$T^* = \left[\frac{T}{T_0}\right] T_0 = (0.8333)(370\text{K}) = 308.3\text{K}$$

$$p^* = \left[\frac{p}{p_0}\right] p_0 = (0.5283)(1.1 \text{ MPa}) = 0.581 \text{ MPa}$$

$$a^* = \sqrt{kRT^*}$$
$$= \sqrt{(1.4)\left(287 \frac{\text{J}}{\text{kg·K}}\right)(308.3\text{K})}$$
$$= 352 \text{ m/s}$$

$$\rho^* = \frac{p^*}{RT^*} = \frac{(0.581 \text{ MPa})\left(10^6 \frac{\text{Pa}}{\text{MPa}}\right)}{\left(287 \frac{\text{J}}{\text{kg·K}}\right)(308.3\text{K})}$$
$$= 6.57 \text{ kg/m}^3$$

The overall nozzle efficiency is $C_D = 0.90$. From $\dot{m} = C_D A v \rho$,

$$A^* = \frac{\dot{m}}{C_D v \rho} = \frac{0.45 \frac{\text{kg}}{\text{s}}}{(0.90)\left(352 \frac{\text{m}}{\text{s}}\right)\left(6.57 \frac{\text{kg}}{\text{m}^3}\right)}$$

$$= \boxed{0.000216 \text{ m}^2}$$

$$D^* = \sqrt{\frac{4A^*}{\pi}} = \sqrt{\frac{(4)(0.000216 \text{ m}^2)}{\pi}}$$
$$= 0.0166 \text{ m}$$

At the exit,

$$p_e = 101.3 \text{ kPa}$$

$$\frac{p_e}{p_0} = \frac{(101.3 \text{ kPa})\left(10^3 \frac{\text{Pa}}{\text{kPa}}\right)}{(1.1 \text{ MPa})\left(10^6 \frac{\text{Pa}}{\text{MPa}}\right)} = 0.0921$$

From the isentropic flow tables at $p/p_0 = 0.0921$, M $= 2.21$ and $[A/A^*] = 2.024$.

$$A_e = \left[\frac{A}{A^*}\right] A^* = (2.024)(0.000216 \text{ m}^2)$$
$$= 0.000437 \text{ m}^2$$

$$D_e = \sqrt{\frac{4A}{\pi}} = \sqrt{\frac{(4)(0.000437 \text{ m}^2)}{\pi}}$$
$$= 0.0236 \text{ m}$$

The longitudinal distance from the throat to the exit is

$$x = \frac{0.0236 \text{ m} - 0.0166 \text{ m}}{(2)(\tan 3^\circ)} = 0.0668 \text{ m}$$

The entrance velocity is not known, so the entrance area cannot be found. However, the longitudinal distance from the entrance to the throat is

$$(0.05)(0.0668 \text{ m}) = 0.00334 \text{ m}$$

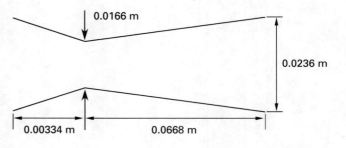

27 Vapor Power Equipment

1. *Customary U.S. Solution*

From App. 24.B, for 100 psia, the enthalpy of dry steam is $h_i = 1187.8$ Btu/lbm.

From the Mollier diagram for an isentropic process from 100 psia to 3 psia, $h_2 = 950$ Btu/lbm.

From App. 24.B, for 3 psia,

$$h_f = 109.39 \text{ Btu/lbm}$$
$$h_{fg} = 1013.1 \text{ Btu/lbm}$$
$$h_2' = h_f + xh_{fg}$$
$$= 109.39 \frac{\text{Btu}}{\text{lbm}} + (0.9)\left(1013.1 \frac{\text{Btu}}{\text{lbm}}\right)$$
$$= 1021.2 \text{ Btu/lbm}$$

From Eq. 27.17, the isentropic efficiency is

$$\eta_s = \frac{h_1 - h_2'}{h_1 - h_2} = \frac{1187.8 \dfrac{\text{Btu}}{\text{lbm}} - 1021.2 \dfrac{\text{Btu}}{\text{lbm}}}{1187.8 \dfrac{\text{Btu}}{\text{lbm}} - 950 \dfrac{\text{Btu}}{\text{lbm}}}$$

$$= \boxed{0.701 \quad (70.1\%)}$$

SI Solution

From App. 24.O, for 700 kPa, the enthalpy of dry steam is $h_1 = 2763.5$ kJ/kg.

From the Mollier diagram for an isentropic process from 700 kPa to 20 kPa, $h_2 = 2245$ kJ/kg.

From App. 24.O, for 20 kPa,

$$h_f = 251.4 \text{ kJ/kg}$$
$$h_{fg} = 2358.3 \text{ kJ/kg}$$
$$h_2' = h_f + xh_{fg}$$
$$= 251.4 \frac{\text{kJ}}{\text{kg}} + (0.9)\left(2358.3 \frac{\text{kJ}}{\text{kg}}\right)$$
$$= 2373.9 \text{ kJ/kg}$$

From Eq. 22.17, the isentropic efficiency is

$$\eta_s = \frac{h_1 - h_2'}{h_1 - h_2}$$

$$= \frac{2763.5 \dfrac{\text{kJ}}{\text{kg}} - 2373.9 \dfrac{\text{kJ}}{\text{kg}}}{2763.5 \dfrac{\text{kJ}}{\text{kg}} - 2245 \dfrac{\text{kJ}}{\text{kg}}}$$

$$= \boxed{0.751 \quad (75.1\%)}$$

2. *Customary U.S. Solution*

(a) From App. 24.B, T_{sat} for 200 psia is 381.86°F.

The steam temperature is

$$381.86°\text{F} + 100°\text{F} = 481.86°\text{F}$$

From App. 24.C, $h_1 = 1258.2$ Btu/lbm.

1 in Hg is approximately 0.5 psia. From the Mollier diagram, assuming isentropic expansion, dropping straight down to the 0.5 psia line, $h_2 \approx 870$ Btu/lbm.

For isentropic expansion, $\eta_{\text{turbine}} = 1$, and the steam mass flow rate through the turbine is given by Eq. 27.22.

$$\dot{m} = \frac{P_{\text{turbine}}}{h_1 - h_2}$$

$$= \frac{(5000 \text{ kW})\left(3413 \dfrac{\text{Btu}}{\text{hr-kW}}\right)}{1258.2 \dfrac{\text{Btu}}{\text{lbm}} - 870 \dfrac{\text{Btu}}{\text{lbm}}}$$

$$= 4.396 \times 10^4 \text{ lbm/hr}$$

The water rate is

$$\text{WR} = \frac{\dot{m}}{P_{\text{turbine}}} = \frac{4.396 \times 10^4 \dfrac{\text{lbm}}{\text{hr}}}{5000 \text{ kW}}$$

$$= \boxed{8.792 \text{ lbm/kW-hr}}$$

(b) The loss in available energy per unit mass is

$$\text{loss} = \left(\tfrac{1}{2}\right)(h_1 - h_2)$$
$$= \left(\tfrac{1}{2}\right)\left(1258.2 \frac{\text{Btu}}{\text{lbm}} - 870 \frac{\text{Btu}}{\text{lbm}}\right)$$
$$= \boxed{194.1 \text{ Btu/lbm}}$$

SI Solution

(a) From App. 24.0, T_{sat} for 1.5 MPa is 198.3°C.

The steam temperature is

$$198.3°C + 50°C = 248.3°C$$

From App. 24.P, $h_1 = 2919$ kJ/kg and $s_1 = 6.7000$ kJ/kg·K.

From App. 24.N, for 3.4 kPa, the entropy of saturated liquid, s_f, the entropy of saturated vapor, s_g, the enthalpy of saturated liquid, h_f, and the enthalpy of vaporization, h_{fg}, are

$$s_f = 0.3839 \text{ kJ/kg·K}$$
$$s_g = 8.5329 \text{ kJ/kg·K}$$
$$h_f = 109.82 \text{ kJ/kg}$$
$$h_{fg} = 2439.5 \text{ kJ/kg}$$

For isentropic expansion, $s_1 = s_2 = 6.7000$ kJ/kg·K.

Since $s_2 < s_g$, the expanded steam is in the liquid-vapor region. The quality of the mixture is given by Eq. 24.41.

$$x = \frac{s - s_f}{s_{fg}} = \frac{s - s_f}{s_g - s_f}$$
$$= \frac{6.7000\,\frac{\text{kJ}}{\text{kg·K}} - 0.3839\,\frac{\text{kJ}}{\text{kg·K}}}{8.5329\,\frac{\text{kJ}}{\text{kg·K}} - 0.3839\,\frac{\text{kJ}}{\text{kg·K}}}$$
$$= 0.7751$$

The final enthalpy is given by Eq. 24.40.

$$h = h_f + x h_{fg}$$
$$= 109.82\,\frac{\text{kJ}}{\text{kg}} + (0.7751)\left(2439.5\,\frac{\text{kJ}}{\text{kg}}\right)$$
$$= 2000.7 \text{ kJ/kg}$$

For isentropic expansion, $\eta_{\text{turbine}} = 1$, and the steam mass flow rate through a turbine is given by Eq. 27.22.

$$\dot{m} = \frac{P_{\text{turbine}}}{h_1 - h_2}$$
$$= \frac{5000 \text{ kW}}{2919\,\frac{\text{kJ}}{\text{kg}} - 2000.7\,\frac{\text{kJ}}{\text{kg}}}$$
$$= 5.445 \text{ kg/s}$$

The water rate is

$$\text{WR} = \frac{\dot{m}}{P_{\text{turbine}}} = \frac{5.445\,\frac{\text{kg}}{\text{s}}}{5000 \text{ kW}}$$
$$= \boxed{1.09 \times 10^{-3} \text{ kg/kW·s}}$$

(b) Loss in availability per unit mass is

$$\text{loss} = \left(\tfrac{1}{2}\right)(h_1 - h_2)$$
$$= \left(\tfrac{1}{2}\right)\left(2919\,\frac{\text{kJ}}{\text{kg}} - 2000.7\,\frac{\text{kJ}}{\text{kg}}\right)$$
$$= \boxed{459.2 \text{ kJ/kg}}$$

3. *Customary U.S. Solution*

From App. 24.C, the enthalpy, h_1, of dry steam at 400 psia and 750°F is $h_1 = 1389.6$ Btu/lbm.

From the Mollier diagram, assuming isentropic expansion, $h_2 = 935$ Btu/lbm.

The adiabatic heat drop is

$$h_1 - h_2 = 1389.6\,\frac{\text{Btu}}{\text{lbm}} - 935\,\frac{\text{Btu}}{\text{lbm}}$$
$$= \boxed{454.6 \text{ Btu/lbm}}$$

SI Solution

From App. 24.P, the enthalpy, h_1, of dry steam at 3.0 MPa and 420°C is $h_1 = 3276.3$ kJ/kg.

From the Mollier diagram, assuming isentropic expansion, $h_2 \approx 2210$ kJ/kg.

The adiabatic heat drop is

$$h_1 - h_2 = 3276.3\,\frac{\text{kJ}}{\text{kg}} - 2210\,\frac{\text{kJ}}{\text{kg}}$$
$$= \boxed{1066.3 \text{ kJ/kg}}$$

4. *Customary U.S. Solution*

The water rate is

$$\text{WR} = \frac{\dot{m}}{P_{\text{turbine}}}$$

The steam flow rate is

$$\dot{m}_{\text{steam}} = (\text{WR})(P_{\text{turbine}})$$
$$= \left(20\,\frac{\text{lbm}}{\text{kW-hr}}\right)(750 \text{ kW})$$
$$= 15,000 \text{ lbm/hr}$$

From App. 24.B, for 165 psia, $T_{\text{sat}} = 365.9°F$.

The steam temperature is

$$365.9°F + 50°F = 415.9°F$$

From App. 24.C, $h_1 = 1225.7$ Btu/lbm.

From Eq. 27.22,

$$P_{\text{turbine}} = \dot{m}(h_1 - h_2)$$

$$h_1 - h_2 = \frac{P_{\text{turbine}}}{\dot{m}} = \frac{(750\text{ kW})\left(3413\,\dfrac{\text{Btu}}{\text{kW-hr}}\right)}{15,000\,\dfrac{\text{lbm}}{\text{hr}}}$$

$$= 170.6\text{ Btu/lbm}$$

$$h_2 = h_1 - 170.6\,\frac{\text{Btu}}{\text{lbm}}$$

$$= 1225.7\,\frac{\text{Btu}}{\text{lbm}} - 170.6\,\frac{\text{Btu}}{\text{lbm}}$$

$$= 1055.1\text{ Btu/lbm}$$

$$p_2 = (26\text{ in Hg})\left(0.491\,\frac{\text{lbf}}{\text{in}^3}\right)$$

$$= 12.77\text{ psia}$$

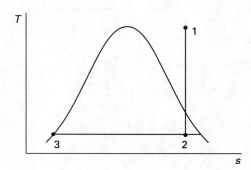

From App. 24.B, for $p_2 = 12.77$ psia,

$$T_{\text{sat}} = T_2 = T_3 \approx 204°\text{F}$$

$$h_{f,3} \approx 171.6\text{ Btu/lbm}$$

From App. 35.A, the specific heat of water at 65°F is $c_{p\text{water}} = 0.999$ Btu.

Assuming the water and steam leave in thermal equilibrium, the heat lost by steam is equal to the heat gained by water.

$$\dot{m}_{\text{water}}c_{p\text{water}}(T_{\text{water,out}} - T_{\text{water,in}}) = \dot{m}_{\text{steam}}(h_2 - h_{f,3})$$

Since the terminal temperature difference is zero, $T_{\text{water,out}} = T_3$.

$$\dot{m}_{\text{water}}\left(0.999\,\frac{\text{Btu}}{\text{lbm-°F}}\right)(204°\text{F} - 65°\text{F})$$

$$= \left(15,000\,\frac{\text{lbm}}{\text{hr}}\right)\left(1055.1\,\frac{\text{Btu}}{\text{lbm}} - 171.6\,\frac{\text{Btu}}{\text{lbm}}\right)$$

$$\dot{m}_{\text{water}} = \boxed{9.54 \times 10^4\text{ lbm/hr}}$$

SI Solution

The steam flow rate is

$$\dot{m}_{\text{steam}} = (\text{WR})(P_{\text{turbine}})$$

$$= \left(2.5 \times 10^{-3}\,\frac{\text{kg}}{\text{kW·s}}\right)(750\text{ kW})$$

$$= 1.875\text{ kg/s}$$

From App. 24.O for 1 MPa, $T_{\text{sat}} = 179.9°\text{C}$.

The steam temperature is

$$179.9°\text{C} + 30°\text{C} = 209.9°\text{C}$$

From App. 24.P, $h_1 = 2850.6$ kJ/kg.

From Eq. 27.22,

$$P_{\text{turbine}} = \dot{m}(h_1 - h_2)$$

$$h_1 - h_2 = \frac{P_{\text{turbine}}}{\dot{m}} = \frac{750\text{ kW}}{1.875\,\dfrac{\text{kg}}{\text{s}}}$$

$$= 400\text{ kJ/kg}$$

$$h_2 = h_1 - 400\,\frac{\text{kJ}}{\text{kg}}$$

$$= 2850.6\,\frac{\text{kJ}}{\text{kg}} - 400\,\frac{\text{kJ}}{\text{kg}}$$

$$= 2450.6\text{ kJ/kg}$$

From App. 24.O for $p_2 = 90$ kPa,

$$T_{\text{sat}} = T_2 = T_3 = 96.71°\text{C}$$

$$h_{f,3} = 405.15\text{ kJ/kg}$$

From App. 35.B, the specific heat of water at 18°C is $c_p = 4.186$ kJ/kg·K.

Assuming water and steam leave in thermal equilibrium, the heat lost by steam is equal to the heat gained by water.

$$\dot{m}_{\text{water}}c_{p,\text{water}}(T_{\text{water,out}} - T_{\text{water,in}}) = \dot{m}_{\text{steam}}(h_2 - h_{f,3})$$

Since the terminal difference is zero, $T_{\text{water,out}} = T_3$.

$$\dot{m}_{\text{water}}\left(4.186\,\frac{\text{kJ}}{\text{kg·K}}\right)(96.71°\text{C} - 18°\text{C})$$

$$= \left(1.875\,\frac{\text{kg}}{\text{s}}\right)\left(2450.6\,\frac{\text{kJ}}{\text{kg}} - 405.15\,\frac{\text{kJ}}{\text{kg}}\right)$$

$$\dot{m}_{\text{water}} = \boxed{11.64\text{ kg/s}}$$

Power Cycles

5. *Customary U.S. Solution*

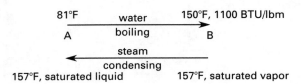

(a) From App. 24.B, for 4.45 psia, $T_{sat} = 157°F$. The average water temperature is

$$\left(\tfrac{1}{2}\right)(81°F + 150°F) = 115.5°F$$

From App. 35.A, the specific heat of water at 115.5°F is $c_{p\text{water}} = 0.999$ Btu/lbm-°F.

From App. 24.A, $h_{\text{water},1} = 49.08$ Btu/lbm.

The heat transferred to the water is

$$Q = \dot{m}_{\text{water}}(h_{\text{water},2} - h_{\text{water},1})$$
$$= \left(332{,}000\ \frac{\text{lbm}}{\text{hr}}\right)\left(1100\ \frac{\text{Btu}}{\text{lbm}} - 49.08\ \frac{\text{Btu}}{\text{lbm}}\right)$$
$$= 3.489 \times 10^8\ \text{Btu/hr}$$

The two end temperature differences are

$$\Delta T_A = 157°F - 81°F = 76°F$$
$$\Delta T_B = 157°F - 150°F = 7°F$$

The logarithmic mean temperature difference from Eq. 36.69 is

$$\Delta T_{lm} = \frac{\Delta T_A - \Delta T_B}{\ln\left(\dfrac{\Delta T_A}{\Delta T_B}\right)}$$
$$= \frac{76°F - 7°F}{\ln\left(\dfrac{76°F}{7°F}\right)} = 28.93°F$$

Since $T_{\text{steam},A} = T_{\text{steam},B}$, the correction factor (F_c) for ΔT_{lm} is 1.

The overall heat transfer coefficient is calculated from Eq. 36.70.

$$Q = UAF_c\Delta T_{lm}$$
$$U = \frac{Q}{AF_c\Delta T_{lm}}$$
$$= \frac{3.489 \times 10^8\ \dfrac{\text{Btu}}{\text{hr}}}{(1850\ \text{ft}^2)(1)(28.93°F)}$$
$$= \boxed{6519\ \text{Btu/hr-ft}^2\text{-°F}}$$

(b) From App. 24.B, the enthalpy of saturated steam at 4.45 psia is $h_1 = 1129$ Btu/lbm.

From App. 24.B, the enthalpy of saturated water at 4.45 psia is $h_2 = 125.1$ Btu/lbm.

The enthalpy change for steam during condensation is

$$\Delta h = h_1 - h_2$$
$$= 1129\ \frac{\text{Btu}}{\text{lbm}} - 125.1\ \frac{\text{Btu}}{\text{lbm}}$$
$$= 1003.9\ \text{Btu/lbm}$$

The heat transferred (Q) from the steam is equal to the heat gained by water.

$$Q = \dot{m}_{\text{steam}}\Delta h$$
$$\dot{m}_{\text{steam}} = \frac{Q}{\Delta h} = \frac{3.489 \times 10^8\ \dfrac{\text{Btu}}{\text{hr}}}{1003.9\ \dfrac{\text{Btu}}{\text{lbm}}}$$
$$= \boxed{3.475 \times 10^5\ \text{lbm/hr}}$$

SI Solution

The extraction rate is

$$\dot{m}_{\text{steam}}h_1 = \left(3.475 \times 10^5\ \frac{\text{lbm}}{\text{hr}}\right)\left(1129\ \frac{\text{Btu}}{\text{lbm}}\right)$$
$$= \boxed{3.92 \times 10^8\ \text{Btu/hr}}$$

From App. 24.O, for 30 kPa, $T_{sat} = 69.10°C$.

(a) The average water temperature is

$$\left(\tfrac{1}{2}\right)(27°C + 65°C) = 46°C$$

From App. 35.B, the specific heat of water at 46°C is $c_{p\text{water}} = 4.184$ kJ/kg·K.

From App. 24.N, $h_{\text{water},1} = 113.25$ kJ/kg.

The heat transferred to the water is

$$Q = \dot{m}_{\text{water}}(h_{\text{water},2} - h_{\text{water},1})$$
$$= \left(41.8\ \frac{\text{kg}}{\text{s}}\right)\left[\left(2.56\ \frac{\text{MJ}}{\text{kg}}\right)\left(1000\ \frac{\text{kJ}}{\text{MJ}}\right)\right.$$
$$\left. - 113.25\ \frac{\text{kJ}}{\text{kg}}\right]$$
$$= 102\,274\ \text{kJ/s}$$

The two end temperature differences are

$$\Delta T_A = 69.10°C - 27°C = 42.1°C$$

$$\Delta T_B = 69.10°C - 65°C = 4.1°C$$

The logarithmic mean temperature difference is calculated from Eq. 36.69.

$$\Delta T_{lm} = \frac{\Delta T_A - \Delta T_B}{\ln\left(\frac{\Delta T_A}{\Delta T_B}\right)} = \frac{42.1°C - 4.1°C}{\ln\left(\frac{42.1°C}{4.1°C}\right)}$$

$$= 16.32°C$$

Since $T_{\text{steam},A} = T_{\text{steam},B}$, the correction factor (F_c) for ΔT_{lm} is 1.

The overall heat transfer coefficient is calculated from Eq. 36.70.

$$Q = UAF_c\Delta T_{lm}$$

$$U = \frac{Q}{AF_c\Delta T_{lm}} = \frac{\left(102\,274\,\frac{\text{kJ}}{\text{s}}\right)\left(1000\,\frac{\text{W}}{\text{kW}}\right)}{(170\,\text{m}^2)(1)(16.32°C)}$$

$$= \boxed{36\,863\,\text{W/m}^2\text{·}°C}$$

(b) From App. 24.O, the enthalpy of saturated steam at 30 kPa is $h_1 = 2625.3$ kJ/kg.

From App. 24.O, the enthalpy of saturated water at 30 kPa is $h_2 = 289.23$ kJ/kg.

The enthalpy change for steam during condensation is

$$\Delta h = h_1 - h_2$$

$$= 2625.3\,\frac{\text{kJ}}{\text{kg}} - 289.23\,\frac{\text{kJ}}{\text{kg}}$$

$$= 2336.1\,\text{kJ/kg}$$

The heat transfer (Q) from the steam is equal to the heat gained by water.

$$Q = \dot{m}_{\text{steam}}\Delta h$$

$$\dot{m}_{\text{steam}} = \frac{Q}{\Delta h} = \frac{102\,274\,\frac{\text{kJ}}{\text{s}}}{2336.1\,\frac{\text{kJ}}{\text{kg}}} = \boxed{43.78\,\text{kg/s}}$$

The extraction rate is

$$\dot{m}_{\text{steam}}h_1 = \left(43.78\,\frac{\text{kg}}{\text{s}}\right)\left(2625.3\,\frac{\text{kJ}}{\text{kg}}\right)$$

$$= 114\,936\,\text{kW}\quad(114.9\,\text{MW})$$

6.

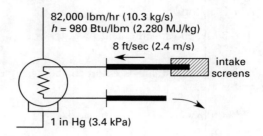

Customary U.S. Solution

(a) From App. 16.B, the dimensions of extra strong 30 in steel pipe are

$$D_i = 2.4167\,\text{ft}$$

$$A_i = 4.5869\,\text{ft}^2$$

From Table 17.2, the specific roughness for steel is $\epsilon = 0.0002$ ft.

$$\frac{\epsilon}{D} = \frac{0.0002\,\text{ft}}{2.4187\,\text{ft}} = 0.000083$$

From the Moody friction factor chart for fully turbulent flow, $f \approx 0.012$.

The head loss from Eq. 17.22 is

$$h_f = \frac{fL\text{v}^2}{2Dg}$$

$$= \frac{(0.012)(120\,\text{ft})\left(8\,\frac{\text{ft}}{\text{sec}}\right)^2}{(2)(2.4187\,\text{ft})\left(32.2\,\frac{\text{ft}}{\text{sec}^2}\right)} = 0.59\,\text{ft}$$

The screen loss is

$$6\,\text{in wg} = (6\,\text{in})\left(\frac{1\,\text{ft}}{12\,\text{in}}\right)$$

$$= 0.5\,\text{ft}$$

$$\text{velocity head} = \frac{\text{v}^2}{2g}$$

$$= \frac{\left(8\,\frac{\text{ft}}{\text{sec}}\right)^2}{(2)\left(32.2\,\frac{\text{ft}}{\text{sec}^2}\right)} = 0.99\,\text{ft}$$

The total head added by a coolant pump (not shown) not including losses inside the condenser is

$$0.59\,\text{ft} + 0.5\,\text{ft} + 0.99\,\text{ft} = \boxed{2.08\,\text{ft}}$$

(b) The condenser pressure is

$$(1\,\text{in wg})\left(0.491\,\frac{\text{lbm}}{\text{in}^3}\right) = 0.5\,\text{lbf/in}^2$$

From App. 24.B, the enthalpy of the saturated liquid is $h_f = 47.11$ Btu/lbm.

From App. 35.A, the specific heat of water is $c_{p,\text{water}} = 1$ Btu/lbm-°F.

The heat lost by the steam is equal to the heat gained by the water.

$$\dot{m}_{\text{water}} c_{p,\text{water}} (\Delta T) = \dot{m}_{\text{steam}} (h_2 - h_f)$$

$$\dot{m}_{\text{water}} \left(1 \frac{\text{Btu}}{\text{lbm-°F}} \right) (10\text{°F})$$

$$= \left(82{,}000 \frac{\text{lbm}}{\text{hr}} \right) \left(980 \frac{\text{Btu}}{\text{lbm}} - 47.11 \frac{\text{Btu}}{\text{lbm}} \right)$$

$$\dot{m}_{\text{water}} = 7.6497 \times 10^6 \text{ lbm/hr}$$

From App. 35.A, the density of water, ρ, is 62.4 lbm/ft³.

$$Q = \frac{\dot{m}_{\text{water}}}{\rho}$$

$$= \frac{\left(7.6497 \times 10^6 \frac{\text{lbm}}{\text{hr}} \right) \left(\frac{1 \text{ hr}}{60 \text{ min}} \right) \left(7.48 \frac{\text{gal}}{\text{ft}^3} \right)}{62.4 \frac{\text{lbm}}{\text{ft}^3}}$$

$$= \boxed{1.528 \times 10^4 \text{ gal/min}}$$

(The flow rate can also be determined from the velocity and pipe area. However, this does not use the 10° data or perform an energy balance.)

SI Solution

(a) From App. 16.B, the dimensions of extra strong 30 in steel pipe, using the footnote from the table, are

$$D_i = (29.00 \text{ in}) \left(25.4 \frac{\text{mm}}{\text{in}} \right) \left(\frac{1 \text{ m}}{1000 \text{ mm}} \right)$$

$$= 0.7366 \text{ m}$$

$$A_i = (660.52 \text{ in}^2) \left(645 \frac{\text{mm}^2}{\text{in}^2} \right) \left(\frac{1 \text{ m}}{1000 \text{ mm}} \right)^2$$

$$= 0.4260 \text{ m}^2$$

From Table 17.2, the specific roughness for steel is $\epsilon = 6.0 \times 10^{-5}$ m.

$$\frac{\epsilon}{D} = \frac{6.0 \times 10^{-5} \text{ m}}{0.7366 \text{ m}} = 0.0000815$$

From the Moody friction factor chart for fully turbulent flow, $f \approx 0.012$.

The head loss from Eq. 17.22 is

$$h_f = \frac{f L \text{v}^2}{2g}$$

$$= \frac{(0.012)(36 \text{ m}) \left(2.4 \frac{\text{m}}{\text{s}} \right)^2}{(2) \left(9.81 \frac{\text{m}}{\text{s}^2} \right)} = 0.1268 \text{ m}$$

$$p_f = \rho g h$$

$$= \left(1000 \frac{\text{kg}}{\text{m}^3} \right) \left(9.81 \frac{\text{m}}{\text{s}^2} \right) (0.1268 \text{ m}) \left(\frac{1 \text{ kPa}}{1000 \text{ Pa}} \right)$$

$$= 1.24 \text{ kPa}$$

The screen loss is 1.5 kPa.

The velocity head is

$$\frac{\text{v}^2}{2g} = \frac{\left(2.4 \frac{\text{m}}{\text{s}} \right)^2}{(2) \left(9.81 \frac{\text{m}}{\text{s}^2} \right)} = 0.2936 \text{ m}$$

$$p_\text{v} = \rho g h$$

$$= \left(1000 \frac{\text{kg}}{\text{m}^3} \right) \left(9.81 \frac{\text{m}}{\text{s}^2} \right) (0.2936 \text{ m}) \left(\frac{1 \text{ kPa}}{1000 \text{ Pa}} \right)$$

$$= 2.88 \text{ kPa}$$

The total head added by a coolant (not shown) not including losses inside the condenser is

$$1.24 \text{ kPa} + 1.5 \text{ kPa} + 2.88 \text{ kPa} = \boxed{5.62 \text{ kPa}}$$

(b) The condenser pressure is 3.4 kPa.

From App. 24.N, the enthalpy of saturated liquid is $h_f = 109.8$ kJ/kg.

From App. 35.B, the specific heat of water is $c_{p,\text{water}} = 4.187$ kJ/kg·K.

The heat lost by the steam is equal to the heat gained by the water.

$$\dot{m}_{\text{water}} c_{p,\text{water}} (\Delta T) = \dot{m}_{\text{steam}} (h_2 - h_f)$$

$$\dot{m}_{\text{water}} \left(4.187 \frac{\text{kJ}}{\text{kg·K}} \right) (5.6\text{°C})$$

$$= \left(10.3 \frac{\text{kg}}{\text{s}} \right) \left[\left(2.280 \frac{\text{MJ}}{\text{kg}} \right) \left(1000 \frac{\text{kJ}}{\text{MJ}} \right) - 109.8 \frac{\text{kJ}}{\text{kg}} \right]$$

$$\dot{m}_{\text{water}} = 953.3 \text{ kg/s}$$

From App. 35.B, the density of water, ρ, is 1000 kg/m³.

$$Q = \frac{\dot{m}_{\text{water}}}{\rho}$$

$$= \left(\frac{953.3 \frac{\text{kg}}{\text{s}}}{1000 \frac{\text{kg}}{\text{m}^3}} \right) \left(1000 \frac{\text{L}}{\text{m}^3} \right) \left(60 \frac{\text{s}}{\text{min}} \right)$$

$$= \boxed{57\,200 \text{ L/min}}$$

7. *Customary U.S. Solution*

From App. 24.A, the enthalpy of saturated liquid at 60°F is $h_1 = 28.08$ Btu/lbm.

From App. 24.B, the enthalpy of saturated steam at 14.7 psia is $h_2 = 1150.5$ Btu/lbm.

The heat transfer rate to the water is

$$Q = \dot{m}(h_2 - h_1)$$
$$= \left(100 \; \frac{\text{lbm}}{\text{hr}}\right)\left(1150.5 \; \frac{\text{Btu}}{\text{lbm}} - 28.08 \; \frac{\text{Btu}}{\text{lbm}}\right)$$
$$= 1.122 \times 10^5 \; \text{Btu/hr}$$
$$= \left(1.122 \times 10^5 \; \frac{\text{Btu}}{\text{hr}}\right)\left(0.2931 \; \frac{\text{W-hr}}{\text{Btu}}\right)\left(\frac{1 \; \text{W}}{1000 \; \text{kW}}\right)$$
$$= 32.89 \; \text{kW}$$

$$\text{cost} = \frac{(32.89 \; \text{kW})\left(\dfrac{\$0.04}{\text{kW-hr}}\right)}{1 - 0.35}$$
$$= \boxed{\$2.02/\text{hr}}$$

SI Solution

From App. 24.N, for saturated liquid at 16°C, $h_1 = 67.19$ kJ/kg.

From App. 24.N, the enthalpy of saturated steam at 101.3 kPa is $h_2 = 2676.1$ kJ/kg.

The heat transfer rate to the water is

$$Q = \dot{m}(h_2 - h_1)$$
$$= \left(0.013 \; \frac{\text{kg}}{\text{s}}\right)\left(2676.1 \; \frac{\text{kJ}}{\text{kg}} - 67.19 \; \frac{\text{kJ}}{\text{kg}}\right)$$
$$= 33.916 \; \text{kW}$$

$$\text{cost} = \frac{(33.916 \; \text{kW})\left(\dfrac{\$0.04}{\text{kW·h}}\right)}{1 - 0.35}$$
$$= \boxed{\$2.09/\text{h}}$$

8. *Customary U.S. Solution*

From App. 24.A, the enthalpy of saturated liquid at 60°F is $h_1 = 28.08$ Btu/lbm.

From App. 24.A, for 40 psia steam, the enthalpy of saturated liquid, h_f, is 236.16 Btu/lbm. The heat of vaporization, h_{fg}, is 933.8 Btu/lbm. The enthalpy is given by Eq. 24.40.

$$h_2 = h_f + x h_{fg}$$
$$= 236.16 \; \frac{\text{Btu}}{\text{lbm}} + (0.98)\left(933.8 \; \frac{\text{Btu}}{\text{lbm}}\right)$$
$$= 1151.28 \; \text{Btu/lbm}$$

The heat transfer rate is

$$Q = \dot{m}(h_2 - h_1)$$
$$= \left(250 \; \frac{\text{lbm}}{\text{hr}}\right)\left(1151.28 \; \frac{\text{Btu}}{\text{lbm}} - 28.08 \; \frac{\text{Btu}}{\text{lbm}}\right)$$
$$\times \left(\frac{1 \; \text{hr}}{60 \; \text{min}}\right)$$
$$= 4680.0 \; \text{Btu/min}$$

Find the volume of gas used at standard conditions for a heating gas (60°F).

$$\dot{V}_{\text{std}} = \dot{V}\left(\frac{T_0}{T}\right)\left(\frac{p}{p_0}\right)$$
$$= \left(13.5 \; \frac{\text{ft}^3}{\text{min}}\right)\left(\frac{460 + 60°\text{F}}{460 + 80°\text{F}}\right)$$
$$\times \left[\frac{(4 \; \text{in Hg} + 30.2 \; \text{in Hg})\left(0.491 \; \dfrac{\text{lbm}}{\text{in}^3}\right)}{14.7 \; \dfrac{\text{lbf}}{\text{in}^2}}\right]$$
$$= 14.85 \; \text{SCFM}$$

The efficiency of the boiler is

$$\eta = \frac{Q}{\text{heat input}}$$
$$= \frac{4680.0 \; \dfrac{\text{Btu}}{\text{lbm}}}{\left(14.85 \; \dfrac{\text{ft}^3}{\text{min}}\right)\left(550 \; \dfrac{\text{Btu}}{\text{ft}^3}\right)} = \boxed{0.573 \; (57.3\%)}$$

SI Solution

From App. 24.N, the enthalpy of saturated liquid at 16°C is $h_1 = 67.19$ kJ/kg.

From App. 24.O, for 300 kPa steam, the enthalpy of saturated liquid, h_f, is 561.47 kJ/kg. The enthalpy of vaporization, h_{fg}, is 2163.8 kJ/kg. The enthalpy is given by Eq. 24.40.

$$h_2 = h_f + x h_{fg}$$
$$= 561.47 \; \frac{\text{kJ}}{\text{kg}} + (0.98)\left(2163.8 \; \frac{\text{kJ}}{\text{kg}}\right)$$
$$= 2682.0 \; \text{kJ/kg}$$

The heat transfer rate is

$$Q = \dot{m}(h_2 - h_1)$$
$$= \left(0.032 \; \frac{\text{kg}}{\text{s}}\right)\left(2682.0 \; \frac{\text{kJ}}{\text{kg}} - 67.19 \; \frac{\text{kJ}}{\text{kg}}\right)$$
$$= 83.67 \; \text{kJ/s}$$

Power Cycles

Find the volume of the gas used at standard conditions for a heating gas (16°C).

$$\dot{V}_{\text{std}} = \dot{V}\left(\frac{T_0}{T}\right)\left(\frac{p}{p_0}\right)$$

$$= \left(6.4 \ \frac{\text{L}}{\text{s}}\right)\left(\frac{1 \ \text{m}^3}{1000 \ \text{L}}\right)\left(\frac{16°\text{C}+273}{26°\text{C}+273}\right)$$

$$\times \left(\frac{13.6 \ \text{kPa} + 102.4 \ \text{kPa}}{101.3 \ \text{kPa}}\right)$$

$$= 0.00708 \ \text{m}^3/\text{s}$$

The efficiency of the boiler is

$$\eta = \frac{Q}{\text{heat input}}$$

$$= \frac{83.67 \ \dfrac{\text{kJ}}{\text{s}}}{\left(0.00708 \ \dfrac{\text{m}^3}{\text{s}}\right)\left(20.5 \ \dfrac{\text{MJ}}{\text{m}^3}\right)\left(1000 \ \dfrac{\text{kJ}}{\text{MJ}}\right)}$$

$$= \boxed{0.576 \quad (57.6\%)}$$

9. *Customary U.S. Solution*

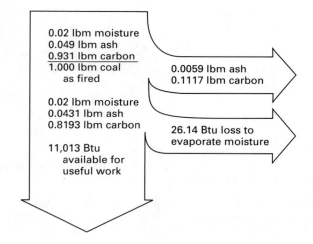

step 1: Determine the actual gravimetric analysis of the coal as fired. Use the successive deletion method on a per-pound basis. 1 lbm of coal contains 0.02 lbm moisture, leaving 0.98 lbm dry coal. Of this, 5% is ash, so the weight of ash is $(0.05)(0.98) = 0.049$ lbm. The remainder $(0.98 \ \text{lbm} - 0.049 \ \text{lbm} = 0.931 \ \text{lbm})$ is assumed to be carbon.

step 2: Determine the ash pit material losses. 12% of dry coal goes to the ash pit.

$$(0.049 \ \text{lbm})(0.12) = 0.0059 \ \text{lbm ash}$$

$$(0.931 \ \text{lbm})(0.12) = 0.1117 \ \text{unburned carbon}$$

step 3: Determine what remains.

0.02 lbm moisture

$$0.049 \ \text{lbm} - 0.0059 \ \text{lbm} = 0.0431 \ \text{lbm ash}$$

$$0.931 \ \text{lbm} - 0.1117 \ \text{lbm} = 0.8193 \ \text{lbm carbon}$$

step 4: Determine energy losses. The 0.02 lbm moisture has to be evaporated. The enthalpy of water at 60°F is read from App. 24.A as 28.08 Btu/lbm. For a constant pressure of 14.7 psia, the enthalpy of water vapor at a combustion temperature of 600°F is read from App. 24.C as 1335.2 Btu/lbm. The energy loss in water evaporation is

$$Q = m(h_2 - h_1)$$

$$= (0.02 \ \text{lbm})\left(1335.2 \ \frac{\text{Btu}}{\text{lbm}} - 28.08 \ \frac{\text{Btu}}{\text{lbm}}\right)$$

$$= 26.14 \ \text{Btu}$$

step 5: Calculate the heating value of the remaining coal. The heating value is given per pound of coal, not per pound of carbon.

$$\text{mass of coal} = 0.0431 \ \text{lbm} + 0.8193 \ \text{lbm}$$

$$= 0.8624 \ \text{lbm}$$

Assume the heating value of coal $\approx$ 12,800 Btu/lbm. The heating value of the remaining coal is

$$(0.8624 \ \text{lbm})\left(12,800 \ \frac{\text{Btu}}{\text{lbm}}\right) = 11,039 \ \text{Btu}$$

step 6: Subtract the losses.

$$11,039 \ \text{Btu} - 26.14 \ \text{Btu} = 11,013 \ \text{Btu}$$

step 7: Find the energy (Q) required to produce steam. From App. 24.A, the enthalpy of water at 120°F is $h_1 = 88.00$ Btu/lbm.

From App. 24.B, the enthalpy of saturated steam at 100 psia is $h_2 = 1187.8$ Btu/lbm.

$$Q = m(h_2 - h_1)$$

$$= (8.23 \ \text{lbm})\left(1187.8 \ \frac{\text{Btu}}{\text{lbm}} - 88.00 \ \frac{\text{Btu}}{\text{lbm}}\right)$$

$$= 9051.3 \ \text{Btu}$$

step 8: The combustion efficiency is

$$\eta = \frac{Q}{HV} = \frac{9051.3 \ \text{Btu}}{11,013 \ \text{Btu}} = \boxed{0.822 \quad (82.2\%)}$$

SI Solution

Since boiler data are based on 1 unit mass of coal fired, steps 1–3 will be the same as for the Customary U.S. Solution. Repeat the rest of the steps as follows.

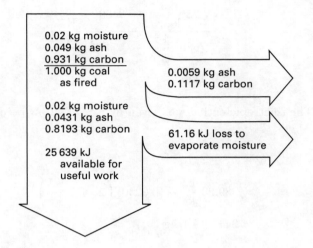

0.02 kg moisture
0.049 kg ash
0.931 kg carbon
1.000 kg coal
as fired

0.0059 kg ash
0.1117 kg carbon

0.02 kg moisture
0.0431 kg ash
0.8193 kg carbon

61.16 kJ loss to
evaporate moisture

25 639 kJ
available for
useful work

step 4: Determine the energy losses due to 0.02 kg moisture evaporation. The enthalpy of water at 16°C is taken from App. 24.N as 67.19 kJ/kg. For constant pressure of 101.3 kPa, the enthalpy of 315°C steam is read from App. 24.P as $\approx$ 312.50 kJ/kg. The energy loss in water evaporation is

$$Q = m(h_2 - h_1)$$
$$= (0.02 \text{ kg}) \left(3125.0 \ \frac{\text{kJ}}{\text{kg}} - 67.19 \ \frac{\text{kJ}}{\text{kg}} \right)$$
$$= 61.16 \text{ kJ}$$

step 5: Calculate the heating value of the remaining coal. The heating value is given per kilogram of coal, not per kilogram of carbon.

$$\text{mass of coal} = 0.0431 \text{ kg} + 0.8193 \text{ kg}$$
$$= 0.8624 \text{ kg}$$

Assume the heating value of coal $\approx$ 29.80 MJ/kg. The heating value of the remaining coal is

$$(0.8624 \text{ kg}) \left(29.80 \ \frac{\text{MJ}}{\text{kg}} \right) \left(1000 \ \frac{\text{kJ}}{\text{MJ}} \right)$$
$$= 25\,700 \text{ kJ}$$

step 6: Subtract the losses to get a heating value of

$$25\,700 \text{ kJ} - 61.16 \text{ kJ} = 25\,639 \text{ kJ}$$

step 7: Find the energy (Q) required to produce steam. From App. 24.N, the enthalpy of water at 50°C is $h_1 = 209.33$ kJ/kg.

From App. 24.O, the enthalpy of saturated steam at 700 kPa is $h_2 = 2763.5$ kJ/kg.

$$Q = m(h_2 - h_1)$$
$$= (8.23 \text{ kg}) \left(2763.5 \ \frac{\text{kJ}}{\text{kg}} - 209.33 \ \frac{\text{kJ}}{\text{kg}} \right)$$
$$= 21\,021 \text{ kJ}$$

step 8: The combustion efficiency is

$$\eta = \frac{Q}{\text{HV}} = \frac{21\,021 \text{ kJ}}{25\,639 \text{ kJ}} = \boxed{0.820 \quad (82.0\%)}$$

10. *Customary U.S. Solution*

(a) Refer to Fig. 28.1.

At point D (leaving the superheater and entering the turbine), the enthalpy, h_D, and entropy, s_D, can be obtained from App. 24.C.

$$h_D = 1520.7 \text{ Btu/lbm}$$
$$s_D = 1.7471 \text{ Btu/lbm-°F}$$

For isentropic expansion through the turbine, $s_E = s_D$. From App. 24.B, the enthalpy of saturated liquid, h_f, the enthalpy of evaporation, h_{fg}, the entropy of saturated liquid, s_f, and the entropy of evaporation, s_{fg}, are

$$h_f = 130.17 \text{ Btu/lbm}$$
$$h_{fg} = 1000.9 \text{ Btu/lbm}$$
$$s_f = 0.2349 \text{ Btu/lbm-°F}$$
$$s_{fg} = 1.6093 \text{ Btu/lbm-°F}$$

The quality of the mixture for an isentropic process is given by Eq. 24.41 (at point E).

$$x_E = \frac{s_E - s_f}{s_{fg}}$$
$$= \frac{1.7471 \ \dfrac{\text{Btu}}{\text{lbm-°F}} - 0.2349 \ \dfrac{\text{Btu}}{\text{lbm-°F}}}{1.6093 \ \dfrac{\text{Btu}}{\text{lbm-°F}}}$$
$$= 0.9397$$

The isentropic enthalpy is given by Eq. 24.40 (at point E).

$$h_E = h_f + x_E h_{fg}$$
$$= 130.17 \ \frac{\text{Btu}}{\text{lbm}} + (0.9397) \left(1000.9 \ \frac{\text{Btu}}{\text{lbm}} \right)$$
$$= 1070.7 \text{ Btu/lbm}$$

Power Cycles

From Eq. 27.17, the actual enthalpy of steam at point E is

$$h'_E = h_D - \eta_s(h_D - h_E)$$

$$= 1520 \, \frac{\text{Btu}}{\text{lbm}} - (0.75) \left(1520 \, \frac{\text{Btu}}{\text{lbm}} - 1070.7 \, \frac{\text{Btu}}{\text{lbm}} \right)$$

$$= 1183.0 \, \text{Btu/lbm}$$

Since the pump work is negligible, the mass flow rate of steam is

$$\dot{m} = \frac{P}{W_{\text{turbine}}} = \frac{P}{h_D - h'_E}$$

$$= \frac{(200 \, \text{MW}) \left(10^6 \, \frac{\text{W}}{\text{MW}} \right) \left(3.4121 \, \frac{\text{Btu}}{\text{hr}} \right)}{1520 \, \frac{\text{Btu}}{\text{lbm}} - 1183.0 \, \frac{\text{Btu}}{\text{lbm}}}$$

$$= \boxed{2.025 \times 10^6 \, \text{lbm/hr}}$$

(b) The heat removed by the condenser is given by Eq. 27.30.

$$\dot{Q} = \dot{m}(h'_E - h_F)$$

From App. 24.B, at 5 psia, $h_F = 130.17$ Btu/lbm.

$$\dot{Q} = \left(2.025 \times 10^6 \, \frac{\text{lbm}}{\text{hr}} \right) \left(1183.0 \, \frac{\text{Btu}}{\text{lbm}} - 130.17 \, \frac{\text{Btu}}{\text{lbm}} \right)$$

$$= \boxed{2.132 \times 10^9 \, \text{Btu/hr}}$$

SI Solution

(a) Refer to Fig. 28.1.

At point D (leaving the superheater and entering the turbine), the enthalpy, h_D, and entropy, s_D, can be obtained from the Mollier diagram.

$$h_D \approx 3430 \, \text{kJ/kg}$$

$$s_D \approx 7.25 \, \text{kJ/kg·K}$$

For isentropic expansion through the turbine, $s_E = s_D$. From App. 24.O, the enthalpy of saturated liquid, h_f, the enthalpy of evaporation, h_{fg}, the entropy of saturated liquid, s_f, and the entropy of saturated vapor, s_g, are

$$h_f = 289.23 \, \text{kJ/kg}$$

$$h_{fg} = 2336.1 \, \text{kJ/kg}$$

$$s_f = 0.9439 \, \text{kJ/kg·K}$$

$$s_g = 7.7686 \, \text{kJ/kg·K}$$

The quality of the mixture for an isentropic process is given by Eq. 24.41 (at point ϵ) as

$$x_E = \frac{s_E - s_f}{s_{fg}} = \frac{s_E - s_f}{s_g - s_f}$$

$$= \frac{7.25 \, \frac{\text{kJ}}{\text{kg·K}} - 0.9439 \, \frac{\text{kJ}}{\text{kg·K}}}{7.7686 \, \frac{\text{kJ}}{\text{kg·K}} - 0.9439 \, \frac{\text{kJ}}{\text{kg·K}}}$$

$$= 0.9240$$

The isentropic enthalpy is given by Eq. 24.40 (at point E) as

$$h_E = h_f + x_E h_{fg}$$

$$= 289.23 \, \frac{\text{kJ}}{\text{kg}} + (0.9240) \left(2336.1 \, \frac{\text{kJ}}{\text{kg}} \right)$$

$$= 2447.8 \, \text{kJ/kg}$$

From Eq. 27.17, the actual enthalpy of steam at point E is

$$h'_E = h_D - \eta_s(h_D - h_E)$$

$$= 3430 \, \frac{\text{kJ}}{\text{kg}} - (0.75) \left(3430 \, \frac{\text{kJ}}{\text{kg}} - 2447.8 \, \frac{\text{kJ}}{\text{kg}} \right)$$

$$= 2693.4 \, \text{kJ/kg}$$

Since the pump work is negligible, the mass flow rate of steam is

$$\dot{m} = \frac{P}{W_{\text{turbine}}} = \frac{P}{h_D - h'_E}$$

$$= \frac{(200 \, \text{MW}) \left(10^3 \, \frac{\text{kW}}{\text{MW}} \right)}{3430 \, \frac{\text{kJ}}{\text{kg}} - 2693.4 \, \frac{\text{kJ}}{\text{kg}}}$$

$$= \boxed{271.5 \, \text{kg/s}}$$

(b) The heat removed by the condenser is given by Eq. 27.30.

$$\dot{Q} = \dot{m}(h'_E - h_F)$$

From App. 24.O at 30 kPa, $h_F = 289.23$ kJ/kg.

$$\dot{Q} = \left(271.5 \, \frac{\text{kg}}{\text{s}} \right) \left(2693.4 \, \frac{\text{kJ}}{\text{kg}} - 289.23 \, \frac{\text{kJ}}{\text{kg}} \right)$$

$$= \boxed{6.527 \times 10^5 \, \text{kW}}$$

11. *Customary U.S. Solution*

The following illustration shows one of N layers. Each layer consists of 24 tubes, only 3 of which are shown.

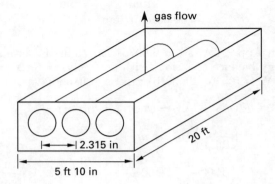

Assume stack gases consist primarily of nitrogen. The average gas temperature is

$$T_{\text{ave}} = \left(\tfrac{1}{2}\right)(635°F + 470°F) + 460 = 1012.5°R$$

The specific heat of nitrogen is calculated from Eq. 24.94 using constants given in Table 24.9.

$$c_p = A + BT + CT^2 + \frac{D}{\sqrt{T}}$$
$$= 0.2510 + (-1.63 \times 10^{-5})(1012.5°R)$$
$$+ (20.4 \times 10^{-9})(1012.5°R)^2 + 0$$
$$= 0.2554 \text{ Btu/lbm-°R}$$

Assume counterflow operation. The two end temperature differences are

$$\Delta T_A = 635°F - 285°F = 350°F$$
$$\Delta T_B = 470°F - 212°F = 258°F$$

635°F	gases →	470°F
$\Delta T = 350°F$		$\Delta T = 258°F$
285°F	← water	212°F

The logarithmic temperature difference is

$$\Delta T_{lm} = \frac{\Delta T_A - \Delta T_B}{\ln\left(\dfrac{\Delta T_A}{\Delta T_B}\right)} = \frac{350°F - 258°F}{\ln\left(\dfrac{350°F}{258°F}\right)}$$
$$= 301.7°F$$

The heat transfer from the temperature gain of water is equal to the heat transfer based on the logarithmic mean temperature difference.

$$Q = \dot{m}c_p\Delta T = U_0 A_0 \Delta T_{lm}$$
$$\left(191{,}000 \ \frac{\text{lbm}}{\text{hr}}\right)\left(0.2554 \ \frac{\text{Btu}}{\text{lbm-°R}}\right)(635°F - 470°F)$$
$$= \left(10 \ \frac{\text{Btu}}{\text{hr-ft}^2\text{-°F}}\right)A_0(301.7°F)$$
$$A_0 = 2667.9 \text{ ft}^2$$

The tube area per bank is

$$A_{\text{bank}} = N\pi D_0 L$$
$$= 24\pi(1.315 \text{ in})\left(\frac{1 \text{ ft}}{12 \text{ in}}\right)(20 \text{ ft})$$
$$= 165.2 \text{ ft}^2$$

$$\text{no. of layers} = \frac{A_0}{A_{\text{bank}}}$$
$$= \frac{2667.9 \text{ ft}^2}{165.2 \text{ ft}^2} = \boxed{16.1 \quad [\text{say } 17]}$$

SI Solution

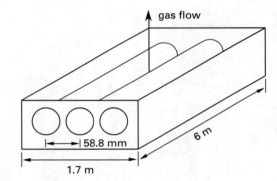

Assume stack gas consists primarily of nitrogen. The average gas temperature is

$$T_{\text{ave}} = \left(\tfrac{1}{2}\right)(335°C + 240°C) + 273 = 560.5\text{K} \quad (1009°R)$$

Use the value of the specific heat of nitrogen that was calculated for the Customary U.S. Solution since the two temperatures are almost the same.

$$c_p = \left(0.2554 \ \frac{\text{Btu}}{\text{lbm-°R}}\right)\left(4186.8 \ \frac{\frac{\text{J}}{\text{kg·°C}}}{\frac{\text{Btu}}{\text{lbm-°R}}}\right)$$
$$= 1069 \text{ J/kg·°C}$$

Assume counterflow operation. The two end temperature differences are

$$\Delta T_A = 335°C - 140°C = 195°C$$
$$\Delta T_B = 240°C - 100°C = 140°C$$

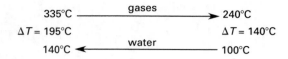

The logarithmic mean temperature difference is

$$\Delta T_{lm} = \frac{\Delta T_A - \Delta T_B}{\ln\left(\dfrac{\Delta T_A}{\Delta T_B}\right)} = \frac{195°C - 140°C}{\ln\left(\dfrac{195°C}{140°C}\right)}$$

$$= 166.0°C$$

The heat transfer from the temperature gain of water is equal to the heat transfer based on the logarithmic mean temperature difference.

$$Q = \dot{m}c_p\Delta T = U_0 A_0 \Delta T_{lm}$$

$$\left(24\ \frac{kg}{s}\right)\left(1069\ \frac{J}{kg·°C}\right)(335°C - 240°C)$$

$$= \left(57\ \frac{W}{m^2·°C}\right) A_0(166.0°C)$$

$$A_0 = 257.6\ m^2$$

The tube area per bank is

$$A_{bank} = N\pi D_0 L$$

$$= 24\pi(33.4\ mm)\left(\frac{1\ m}{1000\ mm}\right)(6\ m)$$

$$= 15.1\ m^2$$

$$\text{no. of layers} = \frac{A_0}{A_{bank}}$$

$$= \frac{257.6\ m^2}{15.1\ m^2} = \boxed{17.1 \quad [\text{say } 18]}$$

12.

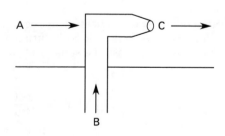

Customary U.S. Solution

(a) The enthalpy, h_A, and entropy, s_A, for steam at 600°F and 200 psia can be obtained from App. 24.C.

$$h_A = 1322.1\ Btu/lbm$$

$$s_A = 1.6767\ Btu/lbm·°R$$

For water at 82°F, enthalpy can be obtained for saturated water from App. 24.A and corrected for compression using App. 24.D.

$$h_B = 50.08\ \frac{Btu}{lbm} + 0.55\ \frac{Btu}{lbm}$$

$$= 50.63\ Btu/lbm$$

From App. 24.A, $s_B = 0.09701$ Btu/lbm-°F. From an energy balance equation (with $Q = 0$, $v_1 = 0$, $\Delta z = 0$, and $W = 0$), Eq. 25.30(b) can be written as

$$0 = h_C(m_A + m_B) - (h_A m_A + h_B m_B)$$

$$\quad - \left(\frac{v_C^2}{2g_c J}\right)(m_A + m_B)$$

$$= h_C\left(1000\ \frac{lbm}{hr} + 50\ \frac{lbm}{hr}\right) - \left[\left(1322.1\ \frac{Btu}{lbm}\right)\right.$$

$$\times \left(1000\ \frac{lbm}{hr}\right) + \left.\left(50.08\ \frac{Btu}{lbm}\right)\left(50\ \frac{lbm}{hr}\right)\right]$$

$$\quad - \frac{\left(2000\ \dfrac{ft}{sec}\right)^2\left(1000\ \dfrac{lbm}{hr} + 50\ \dfrac{lbm}{hr}\right)}{(2)\left(32.2\ \dfrac{lbm\text{-}ft}{lbf\text{-}sec^2}\right)\left(778\ \dfrac{ft\text{-}lbf}{Btu}\right)}$$

$$h_C = 1181.7\ Btu/lbm$$

$$p_C = 100\ psia$$

Since the enthalpy of saturated steam at 100 psia, h_g, from App. 24.B, is greater than h_C, steam leaving the desuperheater is not 100% saturated. From App. 24.B, the temperature of the saturated steam mix is $\boxed{327.86°F.}$

(b) The quality of the steam leaving can be determined using Eq. 24.40.

$$h_C = h_f + x h_{fg}$$

From App. 24.B, for 100 psia, $h_f = 298.6$ Btu/lbm and $h_{fg} = 889.2$ Btu/lbm.

$$x = \frac{1181.7\ \dfrac{Btu}{lbm} - 298.6\ \dfrac{Btu}{lbm}}{889.2\ \dfrac{Btu}{lbm}}$$

$$= \boxed{0.993}$$

SI Solution

(a) The enthalpy, h_A, and entropy, s_A, for steam at 300°C and 1.5 MPa can be obtained from App. 24.P.

$$h_A = 3037.6\ kJ/kg$$

$$s_A = 6.9179\ kJ/kg·K$$

App. 24.Q does not go down to 1.5 MPa, so disregard the effect of compression. For water at 28°C from App. 24.N, $h_B = 117.43$ kJ/kg.

Similarly, from App. 24.N, $s_B = 0.4093$ kJ/kg·K.

From an energy balance equation (with $Q = 0$, $v_1 = 0$, $\Delta z = 0$, and $W = 0$), Eq. 25.30(a) can be written as

$$0 = h_C(m_A + m_B) - (m_A h_A + m_B h_B)$$
$$- \left(\frac{v_C^2}{2}\right)(m_A + m_B)$$
$$= h_C \left(0.13 \ \frac{kg}{s} + 0.0063 \ \frac{kg}{s}\right) - \left[\left(0.13 \ \frac{kg}{s}\right)\right.$$
$$\times \left(3037.6 \ \frac{kJ}{kg}\right) + \left(0.0063 \ \frac{kg}{s}\right)\left(117.43 \ \frac{kJ}{kg}\right)\right]$$
$$- \left(\frac{\left(600 \ \frac{m}{s}\right)^2}{2}\right)\left(0.13 \ \frac{kg}{s} + 0.0063 \ \frac{kg}{s}\right)$$
$$\times \left(\frac{1 \ kJ}{1000 \ J}\right)$$

$h_C = 2722.6$ kJ/kg

$p_C = 700$ kPa

Since the enthalpy of saturated steam at 700 kPa, from App. 24.O, is greater than h_C, steam leaving the desuperheater is not 100% saturated. From App. 24.O, the temperature of the steam mix is $\boxed{165.0°C.}$

(b) The quality of steam leaving can be determined using Eq. 24.40.

$$h_C = h_f + x h_{fg}$$

From App. 24.O, for 700 kPa, $h_f = 697.22$ kJ/kg and $h_{fg} = 2066.3$ kJ/kg.

$$x = \frac{2722.6 \ \frac{kJ}{kg} - 697.22 \ \frac{kJ}{kg}}{2066.3 \ \frac{kJ}{kg}} = \boxed{0.9802}$$

13. *Customary U.S. Solution*

(a) Work with the original system to find the steam flow.

From App. 24.C, at 100 psia and 400°F, $h_A = 1227.5$ Btu/lbm.

From App. 24.A, at 70°F, $h_B = 38.09$ Btu/lbm.

From App. 24.A, at 180°F, $h_C = 147.99$ Btu/lbm.

Let $x =$ fraction of steam in mixture.

From the energy balance equation,

$$m_A h_A + m_B h_B = m_C h_C$$

$$x\left(1227.5 \ \frac{Btu}{lbm}\right)$$
$$+ (1-x)\left(38.09 \ \frac{Btu}{lbm}\right) = (1)\left(147.99 \ \frac{Btu}{lbm}\right)$$
$$x = 0.0924$$

The steam flow is

$$\dot{m} = x\left(2000 \ \frac{lbm}{hr}\right) = (0.0924)\left(2000 \ \frac{lbm}{hr}\right)$$
$$= 184.8 \ lbm/hr$$

Since the pressure drop across the heater is 5 psi,

$$p_D = p_F + 5 \ psi$$
$$= 20 \ psia + 5 \ psi = 25 \ psia$$

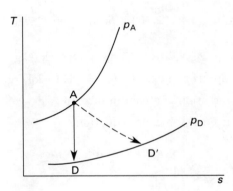

With isentropic expansion through the turbine, using the Mollier diagram, $h_D \approx 1115$ Btu/lbm (liquid-vapor mixture).

From Eq. 27.17,

$$h'_D = h_A - \eta_s(h_A - h_D)$$
$$= 1227.5 \ \frac{Btu}{lbm} - (0.60)\left(1227.5 \ \frac{Btu}{lbm} - 1115 \ \frac{Btu}{lbm}\right)$$
$$= 1160 \ Btu/lbm$$

The power output is

$$P = \eta \dot{m}(h_A - h'_D)$$

$$= \frac{(0.96)\left(184.8 \ \frac{lbm}{hr}\right)}{\times \left(1227.5 \ \frac{Btu}{lbm} - 1160 \ \frac{Btu}{lbm}\right)\left(778 \ \frac{ft\text{-}lbf}{Btu}\right)}{\left(3600 \ \frac{sec}{hr}\right)\left(550 \ \frac{ft\text{-}lbf}{hp\text{-}sec}\right)}$$

$$= \boxed{4.71 \ hp}$$

(b) Let x = fraction of steam entering the heater.

From the energy balance equation,

$$m_A h_D' + m_B h_B = m_C h_C$$

$$x \left(1160 \ \frac{\text{Btu}}{\text{lbm}}\right)$$

$$+ (1-x)\left(38.09 \ \frac{\text{Btu}}{\text{lbm}}\right) = (1)\left(147.99 \ \frac{\text{Btu}}{\text{lbm}}\right)$$

$$x = 0.098$$

$$\dot{m}_F = \frac{184.8 \ \frac{\text{lbm}}{\text{hr}}}{0.098}$$

$$= \boxed{1886 \ \text{lbm/hr}}$$

SI Solution

(a) Work with the original system to find the steam flow.

From App. 24.N, at 700 kPa and 200°C, h_A = 2884.8 kJ/kg.

From App. 24.N, at 21°C, h_B = 88.14 kJ/kg.

From App. 24.N, at 80°C, h_C = 334.91 kJ/kg.

Let x = fraction of steam in mixture.

From the energy balance equation,

$$m_A h_A + m_B h_B = m_C h_C$$

$$x \left(2884.8 \ \frac{\text{kJ}}{\text{kg}}\right)$$

$$+ (1-x)\left(88.14 \ \frac{\text{kJ}}{\text{kg}}\right) = (1)\left(334.91 \ \frac{\text{kJ}}{\text{kg}}\right)$$

$$x = 0.0882$$

The steam flow is

$$\dot{m} = x \left(0.25 \ \frac{\text{kg}}{\text{s}}\right) = (0.0882)\left(0.25 \ \frac{\text{kg}}{\text{s}}\right)$$

$$= 0.0221 \ \text{kg/s}$$

Since the pressure drop across the heater is 30 kPa,

$$p_D = p_F + 30 \ \text{kPa}$$

$$= 150 \ \text{kPa} + 30 \ \text{kPa}$$

$$= 180 \ \text{kPa}$$

For isentropic expansion through the turbine from the Mollier diagram, $h_D \approx 2583$ kJ/kg (liquid-vapor mixture).

From Eq. 27.17,

$$h_D' = h_A - \eta_s (h_A - h_D)$$

$$= 2884.8 \ \frac{\text{kJ}}{\text{kg}} - (0.60)\left(2884.8 \ \frac{\text{kJ}}{\text{kg}} - 2583 \ \frac{\text{kJ}}{\text{kg}}\right)$$

$$= 2703.7 \ \text{kJ/kg}$$

The power output is

$$P = \eta \dot{m}(h_A - h_D')$$

$$= (0.96)\left(0.0221 \ \frac{\text{kg}}{\text{s}}\right)\left(2884.8 \ \frac{\text{kJ}}{\text{kg}} - 2703.7 \ \frac{\text{kJ}}{\text{kg}}\right)$$

$$= \boxed{3.84 \ \text{kW}}$$

(b) Let x = fraction of steam entering the heater.

From the energy balance equation,

$$m_A h_D' + m_B h_B = m_C h_C$$

$$x \left(2703.7 \ \frac{\text{kJ}}{\text{kg}}\right)$$

$$+ (1-x)\left(88.14 \ \frac{\text{kJ}}{\text{kg}}\right) = (1)\left(334.91 \ \frac{\text{kJ}}{\text{kg}}\right)$$

$$x = 0.0943$$

$$\dot{m}_F = \frac{0.0221 \ \frac{\text{kg}}{\text{s}}}{0.0943}$$

$$= \boxed{0.234 \ \text{kg/s}}$$

1. Customary U.S. Solution

The maximum possible thermal efficiency is given by the Carnot cycle. From Eq. 28.8,

$$\eta_{th} = \frac{T_{high} - T_{low}}{T_{high}}$$

The absolute temperatures are

$$T_{high} = 650°F + 460 = 1110°R$$
$$T_{low} = 100°F + 460 = 560°F$$
$$\eta_{th} = \frac{1110°R - 560°R}{1110°R} = \boxed{0.495 \quad (49.5\%)}$$

SI Solution

The maximum possible thermal efficiency is given by the Carnot cycle. From Eq. 28.8,

$$\eta_{th} = \frac{T_{high} - T_{low}}{T_{high}}$$

The absolute temperatures are

$$T_{high} = 340°C + 273 = 613K$$
$$T_{low} = 38°C + 273 = 311K$$
$$\eta_{th} = \frac{613K - 311K}{613K} = \boxed{0.493 \quad (49.3\%)}$$

2. Customary U.S. Solution

Refer to the Carnot cycle (Fig. 28.2).

At point A, from App. 24.A, for saturated liquid at $T_A = 650°F$,

$$h_A = 696.5 \text{ Btu/lbm}$$
$$s_A = 0.8836 \text{ Btu/lbm-°F}$$

At point B, from App. 24.A, for saturated vapor at $T_B = 650°F$,

$$h_B = 1118.7 \text{ Btu/lbm}$$
$$s_B = 1.2643 \text{ Btu/lbm}$$

At point C,

$$T_C = 100°F$$
$$s_C = s_B = 1.2643 \text{ Btu/lbm-°F}$$

From App. 24.A,

$$s_f = 0.1296 \text{ Btu/lbm-°F}$$
$$s_g = 1.9822 \text{ Btu/lbm-°F}$$
$$h_f = 68.05 \text{ Btu/lbm}$$
$$h_{fg} = 1037 \text{ Btu/lbm}$$

$$x_C = \frac{s_C - s_f}{s_g - s_f} = \frac{1.2643 \frac{\text{Btu}}{\text{lbm-°F}} - 0.1296 \frac{\text{Btu}}{\text{lbm-°F}}}{1.9822 \frac{\text{Btu}}{\text{lbm-°F}} - 0.1296 \frac{\text{Btu}}{\text{lbm-°F}}}$$

$$= 0.612$$

$$h_C = h_f + x_C h_{fg}$$
$$= 68.05 \frac{\text{Btu}}{\text{lbm}} + (0.612)\left(1037 \frac{\text{Btu}}{\text{lbm}}\right)$$
$$= 702.7 \text{ Btu/lbm}$$

At point D,

$$T_D = 100°F$$
$$s_D = s_A = 0.8836 \text{ Btu/lbm-°F}$$

$$x_D = \frac{s_D - s_f}{s_g - s_f} = \frac{0.8836 \frac{\text{Btu}}{\text{lbm-°F}} - 0.1296 \frac{\text{Btu}}{\text{lbm-°F}}}{1.9822 \frac{\text{Btu}}{\text{lbm-°F}} - 0.1296 \frac{\text{Btu}}{\text{lbm-°F}}}$$

$$= 0.407$$

$$h_D = h_f + x_D h_{fg}$$
$$= 68.05 \frac{\text{Btu}}{\text{lbm}} + (0.407)\left(1037 \frac{\text{Btu}}{\text{lbm}}\right)$$
$$= 490.1 \text{ Btu/lbm}$$

From Eq. 28.9, due to the inefficiency of the turbine,

$$h'_C = h_B - \eta_{s,turbine}(h_B - h_C)$$
$$= 1118.7 \frac{\text{Btu}}{\text{lbm}} - (0.9)\left(1118.7 \frac{\text{Btu}}{\text{lbm}} - 702.7 \frac{\text{Btu}}{\text{lbm}}\right)$$
$$= 744.3 \text{ Btu/lbm}$$

From Eq. 28.10, due to the inefficiency of the pump,

$$h'_A = h_D + \frac{h_A - h_D}{\eta_{s,\text{pump}}}$$

$$= 490.1 \,\frac{\text{Btu}}{\text{lbm}} + \frac{696.5 \,\frac{\text{Btu}}{\text{lbm}} - 490.1 \,\frac{\text{Btu}}{\text{lbm}}}{0.8}$$

$$= 748.1 \text{ Btu/lbm}$$

From Eq. 28.8, the thermal efficiency of the entire cycle is

$$\eta_{\text{th}} = \frac{(h_B - h'_C) - (h'_A - h_D)}{h_B - h'_A}$$

$$= \frac{\left(1118.7 \,\frac{\text{Btu}}{\text{lbm}} - 744.3 \,\frac{\text{Btu}}{\text{lbm}}\right) - \left(748.1 \,\frac{\text{Btu}}{\text{lbm}} - 490.1 \,\frac{\text{Btu}}{\text{lbm}}\right)}{1118.7 \,\frac{\text{Btu}}{\text{lbm}} - 748.1 \,\frac{\text{Btu}}{\text{lbm}}}$$

$$= \boxed{0.314 \ (31.4\%)}$$

SI Solution

At point A, $T_A = 340°C$.

From App. 24.N, for saturated liquid,

$$h_A = 1594.2 \text{ kJ/kg}$$

$$s_A = 3.6594 \text{ kJ/kg·K}$$

At point B, $T_B = 340°C$.

From App. 24.N, for saturated vapor,

$$h_B = 2622.0 \text{ kJ/kg}$$

$$s_B = 5.3357 \text{ kJ/kg·K}$$

At point C,

$$T_C = 38°C$$

$$s_C = s_B = 5.3357 \text{ kJ/kg·K}$$

From App. 24.N,

$$s_f = 0.5458 \text{ kJ/kg·K}$$

$$s_g = 8.2950 \text{ kJ/kg·K}$$

$$h_f = 159.21 \text{ kJ/kg}$$

$$h_{fg} = 2411.5 \text{ kJ/kg}$$

$$x_C = \frac{s_C - s_f}{s_g - s_f} = \frac{5.3357 \,\frac{\text{kJ}}{\text{kg·K}} - 0.5458 \,\frac{\text{kJ}}{\text{kg·K}}}{8.2950 \,\frac{\text{kJ}}{\text{kg·K}} - 0.5458 \,\frac{\text{kJ}}{\text{kg·K}}}$$

$$= 0.618$$

$$h_C = h_f + x_C h_{fg}$$

$$= 159.21 \,\frac{\text{kJ}}{\text{kg}} + (0.618)\left(2411.5 \,\frac{\text{kJ}}{\text{kg}}\right)$$

$$= 1649.5 \text{ kJ/kg}$$

At point D,

$$T_D = 38°C$$

$$s_D = s_A = 3.6594 \text{ kJ/kg·K}$$

$$x_D = \frac{s_D - s_f}{s_g - s_f}$$

$$= \frac{3.6594 \,\frac{\text{kJ}}{\text{kg·K}} - 0.5458 \,\frac{\text{kJ}}{\text{kg·K}}}{8.2950 \,\frac{\text{kJ}}{\text{kg·K}} - 0.5458 \,\frac{\text{kJ}}{\text{kg·K}}}$$

$$= 0.402$$

$$h_D = h_f + x_D h_{fg}$$

$$= 159.21 \,\frac{\text{kJ}}{\text{kg}} + (0.402)\left(2411.5 \,\frac{\text{kJ}}{\text{kg}}\right)$$

$$= 1128.6 \text{ kJ/kg}$$

From Eq. 28.9, due to the inefficiency of the turbine,

$$h'_C = h_B - \eta_{s,\text{turbine}}(h_B - h_C)$$

$$= 2622.0 \,\frac{\text{kJ}}{\text{kg}} - (0.9)\left(2622.0 \,\frac{\text{kJ}}{\text{kg}} - 1649.5 \,\frac{\text{kJ}}{\text{kg}}\right)$$

$$= 1746.7 \text{ kJ/kg}$$

From Eq. 28.10, due to the inefficiency of the pump,

$$h'_A = h_D + \frac{h_A - h_D}{\eta_{s,\text{pump}}}$$

$$= 1128.6 \,\frac{\text{kJ}}{\text{kg}} + \frac{1594.2 \,\frac{\text{kJ}}{\text{kg}} - 1128.6 \,\frac{\text{kJ}}{\text{kg}}}{0.8}$$

$$= 1710.6 \text{ kJ/kg}$$

From Eq. 28.8, the thermal efficiency of the entire cycle is

$$\eta_{\text{th}} = \frac{(h_B - h'_C) - (h'_A - h_D)}{h_B - h'_A}$$

$$= \frac{\left(2622 \,\frac{\text{kJ}}{\text{kg}} - 1746.7 \,\frac{\text{kJ}}{\text{kg}}\right) - \left(1710.6 \,\frac{\text{kJ}}{\text{kg}} - 1128.6 \,\frac{\text{kJ}}{\text{kg}}\right)}{2622 \,\frac{\text{kJ}}{\text{kg}} - 1710.6 \,\frac{\text{kJ}}{\text{kg}}}$$

$$= \boxed{0.322 \ (32.2\%)}$$

3. *Customary U.S. Solution*

From Eq. 28.1, the thermal efficiency is

$$\eta_{th} = \frac{Q_{in} - Q_{out}}{Q_{in}}$$

The condenser load is $Q_{out} = 3.07 \times 10^9$ Btu/hr.

The net work is

$$W_{net} = Q_{in} - Q_{out}$$

The boiler load is

$$Q_{in} = W_{net} + Q_{out}$$

$$= (600 \text{ MW})\left(1000 \frac{\text{kW}}{\text{MW}}\right)\left(3412 \frac{\frac{\text{Btu}}{\text{hr}}}{\text{kW}}\right)$$

$$+ 3.07 \times 10^9 \frac{\text{Btu}}{\text{hr}}$$

$$= 5.12 \times 10^9 \text{ Btu/hr}$$

$$\eta_{th} = \frac{5.12 \times 10^9 \frac{\text{Btu}}{\text{hr}} - 3.07 \times 10^9 \frac{\text{Btu}}{\text{hr}}}{5.12 \times 10^9 \frac{\text{Btu}}{\text{hr}}}$$

$$= \boxed{0.400 \ (40\%)}$$

SI Solution

From Eq. 28.1, the thermal efficiency is

$$\eta_{th} = \frac{Q_{in} - Q_{out}}{Q_{in}}$$

The condenser load is $Q_{out} = 900$ MW.

The boiler load is

$$Q_{in} = W_{net} + Q_{out}$$
$$= 600 \text{ MW} + 900 \text{ MW}$$
$$= 1500 \text{ MW}$$
$$\eta_{th} = \frac{1500 \text{ MW} - 900 \text{ MW}}{1500 \text{ MW}}$$
$$= \boxed{0.400 \ (40\%)}$$

4. *Customary U.S. Solution*

At point A, $p_A = 100$ psia.

From App. 24.B, the enthalpy of saturated liquid is $h_A = 298.6$ Btu/lbm.

At point B, $p_B = 100$ psia.

From App.24.B, the enthalpy and entropy of saturated vapor are

$$h_B = 1187.8 \text{ Btu/lbm}$$
$$s_B = 1.6034 \text{ Btu/lbm-}°\text{R}$$

At point C,

$$p_C = 1 \text{ atm}$$
$$s_C = s_B = 1.6034 \text{ Btu/lbm-}°\text{R}$$

From App. 24.B, the entropy and enthalpy of saturated liquid and entropy and enthalpy of vaporization are

$$s_f = 0.3121 \text{ Btu/lbm-}°\text{R}$$
$$h_f = 180.15 \text{ Btu/lbm}$$
$$s_{fg} = 1.4446 \text{ Btu/lbm-}°\text{R}$$
$$h_{fg} = 970.4 \text{ Btu/lbm}$$

$$x_C = \frac{s_C - s_f}{s_{fg}} = \frac{1.6034 \frac{\text{Btu}}{\text{lbm-}°\text{R}} - 0.3121 \frac{\text{Btu}}{\text{lbm-}°\text{R}}}{1.4446 \frac{\text{Btu}}{\text{lbm-}°\text{R}}}$$

$$= 0.894$$

$$h_C = h_f + x_C h_{fg}$$
$$= 180.15 \frac{\text{Btu}}{\text{lbm}} + (0.894)\left(970.4 \frac{\text{Btu}}{\text{lbm}}\right)$$
$$= 1047.7 \text{ Btu/lbm}$$

At point D, $T = 80°$F and $p_D = 1$ atm (subcooled). h and v are essentially independent of pressure.

From App. 24.A, the enthalpy and specific volume of saturated liquid are

$$h_D = 48.09 \text{ Btu/lbm}$$
$$v_D = 0.01607 \text{ ft}^3/\text{lbm}$$

At point E, $p_E = p_A = 100$ psia.

From Eq. 28.14,

$$h_E = h_D + v_D(p_E - p_D)$$

$$= 48.09 \frac{\text{Btu}}{\text{lbm}} + \left(0.01607 \frac{\text{ft}^3}{\text{lbm}}\right)$$

$$\times \frac{\left(100 \frac{\text{lbf}}{\text{in}^2} - 14.7 \frac{\text{lbf}}{\text{in}^2}\right)\left(144 \frac{\text{in}^2}{\text{ft}^2}\right)}{778 \frac{\text{ft-lbf}}{\text{Btu}}}$$

$$= 48.34 \text{ Btu/lbm}$$

From Eq. 28.18, due to the inefficiency of the turbine,

$$h'_C = h_B - \eta_{s,turbine}(h_B - h_C)$$

$$= 1187.8 \frac{\text{Btu}}{\text{lbm}} - (0.80)\left(1187.8 \frac{\text{Btu}}{\text{lbm}}\right.$$

$$\left. - 1047.7 \frac{\text{Btu}}{\text{lbm}}\right)$$

$$= 1075.7 \text{ Btu/lbm}$$

From Eq. 28.19, due to the inefficiency of the pump,

$$h'_E = h_D + \frac{h_E - h_D}{\eta_{s,pump}}$$

$$= 48.09 \ \frac{Btu}{lbm} + \frac{48.34 \ \frac{Btu}{lbm} - 48.09 \ \frac{Btu}{lbm}}{0.6}$$

$$= 48.51 \ Btu/lbm$$

From Eq. 28.17, the thermal efficiency of the cycle is

$$\eta_{th} = \frac{(h_B - h'_C) - (h'_E - h_D)}{h_B - h'_E}$$

$$= \frac{\left(1187.8 \ \frac{Btu}{lbm} - 1075.7 \ \frac{Btu}{lbm}\right) - \left(48.51 \ \frac{Btu}{lbm} - 48.09 \ \frac{Btu}{lbm}\right)}{1187.8 \ \frac{Btu}{lbm} - 48.51 \ \frac{Btu}{lbm}}$$

$$= \boxed{0.098 \ (9.8\%)}$$

SI Solution

At point A, $p_A = 700$ kPa.

From App. 24.O, the enthalpy of saturated liquid is $h_A = 670.56$ kJ/kg.

At point B, $p_B = 700$ kPa.

From App. 24.O, the enthalpy and entropy of saturated vapor are

$$h_B = 2763.5 \ kJ/kg$$
$$s_B = 6.7080 \ kJ/kg{\cdot}K$$

At point C,

$$p_C = 1 \ atm$$
$$s_C = s_B = 6.7080 \ kJ/kg{\cdot}K$$

From App. 24.O, the entropy and enthalpy of saturated liquid, the entropy of saturated vapor, and the enthalpy of vaporization are

$$s_f = 1.3026 \ kJ/kg{\cdot}K$$
$$h_f = 417.46 \ kJ/kg$$
$$s_g = 7.3594 \ kJ/kg{\cdot}K$$
$$h_{fg} = 2258.0 \ kJ/kg$$

$$x_C = \frac{s_C - s_f}{s_g - s_f}$$

$$= \frac{6.7080 \ \frac{kJ}{kg{\cdot}K} - 1.3026 \ \frac{kJ}{kg{\cdot}K}}{7.3594 \ \frac{kJ}{kg{\cdot}K} - 1.3026 \ \frac{kJ}{kg{\cdot}K}}$$

$$= 0.892$$

$$h_C = h_f + x_C h_{fg}$$

$$= 417.46 \ \frac{kJ}{kg} + (0.892)\left(2258.0 \ \frac{kJ}{kg}\right)$$

$$= 2431.6 \ kJ/kg$$

At point D, $T = 27°C$ and $p_D = 1$ atm (subcooled). h and v are essentially independent of pressure.

From App. 24.N, the enthalpy and specific volume of saturated liquid are

$$h_D = 113.25 \ kJ/kg$$
$$v_D = 1.0035 \ cm^3/g$$

At point E, $p_E = p_A = 700$ kPa.

From Eq. 28.14,

$$h_E = h_D + v_D(p_E - p_D)$$

$$= 113.25 \ \frac{kJ}{kg} + \left(1.0035 \ \frac{cm^3}{g}\right)\left(\frac{1 \ m^3}{10^6 \ cm^3}\right)$$

$$\times \left(1000 \ \frac{g}{kg}\right)(700 \ kPa - 101 \ kPa)$$

$$= 113.85 \ kJ/kg$$

From Eq. 28.18, due to the inefficiency of the turbine,

$$h'_C = h_B - \eta_{s,turbine}(h_B - h_C)$$

$$= 2763.5 \ \frac{kJ}{kg} - (0.80)\left(2763.5 \ \frac{kJ}{kg} - 2431.6 \ \frac{kJ}{kg}\right)$$

$$= 2498.0 \ kJ/kg$$

From Eq. 28.19, due to the inefficiency of the pump,

$$h'_E = h_D + \frac{h_E - h_D}{\eta_{s,pump}}$$

$$= 113.25 \ \frac{kJ}{kg} + \frac{113.85 \ \frac{kJ}{kg} - 113.25 \ \frac{kJ}{kg}}{0.6}$$

$$= 114.25 \ kJ/kg$$

From Eq. 28.17, the thermal efficiency of the cycle is

$$\eta_{th} = \frac{(h_B - h_C') - (h_E' - h_D)}{h_B - h_E'}$$

$$= \frac{\left(2763.5 \ \dfrac{kJ}{kg} - 2498.0 \ \dfrac{kJ}{kg}\right) - \left(114.25 \ \dfrac{kJ}{kg} - 113.25 \ \dfrac{kJ}{kg}\right)}{2763.5 \ \dfrac{kJ}{kg} - 114.25 \ \dfrac{kJ}{kg}}$$

$$= \boxed{0.10 \quad (10\%)}$$

5. *Customary U.S. Solution*

Refer to the reheat cycle (Fig. 28.8).

At point B, $p_B = 600$ psia.

From App. 24.B, the enthalpy of the saturated liquid is $h_B = 471.7$ Btu/lbm.

At point C, $p_C = 600$ psia.

From App. 24.B, the enthalpy of the saturated vapor is $h_C = 1204.1$ Btu/lbm.

At point D,

$$T_D = 600°F$$
$$p_D = 600 \text{ psia}$$

From App. 24.C, the enthalpy and entropy of super-heated vapor are

$$h_D = 1289.5 \text{ Btu/lbm}$$
$$s_D = 1.5320 \text{ Btu/lbm-°R}$$

At point E,

$$p_E = 20 \text{ psia}$$
$$s_E = s_D = 1.5320 \text{ Btu/lbm-°R}$$

From App. 24.B, the various saturation properties are

$$s_f = 0.3358 \text{ Btu/lbm-°R}$$
$$s_{fg} = 1.3962 \text{ Btu/lbm-°R}$$
$$h_f = 196.26 \text{ Btu/lbm}$$
$$h_{fg} = 960.1 \text{ Btu/lbm}$$

$$x_E = \frac{s_E - s_f}{s_g - s_f} = \frac{1.5320 \ \dfrac{Btu}{lbm\text{-}°R} - 0.3358 \ \dfrac{Btu}{lbm\text{-}°R}}{1.3962 \ \dfrac{Btu}{lbm\text{-}°R}}$$

$$= 0.857$$

$$h_E = h_f + x_E h_{fg}$$

$$= 196.26 \ \frac{Btu}{lbm} + (0.857)\left(960.1 \ \frac{Btu}{lbm}\right)$$

$$= 1019.1 \text{ Btu/lbm}$$

From Eq. 28.38, due to the inefficiency of the turbine,

$$h_E' = h_D - \eta_{s,turbine}(h_D - h_E)$$

$$= 1289.5 \ \frac{Btu}{lbm} - (0.88)\left(1289.5 \ \frac{Btu}{lbm} - 1019.1 \ \frac{Btu}{lbm}\right)$$

$$= 1051.5 \text{ Btu/lbm}$$

At point F, the temperature has been returned to 600°F, but the pressure stays at the expansion pressure, p_E.

$$p_F = 20 \text{ psia}$$
$$T_F = 600°F$$

From App. 24.C, the enthalpy and entropy of the superheated vapor is

$$h_F = 1334.8 \text{ Btu/lbm}$$
$$s_F = 1.9395 \text{ Btu/lbm-°R}$$

At point G,

$$T_G = 60°F$$
$$s_G = s_F = 1.9395 \text{ Btu/lbm-°R}$$

From App. 24.A, various saturation properties are

$$s_f = 0.05555 \text{ Btu/lbm-°R}$$
$$s_g = 2.0943 \text{ Btu/lbm-°R}$$
$$h_f = 28.08 \text{ Btu/lbm}$$
$$h_{fg} = 1059.6 \text{ Btu/lbm}$$

$$x_G = \frac{s_G - s_f}{s_g - s_f} = \frac{1.9395 \ \dfrac{Btu}{lbm\text{-}°R} - 0.05555 \ \dfrac{Btu}{lbm\text{-}°R}}{2.0943 \ \dfrac{Btu}{lbm\text{-}°R} - 0.05555 \ \dfrac{Btu}{lbm\text{-}°R}}$$

$$= 0.924$$

$$h_G = h_f + x_G h_{fg}$$

$$= 28.08 \ \frac{Btu}{lbm} + (0.924)\left(1059.6 \ \frac{Btu}{lbm}\right)$$

$$= 1007.2 \text{ Btu/lbm}$$

From Eq. 28.39, due to the inefficiency of the turbine,

$$h_G' = h_F - \eta_{s,turbine}(h_F - h_G)$$

$$= 1334.8 \ \frac{Btu}{lbm} - (0.88)\left(1334.8 \ \frac{Btu}{lbm} - 1007.2 \ \frac{Btu}{lbm}\right)$$

$$= 1046.5 \text{ Btu/lbm}$$

At point H, $T_H = 60°F$.

From App. 24.A, the saturation pressure, enthalpy, and specific volume of the saturated liquid are

$$p_H = 0.2563 \text{ psia}$$
$$h_H = 28.08 \text{ Btu/lbm}$$
$$v_H = 0.01604 \text{ ft}^3/\text{lbm}$$

At point A, $p_A = 600$ psia.

From Eq. 28.14,

$$h_A = h_H + v_H(p_A - p_H)$$

$$= 28.08 \frac{\text{Btu}}{\text{lbm}}$$

$$+ \frac{\left(0.01604 \frac{\text{ft}^3}{\text{lbm}}\right) \times \left(600 \frac{\text{lbf}}{\text{in}^2} - 0.2563 \frac{\text{lbf}}{\text{in}^2}\right) \left(144 \frac{\text{in}^2}{\text{ft}^2}\right)}{778 \frac{\text{lbf-ft}}{\text{Btu}}}$$

$$= 29.86 \text{ Btu/lbm}$$

From Eq. 28.40, due to the inefficiency of the pump,

$$h'_A = h_H + \frac{h_A - h_H}{\eta_{s,\text{pump}}}$$

$$= 28.08 \frac{\text{Btu}}{\text{lbm}} + \frac{29.86 \frac{\text{Btu}}{\text{lbm}} - 28.08 \frac{\text{Btu}}{\text{lbm}}}{0.96}$$

$$= 29.93 \text{ Btu/lbm}$$

From Eq. 28.37, the thermal efficiency of the cycle for a non-isentropic process for the turbine and the pump is

$$\eta_{\text{th}} = \frac{(h_D - h'_A) + (h_F - h'_E) - (h'_G - h_H)}{(h_D - h'_A) + (h_F - h'_E)}$$

$$= \frac{\begin{array}{l}\left(1289.5 \frac{\text{Btu}}{\text{lbm}} - 29.93 \frac{\text{Btu}}{\text{lbm}}\right) \\ + \left(1334.8 \frac{\text{Btu}}{\text{lbm}} - 1051.5 \frac{\text{Btu}}{\text{lbm}}\right) \\ - \left(1051.5 \frac{\text{Btu}}{\text{lbm}} - 28.08 \frac{\text{Btu}}{\text{lbm}}\right)\end{array}}{\begin{array}{l}\left(1289.5 \frac{\text{Btu}}{\text{lbm}} - 29.93 \frac{\text{Btu}}{\text{lbm}}\right) \\ + \left(1334.8 \frac{\text{Btu}}{\text{lbm}} - 1051.5 \frac{\text{Btu}}{\text{lbm}}\right)\end{array}}$$

$$= \boxed{0.337 \ (33.7\%)}$$

SI Solution

Refer to the reheat cycle (Fig. 28.8).

At point B, $p_B = 4$ MPa.

From App. 24.O, the enthalpy of saturated liquid is $h_B = 1087.3$ kJ/kg.

At point C, $p_C = 4$ MPa.

From App. 24.O, the enthalpy of saturated vapor is $h_C = 2801.4$ kJ/kg.

At point D, $p_D = 4$ MPa and $T_D = 300°C$.

From the Mollier diagram, the enthalpy of superheated vapor is $h_D = 2980$ kJ/kg.

At point E, from the Mollier diagram, assuming isentropic expansion, $h_E = 2395$ kJ/kg.

From Eq. 28.38, due to the inefficiency of the turbine,

$$h'_E = h_D - \eta_{s,\text{turbine}}(h_D - h_E)$$

$$= 2980 \frac{\text{kJ}}{\text{kg}} - (0.88)\left(2980 \frac{\text{kJ}}{\text{kg}} - 2395 \frac{\text{kJ}}{\text{kg}}\right)$$

$$= 2465.2 \text{ kJ/kg}$$

At point F,

$$p_F = 150 \text{ kPa}$$
$$T_F = 300°C$$

From App. 24.P, the enthalpy and entropy of the superheated vapor is

$$h_F = 3073.1 \text{ kJ/kg}$$
$$s_F = 8.0720 \text{ kJ/kg·K}$$

At point G,

$$T_G = 16°C$$
$$s_G = s_F = 8.0720 \text{ kJ/kg·K}$$

From App. 24.N, the various saturation properties are

$$s_f = 0.2390 \text{ kJ/kg·K}$$
$$s_g = 8.7582 \text{ kJ/kg·K}$$
$$h_f = 67.19 \text{ kJ/kg}$$
$$h_{fg} = 2463.6 \text{ kJ/kg}$$

$$x_G = \frac{s_G - s_f}{s_g - s_f} = \frac{8.0720 \frac{\text{kJ}}{\text{kg·K}} - 0.2390 \frac{\text{kJ}}{\text{kg·K}}}{8.7582 \frac{\text{kJ}}{\text{kg·K}} - 0.2390 \frac{\text{kJ}}{\text{kg·K}}}$$

$$= 0.919$$

$$h_G = h_f + x_G h_{fg}$$
$$= 67.19 \frac{kJ}{kg} + (0.919)\left(2463.6 \frac{kJ}{kg}\right)$$
$$= 2331.2 \text{ kJ/kg}$$

From Eq. 28.39, due to the inefficiency of the turbine,

$$h'_G = h_F - \eta_{s,turbine}(h_F - h_G)$$
$$= 3073.1 \frac{kJ}{kg} - (0.88)\left(3073.1 \frac{kJ}{kg} - 2331.2 \frac{kJ}{kg}\right)$$
$$= 2420.2 \text{ kJ/kg}$$

At point H, $T_H = 16°C$.

From App. 24.N, the saturation pressure, enthalpy, and specific volume of the saturated liquid are

$$p_H = (0.01818 \text{ bar})\left(100 \frac{kPa}{bar}\right) = 1.818 \text{ kPa}$$
$$h_H = 67.19 \text{ kJ/kg}$$
$$v_H = \left(1.0011 \frac{cm}{g^3}\right)\left(1000 \frac{g}{kg}\right)\left(\frac{1 \text{ m}}{100 \text{ cm}}\right)^3$$
$$= 1.0011 \times 10^{-3} \text{ m}^3/\text{kg}$$

At point A,

$$p_A = (4 \text{ MPa})\left(1000 \frac{kPa}{MPa}\right)$$
$$= 4000 \text{ kPa}$$

From Eq. 28.14,

$$h_A = h_H + v_H(p_A - p_H)$$
$$= 67.19 \frac{kJ}{kg} + \left(1.0011 \times 10^{-3} \frac{m^3}{kg}\right)$$
$$\times (4000 \text{ kPa} - 1.818 \text{ kPa})$$
$$= 71.19 \text{ kJ/kg}$$

From Eq. 28.40, due to the inefficiency of the pump,

$$h'_A = h_H + \frac{h_A - h_H}{\eta_{s,pump}}$$
$$= 67.19 \frac{kJ}{kg} + \frac{71.19 \frac{kJ}{kg} - 67.19 \frac{kJ}{kg}}{0.96}$$
$$= 71.36 \text{ kJ/kg}$$

From Eq. 28.37, the thermal efficiency of the cycle for a non-isentropic process for the turbine and the pump is

$$\eta_{th} = \frac{(h_D - h'_A) + (h_F - h'_E) - (h'_G - h_H)}{(h_D - h'_A) + (h_F - h'_E)}$$

$$= \frac{\begin{pmatrix}2980 \frac{kJ}{kg} - 71.36 \frac{kJ}{kg}\end{pmatrix} + \left(3073.1 \frac{kJ}{kg} - 2465.2 \frac{kJ}{kg}\right) - \left(2420.2 \frac{kJ}{kg} - 67.19 \frac{kJ}{kg}\right)}{\left(2980 \frac{kJ}{kg} - 71.36 \frac{kJ}{kg}\right) + \left(3073.1 \frac{kJ}{kg} - 2465.2 \frac{kJ}{kg}\right)}$$

$$= \boxed{0.331 \ (33.1\%)}$$

6. *Customary U.S. Solution*

Refer to Chap. 28, Sec. 20, and the following diagram.

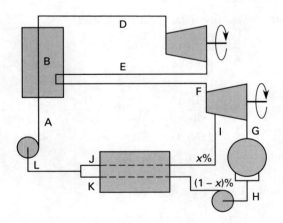

From Prob. 5,

$$h_B = 471.7 \text{ Btu/lbm}$$
$$h_D = 1289.5 \text{ Btu/lbm}$$
$$h'_E = 1046.4 \text{ Btu/lbm}$$
$$h_F = 1334.8 \text{ Btu/lbm}$$
$$h'_G = 1046.5 \text{ Btu/lbm}$$
$$h_H = 28.08 \text{ Btu/lbm}$$
$$s_F = 1.9395 \text{ Btu/lbm-°R}$$

At point I,

$$T_\mathrm{I} = 270°\mathrm{F}$$
$$s_\mathrm{I} = s_\mathrm{F} = 1.9395 \ \mathrm{Btu/lbm\text{-}°R}$$

These conditions are for superheated steam. From App. 24.C,

$$p_\mathrm{I} = 4.5 \ \mathrm{psia}$$
$$h_\mathrm{I} = 1181.0 \ \mathrm{Btu/lbm}$$

From Eq. 28.39, due to the inefficiency of the turbine,

$$h'_\mathrm{I} = h_\mathrm{F} - \eta_{s,\mathrm{turbine}}(h_\mathrm{F} - h_\mathrm{I})$$
$$= 1334.8 \ \frac{\mathrm{Btu}}{\mathrm{lbm}} - (0.88)\left(1334.8 \ \frac{\mathrm{Btu}}{\mathrm{lbm}}\right.$$
$$\left. -1181.0 \ \frac{\mathrm{Btu}}{\mathrm{lbm}}\right)$$
$$= 1199.5 \ \mathrm{Btu/lbm}$$

At point J, from App. 24.A, the saturated liquid enthalpy at 270°F is $h_\mathrm{J} = 239.0 \ \mathrm{Btu/lbm}$.

At point K, the temperature is

$$270°\mathrm{F} \ - 6°\mathrm{F} \ = 264°\mathrm{F}$$

Since the water is subcooled, enthalpy is a function of temperature only.

$$h_\mathrm{K} = 232.88 \ \mathrm{Btu/lbm}$$

From the energy balance in the heater,

$$(1 - x)(h_\mathrm{K} - h_\mathrm{H}) = x(h'_\mathrm{I} - h_\mathrm{J})$$
$$(1 - x)\left(232.88 \ \frac{\mathrm{Btu}}{\mathrm{lbm}}\right.$$
$$\left. - 28.08 \ \frac{\mathrm{Btu}}{\mathrm{lbm}}\right) = x\left(1199.5 \ \frac{\mathrm{Btu}}{\mathrm{lbm}} - 239.0 \ \frac{\mathrm{Btu}}{\mathrm{lbm}}\right)$$
$$1165.3x = 204.8$$
$$x = 0.176$$

At point L,

$$h_\mathrm{L} = xh_\mathrm{J} + (1 - x)h_\mathrm{K}$$
$$= (0.176)\left(239.0 \ \frac{\mathrm{Btu}}{\mathrm{lbm}}\right)$$
$$+ (1 - 0.176)\left(232.88 \ \frac{\mathrm{Btu}}{\mathrm{lbm}}\right)$$
$$= 233.96 \ \mathrm{Btu/lbm}$$

Since this is a subcooled liquid, from App. 24.A,

$$T_\mathrm{L} = 265.1°\mathrm{F}$$
$$p_\mathrm{L} = 38.69 \ \mathrm{psia}$$
$$v_\mathrm{L} = 0.01713 \ \mathrm{ft^3/lbm}$$

At point A, $p_\mathrm{A} = 600$ psia.

From Eq. 28.14,

$$h_\mathrm{A} = h_\mathrm{L} + v_\mathrm{L}(p_\mathrm{A} - p_\mathrm{L})$$
$$= 233.96 \ \frac{\mathrm{Btu}}{\mathrm{lbm}}$$
$$+ \frac{\left(0.01713 \ \frac{\mathrm{ft^3}}{\mathrm{lbm}}\right)}{778 \ \frac{\mathrm{lbf\text{-}ft}}{\mathrm{lbm}}} \times \left(600 \ \frac{\mathrm{lbf}}{\mathrm{in^2}} - 38.69 \ \frac{\mathrm{lbf}}{\mathrm{in^2}}\right)\left(144 \ \frac{\mathrm{in^2}}{\mathrm{ft^2}}\right)$$
$$= 235.74 \ \mathrm{Btu/lbm}$$

From Eq. 28.40, due to the inefficiency of the pump,

$$h'_\mathrm{A} = h_\mathrm{L} + \frac{h_\mathrm{A} - h_\mathrm{L}}{\eta_{s,\mathrm{pump}}}$$
$$= 233.96 \ \frac{\mathrm{Btu}}{\mathrm{lbm}} + \frac{235.74 \ \frac{\mathrm{Btu}}{\mathrm{lbm}} - 233.96 \ \frac{\mathrm{Btu}}{\mathrm{lbm}}}{0.96}$$
$$= 235.81 \ \mathrm{Btu/lbm}$$

From Eq. 28.37, the thermal efficiency of the entire cycle neglecting condensation and drip pump, is

$$\eta_\mathrm{th} = \frac{W_\mathrm{turbines} - W_\mathrm{pump}}{Q_\mathrm{in}}$$
$$= \frac{\begin{array}{c}(h_\mathrm{D} - h'_\mathrm{E}) + (h_\mathrm{F} - h'_\mathrm{I}) \\ + (1 - x)(h'_\mathrm{I} - h'_\mathrm{G}) - (h'_\mathrm{A} - h_\mathrm{L})\end{array}}{(h_\mathrm{D} - h'_\mathrm{A}) + (h_\mathrm{F} - h'_\mathrm{E})}$$

$$= \frac{\begin{array}{c}\left(1289.5 \ \frac{\mathrm{Btu}}{\mathrm{lbm}} - 1046.4 \ \frac{\mathrm{Btu}}{\mathrm{lbm}}\right) \\ + \left(1334.8 \ \frac{\mathrm{Btu}}{\mathrm{lbm}} - 1199.5 \ \frac{\mathrm{Btu}}{\mathrm{lbm}}\right) \\ + (1 - 0.176)\left(1199.5 \ \frac{\mathrm{Btu}}{\mathrm{lbm}} - 1046.5 \ \frac{\mathrm{Btu}}{\mathrm{lbm}}\right) \\ - \left(235.8 \ \frac{\mathrm{Btu}}{\mathrm{lbm}} - 233.96 \ \frac{\mathrm{Btu}}{\mathrm{lbm}}\right)\end{array}}{\begin{array}{c}\left(1289.5 \ \frac{\mathrm{Btu}}{\mathrm{lbm}} - 235.81 \ \frac{\mathrm{Btu}}{\mathrm{lbm}}\right) \\ + \left(1334.8 \ \frac{\mathrm{Btu}}{\mathrm{lbm}} - 1046.4 \ \frac{\mathrm{Btu}}{\mathrm{lbm}}\right)\end{array}}$$

$$= \boxed{0.374 \ (37.4\%)}$$

(Note: In this problem, pressure for the reheat cycle is too low. This results in a superheat condition at point I with a pressure of only 4.5 psia. A pump would be required to raise the pressure of the bleed at I from 4.5 psia to 38.69 psia at L.)

SI Solution

From Prob. 5,

$$h_B = 1087.3 \text{ kJ/kg}$$
$$h_D = 2980 \text{ kJ/kg}$$
$$h'_E = 2465.2 \text{ kJ/kg}$$
$$h_F = 3073.1 \text{ kJ/kg}$$
$$h'_G = 2420.2 \text{ kJ/kg}$$
$$h_H = 67.19 \text{ kJ/kg}$$
$$s_F = 8.0720 \text{ kJ/kg·K}$$

At point I,

$$T_I = 130°C$$
$$s_I = s_F$$
$$= 8.0720 \text{ kJ/kg·K}$$

These conditions are for superheat steam. From App. 24.P,

$$p_I = 37.73 \text{ kPa}$$
$$h_I = 2742.2 \text{ kJ/kg}$$

From Eq. 28.39, due to inefficiency of the turbine,

$$h'_I = h_F - \eta_{s,\text{turbine}}(h_F - h_I)$$
$$= 3073.1 \frac{\text{kJ}}{\text{kg}} - (0.88)\left(3073.1 \frac{\text{kJ}}{\text{kg}} - 2742.2 \frac{\text{kJ}}{\text{kg}}\right)$$
$$= 2781.9 \text{ kJ/kg}$$

At point J, from App. 24.N, the saturated liquid enthalpy at 130°C is $h_J = 546.31$ kJ/kg.

At point K, the temperature is

$$130°C - 3°C = 127°C$$

Since the water is cooled, enthalpy is a function of temperature only.

$$h_K = 533.53 \text{ kJ/kg}$$

From an energy balance in the heater,

$$(1 - x)(h_K - h_H) = x(h'_I - h_J)$$
$$(1 - x)\left(533.53 \frac{\text{kJ}}{\text{kg}} - 67.19 \frac{\text{kJ}}{\text{kg}}\right) = x\left(2781.9 \frac{\text{kJ}}{\text{kg}} - 546.31 \frac{\text{kJ}}{\text{kg}}\right)$$
$$2701.93x = 466.34$$
$$x = 0.173$$

At point L,

$$h_L = x_J + (1 - x)h_K$$
$$= (0.173)\left(546.31 \frac{\text{kJ}}{\text{kg}}\right) + (1 - 0.173)\left(533.53 \frac{\text{kJ}}{\text{kg}}\right)$$
$$= 535.74 \text{ kJ/kg}$$

Since this is a subcooled liquid, from App. 24.N,

$$T_L = 127.5°C$$
$$p_L = 2.522 \text{ bar}$$
$$v_L = 1.0674 \text{ cm}^3/\text{g}$$

At point A, $p_A = 4$ MPa.

From Eq. 28.14,

$$h_A = h_L + v_L(p_A - p_L)$$
$$h_A = 535.74 \frac{\text{kJ}}{\text{kg}} + \left(1.0674 \frac{\text{cm}^3}{\text{g}}\right)\left(1000 \frac{\text{g}}{\text{kg}}\right)$$
$$\times \left(\frac{1 \text{ m}}{100 \text{ cm}}\right)^3 \left[(4 \text{ MPa})\left(1000 \frac{\text{kPa}}{\text{MPa}}\right)\right.$$
$$\left. - (2.522 \text{ bar})\left(100 \frac{\text{kPa}}{\text{bar}}\right)\right]$$
$$= 539.74 \text{ kJ/kg}$$

From Eq. 28.40, due to the inefficiency in the pump,

$$h'_A = h_L + \frac{h_A - h_L}{\eta_{s,\text{pump}}}$$
$$= 535.74 \frac{\text{kJ}}{\text{kg}} + \frac{539.74 \frac{\text{kJ}}{\text{kg}} - 535.74 \frac{\text{kJ}}{\text{kg}}}{0.96}$$
$$= 539.91 \text{ kJ/kg}$$

From Eq. 28.37, the thermal efficiency of the entire cycle, neglecting condensation and drip pump, is

$$\eta_{\text{th}} = \frac{W_{\text{turbine}} - W_{\text{pump}}}{Q_{\text{in}}}$$

$$= \frac{\begin{bmatrix}(h_D - h'_E) + (h_F - h'_I) \\ + (1-x)(h'_I - h'_G)\end{bmatrix} - (h'_A - h_L)}{(h_D - h'_A) + (h_F - h'_E)}$$

$$= \frac{\begin{bmatrix}\left(2980\ \dfrac{\text{kJ}}{\text{kg}} - 2465.2\ \dfrac{\text{kJ}}{\text{kg}}\right) \\[2mm] + \left(3073.1\ \dfrac{\text{kJ}}{\text{kg}} - 2781.9\ \dfrac{\text{kJ}}{\text{kg}}\right) \\[2mm] + (1 - 0.173)\left(2781.9\ \dfrac{\text{kJ}}{\text{kg}} - 2420.2\ \dfrac{\text{kJ}}{\text{kg}}\right)\end{bmatrix}}{\begin{aligned}&\left(2980\ \dfrac{\text{kJ}}{\text{kg}} - 539.91\ \dfrac{\text{kJ}}{\text{kg}}\right)\end{aligned}}$$

$$\frac{- \left(539.91\ \dfrac{\text{kJ}}{\text{kg}} - 535.74\ \dfrac{\text{kJ}}{\text{kg}}\right)}{\quad}$$

$$+ \left(3073.1\ \dfrac{\text{kJ}}{\text{kg}} - 2465.2\ \dfrac{\text{kJ}}{\text{kg}}\right)$$

$$= \boxed{0.361 \quad (36.1\%)}$$

(Note: In this problem, pressure for the reheat cycle is too low. This results in a superheat condition at point I with a pressure of only 0.3773 bar. A pump would be required to raise the pressure of the bleed at I from 0.3773 bar to 2.522 bar at L.)

7. *Customary U.S. Solution*

Refer to the given illustration for Prob. 7 and to the following diagram.

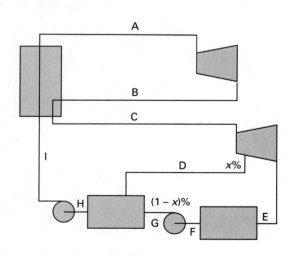

At point A,

$$p_A = 900 \text{ psia}$$
$$T_A = 800°\text{F}$$

Using the superheated steam table, App. 24.C,

$$h_A = 1393.4 \text{ Btu/lbm}$$
$$s_A = 1.5810 \text{ Btu/lbm-}°\text{R}$$

At point B, $h'_B = 1270$ Btu/lbm.

From the Mollier diagram, assuming isentropic expansion to 200 psia, $h_B = 1230$ Btu/lbm.

Isentropic efficiency of the high pressure turbine is

$$\eta_{s,\text{turbine}} = \frac{h_A - h'_B}{h_A - h_B}$$

$$= \left(\frac{1393.4\ \dfrac{\text{Btu}}{\text{lbm}} - 1270\ \dfrac{\text{Btu}}{\text{lbm}}}{1393.4\ \dfrac{\text{Btu}}{\text{lbm}} - 1230\ \dfrac{\text{Btu}}{\text{lbm}}}\right)(100\%)$$

$$= 75.52\%$$

At point C,

$$p_C = 190 \text{ psia}$$
$$T_C = 800°\text{F}$$

Using the superheated steam table from App. 24.C, $h_C = 1425.7$ Btu/lbm.

At point D:	h'_D	$= 1280$ Btu/lbm
At point E:	h'_E	$= 1075$ Btu/lbm
At point F:	h_F	$= 69.73$ Btu/lbm
At point G:	W_{pump}	$= 0.15$ Btu/lbm
	W_{pump}	$= h'_G - h_F$
	h'_G	$= W_{\text{pump}} + h_F$
		$= 0.15\ \dfrac{\text{Btu}}{\text{lbm}} + 69.73\ \dfrac{\text{Btu}}{\text{lbm}}$
		$= 69.88$ Btu/lbm
At point H:	h_H	$= 250.2$ Btu/lbm
At point I:	h'_I	$= 253.1$ Btu/lbm

From an energy balance in the heater,

$$xh'_D + (1-x)h'_G = h_H$$
$$x(h'_D - h'_G) = h_H - h'_G$$
$$x = \frac{h_H - h'_G}{h'_D - h'_G}$$

$$= \frac{250.2\ \dfrac{\text{Btu}}{\text{lbm}} - 69.88\ \dfrac{\text{Btu}}{\text{lbm}}}{1280\ \dfrac{\text{Btu}}{\text{lbm}} - 69.88\ \dfrac{\text{Btu}}{\text{lbm}}}$$

$$= 0.149$$

The thermal efficiency of the cycle is

$$\eta_{th} = \frac{W_{out} - W_{in}}{Q_{in}}$$

$$= \frac{\begin{array}{c}(h_A - h'_B) + (h_C - h'_D) + (1-x)\\ \times (h'_D - h'_E) - (h'_I - h_H) - (1-x)(h'_G - h_F)\end{array}}{(h_A - h'_I) + (h_C - h'_B)}$$

$$= \frac{\begin{array}{c}\left(1393.4\,\frac{Btu}{lbm} - 1270\,\frac{Btu}{lbm}\right)\\ + \left(1425.7\,\frac{Btu}{lbm} - 1280\,\frac{Btu}{lbm}\right)\\ + (1-0.149)\left(1280\,\frac{Btu}{lbm} - 1075\,\frac{Btu}{lbm}\right)\\ + \left(253.1\,\frac{Btu}{lbm} - 250.2\,\frac{Btu}{lbm}\right)\\ - (1-0.149)\left(69.88\,\frac{Btu}{lbm} - 69.73\,\frac{Btu}{lbm}\right)\end{array}}{\begin{array}{c}\left(1393.4\,\frac{Btu}{lbm} - 253.1\,\frac{Btu}{lbm}\right)\\ + \left(1425.7\,\frac{Btu}{lbm} - 1270\,\frac{Btu}{lbm}\right)\end{array}}$$

$$= \boxed{0.344 \;(34.4\%)}$$

SI Solution

Refer to the illustration for Prob. 7 and to the diagram for the Customary U.S. Solution.

At point A,

$$p_A = 6.2 \text{ MPa}$$
$$T_A = 420°C$$

Using the Mollier diagram for steam, App. 24.R,

$$h_A = 3235.0 \text{ kJ/kg}$$
$$s_A = 6.65 \text{ kJ/kg·K}$$

At point B, $h'_B = 2960$ kJ/kg.

From the Mollier diagram, assuming isentropic expansion to 1.5 MPa, $h_B = 2860$ kJ/kg.

Isentropic efficiency of the high pressure turbine is

$$\eta_{s,turbine} = \frac{h_A - h'_B}{h_A - h_B}$$

$$= \frac{3235.0\,\frac{kJ}{kg} - 2960\,\frac{kJ}{kg}}{3235.0\,\frac{kJ}{kg} - 2860\,\frac{kJ}{kg}}$$

$$= 0.733 \;(73.3\%)$$

At point C,

$$p_C = 1.4 \text{ MPa}$$
$$T_C = 420°C$$

Using the superheated steam table from App. 24.P, $h_C = 3300.6$ kJ/kg.

At point D, $h'_D = 2980$ kJ/kg.

At point E, $h'_E = 2500$ kJ/kg.

At point F, $h_F = 162.5$ kJ/kg.

At point G,

$$W_{pump} = 0.3 \text{ kJ/kg}$$
$$= h'_G - h_F$$
$$h'_G = W_{pump} + h_F$$
$$= 0.3\,\frac{kJ}{kg} + 162.5\,\frac{kJ}{kg}$$
$$= 162.8 \text{ kJ/kg}$$

At point H, $h_H = 583.0$ kJ/kg.

At point I, $h'_I = 589.7$ kJ/kg.

From an energy balance in the heater,

$$xh'_D + (1-x)h'_G = h_H$$
$$x(h'_D - h'_G) = h_H - h'_G$$
$$x = \frac{h_H - h'_G}{h'_D - h'_G}$$

$$= \frac{583.0\,\frac{kJ}{kg} - 162.8\,\frac{kJ}{kg}}{2980\,\frac{kJ}{kg} - 162.8\,\frac{kJ}{kg}}$$

$$= 0.149$$

The thermal efficiency of the cycle is

$$\eta_{th} = \frac{W_{out} - W_{in}}{Q_{in}}$$

$$= \frac{\begin{array}{c}(h_A - h'_B) + (h_C - h'_D) + (1-x)\\ \times (h'_D - h'_E) - (h'_I - h_H) - (1-x)(h'_G - h_F)\end{array}}{(h_A - h'_I) + (h_C - h'_B)}$$

$$= \frac{\begin{array}{c}\left(3235.0\,\frac{kJ}{kg} - 2960\,\frac{kJ}{kg}\right)\\ + \left(3300.6\,\frac{kJ}{kg} - 2980\,\frac{kJ}{kg}\right)\\ + (1-0.149)\left(2980\,\frac{kJ}{kg} - 2500\,\frac{kJ}{kg}\right)\\ + \left(598.7\,\frac{kJ}{kg} - 583.0\,\frac{kJ}{kg}\right)\\ - (1-0.149)\left(162.8\,\frac{kJ}{kg} - 162.5\,\frac{kJ}{kg}\right)\end{array}}{\begin{array}{c}\left(3235.0\,\frac{kJ}{kg} - 598.7\,\frac{kJ}{kg}\right)\\ + \left(3300.6\,\frac{kJ}{kg} - 2960\,\frac{kJ}{kg}\right)\end{array}}$$

$$= \boxed{0.342 \;(34.2\%)}$$

8.

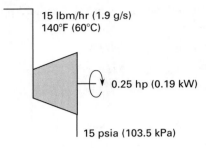

15 lbm/hr (1.9 g/s)
140°F (60°C)

0.25 hp (0.19 kW)

15 psia (103.5 kPa)

Customary U.S. Solution

The drill power is

$$P = 0.25 \text{ hp} \quad [\text{given}]$$

$$= (0.25 \text{ hp}) \left(2545 \frac{\text{Btu}}{\text{hp-hr}} \right) = 636.25 \text{ Btu/hr}$$

The absolute inlet temperature is

$$T_I = 140°F + 460 = 600°R$$

From App. 24.F, the properties of air entering the turbine are

$$h_I = 143.47 \text{ Btu/lbm}$$

$$p_{r,1} = 2.005$$

$$\phi_I = 0.62607 \text{ Btu/lbm-}°R$$

From Eq. 27.18,

$$P = \dot{m}(h_1 - h_2')$$

$$\eta_{s,\text{turbine}} = \frac{h_1 - h_2'}{h_1 - h_2}$$

So,

$$P = \dot{m}\eta_{s,\text{turbine}}(h_1 - h_2)$$

$$h_2 = h_1 - \frac{P}{\dot{m}\eta_{s,\text{turbine}}}$$

$$= 143.47 \frac{\text{Btu}}{\text{lbm}} - \frac{636.25 \frac{\text{Btu}}{\text{hr}}}{\left(15 \frac{\text{lbm}}{\text{hr}} \right)(0.60)}$$

$$= 72.776 \text{ Btu/lbm}$$

Appendix 24.F doesn't go low enough. From the Keenan and Kayes *Gas Tables*, for $h = 72.776$ Btu/lbm,

$$T_2 = 305°R$$

$$p_{r,2} = 0.18851$$

(a) Due to the irreversibility of the expansion from Eq. 27.19,

$$h_2' = h_1 - \eta_s(h_1 - h_2)$$

$$= 143.47 \frac{\text{Btu}}{\text{lbm}}$$

$$- (0.60) \left(143.47 \frac{\text{Btu}}{\text{lbm}} - 72.776 \frac{\text{Btu}}{\text{lbm}} \right)$$

$$= 101.05 \text{ Btu/lbm}$$

From App. 24.F for $h = 101.05$ Btu/lbm,

$$T_2' = \boxed{423°R}$$

$$\phi_2 = 0.54225 \text{ Btu/lbm-}°R$$

(b) Since $p_1/p_2 = p_{r,1}/p_{r,2}$,

$$p_1 = p_2 \left(\frac{p_{r,1}}{p_{r,2}} \right) = (15 \text{ psia}) \left(\frac{2.005}{0.18851} \right)$$

$$= \boxed{159.5 \text{ psia}}$$

(c) From Eq. 24.39, the entropy change is

$$s_2 - s_1 = \phi_2 - \phi_1 - R \ln \left(\frac{p_2}{p_1} \right)$$

From Table 24.7, $R = 53.35$ ft-lbf/lbm-°R.

$$s_2 - s_1 = 0.54225 \frac{\text{Btu}}{\text{lbm-}°R} - 0.62607 \frac{\text{Btu}}{\text{lbm-}°R}$$

$$- \left(\frac{53.35 \frac{\text{ft-lbf}}{\text{lbm-}°R}}{778 \frac{\text{ft-lbf}}{\text{Btu}}} \right) \ln \left(\frac{15 \text{ psia}}{159.5 \text{ psia}} \right)$$

$$= \boxed{0.07829 \text{ Btu/lbm-}°R}$$

SI Solution

The absolute inlet temperature is

$$T_I = 60°C + 273 = 333K$$

From App. 24.S, the properties of air entering the turbine are

$$h_1 = 333.70 \text{ kJ/kg}$$

$$p_{r,1} = 2.0064$$

$$\phi_1 = 1.80784 \text{ kJ/kg·K}$$

From Eq. 27.18,

$$P = \dot{m}(h_1 - h_2')$$

$$\eta_{s,\text{turbine}} = \frac{h_1 - h_2'}{h_1 - h_2}$$

$$P = \dot{m}\eta_{s,\text{turbine}}(h_1 - h_2)$$

$$h_2 = h_1 - \frac{P}{\dot{m}\eta_{s,\text{turbine}}}$$

$$= 333.70 \frac{\text{kJ}}{\text{kg}} - \frac{0.19 \text{ kW}}{\left(1.9 \frac{\text{g}}{\text{s}} \right) \left(\frac{1 \text{ kg}}{1000 \text{ g}} \right)(0.60)}$$

$$= 167.03 \text{ kJ/kg}$$

Appendix 24.S doesn't go low enough. From gas tables, for $h = 167.03$ kJ/kg,

$$T_2 = 164.4\text{K}$$
$$p_{r,2} = 0.16980$$

(a) Due to the irreversibility of the expansion from Eq. 27.19,

$$h_2' = h_1 - \eta_s(h_1 - h_2)$$
$$= 333.70\,\frac{\text{kJ}}{\text{kg}} - (0.60)\left(330.70\,\frac{\text{kJ}}{\text{kg}} - 167.03\,\frac{\text{kJ}}{\text{kg}}\right)$$
$$= 235.50\text{ kJ/kg}$$

From App. 24.S, for $h = 235.50$ kJ/kg,

$$T_2' = \boxed{235.3\text{K}}$$
$$\phi_2 = 1.45819\text{ kJ/kg·K}$$

(b) Since $p_1/p_2 = p_{r,1}/p_{r,2}$,

$$p_1 = (103.5\text{ kPa})\left(\frac{2.0064}{0.16980}\right)$$
$$= \boxed{1223\text{ kPa}}$$

(c) From Table 24.7, $R = 287.03$ kJ/kg·K. From Eq. 24.39, the entropy change is

$$s_2 - s_1 = \phi_2 - \phi_1 - R\ln\left(\frac{p_2}{p_1}\right)$$
$$= 1.45819\,\frac{\text{kJ}}{\text{kg·K}} - 1.80784\,\frac{\text{kJ}}{\text{kg·K}}$$
$$- \left(287.03\,\frac{\text{kJ}}{\text{kg·K}}\right)\left(\frac{1\text{ kJ}}{1000\text{ J}}\right)$$
$$\times \ln\left(\frac{103.5\text{ kPa}}{1223\text{ kPa}}\right)$$
$$= \boxed{0.3592\text{ kJ/kg·K}}$$

29 Combustion Power Cycles

1. *Customary U.S. Solution*

(a) The absolute temperature is

$$T_1 = 1500°\text{F} + 460 = 1960°\text{R}$$

From air tables (App. 24.F) at 1960°R,

$$h_1 = 493.64 \text{ Btu/lbm}$$
$$p_{r,1} = 160.48$$
$$v_{r,1} = 4.53$$

After expansion,

$$p_{r,2} = p_{r,1}\left(\frac{p_2}{p_1}\right)$$
$$= (160.48)\left(\frac{50 \text{ psia}}{200 \text{ psia}}\right)$$
$$= 40.12$$

From air tables (App. 24.F) at $p_{r,2} = 40.12$,

$$T_2 = \boxed{1375°\text{R}}$$
$$h_2 = 336.39 \text{ Btu/lbm}$$
$$v_{r,2} = 12.721$$

(b)
$$\dot{V}_2 = \dot{V}_1\left(\frac{v_{r,2}}{v_{r,1}}\right)$$
$$= \left(10 \text{ } \frac{\text{ft}^3}{\text{sec}}\right)\left(\frac{12.721}{4.53}\right)$$
$$= \boxed{28.1 \text{ ft}^3/\text{sec}}$$

(c) The enthalpy change is

$$\Delta h = h_2 - h_1$$
$$= 336.39 \text{ } \frac{\text{Btu}}{\text{lbm}} - 493.64 \text{ } \frac{\text{Btu}}{\text{lbm}}$$
$$= \boxed{-157.25 \text{ Btu/lbm} \quad [\text{decrease}]}$$

SI Solution

(a) The absolute temperature is

$$T_1 = 820°\text{C} + 273 = 1093\text{K}$$

From air tables (App. 24.S) at 1093K,

$$h_1 = 1153 \text{ kJ/kg}$$
$$p_{r,1} = 162.94$$
$$v_{r,1} = 19.275$$

After expansion,

$$p_{r,2} = p_{r,1}\left(\frac{p_2}{p_1}\right)$$
$$= (162.94)\left(\frac{350 \text{ kPa}}{(1.4 \text{ MPa})\left(1000 \text{ } \frac{\text{kPa}}{\text{MPa}}\right)}\right)$$
$$= 40.74$$

From air tables (App. 24.S) at $p_{r,2} = 40.74$,

$$T_2 = \boxed{767.2\text{K}}$$
$$h_2 = 786.05 \text{ kJ/kg}$$
$$v_{r,2} = 53.99$$

(b)
$$\dot{V}_2 = \dot{V}_1\left(\frac{v_{r,2}}{v_{r,1}}\right)$$
$$= \left(280 \text{ } \frac{\text{L}}{\text{s}}\right)\left(\frac{53.99}{19.275}\right)$$
$$= \boxed{784.3 \text{ L/s}}$$

(c) The enthalpy change is

$$\Delta h = h_2 - h_1$$
$$= 786.05 \text{ } \frac{\text{kJ}}{\text{kg}} - 1153 \text{ } \frac{\text{kJ}}{\text{kg}}$$
$$= \boxed{-366.95 \text{ kJ/kg} \quad [\text{decrease}]}$$

Power Cycles

2. *Customary U.S. Solution*

The actual brake horsepower from Eq. 29.10(b) is

$$\text{BHP} = \frac{nT}{5252} = \frac{(200 \text{ rpm})(600 \text{ ft-lbf})}{5252}$$
$$= 22.85 \text{ hp}$$

From Eq. 29.41, the number of power strokes per minute is

$$N = \frac{(2n)(\text{no. cylinders})}{\text{no. strokes per cycle}}$$
$$= \frac{(2)(200 \text{ rpm})(2)}{4} = 200 \text{ power strokes/min}$$

The stroke is

$$L = (18 \text{ in})\left(\frac{1 \text{ ft}}{12 \text{ in}}\right) = 1.5 \text{ ft}$$

The bore area is

$$\left(\frac{\pi}{4}\right)(10 \text{ in})^2 = 78.54 \text{ in}^2$$

From Eq. 29.40(b), the ideal horsepower is

$$\text{hp} = \frac{pLAN}{33,000}$$
$$= \frac{\left(95 \frac{\text{lbf}}{\text{in}^2}\right)(1.5 \text{ ft})(78.54 \text{ in}^2)\left(200 \frac{\text{strokes}}{\text{min}}\right)}{33,000 \frac{\text{ft-lbf}}{\text{hp-min}}}$$
$$= 67.83 \text{ hp}$$

The friction horsepower is

$$\text{ideal hp} - \text{actual BHP} = 67.83 \text{ hp} - 22.85 \text{ hp}$$
$$= \boxed{44.98 \text{ hp}}$$

SI Solution

The actual brake power from Eq. 29.10(a) is

$$\text{BkW} = \frac{nT}{5252} = \frac{(200 \text{ rpm})(820 \text{ N·m})}{9549}$$
$$= 17.17 \text{ kW}$$

From Eq. 29.41, the number of power strokes per minute is

$$N = \frac{(2n)(\text{no. cylinders})}{\text{no. strokes per cycle}}$$
$$= \frac{(2)(200 \text{ rpm})(2)}{4} = 200 \text{ power strokes/min}$$

The stroke is

$$\frac{460 \text{ mm}}{1000 \frac{\text{mm}}{\text{m}}} = 0.46 \text{ m}$$

The bore area is

$$\left(\frac{\pi}{4}\right)\left(\frac{250 \text{ mm}}{1000 \frac{\text{mm}}{\text{m}}}\right)^2 = 4.909 \times 10^{-2} \text{ m}^2$$

From Eq. 29.40(a), the ideal power is

$$\text{kW} = pLAN$$
$$= \frac{(660 \text{ kPa})(0.46 \text{ m}) \times (4.909 \times 10^{-2} \text{ m}^2)\left(200 \frac{\text{strokes}}{\text{min}}\right)}{60 \frac{\text{s}}{\text{min}}}$$
$$= 49.68 \text{ kW}$$

The friction power is

$$\text{ideal kW} - \text{actual kW} = 49.68 \text{ kW} - 17.17 \text{ kW}$$
$$= \boxed{32.51 \text{ kW}}$$

3. *Customary U.S. Solution*

The number of degrees that the valve is open is

$$180° + 40° = 220°$$

The time that the valve is open is

$$\left(\frac{220°}{360°}\right)\left(\frac{\text{time}}{\text{rev}}\right) = \left(\frac{220°}{360°}\right)\left(\frac{60 \frac{\text{sec}}{\text{min}}}{4000 \text{ rpm}}\right)$$
$$= 9.167 \times 10^{-3} \text{ sec}$$

The displacement is

$$\left(\frac{\pi}{4}\right)(\text{bore})^2(\text{stroke}) = \left(\frac{\pi}{4}\right)(3.1 \text{ in})^2\left(\frac{1 \text{ ft}}{12 \text{ in}}\right)^2$$
$$\times (3.8 \text{ in})\left(\frac{1 \text{ ft}}{12 \text{ in}}\right)$$
$$= 0.0166 \text{ ft}^3$$

The actual incoming volume per intake stroke is

$$V = (\text{volumetric efficiency})(\text{displacement})$$
$$= (0.65)(0.0166 \text{ ft}^3) = 0.01079 \text{ ft}^3$$

The area is

$$A = \frac{V}{vt} = \frac{0.01079 \text{ ft}^3}{\left(100 \dfrac{\text{ft}}{\text{sec}}\right)(9.167 \times 10^{-3} \text{ sec})}$$

$$= \boxed{0.0118 \text{ ft}^2 \quad (1.69 \text{ in}^2)}$$

SI Solution

The number of degrees that the valve is open is

$$180° + 40° = 220°$$

The time that the valve is open is

$$\left(\frac{220°}{360°}\right)\left(\frac{\text{time}}{\text{rev}}\right) = \left(\frac{220°}{360°}\right)\left(\frac{60 \dfrac{\text{s}}{\text{min}}}{4000 \text{ rpm}}\right)$$

$$= 9.167 \times 10^{-3} \text{ s}$$

The displacement is

$$\left(\frac{\pi}{4}\right)(\text{bore})^2(\text{stroke}) = \left(\frac{\pi}{4}\right)(0.08 \text{ m})^2(0.097 \text{ m})$$

$$= 4.876 \times 10^{-4} \text{ m}^3$$

The actual incoming volume per intake stroke is

$$V = (\text{volumetric efficiency})(\text{displacement})$$

$$= (0.65)(4.876 \times 10^{-4} \text{ m}^3) = 3.169 \times 10^{-4} \text{ m}^3$$

The area is

$$A = \frac{V}{vt} = \frac{3.169 \times 10^{-4} \text{ m}^3}{\left(30 \dfrac{\text{m}}{\text{s}}\right)(9.167 \times 10^{-3} \text{ s})}$$

$$= \boxed{1.152 \times 10^{-3} \text{ m}^2}$$

4. *Customary U.S. Solution*

Refer to the air-standard Otto cycle diagram (Fig. 29.3).

(a) At A:

$$V_A = 11 \text{ ft}^3$$

The absolute temperature is

$$T_A = 80°F + 460 = 540°R$$

For an ideal gas, the mass of the air in the intake volume is

$$m = \frac{pV}{RT} = \frac{\left(14.2 \dfrac{\text{lbf}}{\text{in}^2}\right)\left(144 \dfrac{\text{in}^2}{\text{ft}^2}\right)(11 \text{ ft}^3)}{\left(53.3 \dfrac{\text{ft-lbf}}{\text{lbm-°R}}\right)(540°R)}$$

$$= 0.781 \text{ lbm}$$

From air tables (App. 24.F) at 540°R,

$$v_{r,A} = 144.32$$
$$u_A = 92.04 \text{ Btu/lbm}$$

At B:

The compression ratio is a ratio of volumes.

$$V_B = \left(\frac{1}{10}\right)V_A = \left(\frac{1}{10}\right)(11 \text{ ft}^3)$$
$$= 1.1 \text{ ft}^3$$

Since the compression from A to B is isentropic,

$$v_{r,B} = \frac{v_{r,A}}{10} = \frac{144.32}{10}$$
$$= 14.432$$

From the air tables (App. 24.F) for $v_r = 14.432$,

$$T_B \approx 1314°R$$
$$u_B \approx 230.5 \text{ Btu/lbm}$$

At C:

Assume $T_C \approx 2300°R$. At 2300°R from air tables (App. 24.F), $u_C = 431.16$ Btu/lbm.

$$c_v = \frac{\Delta u}{\Delta T} = \frac{u_C - u_B}{T_C - T_B}$$

$$= \frac{431.16 \dfrac{\text{Btu}}{\text{lbm}} - 230.5 \dfrac{\text{Btu}}{\text{lbm}}}{2300°R - 1314°R}$$

$$= 0.2035 \text{ Btu/lbm-°R}$$

From Eq. 29.34,

$$T_C = T_B + \frac{q_{in,B-C}}{c_v} = T_B + \frac{Q_{in,B-C}}{mc_v}$$

$$= 1314°R + \frac{160 \text{ Btu}}{(0.781 \text{ lbm})\left(0.2035 \dfrac{\text{Btu}}{\text{lbm-°R}}\right)}$$

$$= 2321°R$$

From air tables (App. 24.F) at 2321°R,

$$v_{r,C} = 2.689$$
$$u_C = 435.67$$

At D:

Since expansion is isentropic and the ratio of volumes is the same,

$$v_{r,D} = 10v_{r,C} = (10)(2.689)$$
$$= 26.89$$

From air tables (App. 24.F), at $v_r = 26.89$,

$$T_D = 1044°R$$
$$u_D = 180.38 \text{ Btu/lbm}$$

(b) The heat input is

$$q_{in} = \frac{Q}{m} = \frac{160 \text{ Btu}}{0.781 \text{ lbm}}$$
$$= 204.9 \text{ Btu/lbm}$$

The heat rejected during a constant volume process is $q_{out} = \Delta u$.

Heat is rejected between D and A. Therefore,

$$q_{out} = u_D - u_A = 180.38 \frac{\text{Btu}}{\text{lbm}} - 92.04 \frac{\text{Btu}}{\text{lbm}}$$
$$= 88.34 \text{ Btu/lbm}$$

From Eq. 29.38, the thermal efficiency is

$$\eta_{th} = \frac{q_{in} - q_{out}}{q_{in}} = \frac{204.9 \frac{\text{Btu}}{\text{lbm}} - 88.34 \frac{\text{Btu}}{\text{lbm}}}{204.9 \frac{\text{Btu}}{\text{lbm}}}$$
$$= \boxed{0.569 \ (56.9\%)}$$

SI Solution

(a) At A:

The absolute temperature is

$$T_A = 27°C + 273 = 300K$$

From the ideal gas law, the mass of air in the intake volume is

$$m = \frac{pV}{RT} = \frac{(98 \text{ kPa})\left(1000 \frac{\text{Pa}}{\text{kPa}}\right)(0.3 \text{ m}^3)}{\left(287 \frac{\text{J}}{\text{kg·K}}\right)(300K)}$$
$$= 0.3415 \text{ kg}$$

From air tables (App. 24.S) at 300K,

$$v_{r,A} = 621.2$$
$$u_A = 214.07 \text{ kJ/kg}$$

At B:

The compression ratio is a ratio of volumes.

$$V_B = \left(\frac{1}{10}\right)V_A = \frac{0.3 \text{ m}^3}{10}$$
$$= 0.03 \text{ m}^3$$

Since the compression from A to B is isentropic,

$$v_{r,B} = \frac{v_{r,A}}{10} = \frac{621.2}{10}$$
$$= 62.12$$

From air tables (App. 24.S) for this value of $v_{r,B}$,

$$T_B = 730K$$
$$u_B = 536.0 \text{ kJ/kg}$$

At C:

Assume $T_C \approx 1300K$. From App. 24.S, at 1300K,

$$u_C = 1022.82 \text{ kJ/kg}$$
$$c_v = \frac{\Delta u}{\Delta T} = \frac{u_C - u_B}{T_C - T_B}$$
$$= \frac{1022.82 \frac{\text{kJ}}{\text{kg}} - 536.07 \frac{\text{kJ}}{\text{kg}}}{1300K - 730K}$$
$$= 0.8539 \text{ kJ/kg·K}$$

From Eq. 29.34,

$$T_C = T_B + \frac{q_{in,B-C}}{c_v} = T_B + \frac{q_{in,B-C}}{mc_v}$$
$$= 730K + \frac{179 \text{ kJ}}{(0.3415 \text{ kg})\left(0.8539 \frac{\text{kJ}}{\text{kg·K}}\right)}$$
$$= 1344K$$

From air tables (App. 24.S),

$$v_{r,C} = 10.154$$
$$u_C = 1062.57 \text{ kJ/kg·K}$$

At D:

Since expansion is isentropic and the ratio of volumes is the same,

$$v_{r,D} = 10v_{r,C} = (10)(10.154)$$
$$= 101.54$$

From air tables (App. 24.S), at $v_r = 101.54$,

$$T_D = 609.3K$$
$$u_D = 441.9 \text{ kJ/kg}$$

(b) The heat input is

$$q_{in} = \frac{Q}{m} = \frac{179 \text{ kJ}}{0.3415 \text{ kg}}$$
$$= 524.2 \text{ kJ/kg}$$

The heat rejected during a constant volume process is

$$q_{out} = \Delta u$$

Heat is rejected between D and A. Therefore,

$$q_{out} = u_D - u_A = 441.9 \frac{\text{kJ}}{\text{kg}} - 214.07 \frac{\text{kJ}}{\text{kg}}$$
$$= 227.8 \text{ kJ/kg}$$

From Eq. 29.38, the thermal efficiency is

$$\eta_{th} = \frac{q_{in} - q_{out}}{q_{in}} = \frac{524.2 \frac{\text{kJ}}{\text{kg}} - 227.8 \frac{\text{kJ}}{\text{kg}}}{524.2 \frac{\text{kJ}}{\text{kg}}}$$

$$= \boxed{0.565 \quad (56.5\%)}$$

5. *Customary U.S. Solution*

step 1: Find the ideal mass of air ingested.

From Eq. 29.41, the number of power strokes per second is

$$N = \frac{(2n)(\text{no. cylinders})}{\text{no. strokes per cycle}}$$

$$= \frac{(2)\left(1200 \frac{\text{rev}}{\text{min}}\right)\left(\frac{1 \text{ min}}{60 \text{ sec}}\right)(6 \text{ cylinders})}{4 \text{ strokes}}$$

$$= 60/\text{sec}$$

The swept volume is

$$V_s = \left(\frac{\pi}{4}\right)(\text{bore})^2(\text{stroke})$$

$$= \left(\frac{\pi}{4}\right)(4.25 \text{ in})^2 \left(\frac{1 \text{ ft}^2}{144 \text{ in}^2}\right)(6 \text{ in})\left(\frac{1 \text{ ft}}{12 \text{ min}}\right)$$

$$= 0.04926 \text{ ft}^3$$

The ideal volume of air taken in per second is

$$\dot{V}_i = (\text{swept volume})\left(\frac{\text{intake strokes}}{\text{sec}}\right)$$

$$= V_s N$$

$$= (0.04926 \text{ ft}^3)\left(60 \frac{1}{\text{sec}}\right) = 2.956 \text{ ft}^3/\text{sec}$$

The absolute temperature is

$$70°\text{F} + 460 = 530°\text{R}$$

From the ideal gas law, the ideal mass of air in the swept volume is

$$\dot{m} = \frac{p\dot{V}}{RT}$$

$$= \frac{\left(14.7 \frac{\text{lbf}}{\text{in}^2}\right)\left(144 \frac{\text{in}^2}{\text{ft}^2}\right)\left(2.956 \frac{\text{ft}^3}{\text{sec}}\right)}{\left(53.35 \frac{\text{ft-lbf}}{\text{lbm-}°\text{R}}\right)(530°\text{R})}$$

$$= 0.2213 \text{ lbm/sec}$$

step 2: Find the carbon dioxide volume in the exhaust assuming complete combustion when the air/fuel ratio is 15 ($\%CO_2 = 13.7\%$, dry basis).

Air is 76.85% (by weight) nitrogen, so the nitrogen/fuel ratio is

$$(0.7685)(15) = 11.528 \text{ lbm N}_2/\text{lbm fuel}$$

From the ideal gas law, the nitrogen per pound of fuel burned is

$$V_{N_2} = \frac{mRT}{p}$$

$$= \frac{\left(11.528 \frac{\text{lbm N}_2}{\text{lbm fuel}}\right)\left(55.16 \frac{\text{ft-lbf}}{\text{lbm-}°\text{R}}\right)(530°\text{R})}{\left(14.7 \frac{\text{lbf}}{\text{in}^2}\right)\left(144 \frac{\text{in}^2}{\text{ft}^2}\right)}$$

$$= 159.2 \text{ ft}^3/\text{lbm fuel}$$

Similarly, air is 23.15% oxygen by weight, so the oxygen/fuel ratio is

$$(0.2315)(15) = 3.472 \text{ lbm O}_2/\text{lbm fuel}$$

From the ideal gas law, the oxygen per pound of fuel burned is

$$V_{O_2} = \frac{mRT}{p}$$

$$= \frac{\left(3.472 \ \frac{\text{lbm } O_2}{\text{lbm fuel}}\right)\left(48.29 \ \frac{\text{ft-lbf}}{\text{lbm-}°R}\right)(530°R)}{\left(14.7 \ \frac{\text{lbf}}{\text{in}^2}\right)\left(144 \ \frac{\text{in}^2}{\text{ft}^2}\right)}$$

$$= 41.98 \ \text{ft}^3/\text{lbm fuel}$$

When oxygen forms carbon dioxide, the chemical equation is $C + O_2 \longrightarrow CO_2$.

It takes one volume of oxygen to form one volume of carbon dioxide. Considering nitrogen and excess oxygen in the exhaust, the percentage of carbon dioxide in the exhaust is found from

$$\%CO_2 = \frac{\text{vol } CO_2}{\text{vol } CO_2 + \text{vol } O_2 + \text{vol } N_2}$$

$\text{vol } CO_2 = x$ [unknown], in ft^3

$\text{vol } O_2 = 41.98 \ \text{ft}^3 -$ oxygen used to make CO_2

$\quad = 41.98 \ \text{ft}^3 - x$

$\%CO_2 = 0.137$ [given]

$$0.137 = \frac{x}{x + (41.98 \ \text{ft}^3 - x) + 159.3 \ \text{ft}^3}$$

$$x = 27.58 \ \text{ft}^3/\text{lbm fuel}$$

Assuming complete combustion, the volume of CO_2 will be constant regardless of the amount of air used.

step 3: Calculate the excess air if the percentage of carbon dioxide in the exhaust is 9%.

$$\%CO_2 = \frac{\text{vol } CO_2}{\substack{\text{vol } CO_2 + \text{vol } O_2 \\ + \text{vol } N_2 + \text{vol excess air}}}$$

$$0.09 = \frac{27.58 \ \text{ft}^3}{\substack{27.58 \ \text{ft}^3 + (41.99 \ \text{ft}^3 - 27.58 \ \text{ft}^3) \\ + 159.3 \ \text{ft}^3 + \text{vol excess air}}}$$

$$\begin{matrix} \text{vol} \\ \text{excess} \\ \text{air} \end{matrix} = 105.2 \ \text{ft}^3/\text{lbm fuel}$$

From the ideal gas law, the mass of excess air is

$$m_{\text{excess}} = \frac{\left(14.7 \ \frac{\text{lbf}}{\text{in}^2}\right)\left(144 \ \frac{\text{in}^2}{\text{ft}^2}\right)(105.2 \ \text{ft}^3)}{\left(53.35 \ \frac{\text{lbf-ft}}{\text{lbm-}°R}\right)(530°R)}$$

$$= 7.876 \ \text{lbm/lbm fuel}$$

step 4: The actual air/fuel ratio is

$$15 \ \frac{\text{lbm air}}{\text{lbm fuel}} + 7.876 \ \frac{\text{lbm air}}{\text{lbm fuel}}$$

$$= 22.876 \ \text{lbm air/lbm fuel}$$

The actual air mass per second is

$$\left(22.876 \ \frac{\text{lbm air}}{\text{lbm fuel}}\right)\left(28 \ \frac{\text{lbm fuel}}{\text{hr}}\right)\left(\frac{1 \ \text{hr}}{3600 \ \text{sec}}\right)$$

$$= 0.178 \ \text{lbm/sec}$$

step 5: The volumetric efficiency is

$$\eta_v = \frac{0.178 \ \frac{\text{lbm}}{\text{sec}}}{0.2213 \ \frac{\text{lbm}}{\text{sec}}} = \boxed{0.804 \ (80.4\%)}$$

SI Solution

step 1: Find the ideal mass of air ingested.

From Eq. 29.41, the number of power strokes per second is

$$N = \frac{(2n)(\text{no. cylinders})}{\text{no. strokes per cycle}}$$

$$= \frac{(2)\left(1200 \ \frac{\text{rev}}{\text{min}}\right)\left(\frac{1 \ \text{min}}{60 \ \text{s}}\right)(6 \ \text{cylinders})}{4 \ \text{strokes}}$$

$$= 60/\text{s}$$

The swept volume is

$$V_s = \left(\frac{\pi}{4}\right)(\text{bore})^2(\text{stroke})$$

$$= \left(\frac{\pi}{4}\right)(0.110 \ \text{m})^2(0.150 \ \text{m})$$

$$= 1.425 \times 10^{-3} \ \text{m}^3$$

The ideal volume of air taken in per second is

$$\dot{V}_i = (\text{swept volume})\left(\frac{\text{intake strokes}}{\text{s}}\right)$$

$$= V_s N$$

$$= (1.425 \times 10^{-3})\left(60 \ \frac{1}{\text{s}}\right) = 0.0855 \ \text{m}^3/\text{s}$$

The absolute temperature is

$$21°C + 273 = 294K$$

From the ideal gas law, the ideal mass of air in the swept volume is

$$\dot{m} = \frac{p\dot{V}}{RT}$$

$$= \frac{(101.3 \text{ kPa})\left(1000 \dfrac{\text{Pa}}{\text{kPa}}\right)\left(0.0855 \dfrac{\text{m}^3}{\text{s}}\right)}{\left(287.03 \dfrac{\text{J}}{\text{kg·K}}\right)(294\text{K})}$$

$$= 0.1026 \text{ kg/s}$$

step 2: Find the carbon dioxide volume in the exhaust assuming complete combustion when the air/fuel ratio is 15 ($\%CO_2 = 13.7\%$ dry basis).

Air is 76.85% nitrogen by weight, so the nitrogen/fuel ratio is

$$(0.7685)(15) = 11.528 \text{ kg } N_2/\text{kg fuel}$$

From the ideal gas law, the nitrogen per kg of fuel burned is

$$V_{N_2} = \frac{mRT}{p}$$

$$= \frac{\left(11.528 \dfrac{\text{kg } N_2}{\text{kg fuel}}\right)\left(296.77 \dfrac{\text{J}}{\text{kg·K}}\right)(294\text{K})}{(101.3 \text{ kPa})\left(1000 \dfrac{\text{Pa}}{\text{kPa}}\right)}$$

$$= 9.929 \text{ m}^3/\text{kg fuel}$$

Similarly, air is 23.15% oxygen by weight, so the oxygen/fuel ratio is

$$(0.2315)(15) = 3.473 \text{ kg } O_2/\text{kg fuel}$$

From the ideal gas law, the oxygen per kg of fuel burned is

$$V_{O_2} = \frac{mRT}{p}$$

$$= \frac{\left(3.473 \dfrac{\text{kg } O_2}{\text{kg fuel}}\right)\left(259.82 \dfrac{\text{J}}{\text{kg·K}}\right)(294\text{K})}{(101.3 \text{ kPa})\left(1000 \dfrac{\text{Pa}}{\text{kPa}}\right)}$$

$$= 2.619 \text{ m}^3/\text{kg fuel}$$

From the Customary U.S. Solution,

$$\%CO_2 = \frac{\text{vol } CO_2}{\text{vol } CO_2 + \text{vol } O_2 + \text{vol } N_2}$$

vol $CO_2 = x$ [unknown], in m^3

vol $O_2 = 2.619 \text{ m}^3 - O_2$ used to make CO_2

$$= 2.619 \text{ m}^3 - x$$

$\%CO_2 = 0.137$ [given]

$$0.137 = \frac{x}{x + (2.619 \text{ m}^3 - x) + 9.929 \text{ m}^3}$$

$$x = 1.719 \text{ m}^3/\text{kg fuel}$$

Assuming complete combustion, the volume of carbon dioxide will be constant regardless of the amount of air used.

step 3: Calculate the excess air if the percentage of carbon dioxide in the exhaust is 9%. Therefore,

$$\%CO_2 = \frac{\text{vol } CO_2}{\substack{\text{vol } CO_2 + \text{vol } O_2 \\ + \text{ vol } N_2 + \text{vol excess air}}}$$

$$0.09 = \frac{1.719 \text{ m}^3}{\substack{1.719 \text{ m}^3 + (2.619 \text{ m}^3 - 1.719 \text{ m}^3) \\ + \, 9.929 \text{ m}^3 + \text{vol excess air}}}$$

$$\begin{array}{l}\text{vol} \\ \text{excess} \\ \text{air}\end{array} = 6.552 \text{ m}^3/\text{kg fuel}$$

From the ideal gas law, the mass of the excess air is

$$m_{\text{excess}} = \frac{(101.3 \text{ kPa})\left(1000 \dfrac{\text{Pa}}{\text{kPa}}\right)(6.552 \text{ m}^3)}{\left(287.03 \dfrac{\text{J}}{\text{kg·K}}\right)(294\text{K})}$$

$$= 7.865 \text{ kg/kg fuel}$$

step 4: The actual air/fuel ratio is

$$15 \, \frac{\text{kg air}}{\text{kg fuel}} + 7.865 \, \frac{\text{kg air}}{\text{kg fuel}} = 22.865 \text{ kg air/kg fuel}$$

The actual air mass per second is

$$\left(22.865 \, \frac{\text{kg air}}{\text{kg fuel}}\right)\left(0.0035 \, \frac{\text{kg}}{\text{s}}\right) = 0.0800 \text{ kg/s}$$

step 5: The volumetric efficiency is

$$\eta_{\text{v}} = \frac{0.0800 \, \dfrac{\text{kg}}{\text{s}}}{0.1026 \, \dfrac{\text{kg}}{\text{s}}} = \boxed{0.772 \ (77.2\%)}$$

6. *Customary U.S. Solution*

step 1: From App. 26.E,

Altitude 1: standard atmospheric condition, 14.696 psia, 518.7°R

Altitude 2: $z = 5000$ ft, 12.225 psia, 500.9°R

step 2: Calculate the friction power (Eq. 29.68).

$$IHP_1 = \frac{BHP_1}{\eta_{m,1}} = \frac{1000 \text{ hp}}{0.80} = 1250 \text{ hp}$$

Power Cycles

step 3: Not needed since η_m is constant with altitude.

step 4: From the ideal gas law,

$$\rho_{a1} = \frac{p}{RT} = \frac{\left(14.696\ \frac{\text{lbf}}{\text{in}^2}\right)\left(144\ \frac{\text{in}^2}{\text{ft}^2}\right)}{\left(53.35\ \frac{\text{lbf-ft}}{\text{lbm-}°\text{R}}\right)(518.7°\text{R})}$$

$$= 0.0765\ \text{lbm/ft}^3$$

Similarly,

$$\rho_{a2} = \frac{p}{RT} = \frac{\left(12.225\ \frac{\text{lbf}}{\text{in}^2}\right)\left(144\ \frac{\text{in}^2}{\text{ft}^2}\right)}{\left(53.35\ \frac{\text{ft-lbf}}{\text{lbm-}°\text{R}}\right)(500.9°\text{R})}$$

$$= 0.0659\ \text{lbm/ft}^3$$

step 5: Calculate the new frictionless power (Eq. 29.70).

$$\text{IHP}_2 = \text{IHP}_1\left(\frac{\rho_{a2}}{\rho_{a1}}\right)$$

$$= (1250\ \text{hp})\left(\frac{0.0659\ \frac{\text{lbm}}{\text{ft}^3}}{0.0765\ \frac{\text{lbm}}{\text{ft}^3}}\right)$$

$$= 1076.8\ \text{hp}$$

steps 6 and 7: Calculate the new net power using Eq. 29.72.

$$\text{BHP}_2 = \eta_{m,2}(\text{IHP}_2) = (0.80)(1076.8\ \text{hp})$$

$$= 861.4\ \text{hp}$$

step 8: Not needed.

step 9: The original fuel rate (Eq. 29.74) is

$$\dot{m}_{f1} = (\text{BSFC}_1)(\text{BHP}_1)$$

$$= \left(0.45\ \frac{\text{lbm}}{\text{bhp-hr}}\right)(1000\ \text{bhp})$$

$$= 450\ \text{lbm/hr}$$

step 10: Not needed.

step 11: $\dot{m}_{f2} = \dot{m}_{f1} = 450\ \text{lbm/hr}$

step 12: The new fuel consumption (Eq. 29.79) is

$$\text{BSFC}_2 = \frac{\dot{m}_{f2}}{\text{BHP}_2} = \frac{450\ \frac{\text{lbm}}{\text{hr}}}{861.4\ \text{hp}}$$

$$= \boxed{0.522\ \text{lbm/bhp-hr}}$$

SI Solution

step 1: From App. 26.E,

Altitude 1: standard atmospheric condition, 1.01325 bar, 288.15K

Altitude 2: 0.8456 bar, 278.4K

$$z = 1500\ \text{m}$$

step 2: Calculate the friction power (Eq. 29.68).

$$\text{IHP}_1 = \frac{\text{BHP}_1}{\eta_{m,1}} = \frac{750\ \text{kW}}{0.80} = 937.5\ \text{kW}$$

step 3: Not needed since η_m is constant with altitude.

step 4: From the ideal gas law, the air densities are

$$\rho_{a1} = \frac{p}{RI} = \frac{(1.01325\ \text{bar})\left(10^5\ \frac{\text{Pa}}{\text{bar}}\right)}{\left(287.03\ \frac{\text{J}}{\text{kg·K}}\right)(288.15\text{K})}$$

$$= 1.225\ \text{kg/m}^3$$

Similarly,

$$\rho_{a2} = \frac{(0.8456\ \text{bar})\left(10^5\ \frac{\text{Pa}}{\text{bar}}\right)}{\left(287.03\ \frac{\text{J}}{\text{kg·K}}\right)(278.4\text{K})}$$

$$= 1.058\ \text{kg/m}^3$$

step 5: Calculate the new frictionless power (Eq. 29.70).

$$\text{IHP}_2 = \text{IHP}_1\left(\frac{\rho_{a2}}{\rho_{a1}}\right)$$

$$= (937.5\ \text{kW})\left(\frac{1.058\ \frac{\text{kg}}{\text{m}^3}}{1.225\ \frac{\text{kg}}{\text{m}^3}}\right)$$

$$= 809.7\ \text{kW}$$

steps 6 and 7: Calculate the new net power (Eq. 29.72).

$$\text{BHP}_2 = \eta_{m,2}(\text{IHP}_2) = (0.80)(809.7\ \text{kW})$$

$$= 647.8\ \text{kW}$$

step 8: Not needed.

step 9: The original fuel rate (Eq. 29.74) is

$$\dot{m}_{f1} = (\text{BSFC}_1)(\text{BHP}_1)$$

$$= \left(76 \ \frac{\text{kg}}{\text{GJ}}\right)(750 \ \text{kW})\left(\frac{\text{GJ}}{10^6 \ \text{kJ}}\right)$$

$$= 0.057 \ \text{kg/s}$$

step 10: Not needed.

step 11: $\dot{m}_{f2} = \dot{m}_{f1} = 0.057 \ \text{kg/s}$

step 12: The new fuel consumption (Eq. 29.79) is

$$\text{BSFC}_2 = \frac{m_{f2}}{\text{BHP}_2}$$

$$= \frac{0.057 \ \dfrac{\text{kg}}{\text{s}}}{(647.8 \ \text{kW})\left(\dfrac{\text{GW}}{10^6 \ \text{kW}}\right)}$$

$$= \boxed{88.0 \ \text{kg/GJ}}$$

7. *Customary U.S. Solution*

(Use an air table. The SI Solution assumes an ideal gas.) Refer to Fig. 29.11.

At A:

$$T_A = 60°\text{F} + 460 = 520°\text{R} \quad \text{[given]}$$

$$p_A = 14.7 \ \text{psia} \quad \text{[given]}$$

From the air table (App. 24.F),

$$v_{r,A} = 158.58$$

$$p_{r,A} = 1.2147$$

$$h_A = 124.27 \ \text{Btu/lbm}$$

At B:

The process from A to B is isentropic.

$$v_{r,B} = v_{r,A}\left(\frac{V_B}{V_A}\right) = (158.58)\left(\frac{1}{5}\right) = 31.716$$

Locate this volume ratio in the air table (App. 24.F).

$$T_B \approx 980°\text{R}$$

$$h_B \approx 236.02 \ \text{Btu/lbm}$$

$$p_{r,B} = 11.430$$

Since process A-B is isentropic,

$$p_B = \left(\frac{p_{r,B}}{p_{r,A}}\right)p_A = \left(\frac{11.430}{1.2147}\right)(14.7 \ \text{psia}) = 138.3 \ \text{psia}$$

At C:

$$T_C = 1500°\text{F} + 460 = 1960°\text{R} \quad \text{[given]}$$

$$p_C = p_B = 138.3 \ \text{psia}$$

Locate the temperature in the air table.

$$h_C = 493.64 \ \text{Btu/lbm}$$

$$p_{r,C} = 160.48$$

At D:

$$p_D = 14.7 \ \text{psia}$$

Since process C-D is isentropic,

$$p_{r,D} = p_{r,C}\left(\frac{p_D}{p_C}\right) = (160.48)\left(\frac{14.7 \ \text{psia}}{138.3 \ \text{psia}}\right)$$

$$= 17.057$$

Locate this pressure ratio in the air table.

$$T_D = 1094°\text{R}$$

$$h_D = 264.49 \ \text{Btu/lbm}$$

Since the efficiency of compression is 83%, from Eq. 29.98,

$$h'_B = h_A + \frac{h_B - h_A}{\eta_{s,\text{compressor}}}$$

$$= 124.27 \ \frac{\text{Btu}}{\text{lbm}} + \frac{236.02 \ \dfrac{\text{Btu}}{\text{lbm}} - 124.27 \ \dfrac{\text{Btu}}{\text{lbm}}}{0.83}$$

$$= 258.9 \ \text{Btu/lbm}$$

Since the efficiency of the expansion process is 92%, from Eq. 29.100,

$$h'_D = h_C - \eta_{s,\text{turbine}}(h_C - h_D)$$

$$= 493.64 \ \frac{\text{Btu}}{\text{lbm}}$$

$$\quad - (0.92)\left(493.64 \ \frac{\text{Btu}}{\text{lbm}} - 264.49 \ \frac{\text{Btu}}{\text{lbm}}\right)$$

$$= 282.8 \ \text{Btu/lbm}$$

From Eq. 26.96, the thermal efficiency is

$$\eta_{\text{th}} = \frac{(h_C - h'_B) - (h'_D - h_A)}{h_C - h'_B}$$

$$= \frac{\left(493.64 \ \dfrac{\text{Btu}}{\text{lbm}} - 258.9 \ \dfrac{\text{Btu}}{\text{lbm}}\right)}{493.64 \ \dfrac{\text{Btu}}{\text{lbm}} - 258.9 \ \dfrac{\text{Btu}}{\text{lbm}}}$$

$$\frac{\quad - \left(282.8 \ \dfrac{\text{Btu}}{\text{lbm}} - 124.27 \ \dfrac{\text{Btu}}{\text{lbm}}\right)}{}$$

$$= \boxed{0.325 \quad (32.5\%)}$$

SI Solution

Refer to Fig. 29.11.

At A:
$$T_A = 16°C + 273 = 289K \quad \text{[given]}$$
$$p_A = 101.3 \text{ kPa} \quad \text{[given]}$$

At B:
$$T_B = T_A \left(\frac{v_A}{v_B}\right)^{k-1} = (289K)(5)^{1.4-1} = 550.2K$$
$$p_B = p_A \left(\frac{v_A}{v_B}\right)^{k} = (101.3 \text{ kPa})(5)^{1.4} = 964.2 \text{ kPa}$$

At C:
$$T_C = 820°C + 273 = 1093K \quad \text{[given]}$$
$$p_C = p_B = 964.2 \text{ kPa}$$

At D:
$$p_D = 101.3 \text{ kPa} \quad \text{[given]}$$
$$T_D = T_C \left(\frac{p_D}{p_C}\right)^{\frac{k-1}{k}} = (1093K)\left(\frac{101.3 \text{ kPa}}{964.2 \text{ kPa}}\right)^{\frac{1.4-1}{1.4}}$$
$$T_D = 574.2K$$

For ideal gases, the specific heats are constant. Therefore, the change in internal energy (and enthalpy, approximately) is proportional to the change in temperature. The actual temperature (Eq. 29.99) is

$$T_B' = T_A + \frac{T_B - T_A}{\eta_{s,\text{compressor}}}$$
$$= 289K + \frac{550.2K - 289K}{0.83}$$
$$= 603.7K$$

From Eq. 29.101,
$$T_D' = T_C - \eta_{s,\text{turbine}}(T_C - T_D)$$
$$= 1093K - (0.92)(1093K - 574.2K)$$
$$= 615.7K$$

From Eq. 29.97, the thermal efficiency is

$$\eta_{th} = \frac{(T_C - T_B') - (T_D' - T_A)}{T_C - T_B'}$$
$$= \frac{(1093K - 603.7K) - (615.7K - 289K)}{1093K - 603.7K}$$
$$= \boxed{0.332 \quad (33.2\%)}$$

8. *Customary U.S. Solution*

Since specific heats are constant, use ideal gas rather than air tables.

Refer to Fig. 29.12.

At A:
$$T_A = 60°F + 460 = 520°R \quad \text{[given]}$$
$$p_A = 14.7 \text{ psia} \quad \text{[given]}$$

At B:
$$T_B = T_A \left(\frac{v_A}{v_B}\right)^{k-1} = (520°R)(5)^{1.4-1} = 989.9°R$$
$$p_B = p_A \left(\frac{v_A}{v_B}\right)^{k} = (14.7 \text{ psia})(5)^{1.4}$$
$$= 139.9 \text{ psia}$$

At D:
$$T_D = 1500°F + 460 = 1960°R \quad \text{[given]}$$
$$p_D = p_B = 139.9 \text{ psia}$$

At E:
$$p_E = 14.7 \text{ psia} \quad \text{[given]}$$
$$T_E = T_D \left(\frac{p_E}{p_D}\right)^{\frac{k-1}{k}} = (1960°R)\left(\frac{14.7 \text{ psia}}{139.9 \text{ psia}}\right)^{\frac{1.4-1}{1.4}}$$
$$= 1029.6°R$$

From Eq. 29.99,
$$T_B' = T_A + \frac{T_B - T_A}{\eta_{s,\text{compressor}}} = 520°R + \frac{989.9°R - 520°R}{0.83}$$
$$= 1086.1°R$$

From Eq. 29.101,
$$T_E' = T_D - \eta_{s,\text{turbine}}(T_D - T_E)$$
$$= 1960°R - (0.92)(1960°R - 1029.6°R)$$
$$= 1104.0°R$$

From Eq. 29.102,
$$\eta_{\text{regenerator}} = \frac{h_C - h_B'}{h_E' - h_B'}$$

For $c_p \approx$ constant,
$$\eta_{\text{regenerator}} = \frac{T_C - T_B'}{T_E' - T_B'}$$
$$0.65 = \frac{T_C - 1086.1°R}{1104.0°R - 1086.1°R}$$
$$T_C = 1097.7°R$$

From Eq. 29.103 with constant specific heats,

$$\eta_{th} = \frac{(T_D - T_E') - (T_B' - T_A)}{T_D - T_C}$$

$$= \frac{(1960°R - 1104.0°R) - (1086.1°R - 520°R)}{1960°R - 1097.7°R}$$

$$= \boxed{0.336 \ (33.6\%)}$$

SI Solution

Refer to Fig. 29.12. From Prob. 7,

$$T_A = 289K$$
$$T_B' = 603.7K$$
$$T_D = 1093K$$
$$T_E' = 615.7K$$

For constant specific heats and from Eq. 29.102,

$$\eta_{regenerator} = \frac{T_C - T_B'}{T_E' - T_B'}$$

$$0.65 = \frac{T_C - 603.7K}{615.7K - 603.7K}$$

$$T_C = 611.5K$$

From Eq. 29.103 with constant specific heats,

$$\eta_{th} = \frac{(T_D - T_E') - (T_B' - T_A)}{T_D - T_C}$$

$$= \frac{(1093K - 615.7K) - (603.7K - 289K)}{1093K - 611.5K}$$

$$= \boxed{0.338 \ (33.8\%)}$$

9. *Customary U.S. Solution*

(a) From Eq. 29.41, the number of power strokes per minute is

$$N = \frac{(2n)(\text{no. cylinders})}{\text{no. strokes per cycle}}$$

$$= \frac{\left(2 \ \frac{\text{strokes}}{\text{rev}}\right)\left(4600 \ \frac{\text{rev}}{\text{min}}\right)(8 \text{ cylinders})}{4 \ \frac{\text{strokes}}{\text{power stroke}}}$$

$$= 18,400 \text{ power strokes/min}$$

The net work per cycle is

$$W_{net} = W_{out} - W_{in} = 1500 \text{ ft-lbf} - 1200 \text{ ft-lbf}$$
$$= 300 \text{ ft-lbf/cycle}$$

The indicated horsepower is

$$IHP = \frac{\left(18,400 \ \frac{\text{power strokes}}{\text{min}}\right)(300 \text{ ft-lbf})}{33,000 \ \frac{\text{ft-lbf}}{\text{hp-min}}}$$

$$= \boxed{167.27 \text{ hp}}$$

(b) From Eq. 29.3, the thermal efficiency is

$$\eta_{th} = \frac{W_{out} - W_{in}}{Q_{in}} = \frac{W_{net}}{Q_{in}}$$

$$= \frac{300 \ \frac{\text{ft-lbf}}{\text{cycle}}}{\left(1.27 \ \frac{\text{Btu}}{\text{cycle}}\right)\left(778 \ \frac{\text{ft-lbf}}{\text{Btu}}\right)}$$

$$= \boxed{0.304 \ (30.4\%)}$$

(c) The lower heating value of gasoline is LHV = 18,900 Btu/lbm.

The fuel consumption is

$$\dot{m}_F = \frac{\left(1.27 \ \frac{\text{Btu}}{\text{cycle}}\right)\left(18,400 \ \frac{\text{power strokes}}{\text{min}}\right)\left(60 \ \frac{\text{min}}{\text{hr}}\right)}{18,900 \ \frac{\text{Btu}}{\text{lbm}}}$$

$$= \boxed{74.18 \text{ lbm/hr}}$$

(d) Specific fuel consumption is given by Eq. 29.8.

$$SFC = \frac{\text{fuel usage rate}}{\text{power generated}} = \frac{74.18 \ \frac{\text{lbm}}{\text{hr}}}{167.27 \text{ hp}}$$

$$= \boxed{0.443 \text{ lbm/hp-hr}}$$

SI Solution

(a) From Eq. 29.41, the number of power strokes per minute is

$$N = \frac{(2n)(\text{no. cylinders})}{\text{no. strokes per cycle}}$$

$$= \frac{\left(2 \ \frac{\text{strokes}}{\text{rev}}\right)\left(4600 \ \frac{\text{rev}}{\text{min}}\right)(8 \text{ cylinders})}{4 \text{ strokes per power stroke}}$$

$$= 18\,400 \text{ power strokes/min}$$

The net work per cycle is

$$W_{\text{net}} = W_{\text{out}} - W_{\text{in}} = 2.0 \text{ kJ} - 1.6 \text{ kJ}$$
$$= 0.4 \text{ kJ/cycle}$$

The indicated power is

$$\text{IkW} = \left(18\,400 \frac{\text{power strokes}}{\text{min}}\right)\left(\frac{1 \text{ min}}{60 \text{ sec}}\right)(0.4 \text{ kJ})$$
$$= \boxed{122.7 \text{ kW}}$$

(b) From Eq. 29.3, the thermal efficiency is

$$\eta_{\text{th}} = \frac{W_{\text{out}} - W_{\text{in}}}{Q_{\text{in}}} = \frac{W_{\text{net}}}{Q_{\text{in}}}$$
$$= \frac{0.4 \frac{\text{kJ}}{\text{cycle}}}{1.33 \frac{\text{kJ}}{\text{cycle}}} = \boxed{0.300 \quad (30\%)}$$

(c) The heating value of gasoline is LHV = 44 MJ/kg. The fuel consumption is

$$\dot{m}_F = \frac{\left(1.33 \frac{\text{kJ}}{\text{cycle}}\right)\left(18\,400 \frac{\text{power strokes}}{\text{min}}\right)\left(\frac{1 \text{ min}}{60 \text{ s}}\right)}{\left(44 \frac{\text{MJ}}{\text{kg}}\right)\left(1000 \frac{\text{kJ}}{\text{MJ}}\right)}$$
$$= \boxed{0.00927 \text{ kg/s}}$$

(d) The specific fuel consumption (Eq. 29.8) is

$$\text{SFC} = \frac{\text{fuel usage rate}}{\text{power generated}} = \frac{0.00927 \frac{\text{kg}}{\text{s}}}{122.7 \text{ kW}}$$
$$= \boxed{7.555 \times 10^{-5} \text{ kg/kJ}}$$

10. *Customary U.S. Solution*

(a) At A:
$$T_A = 520°\text{R}$$
$$p_A = 14.7 \text{ psia}$$

At C:
$$T_C = 1600°$$
$$p_C = 568.6 \text{ psia}$$

For isentropic process C-A, from Eq. 25.91,

$$p_A = p_C \left(\frac{T_A}{T_C}\right)^{\frac{k}{k-1}}$$

Therefore,

$$14.7 \text{ psia} = (568.6 \text{ psia})\left(\frac{520°\text{R}}{1600°\text{R}}\right)^{\frac{k}{k-1}}$$
$$0.02585 = (0.325)^{\frac{k}{k-1}}$$
$$\log(0.02585) = \left(\frac{k}{k-1}\right)\log(0.325)$$
$$\frac{k}{k-1} = 3.252$$
$$k = 1.444$$

From Eq. 24.54, the molar specific heat of the mixture is

$$C_{p,\text{mixture}} = \frac{R^* k}{k-1}$$
$$= \frac{\left(1545 \frac{\text{ft-lbf}}{\text{lbmol-°R}}\right)(1.444)}{\left(778 \frac{\text{ft-lbf}}{\text{Btu}}\right)(1.444 - 1)}$$
$$= 6.459 \text{ Btu/lbmol-°R}$$

From Table 24.7,

$$(c_p)_{\text{He}} = 1.240 \text{ Btu/lbm-°R}$$
$$(\text{MW})_{\text{He}} = 4.003 \text{ lbm/lbmol}$$
$$(c_p)_{CO_2} = 0.207 \text{ Btu/lbm-°R}$$
$$(\text{MW})_{CO_2} = 44.011 \text{ lbm/lbmol}$$
$$C_{p,\text{He}} = (\text{MW})_{\text{He}}(c_p)_{\text{He}}$$
$$= \left(4.003 \frac{\text{lbm}}{\text{lbmol}}\right)\left(1.240 \frac{\text{Btu}}{\text{lbm-°R}}\right)$$
$$= 4.96 \text{ Btu/lbmol-°R}$$
$$C_{p,CO_2} = (\text{MW})_{CO_2}(c_p)_{CO_2}$$
$$= \left(44.011 \frac{\text{lbm}}{\text{lbmol}}\right)\left(0.207 \frac{\text{Btu}}{\text{lbm-°R}}\right)$$
$$= 9.11 \text{ Btu/lbmol-°R}$$

Let x be the mole fraction of helium in the mixture.

$$x = \frac{n_{\text{He}}}{n_{\text{He}} + n_{CO_2}}$$

From Eq. 24.82, on a mole basis,

$$c_{p,\text{mixture}} = x(c_p)_{\text{He}} + (1-x)(c_p)_{CO_2}$$
$$6.459 \frac{\text{Btu}}{\text{lbmol-°R}} = x\left(4.96 \frac{\text{Btu}}{\text{lbmol-°R}}\right)$$
$$+ (1-x)\left(9.11 \frac{\text{Btu}}{\text{lbmol-°R}}\right)$$
$$x = 0.639$$

On a per mole basis, the mass of helium would be

$$m_{He} = x(MW)_{He}$$
$$= (0.639)\left(4.003 \frac{lbm}{lbmol}\right)$$
$$= 2.558 \ lbm$$

Similarly, the mass of carbon dioxide on a per mole basis would be

$$m_{CO_2} = (1-x)(MW)_{CO_2}$$
$$= (1 \ lbmol - 0.639 \ lbmol)\left(44.011 \frac{lbm}{lbmol}\right)$$
$$= 15.888 \ lbm$$

The molecular weight of the mixture is

$$(MW)_{mixture} = 2.558 \ lbm + 15.888 \ lbm$$
$$= 18.446 \ lbm/lbmol$$

The gravimetric (mass) fraction of the gases is

$$G_{He} = \frac{m_{He}}{m_{He} + m_{CO_2}}$$
$$= \frac{2.558 \ lbm}{2.558 \ lbm + 15.888 \ lbm} = \boxed{0.139}$$
$$G_{CO_2} = 1 - G_{He} = 1 - 0.139 = \boxed{0.861}$$

(b) From Eq. 24.52,

$$C_{v,mixture} = C_{p,mixture} - R^*$$
$$= 6.459 \frac{Btu}{lbmol\text{-}°R} - \frac{1545 \frac{ft\text{-}lbf}{lbmol\text{-}°R}}{778 \frac{ft\text{-}lbf}{Btu}}$$
$$= \boxed{4.473 \ Btu/lbmol\text{-}°R}$$

From Eq. 25.102, the work done during the isentropic expansion process is

$$W = c_v(T_1 - T_2) = \left(\frac{C_v}{MW}\right)_{mixture} \times (T_C - T_A)$$
$$= \left(\frac{4.473 \frac{Btu}{lbmol\text{-}°R}}{18.446 \frac{lbm}{lbmol}}\right)(1600°R - 520°R)$$
$$= \boxed{261.9 \ Btu/lbm}$$

(c)

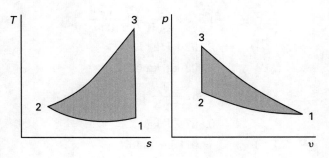

SI Solution

(a) At A:
$$T_A = 290K$$
$$p_A = 101.3 \ kPa$$

At C:
$$T_C = 890K$$
$$p_C = 3.920 \ MPa$$

For isentropic process C-A from Eq. 25.91,

$$p_A = p_C\left(\frac{T_A}{T_C}\right)^{\frac{k}{k-1}}$$

Therefore,

$$101.3 \ kPa = (3.920 \ MPa)\left(1000 \frac{kPa}{MPa}\right)\left(\frac{290K}{890K}\right)^{\frac{k}{k-1}}$$
$$0.02584 = (0.3258)^{\frac{k}{k-1}}$$
$$\log(0.02584) = \left(\frac{k}{k-1}\right)\log(0.3258)$$
$$\frac{k}{k-1} = 3.2599$$
$$k = 1.442$$

From Eq. 24.54, the molar specific heat of the mixture is

$$C_{p,mixture} = \frac{R^*k}{k-1}$$
$$= \frac{\left(8.3143 \frac{kJ}{kmol\cdot K}\right)(1.442)}{1.442 - 1}$$
$$= 27.125 \ kJ/kmol\cdot K$$

From Table 24.7,

$$(c_p)_{He} = \left(5192 \; \frac{J}{kg \cdot K}\right)\left(\frac{1 \; kJ}{1000 \; J}\right)$$

$$= 5.192 \; kJ/kg \cdot K$$

$$(MW)_{He} = 4.003 \; kg/kmol$$

$$(c_p)_{CO_2} = \left(867 \; \frac{J}{kg \cdot K}\right)\left(\frac{1 \; kJ}{1000 \; J}\right)$$

$$= 0.867 \; kJ/kg \cdot K$$

$$(MW)_{CO_2} = 44.011 \; kg/kmol$$

$$C_{p,He} = (MW)_{He}(c_p)_{He}$$

$$= \left(4.003 \; \frac{kg}{kmol}\right)\left(5.192 \; \frac{kJ}{kmol}\right)$$

$$= 20.784 \; kJ/kmol \cdot K$$

$$C_{p,CO_2} = (MW)_{CO_2}(c_p)_{CO_2}$$

$$= \left(44.011 \; \frac{kg}{kmol}\right)\left(0.867 \; \frac{kJ}{kg \cdot K}\right)$$

$$= 38.158 \; kJ/kmol \cdot K$$

Let x be the mole fraction of helium in the mixture.

$$x = \frac{n_{He}}{n_{He} + n_{CO_2}}$$

From Eq. 24.82 on a mole basis,

$$c_{p,mixture} = x(c_p)_{He} + (1-x)(c_p)_{CO_2}$$

$$27.125 \; \frac{kJ}{kmol \cdot K} = x\left(20.784 \; \frac{kJ}{kmol \cdot K}\right)$$

$$+ (1-x)\left(38.158 \; \frac{kJ}{kmol \cdot K}\right)$$

$$x = 0.635 \; kmol$$

On a per mole basis, the mass of helium would be

$$m_{He} = x(MW)_{He}$$

$$= (0.635 \; kmol)\left(4.003 \; \frac{kg}{kmol}\right)$$

$$= 2.542 \; kg$$

Similarly, the mass of CO_2 on a per mole basis would be

$$m_{CO_2} = (1-x)(MW)_{CO_2}$$

$$= (1 \; kmol - 0.635 \; kmol)\left(44.011 \; \frac{kg}{kmol}\right)$$

$$= 16.064 \; kg$$

The molecular weight of the mixture is

$$(MW)_{mixture} = 2.542 \; kg + 16.064 \; kg$$

$$= 18.606 \; kg/kmol$$

The gravimetric (mass) fraction of the gases is

$$G_{He} = \frac{m_{He}}{m_{He} + m_{CO_2}}$$

$$= \frac{2.542 \; kg}{2.542 \; kg + 16.064 \; kg} = \boxed{0.137}$$

$$G_{CO_2} = 1 - G_{He} = 1 - 0.137 = \boxed{0.863}$$

(b) From Eq. 24.52,

$$C_{v,mixture} = C_{p,mixture} - R^*$$

$$= 27.125 \; \frac{kJ}{kmol \cdot K} - 8.3143 \; \frac{kJ}{kmol \cdot K}$$

$$= \boxed{18.811 \; kJ/kmol \cdot K}$$

From Eq. 25.102, the work done during the isentropic expansion process is

$$W = c_v(T_1 - T_2) = \left(\frac{C_v}{MW}\right)_{mixture} \times (T_C - T_A)$$

$$= \left(\frac{18.811 \; \frac{kJ}{kmol \cdot K}}{18.606 \; \frac{kg}{kmol}}\right)(890K - 290K)$$

$$= \boxed{606.6 \; kJ/kg}$$

(c)

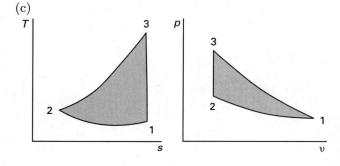

11. *Customary U.S. Solution*

step 1: Not needed.

step 2: From Eq. 29.68, calculate the frictionless power.

$$IHP_1 = \frac{BHP_1}{\eta_{m,1}} = \frac{200 \; hp}{0.86} = 232.6 \; hp$$

step 3: From Eq. 29.69, calculate the friction power, which is assumed to be constant at constant speed.

$$FHP = IHP_1 - BHP_1$$

$$= 232.6 \; hp - 200 \; hp = 32.6 \; hp$$

step 4: Calculate the air densities ρ_{a1} and ρ_{a2} from the ideal gas law. The absolute temperatures are

$$T_1 = 80°F + 460 = 540°R$$
$$T_2 = 60°F + 460 = 520°R$$

$$\rho_{a1} = \frac{p_1}{RT_1} = \frac{\left(14.7 \frac{\text{lbf}}{\text{in}^2}\right)\left(144 \frac{\text{in}^2}{\text{ft}^2}\right)}{\left(53.3 \frac{\text{lbf-ft}}{\text{lbm-}°R}\right)(540°R)}$$

$$= 0.0735 \text{ lbm/ft}^3$$

$$\rho_{a2} = \frac{p_2}{RT_1} = \frac{\left(12.2 \frac{\text{lbf}}{\text{in}^2}\right)\left(144 \frac{\text{in}^2}{\text{ft}^2}\right)}{\left(53.3 \frac{\text{lbf-ft}}{\text{lbm-}°R}\right)(520°R)}$$

$$= 0.0634 \text{ lbm/ft}^3$$

step 5: From Eq. 29.70, calculate the new frictionless power.

$$\text{IHP}_2 = \text{IHP}_1\left(\frac{\rho_{a2}}{\rho_{a1}}\right)$$

$$= (232.6 \text{ hp})\left(\frac{0.0634 \frac{\text{lbm}}{\text{ft}^3}}{0.0735 \frac{\text{lbm}}{\text{ft}^3}}\right)$$

$$= 200.6 \text{ hp}$$

step 6: From Eq. 29.71, calculate the new net power.

$$\text{BHP}_2 = \text{IHP}_2 - \text{FHP}$$
$$= 200.6 \text{ hp} - 32.6 \text{ hp}$$
$$= \boxed{168.0 \text{ hp}}$$

step 7: From Eq. 29.72, calculate the new efficiency.

$$\eta_{m,2} = \frac{\text{BHP}_2}{\text{IHP}_2}$$

$$= \frac{168.0 \text{ hp}}{200.6 \text{ hp}}$$

$$= \boxed{0.837}$$

step 8: From Eq. 29.73, the volumetric air flow rates are the same since the engine speed is constant.

$$\dot{V}_{a2} = \dot{V}_{a1}$$

step 9: The original air and fuel rates from Eqs. 29.74 through 29.76 are

$$\dot{m}_{f1} = (\text{BSFC}_1)(\text{BHP}_1)$$

$$= \left(0.48 \frac{\text{lbm}}{\text{hp-hr}}\right)(200 \text{ hp}) = 96 \text{ lbm/hr}$$

$$\dot{m}_{a1} = (\text{AFR})(\dot{m}_{f1})$$

$$= (22)\left(96 \frac{\text{lbm}}{\text{hr}}\right) = 2112 \text{ lbm/hr}$$

$$\dot{V}_{a1} = \frac{\dot{m}_{a1}}{\rho_{a1}}$$

$$= \frac{2112 \frac{\text{lbm}}{\text{hr}}}{0.0735 \frac{\text{lbm}}{\text{ft}^3}} = 28{,}735 \text{ ft}^3/\text{hr}$$

$$\dot{V}_{a2} = \dot{V}_{a1} = 28{,}735 \text{ ft}^3/\text{hr}$$

step 10: From Eq. 29.77, the new air mass flow rate is

$$\dot{m}_{a2} = \dot{V}_{a2}\rho_{a2}$$

$$= \left(28{,}735 \frac{\text{ft}^3}{\text{hr}}\right)\left(0.0634 \frac{\text{lbm}}{\text{ft}^3}\right)$$

$$= 1821.8 \text{ lbm/hr}$$

step 11: For engines with metered injection,

$$\dot{m}_{f2} = \dot{m}_{f1} = 96 \text{ lbm/hr}$$

step 12: From Eq. 29.79, the new fuel consumption is

$$\text{BSFC}_2 = \frac{\dot{m}_{f2}}{\text{BHP}_2} = \frac{96 \frac{\text{lbm}}{\text{hr}}}{168.0 \text{ hp}}$$

$$= \boxed{0.571 \text{ lbm/hp-hr}}$$

From Eq. 29.75, the new air/fuel ratio is

$$\text{AFR}_2 = \frac{\dot{m}_{a2}}{\dot{m}_{f2}} = \frac{1821.8 \frac{\text{lbm}}{\text{hr}}}{96 \frac{\text{lbm}}{\text{hr}}} = \boxed{18.98}$$

SI Solution

step 1: Not needed.

step 2: From Eq. 29.68, calculate the frictionless power.

$$\text{IkW}_1 = \frac{\text{BkW}_1}{\eta_{m,1}} = \frac{150 \text{ kW}}{0.86} = 174.4 \text{ kW}$$

Power Cycles

step 3: From Eq. 29.69, calculate the friction power, which is assumed to be constant at constant speed.

$$\text{FkW} = \text{IkW}_1 - \text{BkW}_1$$
$$= 174.4 \text{ kW} - 150 \text{ kW} = 24.4 \text{ kW}$$

step 4: Calculate the air densities ρ_{a1} and ρ_{a2} from the ideal gas law. The absolute temperatures are

$$T_1 = 27°\text{C} + 273 = 300\text{K}$$
$$T_2 = 16°\text{C} + 273 = 289\text{K}$$

$$\rho_{a1} = \frac{p_1}{RT_1} = \frac{(101.3 \text{ kPa})\left(1000 \frac{\text{Pa}}{\text{kPa}}\right)}{\left(287.03 \frac{\text{kJ}}{\text{kg·K}}\right)(300\text{K})}$$
$$= 1.176 \text{ kg/m}^3$$

$$\rho_{a2} = \frac{p_2}{RT_2} = \frac{(84 \text{ kPa})\left(1000 \frac{\text{Pa}}{\text{kPa}}\right)}{\left(287.03 \frac{\text{kJ}}{\text{kg·K}}\right)(289\text{K})}$$
$$= 1.013 \text{ kg/m}^3$$

step 5: From Eq. 29.70, calculate the new frictionless power.

$$\text{IkW}_2 = \text{IkW}_1 \left(\frac{\rho_{a2}}{\rho_{a1}}\right)$$
$$= (174.4 \text{ kW})\left(\frac{1.013 \frac{\text{kg}}{\text{m}^3}}{1.176 \frac{\text{kg}}{\text{m}^3}}\right) = 150.2 \text{ kW}$$

step 6: From Eq. 29.71, calculate the new net power.

$$\text{BkW}_2 = \text{IkW}_2 - \text{FkW} = 150.2 \text{ kW} - 24.4 \text{ kW}$$
$$= \boxed{125.8 \text{ kW}}$$

step 7: From Eq. 29.72, calculate the new efficiency.

$$\eta_{m,2} = \frac{\text{BkW}_2}{\text{IkW}_2} = \frac{125.8 \text{ kW}}{150.2 \text{ kW}} = \boxed{0.838}$$

step 8: From Eq. 29.73, the volumetric air flow rates are the same since the engine speed is constant.

$$\dot{V}_{a2} = \dot{V}_{a1}$$

step 9: The original air and fuel rates from Eqs. 29.74 through 29.76 are

$$\dot{m}_{f1} = (\text{BSFC}_1)(\text{BkW}_1)$$
$$= \left(81 \frac{\text{kg}}{\text{GJ}}\right)\left(\frac{1 \text{ GJ}}{10^6 \text{ J}}\right)(150 \text{ kW})$$
$$= 0.01215 \text{ kg/s}$$

$$\dot{m}_{a1} = (\text{AFR})\dot{m}_{f1}$$
$$= (22)\left(0.01215 \frac{\text{kg}}{\text{s}}\right) = 0.2673 \text{ kg/s}$$

$$\dot{V}_{a1} = \frac{\dot{m}_{a1}}{\rho_{a1}} = \frac{0.2673 \frac{\text{kg}}{\text{s}}}{1.176 \frac{\text{kg}}{\text{m}^3}} = 0.2273 \text{ m}^3/\text{s}$$

$$\dot{V}_{a2} = \dot{V}_{a1} = 0.2273 \text{ m}^3/\text{s}$$

step 10: From Eq. 29.77, the new air mass flow rate is
$$\dot{m}_{a2} = \dot{V}_{a2}\rho_{a2}$$
$$= \left(0.2273 \frac{\text{m}^3}{\text{s}}\right)\left(1.013 \frac{\text{kg}}{\text{m}^3}\right) = 0.2303 \text{ kg/s}$$

step 11: For engines with metered injection,
$$\dot{m}_{f2} = \dot{m}_{f1} = 0.01215 \text{ kg/s}$$

step 12: From Eq. 29.79, the new fuel consumption is
$$\text{BSFC}_2 = \frac{\dot{m}_{f2}}{\text{BkW}_2}$$
$$= \frac{0.01215 \frac{\text{kg}}{\text{s}}}{(125.8 \text{ kW})\left(\frac{1 \text{ GJ}}{10^6 \text{ kJ}}\right)}$$
$$= \boxed{96.58 \text{ kg/GJ}}$$

From Eq. 29.75, the new air/fuel ratio is

$$\text{AFR}_2 = \frac{\dot{m}_{a2}}{\dot{m}_{f2}} = \frac{0.2303 \frac{\text{kg}}{\text{s}}}{0.01215 \frac{\text{kg}}{\text{s}}}$$
$$= \boxed{18.95}$$

12.

LHV = 19,000 Btu/lbm (44 MJ/kg)
$\eta_i = 0.85$
turbine $\eta_t = 0.80$
area = 254 ft² (22.9 m²)

Customary U.S. Solution

At 7000 ft altitude:

$$\dot{V}_{a1} = 50{,}000 \ \text{ft}^3/\text{min}$$
$$BHP_1 = 6000 \ \text{hp}$$
$$BSCF_1 = 0.609 \ \text{lbm/hp-hr}$$

At A:

$$p_A = 12 \ \text{psia}$$
$$T_A = 35°\text{F}$$

The absolute temperature at A is

$$T_A = 35°\text{F} + 460 = 495°\text{R}$$

Interpolating from App. 24.F (air table),

$$h_A = 118.28 \ \text{Btu/lbm}$$
$$p_{r,a} = 1.0238$$

From the ideal gas law, air density is

$$\rho_{a1} = \frac{p_A}{RT_A} = \frac{\left(12 \ \frac{\text{lbf}}{\text{in}^2}\right)\left(144 \ \frac{\text{in}^2}{\text{ft}^2}\right)}{\left(53.35 \ \frac{\text{ft-lbf}}{\text{lbm-}°\text{R}}\right)(495°\text{R})}$$
$$= 0.0654 \ \text{lbm/ft}^3$$

From Eq. 29.76,

$$\dot{m}_{a1} = \dot{V}_{a1}\rho_{a1}$$
$$= \left(50{,}000 \ \frac{\text{ft}^3}{\text{min}}\right)\left(0.0654 \ \frac{\text{lbm}}{\text{ft}^3}\right)$$
$$= 3270 \ \text{lbm/min}$$

At B:
$$p_B = 8p_A = (8)(12 \ \text{psia}) = 96 \ \text{psia}$$

Assuming isentropic compression,

$$p_{r,B} = 8p_{r,A} = (8)(1.0238)$$
$$= 8.1904$$

From App. 24.F (air table), this $p_{r,B}$ corresponds to

$$T_B = 893.3°\text{R}$$
$$h_B = 214.62 \ \text{Btu/lbm}$$

Due to the inefficiency of the compressor, from Eq. 29.99,

$$h'_B = h_A + \frac{h_B - h_A}{\eta_{s,\text{compression}}}$$
$$= 118.28 \ \frac{\text{Btu}}{\text{lbm}} + \frac{214.62 \ \frac{\text{Btu}}{\text{lbm}} - 118.28 \ \frac{\text{Btu}}{\text{lbm}}}{0.85}$$
$$= 231.62 \ \text{Btu/lbm}$$

From App. 24.F, this corresponds to $T'_B = 962.3°\text{R}$.

$$W_{\text{compression}} = h'_B - h_A$$
$$= 231.62 \ \frac{\text{Btu}}{\text{lbm}} - 118.28 \ \frac{\text{Btu}}{\text{lbm}}$$
$$= 113.34 \ \text{Btu/lbm}$$

At C:

The absolute temperature is

$$T_C = 1800°\text{F} + 460 = 2260°\text{R} \quad \text{[no change if moved]}$$

Assuming there is no pressure drop across the combustor, $p_C = 96$ psia.

From App. 24.F (air table),

$$h_C = 577.52 \ \text{Btu/lbm}$$
$$p_{r,C} = 286.7$$

The energy requirement from the fuel is

$$\dot{m}\Delta h = \dot{m}_{a1}(h_C - h'_B)$$
$$= \left(3270 \ \frac{\text{lbm}}{\text{min}}\right)\left(577.52 \ \frac{\text{Btu}}{\text{lbm}} - 231.62 \ \frac{\text{Btu}}{\text{lbm}}\right)$$
$$= 1.133 \times 10^6 \ \text{Btu/min}$$

The ideal fuel rate is

$$\frac{\dot{m}\Delta h}{\text{LHV}} = \frac{\left(1.133 \times 10^6 \ \frac{\text{Btu}}{\text{min}}\right)\left(60 \ \frac{\text{min}}{\text{hr}}\right)}{19{,}000 \ \frac{\text{Btu}}{\text{lbm}}}$$
$$= 3577.9 \ \text{lbm/hr}$$

From Eq. 29.74, the ideal BSFC is

$$(BSFC)_{\text{ideal}} = \frac{3577.9 \ \frac{\text{lbm}}{\text{hr}}}{6000 \ \text{hp}} = 0.596 \ \text{lbm/hp-hr}$$

The combustor efficiency is

$$\eta_{\text{combustor}} = \frac{(BSFC)_{\text{ideal}}}{(BSFC)_{\text{actual}}} = \frac{0.596 \ \frac{\text{lbm}}{\text{hp-hr}}}{0.609 \ \frac{\text{lbm}}{\text{hp-hr}}}$$
$$= 0.979 \quad (97.9\%)$$

Power Cycles

At D:

As determined by atmospheric conditions, $p_D = 12$ psia.

If expansion is isentropic,

$$p_{r,D} = \frac{p_{r,C}}{8} = \frac{286.7}{8} = 35.8375$$

From App. 24.F (air table) this $p_{r,D}$ corresponds to

$$T_D = 1334.8°R$$
$$h_D = 325.95 \text{ Btu/lbm}$$

Due to the inefficiency of the turbine, from Eq. 29.101,

$$h'_D = h_C - \eta_{s,\text{turbine}}(h_C - h_D)$$
$$= 577.52 \frac{\text{Btu}}{\text{lbm}} - (0.80)\left(577.52 \frac{\text{Btu}}{\text{lbm}}\right.$$
$$\left. - 325.95 \frac{\text{Btu}}{\text{lbm}}\right)$$
$$= 376.26 \frac{\text{Btu}}{\text{lbm}}$$

$$W_{\text{turbine}} = h_C - h'_D = 577.52 \frac{\text{Btu}}{\text{lbm}} - 376.26 \frac{\text{Btu}}{\text{lbm}}$$
$$= 201.26 \text{ Btu/lbm}$$

The theoretical net horsepower is

$$\text{IHP} = \dot{m}_{a1}\left(W_{\text{turbine}} - W_{\text{compression}}\right)$$
$$= \frac{\left(3270 \frac{\text{lbm}}{\text{min}}\right)\left(201.26 \frac{\text{Btu}}{\text{lbm}}\right.}{33,000 \frac{\text{ft-lbf}}{\text{hp-min}}}$$
$$\frac{\left. - 113.34 \frac{\text{Btu}}{\text{lbm}}\right)\left(778 \frac{\text{ft-lbf}}{\text{Btu}}\right)}{}$$
$$= 6778 \text{ hp}$$

From Eq. 29.69, the friction horsepower is

$$\text{FHP} = \text{IHP} - \text{BHP} = 6778 \text{ hp} - 6000 \text{ hp}$$
$$= 778 \text{ hp}$$

At sea level (zero altitude):

At A:

The absolute temperature is

$$T_A = 70°F + 460 = 530°R$$
$$p_A = 14.7 \text{ psia}$$

From App. 24.F (air table),

$$h_A = 126.86 \text{ Btu/lbm}$$
$$p_{r,A} = 1.2998$$

From the ideal gas law, the air density is

$$\rho_{a2} = \frac{p_A}{RT_A} = \frac{\left(14.7 \frac{\text{lbf}}{\text{in}^2}\right)\left(144 \frac{\text{in}^2}{\text{ft}^2}\right)}{\left(53.35 \frac{\text{lbf-ft}}{\text{lbm-°R}}\right)(530°R)}$$
$$= 0.0749 \text{ lbm/ft}^3$$

From Eq. 29.76, the air mass flow rate is

$$\dot{m}_{a2} = \dot{V}_{a2}\rho_{a2}$$
$$= \left(50,000 \frac{\text{ft}^3}{\text{min}}\right)\left(0.0749 \frac{\text{lbm}}{\text{ft}^3}\right)$$
$$= 3745 \text{ lbm/min}$$

At B:

$$p_B = 8p_A = (8)(14.7 \text{ psia}) = 117.6 \text{ psia}$$

Assuming isentropic compression,

$$p_{r,B} = 8p_{r,A} = (8)(1.2998) = 10.3984$$

From App. 24.F (air table), this $p_{r,B}$ corresponds to

$$T_B = 954.5°R$$
$$h_B = 229.70 \text{ Btu/lbm}$$

Due to the inefficiency of the compressor, from Eq. 29.99,

$$h'_B = h_A + \frac{h_B - h_A}{\eta_{s,\text{compression}}}$$
$$= 126.86 \frac{\text{Btu}}{\text{lbm}} + \frac{229.70 \frac{\text{Btu}}{\text{lbm}} - 126.86 \frac{\text{Btu}}{\text{lbm}}}{0.85}$$
$$= 247.85 \text{ Btu/lbm}$$

From App. 24.F (air table), $h_B = 247.85$ Btu/lbm corresponds to $T'_B = 1027.6°R$.

$$W_{\text{compression}} = h'_B - h_A$$
$$= 247.85 \frac{\text{Btu}}{\text{lbm}} - 126.86 \frac{\text{Btu}}{\text{lbm}}$$
$$= 120.99 \text{ Btu/lbm}$$

At C:

The absolute temperature is

$$T_C = 2260°R \quad [\text{no change}]$$

Assuming there is no pressure drop across the combustor, $p_C = 117.6$ psia.

From App. 24.F (air table),

$$h_C = 577.52 \text{ Btu/lbm}$$
$$p_{r,C} = 286.7$$

The energy requirement from the fuel is $\dot{m}\Delta h$.

$$\dot{m}_{a2}(h_C - h'_B)$$
$$= \left(3745 \frac{\text{lbm}}{\text{min}}\right)\left(577.52 \frac{\text{Btu}}{\text{lbm}} - 247.85 \frac{\text{Btu}}{\text{lbm}}\right)$$
$$= 1.235 \times 10^6 \text{ Btu/min}$$

Assuming a constant combustion efficiency of 97.9%, the ideal fuel rate is

$$\frac{\dot{m}\Delta h}{\text{LHV}} = \frac{\left(1.235 \times 10^6 \frac{\text{Btu}}{\text{min}}\right)\left(60 \frac{\text{min}}{\text{hr}}\right)}{\left(19,000 \frac{\text{Btu}}{\text{lbm}}\right)(0.979)}$$
$$= 3983.7 \text{ lbm/hr}$$

At D:
$$p_D = 14.7 \text{ psia}$$

If expansion is isentropic,

$$p_{r,D} = \frac{p_{r,C}}{8} = \frac{286.7}{8} = 35.8375 \quad \text{[no change]}$$

From App. 24.F (air table), this corresponds to

$$T_D = 1334.8°\text{R}$$
$$h_D = 325.95 \text{ Btu/lbm}$$
$$h'_D = 376.26 \text{ Btu/lbm} \quad \text{[no change]}$$
$$W_{\text{turbine}} = 201.26 \text{ Btu/lbm} \quad \text{[no change]}$$

The theoretical net horsepower is

$$\text{IHP} = \dot{m}_{a2}(W_{\text{turbine}} - W_{\text{compression}})$$

$$= \frac{\left(3745 \frac{\text{lbm}}{\text{min}}\right)\left(201.26 \frac{\text{Btu}}{\text{lbm}} - 120.99 \frac{\text{Btu}}{\text{lbm}}\right)\left(778 \frac{\text{ft-lbf}}{\text{Btu}}\right)}{33,000 \frac{\text{ft-lbf}}{\text{hp-min}}}$$
$$= 7087 \text{ hp}$$

Assuming the frictional horsepower is constant,

$$\text{BHP} = \text{IHP} - \text{FHP}$$
$$= 7087 \text{ hp} - 778 \text{ hp}$$
$$= \boxed{6309 \text{ hp}}$$

From Eq. 29.14, BSFC is

$$\text{BSFC} = \frac{3983.7 \frac{\text{lbm}}{\text{hr}}}{6309 \text{ hp}} = \boxed{0.631 \text{ lbm/hp-hr}}$$

SI Solution

At 2100 m altitude:

At A:
$$p_A = 82 \text{ kPa} \quad \text{[given]}$$

The absolute temperature is

$$T_A = 2°\text{C} + 273 = 275\text{K} \quad \text{[given]}$$

From App. 24.S (air table),

$$h_A = 275.12 \text{ kJ/kg}$$
$$p_{r,A} = 1.0240$$

From the ideal gas law, the air density is

$$\rho_{a1} = \frac{p_A}{RT_A} = \frac{(82 \text{ kPa})\left(1000 \frac{\text{Pa}}{\text{kPa}}\right)}{\left(287.03 \frac{\text{J}}{\text{kg·K}}\right)(275\text{K})}$$
$$= 1.0389 \text{ kg/m}^3$$

From Eq. 29.76, the air mass flow rate is

$$\dot{m}_{a1} = \dot{V}_{a1}\rho_{a1}$$
$$= \left(23,500 \frac{\text{L}}{\text{s}}\right)\left(\frac{1 \text{ m}^3}{1000 \text{ L}}\right)\left(1.0389 \frac{\text{kg}}{\text{m}^3}\right)$$
$$= 24.41 \text{ kg/s}$$

At B:
$$p_C = 8p_A = (8)(82 \text{ kPa}) = 656 \text{ kPa}$$

Assuming isentropic compression,

$$p_{r,B} = 8p_{r,A} = (8)(1.0240) = 8.192$$

From App. 24.S (air table), this $p_{r,B}$ corresponds to

$$T_B = 496.3\text{K}$$
$$h_B = 499.33 \text{ kJ/kg}$$

Due to the inefficiency of the compressor, from Eq. 29.99,

$$h'_B = h_A + \frac{h_B - h_A}{\eta_{s,\text{compression}}}$$
$$= 275.12 \frac{\text{kJ}}{\text{kg}} + \frac{499.33 \frac{\text{kJ}}{\text{kg}} - 275.12 \frac{\text{kJ}}{\text{kg}}}{0.85}$$
$$= 538.90 \text{ kJ/kg}$$

From App. 24.S (air table), this value of $h = 538.90$ kJ/kg corresponds to $T_B' = 534.7$K.

$$W_{compression} = h_B' - h_A$$

$$= 538.90 \frac{kJ}{kg} - 275.12 \frac{kJ}{kg} = 263.78 \text{ kJ/kg}$$

At C:

The absolute temperature is

$$T_C = 980°C + 273 = 1253K$$

Assuming there is no pressure drop across the combustor, $p_C = 656$ kPa.

From App. 24.S (air table),

$$h_C = 1340.28 \text{ kJ/kg}$$

$$p_{r,C} = 284.3$$

The energy requirement from the fuel is

$$\dot{m}\Delta h = \dot{m}_{a1}(h_C - h_B')$$

$$= \left(24.41 \frac{kg}{s}\right)\left(1340.28 \frac{kJ}{kg} - 538.90 \frac{kJ}{kg}\right)$$

$$= 19\,562 \text{ kJ/s}$$

The ideal fuel rate is

$$\frac{\dot{m}\Delta h}{\text{LHV}} = \frac{19\,562 \frac{kJ}{s}}{\left(44 \frac{MJ}{kg}\right)\left(1000 \frac{kJ}{MJ}\right)} = 0.4446 \text{ kg/s}$$

From Eq. 29.74, the ideal BSFC is

$$(\text{BSFC})_{ideal} = \left(\frac{0.4446 \frac{kg}{s}}{4.5 \text{ MW}}\right)\left(1000 \frac{MW}{GW}\right)$$

$$= 98.8 \text{ kg/GJ}$$

The combustor efficiency is

$$\eta_{combustor} = \frac{(\text{BSFC})_{ideal}}{(\text{BSFC})_{actual}} = \frac{98.8 \frac{kg}{GJ}}{100 \frac{kg}{GJ}}$$

$$= 0.988 \quad (98.8\%)$$

At D:

Determined by atmospheric conditions, $p_D = 82$ kPa.

If expansion is isentropic,

$$p_{r,D} = \frac{p_{r,C}}{8} = \frac{284.3}{8} = 35.54$$

From App. 24.S (air table), this $p_{r,D}$ corresponds to

$$T_D = 740K$$

$$h_D = 756.44 \text{ kJ/kg}$$

From Eq. 29.101, due to the inefficiency of the turbine,

$$h_D' = h_C - \eta_{s,turbine}(h_C - h_D)$$

$$= 1340.28 \frac{kJ}{kg} - (0.80)\left(1340.28 \frac{kJ}{kg}\right.$$

$$\left. - 756.44 \frac{kJ}{kg}\right)$$

$$= 873.21 \text{ kJ/kg}$$

$$W_{turbine} = h_C - h_D' = 1340.28 \frac{kJ}{kg} - 873.21 \frac{kJ}{kg}$$

$$= 467.07 \text{ kJ/kg}$$

The theoretical net power is

$$\text{IkW} = \dot{m}_{a1}(W_{turbine} - W_{compression})$$

$$= \left(24.41 \frac{kg}{s}\right)\left(467.07 \frac{kJ}{kg} - 263.78 \frac{kJ}{kg}\right)$$

$$\times \left(\frac{1 \text{ MW}}{1000 \text{ kW}}\right) = 4.962 \text{ MW}$$

From Eq. 29.69, the friction horsepower is

$$\text{FkW} = \text{IkW} - \text{BkW} = 4.962 \text{ MW} - 4.5 \text{ MW}$$

$$= 0.462 \text{ MW}$$

At sea level (zero altitude):

At A:

The absolute temperature is

$$T_A = 21°C + 273 = 294K$$

$$p_A = 101.3 \text{ kPa}$$

From App. 24.S,

$$h_A = 294.17 \text{ kJ/kg}$$

$$p_{r,A} = 1.2917$$

From the ideal gas law, the air density is

$$\rho_{a2} = \frac{p_A}{RT_A} = \frac{(101.3 \text{ kPa})\left(1000 \frac{Pa}{kPa}\right)}{\left(287.03 \frac{J}{kg \cdot K}\right)(294K)}$$

$$= 1.2004 \text{ kg/m}^3$$

From Eq. 29.76, the air mass flow rate is

$$\dot{m}_{a2} = \dot{V}_{a2}\rho_{a2}$$
$$= \left(23\,500\,\frac{L}{s}\right)\left(\frac{1\,m^3}{1000\,L}\right)\left(1.2004\,\frac{kg}{m^3}\right)$$
$$= 28.21\,kg/s$$

At B:

$$p_B = 8p_A = (8)(101.3\,kPa) = 810.4\,kPa$$

Assuming isentropic expansion,

$$p_{r,B} = 8p_{r,A} = (8)(1.2917) = 10.3336$$

From App. 24.S (air table), this $p_{r,B}$ corresponds to

$$T_B = 529.5K$$
$$h_B = 533.46\,kJ/kg$$

Due to the inefficiency of the compressor, from Eq. 29.99,

$$h'_B = h_A + \frac{h_B - h_A}{\eta_{s,compression}}$$
$$= 294.17\,\frac{kJ}{kg} + \frac{533.46\,\frac{kJ}{kg} - 294.17\,\frac{kJ}{kg}}{0.85}$$
$$= 575.69\,kJ/kg$$

From App. 24.S (air table), this value of h_B corresponds to

$$T'_B = 570K$$
$$W_{compression} = h'_B - h_A$$
$$= 575.69\,\frac{kJ}{kg} - 294.17\,\frac{kJ}{kg}$$
$$= 281.52\,kJ/kg$$

At C:

The absolute temperature is

$$T_C = 1253K \quad [\text{no change}]$$

Assuming there is no pressure drop across the combustor, $p_C = 810.4\,kPa$.

From App. 24.S (air table),

$$h_C = 1340.28\,kJ/kg$$
$$p_{r,C} = 284.3$$

The energy requirement from the fuel is

$$\dot{m}\Delta h = \dot{m}_{a2}(h_C - h'_B)$$
$$= \left(28.21\,\frac{kg}{s}\right)\left(1340.28\,\frac{kJ}{kg} - 575.69\,\frac{kJ}{kg}\right)$$
$$= 21\,569\,kJ/s$$

Assuming a constant combustion efficiency of 91.9%, the ideal fuel rate is

$$\frac{\dot{m}\Delta h}{LHV} = \frac{\left(21\,569\,\frac{kJ}{s}\right)\left(\frac{1\,MJ}{1000\,kJ}\right)}{44\,\frac{MJ}{kg}} = 0.490\,kg/s$$

At D:

$$p_D = 101.3\,kPa$$

If expansion is isentropic,

$$p_{r,D} = \frac{p_{r,C}}{8} = \frac{284.3}{8} = 35.538 \quad [\text{no change}]$$

From App. 24.S (air table), this $p_{r,D}$ corresponds to

$$T_D = 740K$$
$$h_D = 756.44\,kJ/kg$$
$$h'_D = 873.21\,kJ/kg \quad [\text{no change}]$$
$$W_{turbine} = 467.07\,kJ/kg$$

The theoretical net power is

$$IkW = \dot{m}_{a2}(W_{turbine} - W_{compression})$$
$$= \left(28.21\,\frac{kg}{s}\right)\left(467.07\,\frac{kJ}{kg} - 281.52\,\frac{kJ}{kg}\right)$$
$$\times \left(\frac{1\,MW}{1000\,kW}\right) = 5.234\,MW$$

Assuming the frictional horsepower is constant,

$$BkW = IkW - FkW = 5.234\,MW - 0.462\,MW$$
$$= \boxed{4.772\,MW}$$

From Eq. 29.74,

$$BSFC = \frac{0.490\,\frac{kg}{s}}{(4.772\,MW)\left(\frac{1\,GW}{1000\,MW}\right)}$$
$$= \boxed{102.7\,kg/GJ}$$

31 Advanced and Alternative Power-Generating Systems

1. *Customary U.S. Solution*

The maximum achievable thermal efficiency is achieved with the Carnot cycle and is given by Eq. 28.8.

$$\eta_{th} = \frac{T_{high} - T_{low}}{T_{high}}$$

$$T_{high} = 82°F + 460 = 542°R$$

$$T_{low} = 40°F + 460 = 500°R$$

$$\eta_{th} = \frac{542°R - 500°R}{542°R} = \boxed{0.0775 \ (7.75\%)}$$

SI Solution

The maximum achievable thermal efficiency is achieved with the Carnot cycle and is given by Eq. 28.8.

$$\eta_{th} = \frac{T_{high} - T_{low}}{T_{high}}$$

$$T_{high} = 27.8°C + 273 = 300.8K$$

$$T_{low} = 4.4°C + 273 = 277.4K$$

$$\eta_{th} = \frac{300.8K - 277.4K}{300.8K} = \boxed{0.0778 \ (7.78\%)}$$

32 Gas Compression Cycles

1.

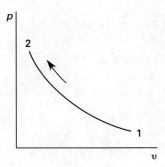

Customary U.S. Solution

Assume air is an ideal gas.

From Eq. 29.18, the isentropic temperature at point 2 is

$$T_2 = T_1 \left(\frac{p_2}{p_1}\right)^{\frac{k-1}{k}}$$

The absolute temperature at point 1 is

$$T_1 = -10°\text{F} + 460 = 450°\text{R}$$

$$T_2 = (450°\text{R}) \left(\frac{40 \text{ psia}}{8 \text{ psia}}\right)^{\frac{1.4-1}{1.4}}$$

$$= 712.7°\text{R}$$

$$T_2 = 712.7°\text{R} - 460 = 252.7°\text{F}$$

The efficiency of the compressor is given by Eq. 29.99.

$$\eta_{s,\text{compressor}} = \frac{T_2 - T_1}{T_2' - T_1}$$

$$= \frac{252.7°\text{F} - (-10°\text{F})}{315°\text{F} - (-10°\text{F})}$$

$$= \boxed{0.808 \ (80.8\%)}$$

SI Solution

Assume air is an ideal gas.

From Eq. 29.18, the isentropic temperature at point 2 is

$$T_2 = T_1 \left(\frac{p_2}{p}\right)^{\frac{k-1}{k}}$$

The absolute temperature at point 1 is

$$T_1 = -20°\text{C} + 273 = 253\text{K}$$

$$T_2 = (253\text{K}) \left(\frac{275 \text{ kPa}}{55 \text{ kPa}}\right)^{\frac{1.4-1}{1.4}}$$

$$= 400.7\text{K}$$

$$T_2 = 400.7\text{K} - 273 = 127.7°\text{C}$$

The efficiency of the compressor is given by Eq. 29.99.

$$\eta_{s,\text{compressor}} = \frac{T_2 - T_1}{T_2' - T_1}$$

$$= \frac{127.7°\text{C} - (-20°\text{C})}{160°\text{C} - (-20°\text{C})}$$

$$= \boxed{0.821 \ (82.1\%)}$$

2.

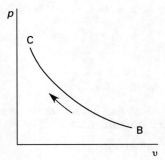

Customary U.S. Solution

The compression ratio for a reciprocating compressor is defined by Eq. 32.4.

$$r_p = \frac{p_\text{C}}{p_\text{B}}$$

$$= \frac{65 \text{ psia}}{14.7 \text{ psia}} = 4.42$$

The volumetric efficiency is given by Eq. 32.6.

$$\eta_\text{v} = 1 - \left(r_p^{\frac{1}{n}} - 1\right)\left(\frac{c}{100}\right)$$

$$= 1 - \left(4.42^{\frac{1}{1.33}} - 1\right)\left(\frac{7\%}{100}\right)$$

$$= 0.856 \ (85.6\%)$$

Power Cycles

The mass of air compressed per minute from Eq. 32.8 is

$$\dot{m} = \frac{\dot{m}_{\text{actual}}}{\eta_v} = \frac{48 \frac{\text{lbm}}{\text{min}}}{0.856}$$

$$= \boxed{56.07 \text{ lbm/min}}$$

SI Solution

The compression ratio for the reciprocating compressor is defined by Eq. 32.4.

$$r_p = \frac{p_C}{p_B} = \frac{450 \text{ kPa}}{101 \text{ kPa}} = 4.46$$

The volumetric efficiency is given by Eq. 32.6.

$$\eta_v = 1 - \left(r_p^{\frac{1}{n}} - 1\right)\left(\frac{c}{100}\right)$$

$$= 1 - \left(4.46^{\frac{1}{1.33}} - 1\right)\left(\frac{7\%}{100}\right)$$

$$= 0.855 \quad (86\%)$$

The mass of air compressed per minute from Eq. 32.8 is

$$\dot{m} = \frac{\dot{m}_{\text{actual}}}{\eta_v} = \frac{0.36 \frac{\text{kg}}{\text{s}}}{0.855}$$

$$= \boxed{0.4211 \text{ kg/s}}$$

3. *Customary U.S. Solution*

Although the ideal gas laws can be used, it is more expedient to use air tables for the low pressures.

The absolute inlet temperature is

$$T_1 = 500°\text{F} + 460 = 960°\text{R}$$

From App. 24.F,

$$h_1 = 231.06 \text{ Btu/lbm}$$

$$p_{r,1} = 10.61$$

$$\phi_1 = 0.74030 \text{ Btu/lbm-}°\text{R}$$

Since $p_1/p_2 = p_{r,1}/p_{r,2}$ and the compression ratio is 6, for isentropic compression,

$$p_{r,2} = 6p_{r,1}$$
$$= (6)(10.61) = 63.66$$

From App. 24, at $p_{r,2} = 63.66$,

$$T_2 = 1552°\text{R}$$

$$h_2 = 382.95 \text{ Btu/lbm}$$

The actual enthalpy from the definition of isentropic efficiency is

$$h_2' = h_1 + \frac{h_2 - h_1}{\eta_s}$$

$$= 231.06 \frac{\text{Btu}}{\text{lbm}} + \frac{382.95 \frac{\text{Btu}}{\text{lbm}} - 231.06 \frac{\text{Btu}}{\text{lbm}}}{0.65}$$

$$= 464.74 \text{ Btu/lbm}$$

From App. 24.F, this corresponds to $T_2' = 1855°\text{R}$ and $\phi_2' = 0.91129 \text{ Btu/lbm-}°\text{R}$.

The compression work is

$$W = h_2' - h_1 = 464.74 \frac{\text{Btu}}{\text{lbm}} - 231.06 \frac{\text{Btu}}{\text{lbm}}$$

$$= 233.68 \text{ Btu/lbm}$$

From Eq. 24.39, the increase in entropy is

$$\Delta s = \phi_2' - \phi_1 - R\ln\left(\frac{p_2}{p_1}\right)$$

$$= 0.91129 \frac{\text{Btu}}{\text{lbm-}°\text{R}} - 0.74030 \frac{\text{Btu}}{\text{lbm-}°\text{R}}$$

$$- \left(\frac{53.3 \frac{\text{ft-lbf}}{\text{lbm-}°\text{R}}}{778 \frac{\text{ft-lbf}}{\text{Btu}}}\right) \ln\left(\frac{6 \text{ atm}}{1 \text{ atm}}\right)$$

$$= \boxed{0.04824 \text{ Btu/lbm-}°\text{R}}$$

SI Solution

Although the ideal gas laws can be used, it is more expedient to use air tables for the lower pressures.

The absolute inlet temperature is

$$T_1 = 260°\text{C} + 273 = 533\text{K}$$

From App. 24.S,

$$h_1 = 537.09 \text{ kJ/kg}$$

$$p_{r,1} = 10.59$$

$$\phi_1 = 2.28161 \text{ kJ/kg·K}$$

Since $p_1/p_2 = p_{r,1}/p_{r,2}$ and the compression ratio is 6, for isentropic compression,

$$p_{r,2} = 6p_{r,1}$$
$$= (6)(10.59) = 63.54$$

From App. 24.S, at $p_{r,2} = 63.54$,

$$T_2 = 861.5\text{K}$$

$$h_2 = 889.9 \text{ kJ/kg}$$

The actual enthalpy from the definition of isentropic efficiency is

$$h_2' = h_1 + \frac{h_2 - h_1}{\eta_s}$$

$$= 537.09 \ \frac{kJ}{kg} + \frac{889.9 \ \frac{kJ}{kg} - 537.09 \ \frac{kJ}{kg}}{0.65}$$

$$= 1079.87 \ kJ/kg$$

From App. 24.S, this corresponds to $T_2' = 1029.6$K and $\phi_2' = 3.00099$ kJ/kg·K.

The compression work is

$$W = h_2' - h_1 = 1079.87 \ \frac{kJ}{kg} - 537.09 \ \frac{kJ}{kg}$$

$$= 542.78 \ kJ/kg$$

From Eq. 24.39, the increase in entropy is

$$\Delta s = \phi_2' - \phi_1 - R \ln\left(\frac{p_2}{p_1}\right)$$

$$= 3.00099 \ \frac{kJ}{kg \cdot K} - 2.28161 \ \frac{kJ}{kg \cdot K}$$

$$- \left(287.03 \ \frac{J}{kg \cdot K}\right)\left(\frac{1 \ kJ}{1000 \ J}\right) \ln\left(\frac{6 \ atm}{1 \ atm}\right)$$

$$= \boxed{0.20509 \ kJ/kg \cdot K}$$

4. *Customary U.S. Solution*

The absolute temperature for process C is $85°F + 460 = 545°R$. Using ideal gas laws, the mass flow rate for process C is

$$\dot{m}_C = \frac{p_C \dot{V}_C}{RT_C} = \frac{\left(80 \ \frac{lbf}{in^2}\right)\left(144 \ \frac{in^2}{ft^2}\right)\left(100 \ \frac{ft^3}{min}\right)}{\left(53.3 \ \frac{ft\text{-}lbf}{lbm\text{-}°R}\right)(545°R)}$$

$$= 39.66 \ lbm/min$$

Similarly, the mass flow rate for process D with an absolute temperature of $80°F + 460 = 540°R$ is

$$\dot{m}_D = \frac{p_D \dot{V}_D}{RT_D} = \frac{\left(85 \ \frac{lbf}{in^2}\right)\left(144 \ \frac{in^2}{ft^2}\right)\left(120 \ \frac{ft^3}{min}\right)}{\left(53.3 \ \frac{ft\text{-}lbf}{lbm\text{-}°R}\right)(540°R)}$$

$$= 51.03 \ lbm/min$$

For process E, the mass flow rate is given as $\dot{m}_E = 8$ lbm/min.

The total mass flow rate for all three processes is

$$\dot{m}_{total} = \dot{m}_C + \dot{m}_D + \dot{m}_E$$

$$= 39.66 \ \frac{lbm}{min} + 51.03 \ \frac{lbm}{min} + 8 \ \frac{lbm}{min}$$

$$= 98.69 \ lbm/min$$

The mass flow rate into compressor A is with an absolute temperature of $80°F + 460 = 540°R$.

$$\dot{m}_A = \frac{p_A \dot{V}_A}{RT_A} = \frac{\left(14.7 \ \frac{lbf}{in^2}\right)\left(144 \ \frac{in^2}{ft^2}\right)\left(600 \ \frac{ft^3}{min}\right)}{\left(53.3 \ \frac{ft\text{-}lbf}{lbm\text{-}°R}\right)(540°R)}$$

$$= 44.13 \ lbm/min$$

The required input for compressor B is

$$\dot{m}_B = \dot{m}_{total} - \dot{m}_A$$

$$= 98.69 \ \frac{lbm}{min} - 44.13 \ \frac{lbm}{min}$$

$$= 54.56 \ lbm/min$$

The volumetric flow rate for compressor B is

$$\dot{V}_B = \frac{\dot{m}_B RT_B}{p_B}$$

$$= \frac{\left(54.56 \ \frac{lbm}{min}\right)\left(53.3 \ \frac{ft\text{-}lbf}{lbm\text{-}°R}\right)(540°R)}{\left(14.7 \ \frac{lbf}{in^2}\right)\left(144 \ \frac{in^2}{ft^2}\right)}$$

$$= \boxed{742 \ cfm}$$

SI Solution

The absolute temperature for process C is $29°C + 273 = 302$K. Using ideal gas laws, the mass flow rate for process C is

$$\dot{m}_C = \frac{p_C \dot{V}_C}{RT_C}$$

$$= \frac{(550 \ kPa)\left(1000 \ \frac{Pa}{kPa}\right)\left(50 \ \frac{L}{s}\right)\left(\frac{1 \ m^3}{1000 \ L}\right)}{\left(287 \ \frac{J}{kg \cdot K}\right)(302K)}$$

$$= 0.3173 \ kg/s$$

The absolute temperature for process D is $27°C + 273 = 300K$. Using ideal gas laws, the mass flow rate for process D is

$$\dot{m}_D = \frac{p_D \dot{V}_D}{RT_D}$$

$$= \frac{(590 \text{ kPa})\left(1000 \frac{\text{Pa}}{\text{kPa}}\right)\left(60 \frac{\text{L}}{\text{s}}\right)\left(\frac{1 \text{ m}^3}{1000 \text{ L}}\right)}{\left(287 \frac{\text{J}}{\text{kg·K}}\right)(300K)}$$

$$= 0.4111 \text{ kg/s}$$

For process E, the mass flow rate is given as $\dot{m}_E = 0.06$ kg/s.

The total mass flow rate for all three processes is

$$\dot{m}_{\text{total}} = \dot{m}_C + \dot{m}_D + \dot{m}_E$$

$$= 0.3173 \frac{\text{kg}}{\text{s}} + 0.4111 \frac{\text{kg}}{\text{s}} + 0.06 \frac{\text{kg}}{\text{s}}$$

$$= 0.7884 \text{ kg/s}$$

The absolute temperature for air into compressors A and B is $27°C + 273 = 300K$.

The mass flow rate into compressor A is

$$\dot{m}_A = \frac{p_A \dot{V}_A}{RT_A}$$

$$= \frac{(101.3 \text{ kPa})\left(1000 \frac{\text{Pa}}{\text{kPa}}\right)\left(300 \frac{\text{L}}{\text{s}}\right)\left(\frac{1 \text{ m}^3}{1000 \text{ L}}\right)}{\left(287 \frac{\text{J}}{\text{kg·K}}\right)(300K)}$$

$$= 0.3530 \text{ kg/s}$$

The required input for compressor B is

$$\dot{m}_B = \dot{m}_{\text{total}} - \dot{m}_A$$

$$= 0.7884 \frac{\text{kg}}{\text{s}} - 0.3530 \frac{\text{kg}}{\text{s}}$$

$$= 0.4354 \text{ kg/s}$$

The volumetric flow rate for compressor B is

$$\dot{V}_B = \frac{\dot{m}_B RT_B}{p_B}$$

$$= \frac{\left(0.4354 \frac{\text{kg}}{\text{s}}\right)\left(287 \frac{\text{J}}{\text{kg·K}}\right)(300K)\left(1000 \frac{\text{L}}{\text{m}^3}\right)}{(101.3 \text{ kPa})\left(1000 \frac{\text{Pa}}{\text{kPa}}\right)}$$

$$= \boxed{370 \text{ L/s}}$$

5.

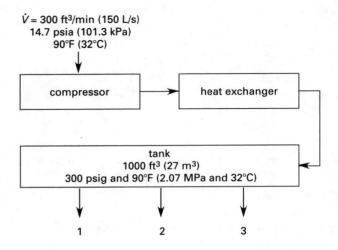

$\dot{V} = 300$ ft³/min (150 L/s)
14.7 psia (101.3 kPa)
90°F (32°C)

compressor → heat exchanger

tank
1000 ft³ (27 m³)
300 psig and 90°F (2.07 MPa and 32°C)

1   2   3

Customary U.S. Solution

Assume steady flow and constant properties.

The absolute temperature for compressor air is $90°F + 460 = 550°R$.

Using ideal gas laws, the mass flow rate of air into the compressor is

$$\dot{m} = \frac{p\dot{V}}{RT}$$

$$= \frac{\left(14.7 \frac{\text{lbf}}{\text{in}^2}\right)\left(144 \frac{\text{in}^2}{\text{ft}^2}\right)\left(300 \frac{\text{ft}^3}{\text{min}}\right)}{\left(53.3 \frac{\text{ft-lbf}}{\text{lbm-°R}}\right)(550°R)}$$

$$= 21.7 \text{ lbm/min}$$

The absolute temperature and absolute pressure of stored compressed air are

$$T = 90°F + 460$$

$$= 550°R$$

$$p = 300 \text{ psig} + 14.7$$

$$= 314.7 \text{ psia}$$

The mass of stored compressed air in a 1000 ft³ tank is

$$m_{\text{tank}} = \frac{pV}{RT}$$

$$= \frac{\left(314.7 \frac{\text{lbf}}{\text{in}^2}\right)\left(144 \frac{\text{in}^2}{\text{ft}^2}\right)(1000 \text{ ft}^3)}{\left(53.3 \frac{\text{ft-lbf}}{\text{lbm-°R}}\right)(550°R)}$$

$$= 1545.9 \text{ lbm}$$

Assuming that each tool operates at its minimum pressure, the mass leaving the system can be calculated as follows.

Tool 1:

The absolute pressure is

$$90 \text{ psig} + 14.7 = 104.7 \text{ psia}$$

The absolute temperature is

$$90°\text{F} + 460 = 550°\text{R}$$

$$\dot{m}_{\text{tool 1}} = \frac{p\dot{V}}{RT}$$

$$= \frac{\left(104.7 \ \frac{\text{lbf}}{\text{in}^2}\right)\left(144 \ \frac{\text{in}^2}{\text{ft}^2}\right)\left(40 \ \frac{\text{ft}^3}{\text{min}}\right)}{\left(53.3 \ \frac{\text{ft-lbf}}{\text{lbm-°R}}\right)(550°\text{R})}$$

$$= 20.57 \text{ lbm/min}$$

Tool 2:

The absolute pressure is

$$50 \text{ psig} + 14.7 = 64.7 \text{ psia}$$

The absolute temperature is

$$85°\text{F} + 460 = 545°\text{R}$$

$$\dot{m}_{\text{tool 2}} = \frac{p\dot{V}}{RT}$$

$$= \frac{\left(64.7 \ \frac{\text{lbf}}{\text{in}^2}\right)\left(144 \ \frac{\text{in}^2}{\text{ft}^2}\right)\left(15 \ \frac{\text{ft}^3}{\text{min}}\right)}{\left(53.3 \ \frac{\text{ft-lbf}}{\text{lbm-°R}}\right)(545°\text{R})}$$

$$= 4.81 \text{ lbm/min}$$

Tool 3:

$$\dot{m}_{\text{tool 3}} = 6 \text{ lbm/min} \quad \text{[given]}$$

The total mass flow leaving the system is

$$\dot{m}_{\text{total}} = \dot{m}_{\text{tool 1}} + \dot{m}_{\text{tool 2}} + \dot{m}_{\text{tool 3}}$$

$$= 20.57 \ \frac{\text{lbm}}{\text{min}} + 4.81 \ \frac{\text{lbm}}{\text{min}} + 6 \ \frac{\text{lbm}}{\text{min}}$$

$$= 31.38 \text{ lbm/min}$$

The critical pressure of 104.7 psia is required for tool 1 operation. The mass in the tank when critical pressure is achieved is

$$m_{\text{tank,critical}} = \frac{pV}{RT}$$

$$= \frac{\left(104.7 \ \frac{\text{lbf}}{\text{in}^2}\right)\left(144 \ \frac{\text{in}^2}{\text{ft}^2}\right)(1000 \text{ ft}^3)}{\left(53.3 \ \frac{\text{ft-lbf}}{\text{lbm-°R}}\right)(550°\text{R})}$$

$$= 514.3 \text{ lbm}$$

The amount in the tank to be depleted is

$$m_{\text{depleted}} = m_{\text{tank}} - m_{\text{tank,critical}}$$

$$= 1545.9 \text{ lbm} - 514.3 \text{ lbm} = 1031.6 \text{ lbm}$$

The net flow rate of air to the tank is

$$\dot{m}_{\text{net}} = \dot{m}_{\text{in}} - \dot{m}_{\text{out}} = 21.7 \ \frac{\text{lbm}}{\text{min}} - 31.38 \ \frac{\text{lbm}}{\text{min}}$$

$$= -9.68 \text{ lbm/min}$$

The time the system can run is

$$\frac{m_{\text{depleted}}}{\dot{m}_{\text{net}}} = \frac{1031.6 \text{ lbm}}{9.68 \ \frac{\text{lbm}}{\text{min}}} = \boxed{106.6 \text{ min} \quad (1.78 \text{ hr})}$$

SI Solution

The absolute temperature of the compressor air is

$$32°\text{C} + 273 = 305\text{K}$$

Using ideal gas laws, the mass flow rate of air into the compressor is

$$\dot{m} = \frac{p\dot{V}}{RT}$$

$$= \frac{(101.3 \text{ kPa})\left(1000 \ \frac{\text{Pa}}{\text{kPa}}\right)\left(150 \ \frac{\text{L}}{\text{s}}\right)\left(\frac{1 \text{ m}^3}{1000 \text{ L}}\right)}{\left(287 \ \frac{\text{J}}{\text{kg·K}}\right)(305\text{K})}$$

$$= 0.1736 \text{ kg/s}$$

The absolute temperature and pressure of stored compressed air are

$$T = 32°\text{C} + 273 = 305\text{K}$$

$$p = (2.07 \text{ MPa})\left(10^6 \ \frac{\text{Pa}}{\text{MPa}}\right)$$

$$= 2.07 \times 10^6 \text{ Pa}$$

The mass of stored compressed air in a 1000 ft³ tank is

$$m_{\text{tank}} = \frac{pV}{RT}$$

$$= \frac{(2.07 \times 10^6 \text{ Pa})(27 \text{ m}^3)}{\left(287 \ \frac{\text{J}}{\text{kg·K}}\right)(305\text{K})}$$

$$= 638.5 \text{ kg}$$

Power Cycles

Assuming that each tool operates at its minimum pressure, the mass leaving the system can be calculated as follows.

Tool 1:

The absolute temperature is $32°C + 273 = 305K$.

$$\dot{m}_{\text{tool 1}} = \frac{p\dot{V}}{RT}$$

$$= \frac{(620 \text{ kPa})\left(1000 \ \frac{\text{Pa}}{\text{kPa}}\right)\left(19 \ \frac{\text{L}}{\text{s}}\right)\left(\frac{1 \text{ m}^3}{1000 \text{ L}}\right)}{\left(287 \ \frac{\text{J}}{\text{kg·K}}\right)(305K)}$$

$$= 0.1346 \text{ kg/s}$$

Tool 2:

The absolute temperature is $29°C + 273 = 302K$.

$$\dot{m}_{\text{tool 2}} = \frac{p\dot{V}}{RT}$$

$$= \frac{(350 \text{ kPa})\left(1000 \ \frac{\text{Pa}}{\text{kPa}}\right)\left(7 \ \frac{\text{L}}{\text{s}}\right)\left(\frac{1 \text{ m}^3}{1000 \text{ L}}\right)}{\left(287 \ \frac{\text{J}}{\text{kg·K}}\right)(302K)}$$

$$= 0.02827 \text{ kg/s}$$

Tool 3:

$$\dot{m}_{\text{tool 3}} = 0.045 \text{ kg/s} \quad \text{[given]}$$

The total mass flow rate leaving the system is

$$\dot{m}_{\text{total}} = \dot{m}_{\text{tool 1}} + \dot{m}_{\text{tool 2}} + \dot{m}_{\text{tool 3}}$$

$$= 0.1346 \ \frac{\text{kg}}{\text{s}} + 0.02827 \ \frac{\text{kg}}{\text{s}} + 0.045 \ \frac{\text{kg}}{\text{s}}$$

$$= 0.2079 \text{ kg/s}$$

The critical pressure of 620 kPa is required for tool 1 operation. The mass in the tank when critical pressure is achieved is

$$m_{\text{tank,critical}} = \frac{pV}{RT}$$

$$= \frac{(620 \text{ kPa})\left(1000 \ \frac{\text{Pa}}{\text{kPa}}\right)(27 \text{ m}^3)}{\left(287 \ \frac{\text{J}}{\text{kg·K}}\right)(305K)}$$

$$= 191.2 \text{ kg}$$

The amount in the tank to be depleted is

$$m_{\text{depleted}} = m_{\text{tank}} - m_{\text{tank,critical}}$$

$$= 638.5 \text{ kg} - 191.2 \text{ kg} = 447.3 \text{ kg}$$

The net flow rate of air into the tank is

$$\dot{m}_{\text{net}} = \dot{m}_{\text{in}} - \dot{m}_{\text{out}} = 0.1736 \ \frac{\text{kg}}{\text{s}} - 0.2079 \ \frac{\text{kg}}{\text{s}}$$

$$= -0.0343 \text{ kg/s}$$

The time the system can run is

$$\frac{m_{\text{depleted}}}{\dot{m}_{\text{net}}} = \frac{447.3 \text{ kg}}{0.0343 \ \frac{\text{kg}}{\text{s}}} = \boxed{13\,041 \text{ s} \quad (3.62 \text{ h})}$$

33 Refrigeration Cycles

1. Customary U.S. Solution

The coefficient of performance for a heat pump operating on the Carnot cycle is given by Eq. 33.9.

$$\text{COP}_{\text{heat pump}} = \frac{T_{\text{high}}}{T_{\text{high}} - T_{\text{low}}}$$

The absolute temperatures are

$$T_{\text{high}} = 700°\text{F} + 460 = 1160°\text{R}$$
$$T_{\text{low}} = 40°\text{F} + 460 = 500°\text{R}$$
$$\text{COP}_{\text{heat pump}} = \frac{1160°\text{R}}{1160°\text{R} - 500°\text{R}} = \boxed{1.76}$$

SI Solution

The coefficient of performance for a heat pump operating on the Carnot cycle is given by Eq. 33.9.

$$\text{COP}_{\text{heat pump}} = \frac{T_{\text{high}}}{T_{\text{high}} - T_{\text{low}}}$$

The absolute temperatures are

$$T_{\text{high}} = 370°\text{C} + 273 = 643\text{K}$$
$$T_{\text{low}} = 4°\text{C} + 273 = 277\text{K}$$
$$\text{COP}_{\text{heat pump}} = \frac{643\text{K}}{643\text{K} - 277\text{K}} = \boxed{1.76}$$

2. Customary U.S. Solution

The coefficient of performance for a heat pump operating on the Carnot cycle is given by Eq. 33.9.

$$\text{COP}_{\text{heat pump}} = \frac{T_{\text{high}}}{T_{\text{high}} - T_{\text{low}}}$$

The temperature T_{high} is the saturation temperature at 172.4 psia, and the temperature T_{low} is the saturation temperature at 35.7 psia. From App. 24.H,

$$T_{\text{high}} = 120.2°\text{F} + 460 = 580.2°\text{R}$$
$$T_{\text{low}} = 19.5°\text{F} + 460 = 479.5°\text{R}$$
$$\text{COP}_{\text{heat pump}} = \frac{580.2°\text{R}}{580.2°\text{R} - 479.5°\text{R}} = \boxed{5.76}$$

SI Solution

The coefficient of performance for a heat pump operating on the Carnot cycle is given by Eq. 33.9.

$$\text{COP}_{\text{heat pump}} = \frac{T_{\text{high}}}{T_{\text{high}} - T_{\text{low}}}$$

The temperature T_{high} is the saturation temperature at 1190 kPa, and the temperature T_{low} is the saturation temperature at 246 kPa. From App. 24.T,

$$T_{\text{high}} = 49°\text{C} + 273 = 322\text{K}$$
$$T_{\text{low}} = -6.8°\text{C} + 273 = 266.2\text{K}$$
$$\text{COP}_{\text{heat pump}} = \frac{322\text{K}}{322\text{K} - 266.2\text{K}} = \boxed{5.77}$$

3. Customary U.S. Solution

The coefficient of performance for a refrigerator is given by Eq. 33.1.

$$\text{COP}_{\text{refrigerator}} = \frac{Q_{\text{in}}}{W_{\text{in}}}$$

$$= \frac{450 \dfrac{\text{Btu}}{\text{hr}}}{(585\text{W}) \left(3.4121 \dfrac{\frac{\text{Btu}}{\text{hr}}}{\text{W}} \right)}$$

$$= \boxed{0.225}$$

SI Solution

From Eq. 33.1, the coefficient of performance for a refrigerator is

$$\text{COP}_{\text{refrigerator}} = \frac{Q_{\text{in}}}{W_{\text{in}}}$$

$$= \frac{(0.13 \text{ kW}) \left(1000 \dfrac{\text{W}}{\text{kW}} \right)}{585\text{W}}$$

$$= \boxed{0.222}$$

1. Use the value of k at an average temperature of $(^1/_2)(T_1 + T_2)$.

$$T = \left(\tfrac{1}{2}\right)(150° + 350°) = 250°$$

$$k = (0.030)(1 + 0.0015T)$$

$$= (0.030)\big(1 + (0.0015)(250°)\big) = \boxed{0.04125}$$

2. *Customary U.S. Solution*

From Fourier's law of heat conduction (Eq. 34.16),

$$\frac{Q_{1-2}}{A} = \frac{k\Delta T}{L}$$

$$= \frac{\left(0.038 \ \dfrac{\text{Btu-ft}}{\text{hr-ft}^2\text{-°F}}\right)(350°\text{F})}{1.0 \text{ ft}}$$

$$= \boxed{13.3 \text{ Btu/hr-ft}^2}$$

SI Solution

From Fourier's law of heat conduction (Eq. 34.16),

$$\frac{Q_{1-2}}{A} = \frac{k\Delta T}{L}$$

$$= \frac{\left(0.066 \ \dfrac{\text{W}}{\text{m·K}}\right)(195\text{K})}{(30 \text{ cm})\left(\dfrac{1 \text{ m}}{100 \text{ cm}}\right)}$$

$$= \boxed{42.9 \text{ W/m}^2}$$

3.

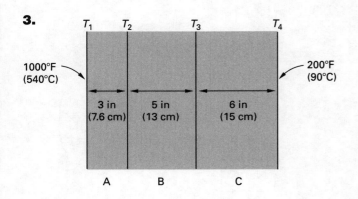

T_1	T_2	T_3	T_4

1000°F (540°C)   200°F (90°C)

3 in (7.6 cm)   5 in (13 cm)   6 in (15 cm)

A   B   C

Customary U.S. Solution

Since the wall temperatures are given, it is not necessary to consider films.

From Eq. 34.21, the heat flow through the composite wall is

$$Q = \frac{A(T_1 - T_4)}{\displaystyle\sum_{i=1}^{n} \frac{L_i}{k_i}}$$

On a per unit area basis,

$$\frac{Q}{A} = \frac{1000°\text{F} - 200°\text{F}}{\dfrac{(3 \text{ in})\left(\dfrac{1 \text{ ft}}{12 \text{ in}}\right)}{0.06 \ \dfrac{\text{Btu-ft}}{\text{hr-ft}^2\text{-°F}}} + \dfrac{(5 \text{ in})\left(\dfrac{1 \text{ ft}}{12 \text{ in}}\right)}{0.5 \ \dfrac{\text{Btu-ft}}{\text{hr-ft}^2\text{-°F}}} + \dfrac{(6 \text{ in})\left(\dfrac{1 \text{ ft}}{12 \text{ in}}\right)}{0.8 \ \dfrac{\text{Btu-ft}}{\text{hr-ft}^2\text{-°F}}}}$$

$$= 142.2 \text{ Btu/hr-ft}^2$$

$$= \frac{T_1 - T_4}{\displaystyle\sum_{i=1}^{n} \frac{L_i}{k_i}} = \frac{T_1 - T_2}{\dfrac{L_A}{k_A}} = \frac{T_2 - T_3}{\dfrac{L_B}{k_B}}$$

To find the temperature at the A-B interface (T_2), use

$$\frac{Q}{A} = \frac{T_1 - T_2}{\dfrac{L_A}{k_A}}$$

$$T_2 = T_1 - \left(\frac{Q}{A}\right)\left(\frac{L_A}{k_A}\right)$$

$$= 1000°\text{F} - \frac{\left(142.2 \ \dfrac{\text{Btu}}{\text{hr-ft}^2}\right)(3 \text{ in})\left(\dfrac{1 \text{ ft}}{12 \text{ in}}\right)}{0.06 \ \dfrac{\text{Btu-ft}}{\text{hr-ft}^2\text{-°F}}}$$

$$= \boxed{407.5°\text{F}}$$

To find the temperature at the B-C interface (T_3), use

$$\frac{Q}{A} = \frac{T_2 - T_3}{\dfrac{L_B}{k_B}}$$

$$T_3 = T_2 - \left(\frac{Q}{A}\right)\left(\frac{L_B}{K_B}\right)$$

$$= 407.5°\text{F} - \left(142.2\ \frac{\text{Btu}}{\text{hr-ft}^2}\right)\left(\frac{(5\ \text{in})\left(\dfrac{1\ \text{ft}}{12\ \text{in}}\right)}{0.5\ \dfrac{\text{Btu-ft}}{\text{hr-ft}^2\text{-}°\text{F}}}\right)$$

$$= \boxed{289°\text{F}}$$

SI Solution

On a per unit area basis,

$$\frac{Q}{A} = \frac{540°\text{C} - 90°\text{C}}{\dfrac{(7.6\ \text{cm})\left(\dfrac{1\ \text{m}}{100\ \text{cm}}\right)}{0.1\ \dfrac{\text{W}}{\text{m·K}}} + \dfrac{(13\ \text{cm})\left(\dfrac{1\ \text{m}}{100\ \text{cm}}\right)}{0.9\ \dfrac{\text{W}}{\text{m·K}}}}$$

$$+ \dfrac{(15\ \text{cm})\left(\dfrac{1\ \text{m}}{100\ \text{cm}}\right)}{1.4\ \dfrac{\text{W}}{\text{m·K}}}$$

$$= 444.8\ \text{W/m}^2$$

$$T_2 = T_1 - \left(\frac{Q}{A}\right)\left(\frac{L_A}{k_A}\right)$$

$$= 540°\text{C} - \left(444.8\ \frac{\text{W}}{\text{m}^2}\right)\left(\frac{(7.6\ \text{cm})\left(\dfrac{1\ \text{m}}{100\ \text{cm}}\right)}{0.1\ \dfrac{\text{W}}{\text{m·K}}}\right)$$

$$= \boxed{202.0°\text{C}}$$

$$T_3 = T_2 - \left(\frac{Q}{A}\right)\left(\frac{L_B}{k_B}\right)$$

$$= 202.0°\text{C} - \left(444.8\ \frac{\text{W}}{\text{m}^2}\right)\left(\frac{(13\ \text{cm})\left(\dfrac{1\ \text{m}}{100\ \text{cm}}\right)}{0.9\ \dfrac{\text{W}}{\text{m·K}}}\right)$$

$$= \boxed{137.8°\text{C}}$$

4. *Customary U.S. Solution*

This is a transient problem. The total time is from 5 P.M. to 1 A.M., which is 8 hr.

The thermal capacitance (capacity), C_e, is given as 100,000 Btu/°F.

The thermal resistance is

$$R_e = \frac{1}{\text{thermal conductance}}$$

$$= \frac{1}{6500\ \dfrac{\text{Btu}}{\text{hr-}°\text{F}}} = 0.0001538\ \text{hr-}°\text{F/Btu}$$

From Eq. 34.50,

$$T_t = T_\infty + (T_0 - T_\infty)e^{-\frac{t}{R_e C_e}}$$

$$T_{8\ \text{hr}} = 40°\text{F} + (70°\text{F} - 40°\text{F})$$

$$\times \exp\left(\frac{-8\ \text{hr}}{\left(0.0001538\ \dfrac{\text{hr-}°\text{F}}{\text{Btu}}\right)\left(100{,}000\ \dfrac{\text{Btu}}{°\text{F}}\right)}\right)$$

$$= \boxed{57.8°\text{F}}$$

SI Solution

The thermal capacitance (capacity) is

$$C_e = \left(60\ \frac{\text{MJ}}{\text{K}}\right)\left(1000\ \frac{\text{kJ}}{\text{MJ}}\right)$$

$$= 60{,}000\ \text{kJ/K} \quad \text{[given]}$$

The thermal resistance is

$$R_e = \frac{1}{\text{thermal conductance}}$$

$$= \frac{1}{1.1\ \dfrac{\text{kW}}{\text{K}}} = 0.909\ \text{K/kW}$$

From Eq. 34.50,

$$T_t = T_\infty + (T_0 - T_\infty)e^{-\frac{t}{R_e C_e}}$$

$$= 4°\text{C} + (21°\text{C} - 4°\text{C})$$

$$\times \exp\left(\frac{(-8\ \text{h})\left(3600\ \dfrac{\text{s}}{\text{h}}\right)}{\left(0.909\ \dfrac{\text{K}}{\text{kW}}\right)\left(60\,000\ \dfrac{\text{kJ}}{\text{K}}\right)}\right)$$

$$= \boxed{14.0°\text{C}}$$

5. *Customary U.S. Solution*

(a) This is a transient problem. Check the Biot number to see if the lumped parameter method can used.

The characteristic site length from Eq. 34.8 is

$$L_c = \frac{V}{A_s} = \frac{\left(\frac{\pi}{6}\right)d^3}{\pi d^2} = \frac{d}{6}$$

For the largest ball, $d = 1.5$ in.

$$L_c = \frac{d}{6} = \frac{(1.5 \text{ in})\left(\frac{1 \text{ ft}}{12 \text{ in}}\right)}{6} = 0.0208 \text{ ft}$$

Evaluate the thermal conductivity, k, of steel at

$$\left(\tfrac{1}{2}\right)(1800°F + 250°F) = 1025°F$$

From App. 34.B, for steel, $k \approx 22.0$ Btu-ft/hr-ft²-°F.

From Eq. 34.10, the Biot number is

$$\text{Bi} = \frac{hL_c}{k} = \frac{\left(56 \frac{\text{Btu}}{\text{hr-ft}^2\text{-°F}}\right)(0.0208 \text{ ft})}{22.0 \frac{\text{Btu-ft}}{\text{hr-ft}^2\text{-°F}}}$$

$$= 0.053$$

For small balls, Bi will be even smaller.

Since Bi < 0.10, the lumped parameter method can be used.

The assumptions are

- homogeneous body temperature
- minimal radiation losses
- oil bath temperature remains constant
- h remains constant

From Eqs. 34.48 and 34.49, the time constant is

$$C_e R_e = c_p\rho V\left(\frac{1}{hA_s}\right) = \left(\frac{c_p\rho}{h}\right)\left(\frac{V}{A_s}\right)$$
$$= \left(\frac{c_p\rho}{h}\right)L_c = \left(\frac{c_p\rho}{h}\right)\left(\frac{d}{6}\right)$$

From App. 34.B, $\rho = 490$ lbm/ft³ and $c_p = 0.11$ Btu/lbm-°F, even though those values are for 32°F.

The time constant is (measuring d in inches),

$$C_e R_e = \left(\frac{\left(0.11 \frac{\text{Btu}}{\text{lbm-°F}}\right)\left(490 \frac{\text{lbm}}{\text{ft}^3}\right)}{56 \frac{\text{Btu}}{\text{hr-ft}^2\text{-°F}}}\right)$$
$$\times \left(\frac{d}{6}\right)\left(\frac{1 \text{ ft}}{12 \text{ in}}\right)$$
$$= \boxed{0.01337d}$$

(b) Taking the natural log of the transient equation (Eq. 34.51),

$$\ln(T_t - T_\infty) = \ln\left(\Delta T e^{-\frac{t}{R_e C_e}}\right)$$
$$= \ln\Delta T + \ln\left(e^{-\frac{t}{R_e C_e}}\right)$$
$$= \ln\Delta T - \frac{t}{R_e C_e}$$

$$T_t = 250°F$$
$$T_\infty = 110°F$$
$$\Delta T = 1800°F - 110°F = 1690°F$$

$$\ln(250°F - 110°F) = \ln(1690°F) - \frac{t}{0.01337d}$$
$$4.942 = 7.432 - \frac{t}{0.01337d}$$
$$t = \boxed{0.0333d}$$

SI Solution

For the largest ball, the characteristic length is

$$L_c = \frac{d}{6} = \frac{(38.1 \text{ mm})\left(\frac{1 \text{ m}}{1000 \text{ mm}}\right)}{6} = 6.35 \times 10^{-3} \text{ m}$$

Evaluate the thermal conductivity, k, of steel at

$$\left(\tfrac{1}{2}\right)(980°C + 120°C) = 550°C$$

From App. 34.B and its footnote,

$$k \approx (22.0)\left(\frac{1.7307 \text{ W·hr·ft}^2\text{·°F}}{\text{m·K·Btu·ft}}\right)$$
$$= 38.08 \text{ W/m·K}$$

From Eq. 34.10, the Biot number is

$$\text{Bi} = \frac{hL_c}{k} = \frac{\left(320 \frac{\text{W}}{\text{m}^2\text{·K}}\right)(6.35 \times 10^{-3} \text{ m})}{38.08 \frac{\text{W}}{\text{m·K}}}$$
$$= 0.053$$

(a) For small balls, Bi will be even smaller.

Since Bi < 0.10, the lumped method can be used. The assumptions are given in the Customary U.S. Solution. From Eqs. 34.48 and 34.49, the time constant is

$$C_e R_e = c_p\rho V\left(\frac{1}{hA_s}\right) = \left(\frac{c_p\rho}{h}\right)\left(\frac{V}{A_s}\right)$$
$$= \left(\frac{c_p\rho}{h}\right)L_c = \left(\frac{c_p\rho}{h}\right)\left(\frac{d}{6}\right)$$

From App. 34.B and its footnote,

$$\rho = \left(490 \ \frac{\text{lbm}}{\text{ft}^3}\right)\left(16.0185 \ \frac{\text{kg·ft}^3}{\text{m}^3\text{·lbm}}\right)$$

$$= 7849.1 \ \text{kg/m}^3$$

$$c_p = (0.11)\left(4186.8 \ \frac{\text{J·lbm·°F}}{\text{kg·K·Btu}}\right)$$

$$= 460.5 \ \text{J/kg·K}$$

$$C_e R_e = \left(\frac{\left(460.5 \ \frac{\text{J}}{\text{kg·K}}\right)\left(7849.1 \ \frac{\text{kg}}{\text{m}^3}\right)}{\left(320 \ \frac{\text{W}}{\text{m}^2\text{·K}}\right)}\right)\left(\frac{d}{6}\right)$$

$$= \boxed{1882.6d}$$

(b)   From the Customary U.S. Solution,

$$\ln(T_t - T_\infty) = \ln\Delta T - \frac{t}{R_e C_e}$$

$$T_t = 120°\text{C}$$

$$T_\infty = 43°\text{C}$$

$$\Delta T = 980°\text{C} - 43°\text{C} = 937°\text{C}$$

$$\ln(120°\text{C} - 43°\text{C}) = \ln(937°\text{C}) - \frac{t}{R_e C_e}$$

$$4.344 = 6.843 - \frac{t}{R_e C_e}$$

$$t = (2.499)R_e C_e$$

$$= (2.499)(1882.6d)$$

$$= \boxed{4704.6d}$$

6. *Customary U.S. Solution*

The volume of the rod is

$$V = \frac{\pi}{4}d^2 L$$

$$\frac{V}{L} = \frac{\pi}{4}d^2 = \left(\frac{\pi}{4}\right)(0.4 \ \text{in})^2\left(\frac{1 \ \text{ft}}{12 \ \text{in}}\right)^2$$

$$= 8.727 \times 10^{-4} \ \text{ft}^3/\text{ft}$$

The heat output per unit length of rod is

$$\frac{Q}{L} = \left(\frac{V}{L}\right)G$$

$$= \left(8.727 \times 10^{-4} \ \frac{\text{ft}^3}{\text{ft}}\right)\left(4 \times 10^7 \ \frac{\text{Btu}}{\text{hr·ft}^3}\right)$$

$$= 3.491 \times 10^4 \ \text{Btu/hr·ft}$$

The diameter of the cladding is

$$d_o = 0.4 \ \text{in} + (2)(0.020 \ \text{in}) = 0.44 \ \text{in}$$

The surface area per unit length of cladding is

$$A = \pi d_o = \pi(0.44 \ \text{in})\left(\frac{1 \ \text{ft}}{12 \ \text{in}}\right) = 0.1152 \ \text{ft}^2/\text{ft}$$

From Eq. 34.23, the surface temperature of the cladding is

$$T_s = \frac{Q}{hA} + T_\infty$$

$$= \frac{3.491 \times 10^4 \ \frac{\text{Btu}}{\text{hr·ft}}}{\left(10{,}000 \ \frac{\text{Btu}}{\text{hr·ft}^2\text{-°F}}\right)\left(0.1152 \ \frac{\text{ft}^2}{\text{ft}}\right)} + 500°\text{F}$$

$$= 530.3°\text{F}$$

For the cladding,

$$r_o = \frac{d_o}{2} = \left(\frac{0.44 \ \text{in}}{2}\right)\left(\frac{1 \ \text{ft}}{12 \ \text{in}}\right) = 0.01833 \ \text{ft}$$

$$r_i = \frac{d}{2} = \left(\frac{0.4 \ \text{in}}{2}\right)\left(\frac{1 \ \text{ft}}{12 \ \text{in}}\right) = 0.01667 \ \text{ft}$$

From App. 34.B, k for stainless steel (at 572°F) is 11 Btu-ft/hr-ft^2-°F. This is reasonable because the inside cladding temperature is greater than the surface temperature (530.3°F).

For a cylinder from Eq. 34.5 and Eq. 34.19,

$$T_{\text{inside}} - T_{\text{outside}} = \frac{Q\ln\left(\frac{r_o}{r_i}\right)}{2\pi k L} = \frac{\left(\frac{Q}{L}\right)\ln\left(\frac{r_o}{r_i}\right)}{2\pi k}$$

$$= \frac{\left(3.491 \times 10^4 \ \frac{\text{Btu}}{\text{hr·ft}}\right)\ln\left(\frac{0.01833 \ \text{ft}}{0.01667 \ \text{ft}}\right)}{2\pi\left(11 \ \frac{\text{Btu-ft}}{\text{hr·ft}^2\text{-°F}}\right)}$$

$$= 47.9°\text{F}$$

$$T_{\underset{\text{cladding}}{\text{inside}}} = T_{\underset{\text{fuel rod}}{\text{outside}}} + 47.9°\text{F}$$

$$= 530.3°\text{F} + 47.9°\text{F} = 578.2°\text{F}$$

From Eq. 34.56,

$$T_{\text{center}} = T_o + \frac{Gr_o^2}{4k}$$

$$= 578.2°\text{F} + \frac{\left(4 \times 10^7 \ \frac{\text{Btu}}{\text{hr·ft}^3}\right)(0.01667 \ \text{ft})^2}{(4)\left(1.1 \ \frac{\text{Btu-ft}}{\text{hr·ft}^2\text{-°F}}\right)}$$

$$= \boxed{3104°\text{F}}$$

SI Solution

$$\frac{V}{L} = \frac{\pi}{4} d = \left(\frac{\pi}{4}\right) (1.0 \text{ cm})^2 \left(\frac{1 \text{ m}}{100 \text{ cm}}\right)^2$$

$$= 7.854 \times 10^{-5} \text{ m}^3/\text{m}$$

The heat output per unit length of rod is

$$\frac{Q}{L} = \left(\frac{V}{L}\right) G = \left(7.854 \times 10^{-5} \frac{\text{m}^3}{\text{m}}\right) \left(4.1 \times 10^8 \frac{\text{W}}{\text{m}^3}\right)$$

$$= 32\,201.4 \text{ W/m}$$

From Eq. 34.23, the surface temperature of the cladding is

$$T_s = \frac{Q}{hA} + T_\infty$$

The diameter of the cladding is

$$d_o = \left(1.0 \text{ cm} + (2)(0.5 \text{ mm}) \left(\frac{1 \text{ cm}}{10 \text{ mm}}\right)\right) \left(\frac{1 \text{ m}}{100 \text{ cm}}\right)$$

$$= 0.011 \text{ m}$$

The surface area per unit length of cladding is

$$A = \pi d_o = \pi(0.011 \text{ m}) = 0.0346 \text{ m}^2/\text{m}$$

$$T_s = \frac{32\,201.4 \frac{\text{W}}{\text{m}}}{\left(57 \frac{\text{kW}}{\text{m}^2 \cdot \text{K}}\right) \left(1000 \frac{\text{W}}{\text{kW}}\right) \left(0.0346 \frac{\text{m}^2}{\text{m}}\right)} + 260°\text{C}$$

$$= 276.3°\text{C}$$

For the cladding,

$$r_o = \frac{d_o}{2} = \frac{0.011 \text{ m}}{2} = 0.0055 \text{ m}$$

$$r_i = \frac{d_i}{2} = \frac{0.01 \text{ m}}{2} = 0.0050 \text{ m}$$

From App. 34.B and the table's footnote, k for stainless steel at 300°C is

$$k \approx \left(11 \frac{\text{Btu-ft}}{\text{hr-ft}^2\text{-°F}}\right) \left(1.7307 \frac{\text{W·hr·ft}^2\text{·°F}}{\text{m·K·Btu·ft}}\right)$$

$$= 19.038 \text{ W/m·K}$$

This is reasonable because the inside cladding temperature is greater than the surface temperature (276.3°C).

For a cylinder from Eqs. 34.5 and 34.19,

$$T_{\text{inside}} - T_{\text{outside}} = \frac{Q \ln\left(\frac{r_o}{r_i}\right)}{2\pi k L} = \left(\frac{Q}{L}\right) \left(\frac{\ln\left(\frac{r_o}{r_i}\right)}{2\pi k}\right)$$

$$= \left(32\,201 \frac{\text{W}}{\text{m}}\right) \left(\frac{\ln\left(\frac{0.0055 \text{ m}}{0.0050 \text{ m}}\right)}{2\pi \left(19.038 \frac{\text{W}}{\text{m·K}}\right)}\right)$$

$$= 25.7°\text{C}$$

$$\underset{\text{cladding}}{T_{\text{inside}}} = \underset{\text{fuel rod}}{T_{\text{outside}}} + 25.7°\text{C}$$

$$= 276.3°\text{C} + 25.7°\text{C} = 302°\text{C}$$

From Eq. 34.56,

$$T_{\text{center}} = T_o + \frac{G r_o^2}{4k}$$

$$= 302°\text{C} + \frac{\left(4.1 \times 10^8 \frac{\text{W}}{\text{m}^3}\right)(0.0050 \text{ m})^2}{(4)\left(1.9 \frac{\text{W}}{\text{m·K}}\right)}$$

$$= \boxed{1651°\text{C}}$$

7. *Customary U.S. Solution*

Consider this an infinite cylindrical fin with

$$T_b = 450°\text{F}$$

$$T_\infty = 80°\text{F}$$

$$h = 3 \text{ Btu/hr-ft}^2\text{-°F}$$

From Eq. 34.66, the perimeter length is

$$P = \pi d = \pi \left(\frac{1}{16} \text{ in}\right) \left(\frac{1 \text{ ft}}{12 \text{ in}}\right) = 0.01636 \text{ ft}$$

From App. 34.B, k at 450°F is approximately 215 Btu-ft/hr-ft^2-°F.

From Eq. 34.65, the cross-sectional area of the fin at its base is

$$A_b = \pi r^2 = \pi \left(\frac{d}{2}\right)^2 = \frac{\pi}{4} d^2$$

$$= \left(\frac{\pi}{4}\right) \left(\frac{1}{16} \text{ in}\right)^2 \left(\frac{1 \text{ ft}}{12 \text{ in}}\right)^2$$

$$= 2.131 \times 10^{-5} \text{ ft}^2$$

From Eq. 34.64, with two fins joined at the middle,

$$Q = 2\sqrt{hPkA_b}(T_b - T_\infty)$$

$$= (2) \sqrt{\begin{array}{c} \left(3 \dfrac{\text{Btu}}{\text{hr-ft}^2\text{-}°\text{F}}\right) (0.01636 \text{ ft}) \\ \times \left(215 \dfrac{\text{Btu-ft}}{\text{hr-ft}^2\text{-}°\text{F}}\right) (2.131 \times 10^{-5} \text{ ft}^2) \end{array}}$$

$$\times (450°\text{F} - 80°\text{F})$$

$$= \boxed{11.1 \text{ Btu/hr}} \quad \text{[This disregards radiation.]}$$

SI Solution

Consider this an infinite cylindrical fin with

$$T_b = 230°\text{C}$$
$$T_\infty = 27°\text{C}$$
$$h = 17 \text{ W/m}^2\text{·K}$$

From Eq. 34.66, the perimeter length is

$$P = \pi d = \pi (1.6 \text{ mm}) \left(\frac{1 \text{ m}}{1000 \text{ mm}}\right) = 5.027 \times 10^{-3} \text{ m}$$

From App. 34.B and the table footnote, k at 230°C is

$$k \approx \left(215 \frac{\text{Btu-ft}}{\text{hr-ft}^2\text{-}°\text{F}}\right) \left(1.7307 \frac{\text{W·hr·ft}^2\text{·}°\text{F}}{\text{m·K·Btu·ft}}\right)$$

$$= 372.1 \text{ W/m·K}$$

From Eq. 34.65, the cross-sectional area of the fin at its base is

$$A_b = \pi r^2 = \pi \left(\frac{d}{2}\right)^2 = \frac{\pi}{4} d^2$$

$$= \left(\frac{\pi}{4}\right) (1.6 \text{ mm})^2 \left(\frac{1 \text{ m}}{1000 \text{ mm}}\right)^2$$

$$= 2.011 \times 10^{-6} \text{ m}^2$$

From Eq. 34.64, with two fins joined at the middle,

$$Q = 2\sqrt{hPkA_b}(T_b - T_\infty)$$

$$= (2) \sqrt{\begin{array}{c} \left(17 \dfrac{\text{W}}{\text{m}^2\text{·K}}\right) (5.027 \times 10^{-3} \text{ m}) \\ \times \left(372.1 \dfrac{\text{W}}{\text{m·K}}\right) (2.011 \times 10^{-6} \text{ m}^2) \end{array}}$$

$$\times (230°\text{C} - 27°\text{C})$$

$$= \boxed{3.25 \text{ W}} \quad \text{[This disregards radiation.]}$$

35 Natural Convection, Evaporation, and Condensation

1. *Customary U.S. Solution*

If the steam is 87% wet, the quality is $x = 0.13$.

From App. 24.B at 50 psia,

$$v_f = 0.01727 \text{ ft}^3/\text{lbm}$$
$$v_g = 8.52 \text{ ft}^3/\text{lbm}$$

From Eq. 24.43, the specific volume of steam is

$$v = v_f + x v_{fg}$$
$$= 0.01727 \frac{\text{ft}^3}{\text{lbm}} + (0.13)\left(8.52 \frac{\text{ft}^3}{\text{lbm}} - 0.01727 \frac{\text{ft}^3}{\text{lbm}}\right)$$
$$= 1.123 \text{ ft}^3/\text{lbm}$$

The density is

$$\rho = \frac{1}{v} = \frac{1}{1.123 \frac{\text{ft}^3}{\text{lbm}}} = \boxed{0.890 \text{ lbm/ft}^3}$$

SI Solution

If the steam is 87% wet, the quality is $x = 0.13$.

From App. 24.O at 350 kPa,

$$v_f = 1.0786 \text{ cm}^3/\text{g}$$
$$v_g = 524.3 \text{ cm}^3/\text{g}$$

From Eq. 24.43, the specific volume of steam is

$$v = v_f + x v_{fg}$$
$$= 1.0786 \frac{\text{cm}^3}{\text{g}} + (0.13)\left(524.3 \frac{\text{cm}^3}{\text{g}}\right)$$
$$= 69.24 \text{ cm}^3/\text{g}$$

The density is

$$\rho = \frac{1}{v} = \left(\frac{1}{69.24 \frac{\text{cm}^3}{\text{g}}}\right)\left(100 \frac{\text{cm}}{\text{m}}\right)^3 \left(\frac{1 \text{ kg}}{1000 \text{ g}}\right)$$
$$= \boxed{14.44 \text{ kg/m}^3}$$

2. *Customary U.S. Solution*

From App. 35.C, the viscosity of water at 100°F is

$$\mu = \left(0.458 \times 10^{-3} \frac{\text{lbm}}{\text{ft-sec}}\right)\left(3600 \frac{\text{sec}}{\text{hr}}\right)$$
$$= \boxed{1.6488 \text{ lbm/ft-hr}}$$

SI Solution

From App. 35.D, the viscosity of water at 38°C is

$$\mu = \boxed{0.682 \times 10^{-3} \text{ kg/m·s}}$$

3. *Customary U.S. Solution*

The midpoint tube temperature is

$$T_s = \left(\tfrac{1}{2}\right)(190°\text{F} + 160°\text{F}) = 175°\text{F}$$
$$T_\infty = 85°\text{F} \quad \text{[given]}$$

From Eq. 35.11, h should be evaluated at $\left(\tfrac{1}{2}\right)(T_s + T_\infty)$.

The film temperature is

$$T_h = \left(\tfrac{1}{2}\right)(175°\text{F} + 85°\text{F}) = \boxed{130°\text{F}}$$

SI Solution

The midpoint tube temperature is

$$T_2 = \left(\tfrac{1}{2}\right)(88°\text{C} + 71°\text{C}) = 79.5°\text{C}$$
$$T_\infty = 29°\text{C} \quad \text{[given]}$$

From Eq. 35.11, h should be evaluated at $\left(\tfrac{1}{2}\right)(T_s + T_\infty)$.

The film temperature is

$$T_h = \left(\tfrac{1}{2}\right)(79.5°\text{C} + 29°\text{C}) = \boxed{54.3°\text{C}}$$

4. *Customary U.S. Solution*

The heat loss per unit length is

$$\frac{Q}{L} = \left(8 \; \frac{W}{ft}\right)\left(3.413 \; \frac{Btu}{hr\text{-}W}\right) = 27.3 \; Btu/hr\text{-}ft$$

From App. 35.C, the air properties are at 100°F film.

$$Pr = 0.72$$

$$\frac{g\beta\rho^2}{\mu^2} = 1.76 \times 10^6 \; \frac{1}{ft^3\text{-}°F}$$

From Eq. 35.4, the Grashof number is

$$Gr = L^3 \Delta T \left(\frac{g\beta\rho^2}{\mu^2}\right)$$

The characteristic length is the wire diameter.

$$L = (0.6 \text{ in})\left(\frac{1 \text{ ft}}{12 \text{ in}}\right) = 0.05 \text{ ft}$$

The temperature gradient is

$$\Delta T = T_s - T_\infty = T_{wire} - 60°F$$

T_{wire} is unknown, so assume $T_{wire} = 150°F$.

$$Gr = (0.05 \text{ ft})^3 (150°F - 60°F)\left(1.76 \times 10^6 \; \frac{1}{ft^3\text{-}°F}\right)$$

$$= 19,800$$

$$PrGr = (0.72)(19,800) = 14,256$$

From Table 35.3,

$$h \approx (0.27)\left(\frac{T_{wire} - T_\infty}{d}\right)^{0.25}$$

$$= (0.27)\left(\frac{150°F - 60°F}{0.05 \text{ ft}}\right)^{0.25}$$

$$= 1.76 \; Btu/hr\text{-}ft^2\text{-}°F$$

The heat transfer from the wire is

$$Q = qA = \pi d L h (T_{wire} - T_\infty)$$

$$\frac{Q}{L} = \pi d h (T_{wire} - T_\infty)$$

$$T_{wire} = \frac{\frac{Q}{L}}{\pi d h} + T_\infty$$

$$= \frac{27.3 \; \frac{Btu}{hr\text{-}ft}}{\pi(0.05 \text{ ft})\left(1.76 \; \frac{Btu}{hr\text{-}ft^2\text{-}°F}\right)} + 60°F$$

$$= 158.7°F$$

Perform one more iteration with $T_{wire} = 158°F$.

$$Gr = (0.05)^3 (158°F - 60°F)\left(1.76 \times 10^6 \; \frac{1}{ft^3\text{-}°F}\right)$$

$$= 21,560$$

$$PrGr = (0.72)(21,560) = 15,523$$

From Table 35.3,

$$h = (0.27)\left(\frac{T_{wire} - T_\infty}{d}\right)^{0.25}$$

$$= (0.27)\left(\frac{158°F - 60°F}{0.05 \text{ ft}}\right)^{0.25}$$

$$= 1.80 \; Btu/hr\text{-}ft^2\text{-}°F$$

$$T_{wire} = \frac{\frac{Q}{L}}{\pi d h} + T_\infty$$

$$= \frac{27.3 \; \frac{Btu}{hr\text{-}ft}}{\pi(0.05 \text{ ft})\left(1.80 \; \frac{Btu}{hr\text{-}ft^2\text{-}°F}\right)} + 60°F$$

$$= \boxed{156.6°F}$$

There is no need to repeat iterations since the assumed temperature and the calculated temperature are about the same.

SI Solution

From App. 35.D, for 38°C film, the air properties are

$$Pr = 0.705$$

$$\frac{g\beta\rho^2}{\mu^2} = 1.12 \times 10^8 \; \frac{1}{K\cdot m^3}$$

From Eq. 35.4, the Grashof number is

$$Gr = L^3 \Delta T \left(\frac{g\beta\rho^2}{\mu^2}\right)$$

The characteristic length is the wire diameter.

$$L = (1.5 \text{ cm})\left(\frac{1 \text{ m}}{100 \text{ cm}}\right) = 0.015 \text{ m}$$

The temperature gradient is

$$\Delta T = T_s - T_\infty = T_{wire} - 15°C$$

$$Gr = (0.015 \text{ m})^3 (T_{wire} - 15°C)\left(1.12 \times 10^8 \; \frac{1}{K\cdot m^3}\right)$$

Assume $T_{\text{wire}} = 70°C$.

$$\text{Gr} = (0.015 \text{ m})^3 (70°C - 15°C) \left(1.12 \times 10^8 \ \frac{1}{\text{K·m}^3} \right)$$

$$= 20\,790$$

$$\text{PrGr} = (0.705)(20\,790) = 14\,657$$

From Table 35.3,

$$h \approx (1.32) \left(\frac{T_{\text{wire}} - T_\infty}{d} \right)^{0.25}$$

$$= (1.32) \left(\frac{70°C - 15°C}{0.015 \text{ m}} \right)^{0.25}$$

$$= 10.27 \text{ W/m}^2\text{·K}$$

From the Customary U.S. Solution,

$$T_{\text{wire}} = \frac{\dfrac{Q}{L}}{\pi d h} + T_\infty$$

$$= \frac{25 \ \dfrac{\text{W}}{\text{m}}}{\pi (0.015 \text{ m}) \left(10.27 \ \dfrac{\text{W}}{\text{m}^2\text{·K}} \right)} + 15°C$$

$$= \boxed{66.7°C}$$

There is no need to perform another iteration since the assumed temperature and the calculated temperature are about the same.

Heat Transfer

36 Forced Convection and Heat Exchangers

1. *Customary U.S. Solution*

The logarithmic mean temperature difference will be different for different types of flow.

Parallel flow:

55°F (15°C) ————————————➤ 87°F (30°C)

        A   B

350°F (175°C) ————————————➤ 270°F (130°C)

$$\Delta T_A = 350°\text{F} - 55°\text{F} = 295°\text{F}$$
$$\Delta T_B = 270°\text{F} - 87°\text{F} = 183°\text{F}$$

From Eq. 36.69, the logarithmic mean temperature difference is

$$\Delta T_{lm} = \frac{\Delta T_A - \Delta T_B}{\ln\left(\dfrac{\Delta T_A}{\Delta T_B}\right)} = \frac{295°\text{F} - 183°\text{F}}{\ln\left(\dfrac{295°\text{F}}{183°\text{F}}\right)} = \boxed{234.6°\text{F}}$$

Counterflow:

55°F (15°C) ————————————➤ 87°F (30°C)

        A   B

270°F (130°C) ◀———————————— 350°F (175°C)

$$\Delta T_A = 270°\text{F} - 55°\text{F} = 215°\text{F}$$
$$\Delta T_B = 350°\text{F} - 87°\text{F} = 263°\text{F}$$

From Eq. 36.69, the logarithmic mean temperature difference is

$$\Delta T_{lm} = \frac{215°\text{F} - 263°\text{F}}{\ln\left(\dfrac{215°\text{F}}{263°\text{F}}\right)} = \boxed{238.2°\text{F}}$$

SI Solution

Parallel flow:

$$\Delta T_A = 175°\text{C} - 15°\text{C} = 160°\text{C}$$
$$\Delta T_B = 130°\text{C} - 30°\text{C} = 100°\text{C}$$

From Eq. 36.69, the logarithmic mean temperature difference is

$$\Delta T_{lm} = \frac{160°\text{C} - 100°\text{C}}{\ln\left(\dfrac{160°\text{C}}{100°\text{C}}\right)} = \boxed{127.7°\text{C}}$$

Counterflow:

$$\Delta T_A = 130°\text{C} - 15°\text{C} = 115°\text{C}$$
$$\Delta T_B = 175°\text{C} - 30°\text{C} = 145°\text{C}$$

From Eq. 36.69, the logarithmic mean temperature difference is

$$\Delta T_{lm} = \frac{115°\text{C} - 145°\text{C}}{\ln\left(\dfrac{115°\text{C}}{145°\text{C}}\right)} = \boxed{129.4°\text{C}}$$

2. *Customary U.S. Solution*

$$\Delta T_A = 190°\text{F} - 85°\text{F} = 105°\text{F}$$
$$\Delta T_B = 160°\text{F} - 85°\text{F} = 75°\text{F}$$

From Eq. 36.69, the logarithmic mean temperature difference is

$$\Delta T_{lm} = \frac{\Delta T_A - \Delta T_B}{\ln\left(\dfrac{\Delta T_A}{\Delta T_B}\right)} = \frac{105°\text{F} - 75°\text{F}}{\ln\left(\dfrac{105°\text{F}}{75°\text{F}}\right)} = \boxed{89.2°\text{F}}$$

SI Solution

$$\Delta T_A = 90°\text{C} - 30°\text{C} = 60°\text{C}$$
$$\Delta T_B = 70°\text{C} - 30°\text{C} = 40°\text{C}$$

From Eq. 36.69, the logarithmic mean temperature difference is

$$\Delta T_{lm} = \frac{60°\text{C} - 40°\text{C}}{\ln\left(\dfrac{60°\text{C}}{40°\text{C}}\right)} = \boxed{49.3°\text{C}}$$

Heat Transfer

3. *Customary U.S. Solution*

$$T_{\text{tank}} = 85°\text{F}$$
$$T_{\text{coil}} = \left(\tfrac{1}{2}\right)(190°\text{F} + 160°\text{F}) = 175°\text{F}$$

The film temperature is

$$T_f = \left(\tfrac{1}{2}\right)(T_{\text{tank}} + T_{\text{coil}})$$
$$= \left(\tfrac{1}{2}\right)(85°\text{F} + 175°\text{F}) = \boxed{130°\text{F}}$$

SI Solution

$$T_{\text{tank}} = 30°\text{C}$$
$$T_{\text{coil}} = \left(\tfrac{1}{2}\right)(90°\text{C} + 70°\text{C}) = 80°\text{C}$$

The film temperature is

$$T_f = \left(\tfrac{1}{2}\right)(T_{\text{tank}} + T_{\text{coil}})$$
$$= \left(\tfrac{1}{2}\right)(30°\text{C} + 80°\text{C}) = \boxed{55°\text{C}}$$

4. *Customary U.S. Solution*

$$T_{\text{coil,initial}} = \left(\tfrac{1}{2}\right)(190°\text{F} + 160°\text{F}) = 175°\text{F}$$

The initial film temperature is

$$T_{f,\text{initial}} = \left(\tfrac{1}{2}\right)(T_{\text{tank,initial}} + T_{\text{coil,initial}})$$
$$= \left(\tfrac{1}{2}\right)(85°\text{F} + 175°\text{F}) = \boxed{130°\text{F}}$$

SI Solution

$$T_{\text{coil,initial}} = \left(\tfrac{1}{2}\right)(90°\text{C} + 70°\text{C}) = 80°\text{C}$$

The initial film temperature is

$$T_{f,\text{initial}} = \left(\tfrac{1}{2}\right)(T_{\text{tank,initial}} + T_{\text{coil,initial}})$$
$$= \left(\tfrac{1}{2}\right)(30°\text{C} + 80°\text{C}) = \boxed{55°\text{C}}$$

5. *Customary U.S. Solution*

The Reynolds number is

$$\text{Re}_d = \frac{\text{v}D}{\nu}$$

$$D = (0.6 \text{ in})\left(\frac{1 \text{ ft}}{12 \text{ in}}\right) = 0.05 \text{ ft}$$

$$\nu = (45 \text{ cS})\left(\frac{1 \text{ S}}{100 \text{ cS}}\right)\left(\frac{1 \text{ ft}^2}{929 \text{ sec-stoke}}\right)$$
$$= 4.84 \times 10^{-4} \text{ ft}^2/\text{sec}$$

$$\text{v} = 2 \text{ ft/sec}$$

$$\text{Re} = \frac{\left(2 \dfrac{\text{ft}}{\text{sec}}\right)(0.05 \text{ ft})}{4.84 \times 10^{-4} \dfrac{\text{ft}^2}{\text{sec}}} = \boxed{206.6}$$

SI Solution

The Reynolds number is

$$\text{Re}_d = \frac{\text{v}D}{\nu}$$

$$D = (1.52 \text{ cm})\left(\frac{1 \text{ m}}{100 \text{ cm}}\right) = 0.0152 \text{ m}$$

$$\text{v} = 0.6 \text{ m/s}$$

$$\nu = (45 \text{ cS})\left(1 \frac{\frac{\mu\text{m}^2}{\text{s}}}{\text{cS·s}}\right)\left(\frac{1 \text{ m}^2}{10^6 \ \mu\text{m}^2}\right)$$
$$= 45 \times 10^{-6} \text{ m}^2/\text{s}$$

$$\text{Re}_d = \frac{\left(0.6 \dfrac{\text{m}}{\text{s}}\right)(0.0152 \text{ m})}{45 \times 10^{-6} \dfrac{\text{m}^2}{\text{s}}} = \boxed{202.7}$$

6. *Customary U.S. Solution*

(a) The exposed duct area is

$$A = (2W + 2H)L$$
$$= ((2)(18 \text{ in}) + (2)(12 \text{ in}))\left(\frac{1 \text{ ft}}{12 \text{ in}}\right)(50 \text{ ft})$$
$$= 250 \text{ ft}^2$$

The duct is noncircular; therefore, the hydraulic diameter of the duct will be used. From Eq. 36.50, the hydraulic diameter is

$$d_H = (4)\left(\frac{\text{area in flow}}{\text{wetted perimeter}}\right) = (4)\left(\frac{WH}{(2)(W + H)}\right)$$
$$= (4)\left(\frac{(18 \text{ in})(12 \text{ in})}{(2)(18 \text{ in} + 12 \text{ in})}\right)\left(\frac{1 \text{ ft}}{12 \text{ in}}\right)$$
$$= 1.2 \text{ ft}$$

From App. 35.C for air at 100°F,

$$\nu = 18.0 \times 10^{-5} \text{ ft}^2/\text{sec}$$
$$\rho = 0.0710 \text{ lbm/ft}^3$$

The Reynolds number is

$$\text{Re} = \frac{\text{v}D}{\nu} = \frac{\left(800 \frac{\text{ft}}{\text{min}}\right)(1.2 \text{ ft})\left(\frac{1 \text{ min}}{60 \text{ sec}}\right)}{18.0 \times 10^{-5} \frac{\text{ft}^2}{\text{sec}}}$$
$$= 8.90 \times 10^4$$

This is a turbulent flow. From Eq. 36.39,

$$h_i \approx (0.00351 + 0.000001583T_{°F})\left[\frac{(G_{\text{lbm/hr-ft}^2})^{0.8}}{(d_{\text{ft}})^{0.2}}\right]$$

$$G = \rho\text{v} = \left(0.0710 \frac{\text{lbm}}{\text{ft}^3}\right)\left(800 \frac{\text{ft}}{\text{min}}\right)\left(60 \frac{\text{min}}{\text{hr}}\right)$$
$$= 3408.0 \text{ lbm/hr-ft}^2$$

$$h_i = (0.00351 + (0.000001583)(100°F))$$
$$\times \left[\frac{\left(3408.0 \frac{\text{lbm}}{\text{hr-ft}^2}\right)^{0.8}}{(1.2 \text{ ft})^{0.2}}\right]$$
$$= 2.37 \text{ Btu/hr-ft}^2\text{-°F}$$

Disregarding the duct thermal resistance, the overall heat transfer coefficient (from Eq. 36.74) is

$$\frac{1}{U} \approx \frac{1}{h_i} + \frac{1}{h_o}$$
$$= \frac{1}{2.37 \frac{\text{Btu}}{\text{hr-ft}^2\text{-°F}}} + \frac{1}{2.0 \frac{\text{Btu}}{\text{hr-ft}^2\text{-°F}}}$$
$$= 0.922 \text{ hr-ft}^2\text{-°F/Btu}$$
$$U = 1.08 \text{ Btu/hr-ft}^2\text{-°F}$$

The heat transfer to the room is

$$Q = UA(T_{\text{ave}} - T_\infty) = UA\left[\left(\tfrac{1}{2}\right)(T_{\text{in}} + T_{\text{out}}) - T_\infty\right]$$

Since T_{out} is unknown, an iteration procedure may be required. Assume $T_{\text{out}} \approx 95°F$.

$$Q = \left(1.08 \frac{\text{Btu}}{\text{hr-ft}^2\text{-°F}}\right)(250 \text{ ft}^2)$$
$$\times \left[\left(\tfrac{1}{2}\right)(100°F + 95°F) - 70°F\right]$$
$$= \boxed{7425 \text{ Btu/hr}}$$

Notice that ΔT (not ΔT_{lm}) is used in accordance with standard conventions in the HVAC industry.

(b) Temperature T_{out} can be verified by using

$$Q = \dot{m}c_p(T_{\text{in}} - T_{\text{out}})$$
$$\dot{m} = GA_{\text{flow}} = GWH$$
$$= \left(3408.0 \frac{\text{lbm}}{\text{hr-ft}^2}\right)(18 \text{ in})(12 \text{ in})$$
$$\times \left(\frac{1 \text{ ft}^2}{144 \text{ in}^2}\right)$$
$$= 5112 \text{ lbm/hr}$$
$$c_p = 0.240 \text{ Btu/lbm-°F}$$
$$\text{[from App. 35.C at 100°F]}$$
$$7425 \frac{\text{Btu}}{\text{hr}} = \left(5112 \frac{\text{lbm}}{\text{hr}}\right)\left(0.240 \frac{\text{Btu}}{\text{lbm-°F}}\right)$$
$$\times (100°F - T_{\text{out}})$$
$$T_{\text{out}} = \boxed{94°F} \quad \text{[close enough]}$$

(c) Assume clean galvanized ductwork with $\epsilon = 0.0005$ ft and about 25 joints per 100 ft. From Eq. 20.33, the equivalent diameter of a rectangular duct is

$$D_e = \frac{(1.3)(\text{short side} \times \text{long side})^{\frac{5}{8}}}{(\text{short side} + \text{long side})^{\frac{1}{4}}}$$
$$= \frac{(1.3)\left[(12 \text{ in})(18 \text{ in})\right]^{\frac{5}{8}}}{(12 \text{ in} + 18 \text{ in})^{\frac{1}{4}}} = 16 \text{ in}$$

The flow rate is

$$\dot{V} = \text{v}A = \frac{\left(800 \frac{\text{ft}}{\text{min}}\right)(12 \text{ in})(18 \text{ in})}{144 \frac{\text{in}^2}{\text{ft}^2}}$$
$$= 1200 \text{ cfm}$$

From Fig. 20.4, the friction loss is 0.066 in wg/100 ft. Therefore,

$$\Delta p = (0.066 \text{ in wg})\left(\frac{50 \text{ ft}}{100 \text{ ft}}\right) = \boxed{0.033 \text{ in wg}}$$

(Notice that the flow rate and not the flow velocity must be used with D_e in Fig. 20.4.)

SI Solution

(a) The exposed duct area is

$$A = (2W + 2H)L$$
$$= ((2)(45 \text{ cm}) + (2)(30 \text{ cm}))\left(\frac{1 \text{ m}}{100 \text{ cm}}\right)(15 \text{ m})$$
$$= 22.5 \text{ m}^2$$

Heat Transfer

The duct is noncircular; therefore, the hydraulic diameter of the duct will be used. From Eq. 36.50, the hydraulic diameter is

$$d_H = (4) \left(\frac{\text{area in flow}}{\text{wetted perimeter}} \right)$$

$$= (4) \left(\frac{WH}{(2)(W+H)} \right)$$

$$= (4) \left(\frac{(45 \text{ cm})(30 \text{ cm})}{(2)(45 \text{ cm} + 30 \text{ cm})} \right) \left(\frac{1 \text{ m}}{100 \text{ cm}} \right)$$

$$= 0.36 \text{ m}$$

From App. 35.D, for air at 40°C,

$$\mu = 1.91 \times 10^{-5} \text{ kg/m·s}$$
$$\rho = 1.130 \text{ kg/m}^3$$
$$c_p = 1.0051 \text{ kJ/kg·K}$$
$$k = 0.02718 \text{ W/m·K}$$

The Reynolds number is

$$\text{Re} = \frac{\rho v D}{\mu} = \frac{\left(1.130 \, \frac{\text{kg}}{\text{m}^3} \right) \left(4.0 \, \frac{\text{m}}{\text{s}} \right) (0.36 \text{ m})}{1.91 \times 10^{-5} \, \frac{\text{kg}}{\text{m·s}}}$$

$$= 8.52 \times 10^4$$

This is a turbulent flow. From Eq. 36.34, the Nusselt number is

$$\text{Nu} = (0.023)(\text{Re}^{0.8})$$

The film coefficient is

$$h = (0.023)(\text{Re}^{0.8}) \left(\frac{k}{d} \right)$$

$$= (0.023)(8.52 \times 10^4)^{0.8} \left(\frac{0.02718 \, \frac{\text{W}}{\text{m·K}}}{0.36 \text{ m}} \right)$$

$$= 15.28 \text{ W/m}^2\text{·K}$$

Disregarding the duct thermal resistance, the overall heat transfer coefficient from Eq. 36.74 is

$$\frac{1}{U} = \frac{1}{h_i} + \frac{1}{h_o}$$

$$= \frac{1}{11 \, \frac{\text{W}}{\text{m}^2\text{·K}}} + \frac{1}{15.28 \, \frac{\text{W}}{\text{m}^2\text{·K}}} = 0.1564 \text{ m}^2\text{·K/W}$$

$$U = 6.39 \text{ W/m}^2\text{·K}$$

The heat transfer to the room is

$$Q = UA(T_{\text{ave}} - T_\infty) = UA \left[\left(\tfrac{1}{2} \right) (T_{\text{in}} + T_{\text{out}}) - T_\infty \right]$$

Since T_{out} is unknown, an iterative procedure may be required. Assume $T_{\text{out}} = 36$°C.

$$Q = \left(6.39 \, \frac{\text{W}}{\text{m}^2\text{·K}} \right) (22.5 \text{ m}^2)$$

$$\times \left(\left(\tfrac{1}{2} \right) (40°C + 36°C) - 21°C \right)$$

$$= \boxed{2444.2 \text{ W}}$$

Notice that ΔT (not ΔT_{lm}) is used in accordance with standard conventions in the HVAC industry.

(b) Verify temperature T_{out}.

$$Q = \dot{m} c_p (T_{\text{in}} - T_{\text{out}})$$
$$\dot{m} = \rho A_{\text{flow}} v$$

$$= \left(1.130 \, \frac{\text{kg}}{\text{m}^3} \right) (45 \text{ cm})(30 \text{ cm}) \left(\frac{1 \text{ m}}{100 \text{ cm}} \right)^2$$

$$\times \left(4 \, \frac{\text{m}}{\text{s}} \right)$$

$$= 0.6102 \text{ kg/s}$$

$$2444.2 \text{ W} = \left(0.6102 \, \frac{\text{kg}}{\text{s}} \right) \left(1.0051 \, \frac{\text{kJ}}{\text{kg·K}} \right) \left(1000 \, \frac{\text{J}}{\text{kJ}} \right)$$

$$\times (40°C - T_{\text{out}})$$

$$T_{\text{out}} = \boxed{36°C} \quad \text{[same as assumed]}$$

(c) Assume clean galvanized ductwork with $\epsilon = 0.15$ mm and about 1 joint per meter. From Eq. 20.33, the equivalent diameter of a rectangular duct is

$$D_e = \frac{(1.3)(\text{short side} \times \text{long side})^{\frac{5}{8}}}{(\text{short side} + \text{long side})^{\frac{1}{4}}}$$

$$= \left(\frac{(1.3)\left[(30 \text{ cm})(45 \text{ cm}) \right]^{\frac{5}{8}}}{(30 \text{ cm} + 45 \text{ cm})^{\frac{1}{4}}} \right) \left(\frac{10 \text{ mm}}{1 \text{ cm}} \right)$$

$$= 400 \text{ mm}$$

The flow rate is

$$\dot{V} = vA = \left(4 \, \frac{\text{m}}{\text{s}} \right) (0.45 \text{ m})(0.30 \text{ m}) \left(1000 \, \frac{\text{L}}{\text{m}^3} \right)$$

$$= 540 \text{ L/s}$$

From Fig. 20.5, the friction loss is 0.5 Pa/m. For 15 m,

$$\Delta p = \left(0.5 \, \frac{\text{Pa}}{\text{m}} \right) (15 \text{ m}) = \boxed{7.5 \text{ Pa}}$$

(Notice that the flow rate and not the flow velocity must be used with D_e in Fig. 20.4.)

7. *Customary U.S. Solution*

Refer to Fig. 34.3. The corresponding radii are

$$r_a = \frac{d_i}{2} = \frac{(3.5 \text{ in})\left(\frac{1 \text{ ft}}{12 \text{ in}}\right)}{2} = 0.1458 \text{ ft}$$

$$r_b = \frac{d_o}{2} = \frac{(4 \text{ in})\left(\frac{1 \text{ ft}}{12 \text{ in}}\right)}{2} = 0.1667 \text{ ft}$$

$$r_c = r_b + t_{\text{insulation}} = 0.1667 \text{ ft} + (2 \text{ in})\left(\frac{1 \text{ ft}}{12 \text{ in}}\right)$$

$$= 0.3334 \text{ ft}$$

From App. 34.B, for steel at 350°F, $k_{\text{pipe}} \approx 25.4$ Btu-ft/hr-ft²-°F.

Initially assume $h_c = 1.5$ Btu/hr-ft²-°F.

For fully developed laminar flow from Eq. 36.28, $\text{Nu}_d = 3.658$.

From App. 35.C, for air at 350°F,

$$k_{\text{air}} \approx 0.0203 \text{ Btu/hr-ft-°F}$$

$$\text{Nu}_d = \frac{h_a d_i}{k_{\text{air}}} = 3.658$$

$$h_a = \frac{(3.658)k_{\text{air}}}{d_i} = \frac{(3.658)\left(0.0203 \frac{\text{Btu}}{\text{hr-ft-°F}}\right)}{(3.5 \text{ in})\left(\frac{1 \text{ ft}}{12 \text{ in}}\right)}$$

$$= 0.255 \text{ Btu/hr-ft}^2\text{-°F}$$

Neglect thermal resistance between pipe and insulation. From Eq. 34.34, the heat transfer is

$$Q = \frac{2\pi L(T_i - T_\infty)}{\dfrac{1}{r_a h_a} + \dfrac{\ln\left(\dfrac{r_b}{r_a}\right)}{k_{\text{pipe}}} + \dfrac{\ln\left(\dfrac{r_c}{r_b}\right)}{k_{\text{insulation}}} + \dfrac{1}{r_c h_c}}$$

$$= \frac{2\pi(100 \text{ ft})(350\text{°F} - 50\text{°F})}{\dfrac{1}{(0.1458 \text{ ft})\left(0.255 \frac{\text{Btu}}{\text{hr-ft}^2\text{-°F}}\right)} + \dfrac{\ln\left(\dfrac{0.1667 \text{ ft}}{0.1458 \text{ ft}}\right)}{25.4 \frac{\text{Btu-ft}}{\text{hr-ft}^2\text{-°F}}}}$$

$$+ \dfrac{\ln\left(\dfrac{0.3334 \text{ ft}}{0.1667 \text{ ft}}\right)}{0.05 \frac{\text{Btu-ft}}{\text{hr-ft}^2\text{-°F}}} + \dfrac{1}{(0.3334 \text{ ft})\left(1.5 \frac{\text{Btu}}{\text{hr-ft}^2\text{-°F}}\right)}$$

$$= \frac{188{,}496 \text{ ft-°F}}{26.90 \frac{\text{hr-ft-°F}}{\text{Btu}} + 0.00527 \frac{\text{hr-ft-°F}}{\text{Btu}}} + 13.863 \frac{\text{hr-ft-°F}}{\text{Btu}} + 2.00 \frac{\text{hr-ft-°F}}{\text{Btu}}$$

$$= 4407 \text{ Btu/hr}$$

Using Eq. 34.34 to find T_2, use all resistances except the outer $(T_i - T_2)$ resistance.

$$\left(\frac{4407 \frac{\text{Btu}}{\text{hr}}}{2\pi(100 \text{ ft})}\right)\left(26.9 \frac{\text{hr-ft-°F}}{\text{Btu}}\right.$$

$$\left. + 0.00527 \frac{\text{hr-ft-°F}}{\text{Btu}} + 13.863 \frac{\text{hr-ft-°F}}{\text{Btu}}\right)$$

$$= 285.9\text{°F}$$

$$T_2 = T_i - 285.9\text{°F} = 350\text{°F} - 285.9\text{°F} = 64.1\text{°F}$$

To evaluate h_c, use film temperature.

$$T_{\text{film}} = \left(\tfrac{1}{2}\right)(T_2 + T_\infty) = \left(\tfrac{1}{2}\right)(64.1\text{°F} + 50\text{°F})$$

$$= 57\text{°F}$$

From App. 35.C air at 57°F,

$$\text{Pr} = 0.72$$

$$\frac{g\beta\rho^2}{\mu^2} = 2.645 \times 10^6 \frac{1}{\text{ft}^3\text{-°F}}$$

From Eq. 35.4, the Grashof number is

$$\text{Gr} = \frac{L^3 g\beta\rho^2(T_2 - T_\infty)}{\mu^2}$$

For pipe,

$$L = d_c = 2r_c = (2)(0.3334 \text{ ft}) = 0.6668 \text{ ft}$$

$$\text{Gr} = (0.6668 \text{ ft})^3\left(2.645 \times 10^6 \frac{1}{\text{ft}^3\text{-°F}}\right)$$

$$\times (64.1\text{°F} - 50\text{°F})$$

$$= 1.1 \times 10^7$$

$$\text{GrPr} = (1.1 \times 10^7)(0.72)$$

$$= 7.9 \times 10^6$$

From Table 35.3,

$$h_c \approx (0.27)\left(\frac{T_2 - T_\infty}{d_c}\right)^{\frac{1}{4}}$$

$$= (0.27)\left(\frac{64.1\text{°F} - 50\text{°F}}{0.6668 \text{ ft}}\right)^{\frac{1}{4}}$$

$$= 0.579 \text{ Btu/hr-ft}^2\text{-°F}$$

Heat Transfer

At the second iteration, the heat transfer is

$$Q = \frac{188{,}496 \text{ ft-}°\text{F}}{26.90 \ \dfrac{\text{hr-ft-}°\text{F}}{\text{Btu}} + 0.00527 \ \dfrac{\text{hr-ft-}°\text{F}}{\text{Btu}}}$$
$$\quad + 13.863 \ \dfrac{\text{hr-ft-}°\text{F}}{\text{Btu}}$$
$$\quad + \dfrac{1}{(0.3334 \text{ ft}) \left(0.579 \ \dfrac{\text{Btu}}{\text{hr-ft-}°\text{F}} \right)}$$

$$= \boxed{4102 \text{ Btu/hr}}$$

Additional iterations will improve the accuracy further.

SI Solution

Refer to Fig. 34.3. The corresponding radii are

$$r_a = \frac{d_i}{2} = \frac{(9.0 \text{ cm}) \left(\dfrac{1 \text{ m}}{100 \text{ cm}} \right)}{2} = 0.045 \text{ m}$$

$$r_b = \frac{d_o}{2} = \frac{(10 \text{ cm}) \left(\dfrac{1 \text{ m}}{100 \text{ cm}} \right)}{2} = 0.050 \text{ m}$$

$$r_c = r_b + t_{\text{insulation}} = 0.050 \text{ m} + (5.0 \text{ cm}) \left(\frac{1 \text{ m}}{100 \text{ cm}} \right)$$

$$= 0.100 \text{ m}$$

From App. 34.B and the table footnote, for steel at 175°C ($\sim$347°F),

$$k_{\text{pipe}} \approx \left(25.4 \ \frac{\text{Btu}}{\text{hr-ft-}°\text{F}} \right) \left(1.7307 \ \frac{\text{W·hr·ft·}°\text{F}}{\text{m·K·Btu}} \right)$$

$$= 43.96 \text{ W/m·K}$$

Initially assume $h_c = 3.5 \text{ W/m}^2\text{·K}$.

For fully developed laminar flow from Eq. 36.28,

$$\text{Nu}_d = \frac{h_a d_i}{k_{\text{air}}} = 3.658$$

From App. 35.D for air at 175°C,

$$k_{\text{air}} \approx 0.03709 \text{ W/m·K}$$

$$h_a = \frac{3.658 k_{\text{air}}}{d_i}$$

$$= \frac{(3.658) \left(0.03709 \ \dfrac{\text{W}}{\text{m·K}} \right)}{(9.0 \text{ cm}) \left(\dfrac{1 \text{ m}}{100 \text{ cm}} \right)}$$

$$= 1.508 \text{ W/m}^2\text{·K}$$

Neglect thermal resistance between pipe and insulation. From Eq. 34.34, the heat transfer is

$$Q = \frac{2\pi L (T_i - T_\infty)}{\dfrac{1}{r_a h_a} + \dfrac{\ln \left(\dfrac{r_b}{r_a} \right)}{k_{\text{pipe}}} + \dfrac{\ln \left(\dfrac{r_c}{r_b} \right)}{k_{\text{insulation}}} + \dfrac{1}{r_c h_c}}$$

$$= \frac{2\pi (30 \text{ m})(175°\text{C} - 10°\text{C})}{\dfrac{1}{(0.045 \text{ m}) \left(1.508 \ \dfrac{\text{W}}{\text{m}^2\text{·K}} \right)} + \dfrac{\ln \left(\dfrac{0.050 \text{ m}}{0.045 \text{ m}} \right)}{43.96 \ \dfrac{\text{W}}{\text{m·K}}}}$$
$$\quad + \dfrac{\ln \left(\dfrac{0.10 \text{ m}}{0.050 \text{ m}} \right)}{0.086 \ \dfrac{\text{W}}{\text{m·K}}} + \dfrac{1}{(0.10 \text{ m}) \left(3.5 \ \dfrac{\text{W}}{\text{m}^2\text{·K}} \right)}$$

$$= \frac{31\,101.8 \text{ m·}°\text{C}}{14.74 \ \dfrac{\text{m·K}}{\text{W}} + 0.00240 \ \dfrac{\text{m·K}}{\text{W}}}$$
$$\quad + 8.06 \ \dfrac{\text{m·K}}{\text{W}} + 2.86 \ \dfrac{\text{m·K}}{\text{W}}$$

$$= 1212 \text{ W}$$

Use Eq. 34.34 to find T_2 by using all resistances except the outer resistance.

$$T_i - T_2 = \left(\frac{1212 \text{ W}}{2\pi (30 \text{ m})} \right)$$
$$\quad \times \left(14.74 \ \frac{\text{m·K}}{\text{W}} + 0.00240 \ \frac{\text{m·K}}{\text{W}} + 8.06 \ \frac{\text{m·K}}{\text{W}} \right)$$
$$= 146.6°\text{C}$$
$$T_2 = T_i - 146.6°\text{C} = 175°\text{C} - 146.6°\text{C}$$
$$= 28.4°\text{C}$$

To evaluate h_c, use film temperature.

$$T_{\text{film}} = \left(\tfrac{1}{2} \right) (T_2 - T_\infty) = \left(\tfrac{1}{2} \right) (28.4°\text{C} + 10°\text{C})$$
$$= 19.2°\text{C}$$

From App. 35.D for air at 19.2°C,

$$\text{Pr} = 0.710$$
$$\frac{g\beta\rho^2}{\mu^2} = 1.52 \times 10^8 \ \frac{1}{\text{K·m}^3}$$

From Eq. 35.4, the Grashof number is

$$\text{Gr} = \frac{L^3 g\beta\rho^2 (T_2 - T_\infty)}{\mu^2}$$

For pipe,

$$L = d_c = 2r_c = (2)(0.10 \text{ m}) = 0.20 \text{ m}$$

$$\text{Gr} = (0.20 \text{ m})^3 \left(1.52 \times 10^8 \, \frac{1}{\text{K·m}^3} \right) (28.4°\text{C} - 10°\text{C})$$

$$= 2.24 \times 10^7$$

$$\text{GrPr} = (2.24 \times 10^7)(0.710)$$

$$= 1.59 \times 10^7$$

From Table 35.3,

$$h_c \approx (1.37) \left(\frac{T_2 - T_\infty}{d_c} \right)^{\frac{1}{4}}$$

$$= (1.37) \left(\frac{28.4°\text{C} - 10°\text{C}}{0.20 \text{ m}} \right)^{\frac{1}{4}}$$

$$= 4.24 \text{ W/m}^2\text{·K} \quad \begin{bmatrix} \text{versus assumed value of} \\ 3.5 \text{ W/m}^2\text{·K} \end{bmatrix}$$

Further iteration will improve accuracy.

$$Q = \frac{31\,101.8 \text{ m·}°\text{C}}{14.74 \, \frac{\text{m·K}}{\text{W}} + 0.00240 \, \frac{\text{m·K}}{\text{W}}}$$
$$+ \; 8.06 \, \frac{\text{m·K}}{\text{W}} + \frac{1}{(0.10 \text{ m}) \left(4.24 \, \frac{\text{W}}{\text{m}^2\text{·K}} \right)}$$

$$= \boxed{1236 \text{ W}}$$

8. *Customary U.S. Solution*

Neglecting pipe resistance (no information for pipe is given), $T_{\text{pipe}} = T_{\text{sat}}$.

From App. 24.B for 300 lbf/in^2 steam, $T_{\text{sat}} = 417.43°\text{F}$. When a vapor condenses, the vapor and condensed liquid are at the same temperature. Therefore, the entire pipe is assumed to be at 417.43°F. The outside film coefficient should be evaluated from Eq. 36.11.

$$T_{\text{film}} = \left(\tfrac{1}{2} \right) (T_s + T_\infty)$$

$$= \left(\tfrac{1}{2} \right) (417.43°\text{F} + 70°\text{F})$$

$$= 243.7°\text{F}$$

From App. 35.C for air at 243.7°F,

$$\text{Pr} = 0.715$$

$$\frac{g\beta\rho^2}{\mu^2} = 0.673 \times 10^6 \, \frac{1}{\text{ft}^3\text{-}°\text{F}}$$

From Eq. 35.4, the Grashof number is

$$\text{Gr} = \frac{L^3 g \beta \rho^2 T_s - T_\infty}{\mu^2}$$

$$L = d_{\text{outside}} = (4 \text{ in}) \left(\frac{1 \text{ ft}}{12 \text{ in}} \right) = 0.3333 \text{ ft}$$

$$\text{Gr} = (0.3333 \text{ ft})^3 \left(0.673 \times 10^6 \, \frac{1}{\text{ft}^3\text{-}°\text{F}} \right)$$
$$\times (417.43°\text{F} - 70°\text{F})$$

$$= 8.66 \times 10^6$$

$$\text{GrPr} = (8.66 \times 10^6)(0.715)$$

$$= 6.19 \times 10^6$$

From Table 35.3,

$$h_c \approx (0.27) \left(\frac{T_s - T_\infty}{d_{\text{outside}}} \right)^{\frac{1}{4}}$$

$$= (0.27) \left(\frac{417.43°\text{F} - 70°\text{F}}{0.3333 \text{ ft}} \right)^{\frac{1}{4}}$$

$$= 1.53 \text{ Btu/hr-ft}^2\text{-}°\text{F}$$

From Eq. 35.1, the heat transfer for the first 50 ft due to convection is

$$Q = h_c A_{\text{outside}} (T_s - T_\infty)$$

$$= h_c (\pi d_{\text{outside}} L)(T_s - T_\infty)$$

$$= \left(1.53 \, \frac{\text{Btu}}{\text{hr-ft}^2\text{-}°\text{F}} \right) \pi (0.3333 \text{ ft})(50 \text{ ft})$$
$$\times (417.43°\text{F} - 70°\text{F})$$

$$Q_{\text{convection}} = 27{,}830 \text{ Btu/hr}$$

To determine heat transfer due to radiation, assume oxidized steel pipe, completely enclosed.

$$F_a = 1$$

The absolute temperatures are

$$T_1 = 417.43°\text{F} + 460 = 877.43°\text{R}$$

$$T_2 = 70°\text{F} + 460 = 530°\text{F}$$

$$F_e = \epsilon_{\text{pipe}} = 0.80$$

The radiation heat transfer is

$$E_{\text{net}} = \sigma F_a F_e \left(T_1^4 - T_2^4 \right)$$

$$= \left(0.1713 \times 10^{-8} \, \frac{\text{Btu}}{\text{hr-ft}^2\text{-}°\text{R}^4} \right)$$
$$\times (1)(0.80) \left[(877.43°\text{R})^4 - (530°\text{R})^4 \right]$$

$$= 704 \text{ Btu/hr-ft}^2$$

$$Q_{\text{radiation}} = E_{\text{net}} A = E_{\text{net}} (\pi d_{\text{outside}} L)$$

$$= \left(704 \, \frac{\text{Btu}}{\text{hr-ft}^2} \right) \pi (0.3333 \text{ ft})(50 \text{ ft})$$

$$= 36{,}858 \text{ Btu/hr}$$

Heat Transfer

The total heat loss is

$$Q_{\text{total}} = Q_{\text{convection}} + Q_{\text{radiation}}$$
$$= 27{,}830 \ \frac{\text{Btu}}{\text{hr}} + 36{,}858 \ \frac{\text{Btu}}{\text{hr}}$$
$$= 64{,}688 \ \text{Btu/hr}$$
$$Q_{\text{total}} = \dot{m}\Delta h$$

The enthalpy decrease per pound is

$$\Delta h = \frac{Q_{\text{total}}}{\dot{m}_{\text{steam}}} = \frac{64{,}688 \ \dfrac{\text{Btu}}{\text{hr}}}{5000 \ \dfrac{\text{lbm}}{\text{hr}}} = 12.94 \ \text{Btu/lbm}$$

This is a quality loss of

$$\Delta x = \frac{\Delta h}{h_{fg}} = \frac{12.94 \ \dfrac{\text{Btu}}{\text{lbm}}}{809.8 \ \dfrac{\text{Btu}}{\text{lbm}}}$$

$$= \boxed{0.0160 \ (1.6\%)}$$

SI Solution

From the Customary U.S. Solution, T_{pipe} is the same for the entire length.

From App. 24.O for 2.1 MPa, $T_{\text{sat}} = 214.72°\text{C}$. The outside film coefficient should be evaluated from Eq. 36.11 as

$$T_{\text{film}} = \left(\tfrac{1}{2}\right)(T_s + T_\infty) = \left(\tfrac{1}{2}\right)(214.72°\text{C} + 21°\text{C})$$
$$= 117.9°\text{C}$$

From App. 35.D for air at $117.9°\text{C}$,

$$\text{Pr} = 0.692$$
$$\frac{g\beta\rho^2}{\mu^2} = 0.403 \times 10^8 \ \frac{1}{\text{K·m}^3}$$

From Eq. 35.4, the Grashof number is

$$\text{Gr} = \frac{L^3 g\beta\rho^2(T_s - T_\infty)}{\mu^2}$$
$$L = d_{\text{outside}} = (10 \ \text{cm})\left(\frac{1 \ \text{m}}{100 \ \text{cm}}\right) = 0.10 \ \text{m}$$
$$\text{Gr} = (0.10 \ \text{m})^3 \left(0.403 \times 10^8 \ \frac{1}{\text{K·m}^3}\right)$$
$$\times \ (214.72°\text{C} - 21°\text{C})$$
$$= 7.807 \times 10^6$$
$$\text{GrPr} = (7.807 \times 10^6)(0.692)$$
$$= 5.40 \times 10^6$$

From Table 35.3,

$$h_c \approx (1.37)\left(\frac{T_s - T_\infty}{d_{\text{outside}}}\right)^{\frac{1}{4}}$$
$$= (1.37)\left(\frac{214.72°\text{C} - 21°\text{C}}{0.10 \ \text{m}}\right)^{\frac{1}{4}}$$
$$= 9.09 \ \text{W/m·K}$$

From Eq. 35.1, the heat transfer for the first 15 m due to convection is

$$Q_{\text{convection}} = h_c(\pi d_{\text{outside}} L)(T_s - T_\infty)$$
$$= \left(9.09 \ \frac{\text{W}}{\text{m·K}}\right)\pi(0.10 \ \text{m})(15 \ \text{m})$$
$$\times \ (214.72°\text{C} - 21°\text{C})$$
$$= 8298 \ \text{W}$$

To determine heat transfer due to radiation, assume oxidized steel pipe, completely enclosed.

$$F_a = 1$$

The absolute temperatures are

$$T_1 = 214.72°\text{C} + 273 = 487.72\text{K}$$
$$T_2 = 21°\text{C} + 273 = 294\text{K}$$
$$F_e = \epsilon_{\text{pipe}} = 0.80$$

The radiation heat transfer is

$$E_{\text{net}} = \sigma F_a F_e \left(T_1^4 - T_2^4\right)$$
$$= \left(5.67 \times 10^{-8} \ \frac{\text{W}}{\text{m}^2\text{·K}^4}\right)$$
$$\times \ (1)(0.80)\left[(487.72\text{K})^4 - (294\text{K})^4\right]$$
$$= 2228 \ \text{W/m}^2$$
$$Q_{\text{radiation}} = E_{\text{net}}(\pi d_{\text{outside}} L)$$
$$= \left(2228 \ \frac{\text{W}}{\text{m}^2}\right)\pi(0.10 \ \text{m})(15 \ \text{m})$$
$$= 10\,499 \ \text{W}$$

The total heat loss is

$$Q_{\text{total}} = Q_{\text{convection}} + Q_{\text{radiation}}$$
$$= 8298 \ \text{W} + 10\,499 \ \text{W}$$
$$= 18\,797 \ \text{W}$$
$$Q_{\text{total}} = \dot{m}\Delta h$$

The enthalpy decrease per kilogram is

$$\Delta h = \frac{Q_{\text{total}}}{\dot{m}_{\text{steam}}} = \frac{(18\,797 \ \text{W})\left(\dfrac{1 \ \text{kJ}}{1000 \ \text{J}}\right)}{0.63 \ \dfrac{\text{kg}}{\text{s}}}$$
$$= 29.84 \ \text{kJ/kg}$$

This is a quality loss of

$$\Delta x = \frac{\Delta h}{h_{fg}} = \frac{29.84\ \frac{\text{kJ}}{\text{kg}}}{1880.8\ \frac{\text{kJ}}{\text{kg}}}$$

$$= \boxed{0.0159\ (1.59\%)}$$

9. *Customary U.S. Solution*

The bulk temperature of the water is

$$T_b = \left(\tfrac{1}{2}\right)(T_{\text{in}} + T_{\text{out}})$$
$$= \left(\tfrac{1}{2}\right)(70°\text{F} + 190°\text{F}) = 130°\text{F}$$

From App. 35.A, the properties of water at 130°F are

$$c_p = 0.999\ \text{Btu/lbm-°F}$$
$$\nu = 0.582 \times 10^{-5}\ \text{ft}^2/\text{sec}$$
$$\text{Pr} = 3.45$$
$$k = 0.376\ \text{Btu/hr-ft-°F}$$

The heat transfer is found from the temperature gain of the water.

$$Q = \dot{m}c_p \Delta T$$
$$= \left(2940\ \frac{\text{lbm}}{\text{hr}}\right)\left(0.999\ \frac{\text{Btu}}{\text{lbm-°F}}\right)(190°\text{F} - 70°\text{F})$$
$$= 352{,}447\ \text{Btu/hr}$$

The Reynolds number is

$$\text{Re} = \frac{\text{v}D}{\nu} = \frac{\left(3\ \frac{\text{ft}}{\text{sec}}\right)(0.9\ \text{in})\left(\frac{1\ \text{ft}}{12\ \text{in}}\right)}{0.582 \times 10^{-5}\ \frac{\text{ft}^2}{\text{sec}}}$$
$$= 3.87 \times 10^4$$

From Eq. 36.33, the film coefficient is

$$h = (0.023)(\text{Re})^{0.8}(\text{Pr})^n \left(\frac{k}{d}\right)$$
$$= (0.023)(3.87 \times 10^4)^{0.8}(3.45)^{0.4}$$
$$\times \left(\frac{0.376\ \frac{\text{Btu}}{\text{hr-ft-°F}}}{(0.9\ \text{in})\left(\frac{1\ \text{ft}}{12\ \text{in}}\right)}\right)$$
$$= 885\ \text{Btu/hr-ft}^2\text{-°F}$$

The saturation temperature for 134 psia steam is $\approx$ 350°F. Assume the wall is 20°F lower ($\approx$ 330°F). The film properties are evaluated at the average of the wall and saturation temperatures.

$$T_h = \left(\tfrac{1}{2}\right)(T_{\text{sat},v} T_s) = \left(\tfrac{1}{2}\right)(350°\text{F} + 330°\text{F})$$
$$= 340°\text{F}$$

Film properties are obtained from App. 35.A for liquid water.

$$k_{340°\text{F}} = 0.392\ \text{Btu/hr-ft-°F}$$
$$\mu_{340°\text{F}} = \left(0.109 \times 10^{-3}\ \frac{\text{lbm}}{\text{sec-ft}}\right)\left(3600\ \frac{\text{sec}}{\text{hr}}\right)$$
$$= 0.392\ \text{lbm/ft-hr}$$
$$\rho_{l,340°\text{F}} = \frac{1}{v_{l,340°\text{F}}} = \frac{1}{0.01787\ \frac{\text{ft}^3}{\text{lbm}}}$$
$$= 55.96\ \text{lbm/ft}^3$$
$$l_{v,340°\text{F}} = \frac{1}{v_{v,340°\text{F}}} = \frac{1}{3.792\ \frac{\text{ft}^3}{\text{lbm}}}$$
$$= 0.2637\ \text{lbm/ft}^3$$
$$h_{fg,134\ \text{psia}} = 871\ \text{Btu/lbm}$$
$$d = (0.9\ \text{in})\left(\frac{1\ \text{ft}}{12\ \text{in}}\right) = 0.075\ \text{ft}$$
$$g = \left(32.2\ \frac{\text{ft}}{\text{sec}^2}\right)\left(3600\ \frac{\text{sec}}{\text{hr}}\right)^2$$
$$= 4.17 \times 10^8\ \text{ft/hr}^2$$

From Eq. 35.31, the film coefficient is

$$h_o = (0.725)\left[\frac{\rho_l(\rho_l - \rho_v)gh_{fg}(k_l)^3}{d\mu_l(T_{\text{sat},v} - T_s)}\right]$$

$$= (0.725)$$

$$\times \left[\frac{\left(55.96\ \frac{\text{lbm}}{\text{ft}^3}\right)\left(55.96\ \frac{\text{lbm}}{\text{ft}^3} - 0.2637\ \frac{\text{lbm}}{\text{ft}^3}\right) \times \left(4.17 \times 10^8\ \frac{\text{ft}}{\text{hr}^2}\right)\left(871\ \frac{\text{Btu}}{\text{lbm}}\right) \times \left(0.392\ \frac{\text{Btu}}{\text{hr-ft-°F}}\right)^3}{(0.075\ \text{ft})\left(0.392\ \frac{\text{lbm}}{\text{ft-hr}}\right)(350°\text{F} - 330°\text{F})}\right]^{\frac{1}{4}}$$

$$= 2379\ \text{Btu/hr-ft}^2\text{-°F}$$

From App. 34.B, for copper alloy (70% Cu), at 330°F, $k = 62$ Btu-ft/hr-ft²-°F.

From Eq. 36.71, the overall heat transfer coefficient based on the outside area is

$$\frac{1}{U_o} = \frac{1}{h_o} + \left(\frac{r_o}{k_{\text{tube}}}\right)\ln\left(\frac{r_o}{r_i}\right) + \frac{r_o}{r_i h_i}$$

$$r_o = \frac{d_o}{2} = \frac{(1\text{ in})\left(\dfrac{1\text{ ft}}{12\text{ in}}\right)}{2} = 0.0417\text{ ft}$$

$$r_i = \frac{d_i}{2} = \frac{(0.9\text{ in})\left(\dfrac{1\text{ ft}}{12\text{ in}}\right)}{2} = 0.0375\text{ ft}$$

$$U_o = \cfrac{1}{\cfrac{1}{2379\ \dfrac{\text{Btu}}{\text{hr-ft}^2\text{-}°\text{F}}} + \left(\cfrac{0.0417\text{ ft}}{62\ \dfrac{\text{Btu-ft}}{\text{hr-ft}^2\text{-}°\text{F}}}\right)\ln\left(\cfrac{0.0417\text{ ft}}{0.0375\text{ ft}}\right) + \cfrac{0.0417\text{ ft}}{(0.0375\text{ ft})\left(885\ \dfrac{\text{Btu}}{\text{hr-ft}^2\text{-}°\text{F}}\right)}}$$

$$= 572\text{ Btu/hr-ft}^2\text{-}°\text{F}$$

For crossflow operation (same result for parallel flow),

$$\Delta T_A = 350°\text{F} - 70°\text{F} = 280°\text{F}$$
$$\Delta T_B = 350°\text{F} - 190°\text{F} = 160°\text{F}$$

From Eq. 36.69, the logarithmic mean temperature difference is

$$\Delta T_{lm} = \frac{\Delta T_A - \Delta T_B}{\ln\left(\dfrac{\Delta T_A}{\Delta T_B}\right)} = \frac{280°\text{F} - 160°\text{F}}{\ln\left(\dfrac{280°\text{F}}{160°\text{F}}\right)} = 214.4°\text{F}$$

The heat transfer is known; therefore, the outside area can be calculated from Eq. 36.70.

$$Q = U_o A_o F_c \Delta T_{lm}$$

For steam condensation, the temperature of steam remains constant. Therefore, $F_c = 1$.

$$A_o = \frac{352{,}447\ \dfrac{\text{Btu}}{\text{hr}}}{\left(572\ \dfrac{\text{Btu}}{\text{hr-ft}^2\text{-}°\text{F}}\right)(1)(214.4°\text{F})} = \boxed{2.87\text{ ft}^2}$$

SI Solution

The bulk temperature of the water is

$$T_b = \left(\tfrac{1}{2}\right)(T_{\text{in}} + T_{\text{out}})$$
$$= \left(\tfrac{1}{2}\right)(21°\text{C} + 90°\text{C}) = 55.5°\text{C}$$

From App. 35.B, the properties of water at 55.5°C are

$$c_p = 4.186\text{ kJ/kg·K}$$
$$\rho = 986.6\text{ kg/m}^3$$
$$\mu = 0.523 \times 10^{-3}\text{ kg/m·s}$$
$$k = 0.6503\text{ W/m·K}$$
$$\text{Pr} = 3.37$$

The heat transfer is found from the temperature gain of the water.

$$Q = \dot{m}c_p \Delta T$$
$$= \left(0.368\ \frac{\text{kg}}{\text{s}}\right)\left(4.186\ \frac{\text{kJ}}{\text{kg·K}}\right)\left(1000\ \frac{\text{J}}{\text{kJ}}\right)$$
$$\times (90°\text{C} - 21°\text{C})$$
$$= 106\,291\text{ W}$$

The Reynolds number is

$$\text{Re} = \frac{\rho v D}{\mu}$$
$$= \frac{\left(986.6\ \dfrac{\text{kg}}{\text{m}^3}\right)\left(0.9\ \dfrac{\text{m}}{\text{s}}\right)(2.29\text{ cm})\left(\dfrac{1\text{ m}}{100\text{ cm}}\right)}{0.523 \times 10^{-3}\ \dfrac{\text{kg}}{\text{m·s}}}$$
$$= 3.89 \times 10^4$$

From Eq. 36.33, the film coefficient is

$$h = (0.023)(\text{Re})^{0.8}(\text{Pr})^n\left(\frac{k}{d}\right)$$
$$= (0.023)(3.89 \times 10^4)^{0.8}(3.37)^{0.4}$$
$$\times \left(\frac{0.6503\ \dfrac{\text{W}}{\text{m·K}}}{(2.29\text{ cm})\left(\dfrac{1\text{ m}}{100\text{ cm}}\right)}\right)$$
$$= 4989\text{ W/m}^2\text{·K}$$

The saturation temperature for 923 kPa steam is 176.4°C. Assume the wall to be at 10°C lower (or 166.4°C). The film properties are evaluated at the average of the wall and saturation temperatures.

$$T_h = \left(\tfrac{1}{2}\right)(T_{\text{sat},v} + T_s) = \left(\tfrac{1}{2}\right)(176.4°\text{C} + 166.4°\text{C})$$
$$= 171.4°\text{C}$$

Film properties are obtained from App. 35.B for liquid water.

$$k_{171.4°C} = 0.6745 \text{ W/m·K}$$

$$\mu_{171.4°C} = 0.1712 \times 10^{-3} \text{ kg/m·s}$$

$$\rho_{l,171.4°C} = \frac{1}{v_{l,171.4°C}}$$

$$= \frac{1}{\left(1.1161 \dfrac{\text{cm}^3}{\text{g}}\right)\left(1000 \dfrac{\text{g}}{\text{kg}}\right)\left(\dfrac{1 \text{ m}}{100 \text{ cm}}\right)^3}$$

$$= 896.0 \text{ kg/m}^3$$

$$\rho_{v,171.4°C} = \frac{1}{v_{g,171.4°C}}$$

$$= \frac{1}{\left(235.3 \dfrac{\text{cm}^3}{\text{g}}\right)\left(1000 \dfrac{\text{g}}{\text{kg}}\right)\left(\dfrac{1 \text{ m}}{100 \text{ cm}}\right)^3}$$

$$= 4.25 \text{ kg/m}^3$$

$$h_{fg,923 \text{ kPa}} = \left(2027.5 \frac{\text{kJ}}{\text{kg}}\right)\left(1000 \frac{\text{J}}{\text{kg}}\right)$$

$$= 2.0275 \times 10^6 \text{ J/kg}$$

$$d = (2.29 \text{ cm})\left(\frac{1 \text{ m}}{100 \text{ cm}}\right) = 0.0229 \text{ m}$$

From Eq. 35.31, the film coefficient is

$$h_o = (0.725)\left[\frac{\rho_l(\rho_l - \rho_\nu)g h_{fg}(k_l)^3}{d\mu_l(T_{\text{sat},v} - T_s)}\right]^{\frac{1}{4}}$$

$$= (0.725)$$

$$\times \left[\frac{\begin{array}{c}\left(896 \dfrac{\text{kg}}{\text{m}^3}\right)\left(896 \dfrac{\text{kg}}{\text{m}^3} - 4.25 \dfrac{\text{kg}}{\text{m}^3}\right)\left(9.81 \dfrac{\text{m}}{\text{s}^2}\right) \\ \times \left(2.0275 \times 10^6 \dfrac{\text{J}}{\text{kg}}\right)\left(0.6745 \dfrac{\text{W}}{\text{m·K}}\right)^3\end{array}}{\begin{array}{c}(0.0229 \text{ m})\left(0.1712 \times 10^{-3} \dfrac{\text{kg}}{\text{m·s}}\right) \\ \times (176.4°C - 166.4°C)\end{array}}\right]^{\frac{1}{4}}$$

$$= 13\,616 \text{ W/m}^2\text{·K}$$

From App. 34.B and the table footnote, for copper alloy (70% Cu) at 166.4°C,

$$k \approx \left(62 \frac{\text{Btu}}{\text{hr·ft·°F}}\right)\left(1.7307 \frac{\text{W·hr·ft·°F}}{\text{m·K·Btu}}\right)$$

$$= 107.3 \text{ W/m·K}$$

From Eq. 36.71, the overall heat transfer coefficient based on outside area is

$$\frac{1}{U_o} = \frac{1}{h_o} + \left(\frac{r_o}{k_{\text{tube}}}\right)\ln\left(\frac{r_o}{r_i}\right) + \frac{r_o}{r_i h_i}$$

$$r_o = \frac{d_o}{2} = \frac{(2.54 \text{ cm})\left(\dfrac{1 \text{ m}}{100 \text{ cm}}\right)}{2} = 0.0127 \text{ m}$$

$$r_i = \frac{d_i}{2} = \frac{0.0229 \text{ m}}{2} = 0.0115 \text{ m}$$

$$U_o = \frac{1}{\begin{array}{c}\dfrac{1}{13\,616 \dfrac{\text{W}}{\text{m}^2\text{·K}}} + \left(\dfrac{0.0127 \text{ m}}{107.3 \dfrac{\text{W}}{\text{m·K}}}\right)\ln\left(\dfrac{0.0127 \text{ m}}{0.0115 \text{ m}}\right) \\ + \dfrac{0.0127 \text{ m}}{(0.0115 \text{ m})\left(4989 \dfrac{\text{W}}{\text{m}^2\text{·K}}\right)}\end{array}}$$

$$= 3262 \text{ W/m}^2\text{·K}$$

$$\begin{array}{ccc} 21°C & \longrightarrow & 90°C \\ A & & B \\ 176.4°C & \longleftarrow & 176.4°C \end{array}$$

$$\Delta T_A = 176.4°C - 21°C = 155.4°C$$

$$\Delta T_B = 176.4°C - 90°C = 86.4°C$$

From Eq. 36.69, the logarithmic mean temperature difference is

$$\Delta T_{lm} = \frac{\Delta T_A - \Delta T_B}{\ln\left(\dfrac{\Delta T_A}{\Delta T_B}\right)} = \frac{155.4°C - 86.4°C}{\ln\left(\dfrac{155.4°C}{86.4°C}\right)}$$

$$= 117.5°C$$

The heat transfer is known; therefore, the outside area can be calculated from Eq. 36.70.

$$Q = U_o A_o F_c \Delta T_{lm}$$

For steam condensation, the temperature of steam remains constant. Therefore, $F_c = 1$.

$$A_o = \frac{106\,291 \text{ W}}{\left(3262 \dfrac{\text{W}}{\text{m}^2\text{·K}}\right)(1)(117.5°C)}$$

$$= \boxed{0.277 \text{ m}^2}$$

Heat Transfer

10.

400°F (205°C), dry
3
↓

1 → ☐ → 2
200°F (100°C)   390°F (200°C)

↓
4
400°F (205°C), liquid

Customary U.S. Solution

From App. 24.A, the enthalpy of each point is

$$h_1 = 168.07 \text{ Btu/lbm}$$
$$h_2 = 364.3 \text{ Btu/lbm}$$
$$h_3 = 1202.0 \text{ Btu/lbm}$$
$$h_4 = 375.1 \text{ Btu/lbm}$$

The heat transfer is due to the temperature gain of water.

$$Q = \dot{m}(h_2 - h_1)$$
$$= \left(500{,}000 \ \frac{\text{lbm}}{\text{hr}}\right)\left(364.3 \ \frac{\text{Btu}}{\text{lbm}} - 168.07 \ \frac{\text{Btu}}{\text{lbm}}\right)$$
$$= 9.812 \times 10^7 \text{ Btu/hr}$$

The mass flow rate per tube is

$$\dot{m}_{\text{tube}} = \rho A_{\text{tube}} \text{v}$$

Select ρ where the volume is greatest (at 390°F). From App. 24.A,

$$v_f = 0.01850 \text{ ft}^3/\text{lbm}$$
$$\rho = \frac{1}{v_f} = \frac{1}{0.01850 \ \dfrac{\text{ft}^3}{\text{lbm}}}$$
$$= 54.05 \text{ lbm/ft}^3$$

The inside diameter of the tube is

$$d_i = d_o - (2)(\text{wall})$$
$$= \frac{7}{8} \text{ in} - (2)\left(\frac{1}{16} \text{ in}\right)$$
$$= 0.750 \text{ in}$$

The area per tube is

$$A_{\text{tube}} = \left(\frac{\pi}{4}\right)(d_i)^2 = \left(\frac{\pi}{4}\right)(0.750 \text{ in})^2 \left(\frac{1 \text{ ft}}{12 \text{ in}}\right)^2$$
$$= 0.003068 \text{ ft}^2$$
$$\dot{m}_{\text{tube}} = \left(54.05 \ \frac{\text{lbm}}{\text{ft}^3}\right)(0.003068 \text{ ft}^2)$$
$$\times \left(5 \ \frac{\text{ft}}{\text{sec}}\right)\left(3600 \ \frac{\text{sec}}{\text{hr}}\right)$$
$$= 2985 \text{ lbm/hr}$$

The required number of tubes is

$$N = \frac{500{,}000 \ \dfrac{\text{lbm}}{\text{hr}}}{2985 \ \dfrac{\text{lbm}}{\text{hr}}} = 167.5 \quad [\text{say } 168]$$

Consider counterflow or parallel flow. Since one fluid temperature remains constant, it will not make a difference. Also, $F_c = 1$.

$$\Delta T_A = 400°\text{F} - 200°\text{F} = 200°\text{F}$$
$$\Delta T_B = 400°\text{F} - 390°\text{F} = 10°\text{F}$$

From Eq. 36.69, the logarithmic mean temperature difference is

$$\Delta T_{lm} = \frac{\Delta T_A - \Delta T_B}{\ln\left(\dfrac{\Delta T_A}{\Delta T_B}\right)} = \frac{200°\text{F} - 10°\text{F}}{\ln\left(\dfrac{200°\text{F}}{10°\text{F}}\right)}$$
$$= 63.4°\text{F}$$

The heat transfer is known. So,

$$Q = UA\Delta T_{lm}F_c$$

The surface area is

$$A = (\pi D_o L)N$$
$$Q = U(\pi D_o L)N\Delta T_{lm}F_c$$
$$L = \frac{Q}{U\pi D_o \Delta T_{lm}F_c N}$$
$$= \frac{9.812 \times 10^7 \ \dfrac{\text{Btu}}{\text{hr}}}{\left(700 \ \dfrac{\text{Btu}}{\text{hr-ft}^2\text{-}°\text{F}}\right)\pi\left(\dfrac{7}{8} \text{ in}\right)}$$
$$\times \left(\dfrac{1 \text{ ft}}{12 \text{ in}}\right)(63.4°\text{F})(1)(168)$$
$$= \boxed{57.4 \text{ ft}}$$

This is the total straight length of the bent tubes.

SI Solution

From App. 24.N, the enthalpy of each point is

$$h_1 = 419.04 \text{ kJ/kg}$$
$$h_2 = 852.45 \text{ kJ/kg}$$
$$h_3 = 2795.9 \text{ kJ/kg}$$
$$h_4 = 875.11 \text{ kJ/kg}$$

The heat transfer is due to the temperature gain of water.

$$Q = \dot{m}(h_2 - h_1)$$
$$= \left(60 \ \frac{\text{kg}}{\text{s}}\right)\left(852.45 \ \frac{\text{kJ}}{\text{kg}} - 419.04 \ \frac{\text{kJ}}{\text{kg}}\right)$$
$$= 26\,005 \text{ kW}$$

The mass flow rate per tube is

$$\dot{m}_{\text{tube}} = \rho A_{\text{tube}} \text{v}$$

Select ρ where the volume is greatest (at 200°C). From App. 24.N,

$$v_f = \left(1.1565 \ \frac{\text{cm}^3}{\text{g}}\right)\left(1000 \ \frac{\text{g}}{\text{kg}}\right)\left(\frac{1 \ \text{m}}{100 \ \text{cm}}\right)^3$$
$$= 1.1565 \times 10^{-3} \ \text{m}^3/\text{kg}$$
$$\rho = \frac{1}{v_f} = \frac{1}{1.1565 \times 10^{-3} \ \frac{\text{m}^3}{\text{kg}}}$$
$$= 864.7 \ \text{kg/m}^3$$

The inside diameter of the tube is

$$d_i = d_o - (2)(\text{wall})$$
$$= \left[2.2 \ \text{cm} - (2)(1.6 \ \text{mm})\left(\frac{1 \ \text{cm}}{10 \ \text{mm}}\right)\right]\left(\frac{1 \ \text{m}}{100 \ \text{cm}}\right)$$
$$= 0.0188 \ \text{m}$$

The area per tube is

$$A_{\text{tube}} = \left(\frac{\pi}{4}\right)(d_i)^2 = \left(\frac{\pi}{4}\right)(0.0188 \ \text{m})^2$$
$$= 2.776 \times 10^{-4} \ \text{m}^2$$
$$\dot{m}_{\text{tube}} = \left(864.7 \ \frac{\text{kg}}{\text{m}^3}\right)(2.776 \times 10^{-4} \ \text{m}^2)\left(1.5 \ \frac{\text{m}}{\text{s}}\right)$$
$$= 0.360 \ \text{kg/s}$$

The required number of tubes are

$$N = \frac{60 \ \frac{\text{kg}}{\text{s}}}{0.360 \ \frac{\text{kg}}{\text{s}}} = 166.7 \quad [\text{say 167}]$$

Since one fluid remains at constant temperature, $F_c = 1$. Also, it will not make a difference whether counterflow or parallel flow is considered.

$$\Delta T_A = 205°C - 100°C = 105°C$$
$$\Delta T_B = 205°C - 200°C = 5°C$$

From Eq. 36.69, the logarithmic mean temperature difference is

$$\Delta T_{lm} = \frac{\Delta T_A - \Delta T_B}{\ln\left(\frac{\Delta T_A}{\Delta T_B}\right)} = \frac{105°C - 5°C}{\ln\left(\frac{105°C}{5°C}\right)}$$
$$= 32.8°C$$

The heat transfer is known. So,

$$Q = UA\Delta T_{lm}F_c$$

The surface area is

$$A = (\pi D_o L)N$$
$$Q = U(\pi D_o L)N\Delta T_{lm}F_c$$
$$L = \frac{Q}{U\pi D_o N\Delta T_{lm}F_c}$$

$$= \frac{(26\,005 \ \text{kW})\left(1000 \ \frac{\text{W}}{\text{kW}}\right)}{\left(700 \ \frac{\text{Btu}}{\text{hr-ft}^2\text{-°F}}\right)\left(5.6783 \ \frac{\text{watt}}{\text{m}^2\text{·°C}}\right)\pi} \\ \times (2.2 \ \text{cm})\left(\frac{1 \ \text{m}}{100 \ \text{cm}}\right)(167)(32.8°C)(1)$$

$$= \boxed{17.3 \ \text{m}}$$

This is the total straight length of the bent tubes.

11. *Customary U.S. Solution*

The water's bulk temperature is

$$T_{b,\text{water}} = \left(\tfrac{1}{2}\right)(70°F + 140°F) = 105°F$$

The fluid properties at 105°F are obtained from App. 35.A.

$$\rho_{105°F} = 61.92 \ \text{lbm/ft}^3$$
$$c_{p,105°F} = 0.998 \ \text{Btu/lbm-°F}$$

The mass flow rate of water is

$$\dot{m}_{\text{water}} = \dot{V}\rho$$
$$= \frac{\left(100 \ \frac{\text{gal}}{\text{min}}\right)\left(60 \ \frac{\text{min}}{\text{hr}}\right)\left(61.92 \ \frac{\text{lbm}}{\text{ft}^3}\right)}{7.48 \ \frac{\text{gal}}{\text{ft}^3}}$$
$$= 49{,}668 \ \text{lbm/hr}$$

The heat transfer is found from the temperature gain of the water.

$$Q_{\text{clean}} = \dot{m}c_p\Delta T$$
$$= \left(49{,}668 \ \frac{\text{lbm}}{\text{hr}}\right)\left(0.998 \ \frac{\text{Btu}}{\text{lbm-°F}}\right) \\ \times (140°F - 70°F)$$
$$= 3.470 \times 10^6 \ \text{Btu/hr}$$
$$\Delta T_A = 230°F - 70°F = 160°F$$
$$\Delta T_B = 230°F - 140°F = 90°F$$

From Eq. 36.69, the logarithmic mean temperature difference is

$$\Delta T_{lm} = \frac{\Delta T_A - \Delta T_B}{\ln\left(\frac{\Delta T_A}{\Delta T_B}\right)} = \frac{160°F - 90°F}{\ln\left(\frac{160°F}{90°F}\right)} = 121.66°F$$

The heat transfer is known. Therefore, the overall heat transfer coefficient can be calculated from Eq. 36.70.

$$Q_{clean} = U_{clean} A F_c \Delta T_{lm}$$

For steam condensation, the temperature of steam remains constant. Therefore, $F_c = 1$.

$$U_{clean} = \frac{Q_{clean}}{A F_c \Delta T_{lm}}$$
$$= \frac{3.470 \times 10^6 \frac{Btu}{hr}}{(50 \text{ ft}^2)(1)(121.66°F)}$$
$$= 570.4 \text{ Btu/hr-ft}^2\text{-}°F$$

After fouling,

$$Q_{fouled} = \left(49{,}668 \frac{lbm}{hr}\right)\left(0.998 \frac{Btu}{lbm\text{-}°F}\right)$$
$$\times (122°F - 70°F)$$
$$= 2.578 \times 10^6 \text{ Btu/hr}$$
$$\Delta T_B = 230°F - 122°F = 108°F$$
$$\Delta T_A = 230°F - 70°F = 160°F$$

From Eq. 36.69, the logarithmic mean temperature difference is

$$\Delta T_{lm} = \frac{160°F - 108°F}{\ln\left(\frac{160°F}{108°F}\right)} = 132.3°F$$

$$U_{fouled} = \frac{2.578 \times 10^6 \frac{Btu}{hr}}{(50 \text{ ft}^2)(1)(132.3°F)} = 389.7 \text{ Btu/hr-ft}^2\text{-}°F$$

From Eq. 36.76, the fouling factor is

$$R_f = \frac{1}{U_{fouled}} - \frac{1}{U_{clean}}$$
$$= \frac{1}{389.7 \frac{Btu}{hr\text{-}ft^2\text{-}°F}} - \frac{1}{570.4 \frac{Btu}{hr\text{-}ft^2\text{-}°F}}$$
$$= \boxed{0.000813 \text{ hr-ft}^2\text{-}°F/Btu}$$

SI Solution

The water's bulk temperature is

$$T_{b,water} = \left(\tfrac{1}{2}\right)(21°C + 60°C) = 40.5°C$$

The fluid properties at 40.5°C are obtained from App. 35.B.

$$\rho_{40.5°C} = 993.5 \text{ kg/m}^3$$
$$c_{p,40.5°C} = 4.183 \text{ kJ/kg·K}$$

The mass flow rate of water is

$$\dot{m}_{water} = \dot{V}\rho$$
$$= \left(6.3 \frac{L}{s}\right)\left(\frac{1 \text{ m}^3}{1000 \text{ L}}\right)\left(993.5 \frac{kg}{m^3}\right)$$
$$= 6.26 \text{ kg/s}$$

The heat transfer is found from the temperature gain of the water.

$$Q_{clean} = \dot{m}c_p\Delta T$$
$$= \left(6.26 \frac{kg}{s}\right)\left(4.183 \frac{kJ}{kg·K}\right)\left(1000 \frac{J}{kg}\right)$$
$$\times (60°C - 21°C)$$
$$= 1.021 \times 10^6 \text{ W}$$
$$\Delta T_A = 110°C - 21°C = 89°C$$
$$\Delta T_B = 110°C - 60°C = 50°C$$

From Eq. 36.69, the logarithmic mean temperature difference is

$$\Delta T_{lm} = \frac{\Delta T_A - \Delta T_B}{\ln\left(\frac{\Delta T_A}{\Delta T_B}\right)} = \frac{89°C - 50°C}{\ln\left(\frac{89°C}{50°C}\right)} = 67.64°C$$

The heat transfer is known. Therefore, the overall heat transfer coefficient can be calculated from Eq. 36.70.

$$Q_{clean} = U_{clean} A F_c \Delta T_{lm}$$

For steam condensation, the temperature of steam remains constant. Therefore, $F_c = 1$.

$$U_{clean} = \frac{Q_{clean}}{A F_c \Delta T_{lm}}$$
$$= \frac{1.021 \times 10^6 \text{ W}}{(4.7 \text{ m}^2)(1)(67.64°C)}$$
$$= 3211.6 \text{ W/m}^2\text{·K}$$

After fouling,

$$Q_{fouled} = \left(6.26 \frac{kg}{s}\right)\left(4.183 \frac{kJ}{kg·K}\right)\left(1000 \frac{J}{kJ}\right)$$
$$\times (50°C - 21°C)$$
$$= 7.594 \times 10^5 \text{ W}$$
$$\Delta T_A = 110°C - 21°C = 89°C$$
$$\Delta T_B = 110°C - 50°C = 60°C$$

From Eq. 36.69, the logarithmic mean temperature difference is

$$\Delta T_{lm} = \frac{89°C - 60°C}{\ln\left(\frac{89°C}{60°C}\right)} = 73.55°C$$

$$U_{fouled} = \frac{7.594 \times 10^5 \text{ W}}{(4.7 \text{ m}^2)(1)(73.55°C)} = 2196.8 \text{ W/m}^2\text{·K}$$

From Eq. 36.76, the fouling factor is

$$R_f = \frac{1}{U_{\text{fouled}}} - \frac{1}{U_{\text{clean}}}$$
$$= \frac{1}{2196.8 \ \frac{\text{W}}{\text{m}^2\cdot\text{K}}} - \frac{1}{3211.6 \ \frac{\text{W}}{\text{m}^2\cdot\text{K}}}$$
$$= \boxed{0.000144 \ \text{m}^2\cdot\text{K/W}}$$

12. *Customary U.S. Solution*

The film temperature of the air from Eq. 35.11 is

$$T_h = \left(\tfrac{1}{2}\right)(T_s + T_\infty) = \left(\tfrac{1}{2}\right)(100°\text{F} + 150°\text{F}) = 125°\text{F}$$

From App. 35.C, the air properties at 125°F are

$$\nu = 0.195 \times 10^{-3} \ \text{ft}^2/\text{sec}$$
$$k = 0.0159 \ \text{Btu/hr-ft-}°\text{F}$$
$$\text{Pr} = 0.72$$

The Reynolds number is

$$\text{Re}_d = \frac{\text{v}d}{\nu} = \frac{\left(100 \ \frac{\text{ft}}{\text{sec}}\right)(0.35 \ \text{in})\left(\frac{1 \ \text{ft}}{12 \ \text{in}}\right)}{0.195 \times 10^{-3} \ \frac{\text{ft}^2}{\text{sec}}}$$
$$= 1.50 \times 10^4$$

From Eq. 36.52, the film coefficient is

$$h = C_1(\text{Re}_d)^n(\text{Pr})^{\frac{1}{3}}\left(\frac{k}{d}\right)$$

From Table 36.3, $C_1 = 0.193$ and $n = 0.618$.

$$h = (0.193)(1.50 \times 10^4)^{0.618}(0.72)^{\frac{1}{3}}$$
$$\times \left(\frac{0.0159 \ \frac{\text{Btu}}{\text{hr-ft-}°\text{F}}}{(0.35 \ \text{in})\left(\frac{1 \ \text{ft}}{12 \ \text{in}}\right)}\right)$$
$$= \boxed{35.9 \ \text{Btu/hr-ft}^2\text{-}°\text{F}}$$

SI Solution

From Eq. 35.11, the film temperature of the air is

$$T_h = \left(\tfrac{1}{2}\right)(T_s + T_\infty) = \left(\tfrac{1}{2}\right)(38°\text{C} + 66°\text{C}) = 52°\text{C}$$

From App. 35.D, the air properties at 52°C are

$$\rho = 1.09 \ \text{kg/m}^3$$
$$\mu = 1.966 \times 10^{-5} \ \text{kg/m}\cdot\text{s}$$
$$k = 0.02815 \ \text{W/m}\cdot\text{K}$$
$$\text{Pr} = 0.703$$

The Reynolds number is

$$\text{Re}_d = \frac{\rho\text{v}d}{\mu}$$
$$= \frac{\left(1.09 \ \frac{\text{kg}}{\text{m}^3}\right)\left(30 \ \frac{\text{m}}{\text{s}}\right)(8.9 \ \text{mm})\left(\frac{1 \ \text{m}}{1000 \ \text{mm}}\right)}{1.966 \times 10^{-5} \ \frac{\text{kg}}{\text{m}\cdot\text{s}}}$$
$$= 1.48 \times 10^4$$

From Eq. 36.52, the film coefficient is

$$h = C_1(\text{Re}_d)^h(\text{Pr})^{\frac{1}{3}}\left(\frac{k}{d}\right)$$

From Table 36.3, $C_1 = 0.193$ and $n = 0.618$.

$$h = (0.193)(1.48 \times 10^4)^{0.618}(0.703)^{\frac{1}{3}}$$
$$\times \left(\frac{0.02815 \ \frac{\text{W}}{\text{m}\cdot\text{K}}}{(8.9 \ \text{mm})\left(\frac{1 \ \text{m}}{1000 \ \text{mm}}\right)}\right)$$
$$= \boxed{205.0 \ \text{W/m}^2\cdot\text{K}}$$

Heat Transfer

37 Radiation and Combined Heat Transfer

1. *Customary U.S. Solution*

The absolute temperatures are

$$T_{\text{furnace}} = 2200°\text{F} + 460 = 2660°\text{R}$$
$$T_\infty = 70°\text{F} + 460 = 530°\text{R}$$

Assuming that the walls are reradiating, nonconducting, and varying in temperature from 2200°F at the inside to 70°F at the outside, Fig. 37.3, curve 6, can be used to find F_{1-2} using $x = 3$ in/6 in $= 0.5$; $F_{1-2} = 0.38$.

The radiation heat loss is

$$\begin{aligned}
Q &= AE_{\text{net}} \\
&= A\sigma F_{1-2}(T_{\text{furnace}}^4 - T_\infty^4) \\
&= (3 \text{ in})^2 \left(\frac{1 \text{ ft}^2}{144 \text{ in}^2}\right) \left(0.1713 \times 10^{-8} \; \frac{\text{Btu}}{\text{hr-ft}^2\text{-}°\text{R}^4}\right) \\
&\quad \times (0.38)\left[(2660°\text{R})^4 - (530°\text{R})^4\right] \\
&= \boxed{2033.6 \text{ Btu/hr}}
\end{aligned}$$

SI Solution

The absolute temperatures are

$$T_{\text{furnace}} = 1200°\text{C} + 273 = 1473\text{K}$$
$$T_\infty = 20°\text{C} + 273 = 293\text{K}$$

Making the same assumptions as for the Customary U.S. Solution, Fig. 37.3, curve 6, can be used to find F_{1-2} using $x = 8$ cm/15 cm $= 0.533$; $F_{1-2} = 0.4$.

The radiation heat loss is

$$\begin{aligned}
Q &= AE_{\text{net}} \\
&= A\sigma F_{1-2}(T_{\text{furnace}}^4 - T_\infty^4) \\
&= (8 \text{ cm})^2 \left(\frac{1 \text{ m}}{100 \text{ cm}}\right)^2 \left(5.67 \times 10^{-8} \; \frac{\text{W}}{\text{m}^2\text{·K}^4}\right) \\
&\quad \times (0.4)\left[(1473\text{K})^4 - (293\text{K})^4\right] \\
&= \boxed{682.3 \text{ W}}
\end{aligned}$$

2. *Customary U.S. Solution*

The absolute temperatures are

$$T_\infty = 80°\text{F} + 460 = 540°\text{R}$$
$$T_{\text{duct}} = 200°\text{F} + 460 = 660°\text{R}$$
$$T_{\text{wall}} = 70°\text{F} + 460 = 530°\text{R}$$

Assume laminar flow. From Table 35.3, the convective film coefficient on the outside of the duct is approximately

$$\begin{aligned}
h_{\text{convective}} &= (0.27)\left(\frac{T_{\text{duct}} - T_\infty}{L}\right)^{0.25} \\
&= (0.27)\left(\frac{660°\text{R} - 540°\text{R}}{(9 \text{ in})\left(\frac{1 \text{ ft}}{12 \text{ in}}\right)}\right)^{0.25} \\
&= 0.96 \text{ Btu/hr-ft}^2\text{-}°\text{F}
\end{aligned}$$

The duct area per unit length is

$$\frac{A}{L} = \pi D = \pi(9 \text{ in})\left(\frac{1 \text{ ft}}{12 \text{ in}}\right) = 2.356 \text{ ft}^2/\text{ft}$$

The convection losses (per unit length) are

$$\begin{aligned}
\frac{Q_{\text{convection}}}{L} &= h\left(\frac{A}{L}\right)\Delta T = h\left(\frac{A}{L}\right)(T_{\text{duct}} - T_\infty) \\
&= \left(0.96 \; \frac{\text{Btu}}{\text{hr-ft}^2\text{-}°\text{F}}\right)\left(2.356 \; \frac{\text{ft}^2}{\text{ft}}\right) \\
&\quad \times (660°\text{R} - 540°\text{R}) \\
&= 271.4 \text{ Btu/hr-ft}
\end{aligned}$$

Assume $\epsilon_{\text{duct}} \approx 0.97$. Then $F_e = \epsilon_{\text{duct}} = 0.97$. $F_a = 1$ since the duct is enclosed. The radiation losses (per unit length) are

$$\begin{aligned}
\frac{E_{\text{net}}}{L} &= \left(\frac{A}{L}\right)\sigma F_a F_e\left[(T_{\text{duct}})^4 - (T_{\text{wall}})^4\right] \\
&= (2.356 \text{ ft}^2)\left(0.1713 \times 10^{-8}\frac{\text{Btu}}{\text{hr-ft}^2\text{-}°\text{R}^4}\right) \\
&\quad \times (1)(0.97)\left[(660°\text{R})^4 - (530°\text{R})^4\right] \\
&= 433.9 \text{ Btu/hr-ft}
\end{aligned}$$

The total heat transfer per unit length is

$$
\begin{aligned}
\frac{Q_{\text{total}}}{L} &= \frac{Q_{\text{convection}}}{L} + \frac{E_{\text{net}}}{L} \\
&= 271.4 \ \frac{\text{Btu}}{\text{hr-ft}} + 433.9 \ \frac{\text{Btu}}{\text{hr-ft}} \\
&= \boxed{705.3 \ \text{Btu/hr-ft length}}
\end{aligned}
$$

SI Solution

The absolute temperatures are

$$
\begin{aligned}
T_{\text{duct}} &= 95^\circ\text{C} + 273 = 368\text{K} \\
T_{\text{wall}} &= 20^\circ\text{C} + 273 = 293\text{K} \\
T_\infty &= 27^\circ\text{C} + 273 = 300\text{K}
\end{aligned}
$$

Assume laminar flow. From Table 35.3, the convective film coefficient on the outside of the duct is approximately

$$
\begin{aligned}
h_{\text{convective}} &= (1.32)\left(\frac{T_{\text{duct}} - T_\infty}{L}\right)^{0.25} \\
&= (1.32)\left(\frac{368\text{K} - 300\text{K}}{(23 \ \text{cm})\left(\dfrac{1 \ \text{m}}{100 \ \text{cm}}\right)}\right)^{0.25} \\
&= 5.47 \ \text{W/m}^2\cdot\text{K}
\end{aligned}
$$

The duct area per unit length is

$$
\frac{A}{L} = \pi D = \pi(23 \ \text{cm})\left(\frac{1 \ \text{m}}{100 \ \text{cm}}\right) = 0.723 \ \text{m}^2/\text{m}
$$

The convective losses per unit length are

$$
\begin{aligned}
\frac{Q_{\text{convective}}}{L} &= h\left(\frac{A}{L}\right)(T_{\text{duct}} - T_\infty) \\
&= \left(5.47 \ \frac{\text{W}}{\text{m}^2\cdot\text{K}}\right)\left(0.723 \ \frac{\text{m}^2}{\text{m}}\right)(368\text{K} - 300\text{K}) \\
&= 268.9 \ \text{W/m}
\end{aligned}
$$

Assuming $\epsilon_{\text{duct}} \approx 0.97$, $F_e = \epsilon_{\text{duct}} = 0.97$. $F_a = 1$ since the duct is enclosed. The radiation losses per unit length are

$$
\begin{aligned}
\frac{E_{\text{net}}}{L} &= \left(\frac{A}{L}\right)\sigma F_a F_e \left[(T_{\text{duct}})^4 - (T_{\text{wall}})^4\right] \\
&= \left(0.723 \ \frac{\text{m}^2}{\text{m}}\right)\left(5.67 \times 10^{-8} \ \frac{\text{W}}{\text{m}^2\cdot\text{K}^4}\right) \\
&\quad \times (1)(0.97)\left[(368\text{K})^4 - (293\text{K})^4\right] \\
&= 436.2 \ \text{W/m}
\end{aligned}
$$

The total heat transfer per unit length is

$$
\begin{aligned}
\frac{Q_{\text{total}}}{L} &= \frac{Q_{\text{convection}}}{L} + \frac{E_{\text{net}}}{L} \\
&= 268.9 \ \frac{\text{W}}{\text{m}} + 436.2 \ \frac{\text{W}}{\text{m}} = \boxed{705.1 \ \text{W/m length}}
\end{aligned}
$$

3.

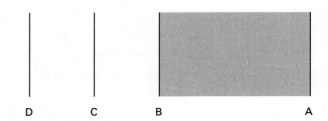

Customary U.S. Solution

(a) The absolute temperatures are

$$
\begin{aligned}
T_{\text{D}} &= -60^\circ\text{F} + 460 = 400^\circ\text{R} \\
T_{\text{A}} &= 80^\circ\text{F} + 460 = 540^\circ\text{F}
\end{aligned}
$$

The conductive heat transfer from A to B per unit area is

$$
\begin{aligned}
\frac{Q_{\text{A-B}}}{A} &= \frac{k(T_{\text{A}} - T_{\text{B}})}{L} \\
&= \frac{\left(0.025 \ \dfrac{\text{Btu}}{\text{hr-ft}^2\text{-}^\circ\text{F}}\right)(540^\circ\text{R} - T_{\text{B}})}{(4 \ \text{in})\left(\dfrac{1 \ \text{ft}}{12 \ \text{in}}\right)} \\
&= 40.5 - 0.075 T_{\text{B}} \quad \text{[Eq. 1]}
\end{aligned}
$$

Since the spaces are evacuated, only radiation should be considered from B to C and from C to D.

The radiation heat transfer per unit area from B to C is

$$
\frac{E_{\text{B-C}}}{A} = \sigma F_e F_a (T_{\text{B}}^4 - T_{\text{C}}^4)
$$

Since the freezer is assumed to be large, $F_a = 1$.

From Table 37.1 for infinite parallel planes,

$$
\begin{aligned}
F_e &= \frac{1}{\dfrac{1}{\epsilon_1} + \dfrac{1}{\epsilon_2} - 1} = \frac{1}{\dfrac{1}{0.5} + \dfrac{1}{0.1} - 1} \\
&= 0.0909
\end{aligned}
$$

$$
\begin{aligned}
\frac{E_{\text{B-C}}}{A} &= \left(0.1713 \times 10^{-8} \ \frac{\text{Btu}}{\text{hr-ft}^2\text{-}^\circ\text{R}^4}\right) \\
&\quad \times (0.0909)(1)(T_{\text{B}}^4 - T_{\text{C}}^4) \\
&= (1.56 \times 10^{-10}) T_{\text{B}}^4 - (1.56 \times 10^{-10}) T_{\text{C}}^4 \quad \text{[Eq. 2]}
\end{aligned}
$$

Similarly, radiation heat transfer per unit area from C to D is

$$\frac{E_{\text{C-D}}}{A} = \left(0.1713 \times 10^{-8} \ \frac{\text{Btu}}{\text{hr-ft}^2\text{-}^{\circ}\text{R}^4}\right)$$
$$\times (0.0909)(1)\left[T_{\text{C}}^4 - (400^{\circ}\text{R})^4\right]$$
$$= (1.56 \times 10^{-10})T_{\text{C}}^4 - 3.99 \quad \text{[Eq. 3]}$$

The heat transfer from B to C is equal to the heat transfer from C to D.

$$\frac{E_{\text{B-C}}}{A} = \frac{E_{\text{C-D}}}{A}$$

$$(1.56 \times 10^{-10})T_{\text{B}}^4$$
$$-(1.56 \times 10^{-10})T_{\text{C}}^4 = (1.56 \times 10^{-10})T_{\text{C}}^4 - 3.99$$
$$T_{\text{B}}^4 - T_{\text{C}}^4 = T_{\text{C}}^4 - 2.56 \times 10^{10}$$
$$T_{\text{B}}^4 + 2.56 \times 10^{10} = 2T_{\text{C}}^4$$
$$T_{\text{C}}^4 = \tfrac{1}{2}T_{\text{B}}^4 + 1.28 \times 10^{10} \quad \text{[Eq. 4]}$$

The heat transfer from A to B is equal to the heat transfer from B to C.

$$\frac{Q_{\text{A-B}}}{A} = \frac{E_{\text{B-C}}}{A}$$
$$40.5 - 0.075T_{\text{B}} = (1.56 \times 10^{-10})T_{\text{B}}^4$$
$$- (1.56 \times 10^{-10})T_{\text{C}}^4$$
$$T_{\text{C}}^4 = T_{\text{B}}^4 + (4.81 \times 10^8)T_{\text{B}}$$
$$- 2.60 \times 10^{11} \quad \text{[Eq. 5]}$$

Since Eq. 4 = Eq. 5,

$$\tfrac{1}{2}T_{\text{B}}^4 + 1.28 \times 10^{10} = T_{\text{B}}^4 + (4.81 \times 10^8)T_{\text{B}}$$
$$- 2.60 \times 10^{11}$$
$$T_{\text{B}}^4 + (9.62 \times 10^8)T_{\text{B}} = 5.456 \times 10^{11}$$

By trial and error, $T_{\text{B}} = 501.4^{\circ}\text{R}$.

From Eq. 1,

$$\frac{Q_{\text{A-B}}}{A} = 40.5 - (0.075)(501.4^{\circ}\text{R})$$

$$= \boxed{2.895 \ \text{Btu/hr-ft}^2}$$

(b) From Eq. 4,

$$T_{\text{C}} = \left[\left(\tfrac{1}{2}\right)(501.4)^4 + 1.28 \times 10^{10}\right]^{\frac{1}{4}}$$

$$= \boxed{459^{\circ}\text{R}}$$

SI Solution

(a) The absolute temperatures are

$$T_{\text{D}} = -50^{\circ}\text{C} + 273 = 223\text{K}$$
$$T_{\text{A}} = 27^{\circ}\text{C} + 273 = 300\text{K}$$

The conductive heat transfer per unit area from A to B is

$$\frac{Q_{\text{A-B}}}{A} = \frac{k(T_{\text{A}} - T_{\text{B}})}{L} = \frac{\left(0.045 \ \frac{\text{W}}{\text{m}\cdot\text{K}}\right)(300\text{K} - T_{\text{B}})}{(10 \ \text{cm})\left(\dfrac{1 \ \text{m}}{100 \ \text{cm}}\right)}$$

$$= 135 - 0.45T_{\text{B}} \quad \text{[Eq. 1]}$$

Since spaces are evacuated, only radiation should be considered from B to C and from C to D.

The radiation heat transfer per unit area from B to C is

$$\frac{E_{\text{B-C}}}{A} = \sigma F_e F_a (T_{\text{B}}^4 - T_{\text{C}}^4)$$

From the Customary U.S. Solution, $F_e = 0.0909$ and $F_a = 1$.

$$\frac{E_{\text{B-C}}}{A} = \left(5.67 \times 10^{-8} \ \frac{\text{W}}{\text{m}^2\cdot\text{K}^4}\right)$$
$$\times (0.0909)(1)(T_{\text{B}}^4 - T_{\text{C}}^4)$$
$$= (5.15 \times 10^{-9})T_{\text{B}}^4 - (5.15 \times 10^9)T_{\text{C}}^4 \quad \text{[Eq. 2]}$$

Similarly, the radiation heat transfer per unit area from C to D is

$$\frac{E_{\text{C-D}}}{A} = \left(5.67 \times 10^{-8} \ \frac{\text{W}}{\text{m}^2\cdot\text{K}^4}\right)$$
$$\times (0.0909)(1)\left(T_{\text{C}}^4 - (223\text{K})^4\right)$$
$$= (5.15 \times 10^{-9})T_{\text{C}}^4 - 12.746 \quad \text{[Eq. 3]}$$

The heat transfer from B to C is equal to the heat transfer from C to D.

$$\frac{E_{\text{B-C}}}{A} = \frac{E_{\text{C-D}}}{A}$$

$$(5.15 \times 10^{-9})T_{\text{B}}^4$$
$$- (5.15 \times 10^{-9})T_{\text{C}}^4 = (5.15 \times 10^{-9})T_{\text{C}}^4 - 12.746$$
$$T_{\text{B}}^4 - T_{\text{C}}^4 = T_{\text{C}}^4 - 2.475 \times 10^9$$
$$T_{\text{B}}^4 + 2.475 \times 10^9 = 2T_{\text{C}}^4$$
$$T_{\text{C}}^4 = \tfrac{1}{2}T_{\text{B}}^4 + 1.237 \times 10^9 \quad \text{[Eq. 4]}$$

The heat transfer from A to B is equal to the heat transfer from B to C.

$$\frac{Q_{\text{A-B}}}{A} = \frac{E_{\text{B-C}}}{A}$$
$$135 - 0.45T_{\text{B}} = (5.15 \times 10^{-9})T_{\text{B}}^4 - (5.15 \times 10^{-9})T_{\text{C}}^4$$
$$T_{\text{C}}^4 = T_{\text{B}}^4 + 8.74 \times 10^7 T_{\text{B}} - 2.62 \times 10^{10}$$

$$\text{[Eq. 5]}$$

Since Eq. 4 = Eq. 5,

$$\tfrac{1}{2}T_B^4 + 1.237 \times 10^9 = T_B^4 + 8.74 \times 10^7 T_B$$
$$- 2.62 \times 10^{10}$$
$$T_B^4 + 17.48 \times 10^7 T_B = 5.49 \times 10^{10}$$

By trial and error, $T_B \approx 278$K.

From Eq. 1,

$$\frac{Q_{A-B}}{A} = 135 - (0.45)(278\text{K}) = \boxed{9.9 \text{ W/m}^2}$$

(b) From Eq. 4,

$$T_C = \left[\left(\tfrac{1}{2}\right)(278\text{K})^4 + 1.237 \times 10^9\right]^{\frac{1}{4}} = \boxed{254.9\text{K}}$$

4. *Customary U.S. Solution*

The absolute temperature of air entering the duct is

$$45°\text{F} + 460 = 505°\text{R}$$

From the ideal gas law, the density of air entering the duct is

$$\rho = \frac{p}{RT}$$
$$= \frac{\left(14.7 \frac{\text{lbf}}{\text{in}^2}\right)\left(144 \frac{\text{in}^2}{\text{ft}^2}\right)}{\left(53.35 \frac{\text{ft-lbf}}{\text{lbm-°R}}\right)(505°\text{R})} = 0.07857 \text{ lbm/ft}^3$$

The mass flow rate of entering air is

$$\dot{m} = \rho\dot{V} = \left(0.07857 \frac{\text{lbm}}{\text{ft}^3}\right)\left(500 \frac{\text{ft}^3}{\text{min}}\right)\left(60 \frac{\text{min}}{\text{hr}}\right)$$
$$= 2357.1 \text{ lbm/hr}$$

The mass velocity is

$$G = \frac{\dot{m}}{A_{\text{flow}}} = \frac{2357.1 \frac{\text{lbm}}{\text{hr}}}{\left(\frac{\pi}{4}\right)(12\text{ in})^2 \left(\frac{1\text{ ft}}{12\text{ in}}\right)^2}$$
$$= 3001.1 \text{ lbm/ft}^2\text{-hr}$$

To calculate the initial film coefficients, estimate the temperature based on the claim. The film coefficients are not highly sensitive to small temperature differences.

$$T_{\text{bulk,air}} = \left(\tfrac{1}{2}\right)(T_{\text{air,in}} + T_{\text{air,out}})$$
$$= \left(\tfrac{1}{2}\right)(45°\text{F} + 50°\text{F}) = 47.5°\text{F}$$

$$T_{\text{surface}} = 70°\text{F} \quad [\text{estimate}]$$

The film coefficient for air flowing inside the duct is given by Eq. 36.39 as

$$h_i \approx (0.00351 + 0.000001583T°\text{F})$$
$$\times \left[\frac{(G_{\text{lbm/hr-ft}^2})^{0.8}}{(d_{\text{ft}})^{0.2}}\right]$$
$$= (0.00351 + (0.000001583)(47.5°\text{F}))$$
$$\times \left[\frac{\left(3001.1 \frac{\text{lbm}}{\text{hr-ft}^2}\right)^{0.8}}{\left((12\text{ in})\left(\frac{1\text{ ft}}{12\text{ in}}\right)\right)^{0.2}}\right]$$
$$h_i = 2.17 \text{ Btu/hr-ft}^2\text{-°F}$$

If Eq. 36.41 was used instead, the value of h_i is approximately 2.01 Btu/hr-ft²-°F, indicating that the temperature is not important.

For natural convection on the outside of the duct, estimate the film temperature.

$$T_{\text{film}} = \left(\tfrac{1}{2}\right)(T_{\text{surface}} + T_\infty) = \left(\tfrac{1}{2}\right)(70°\text{F} + 80°\text{F})$$
$$= 75°\text{F}$$

From App. 35.C, the properties of air at 75°F are

$$\text{Pr} \approx 0.72$$
$$\frac{g\beta\rho^2}{\mu^2} = 2.27 \times 10^6 \frac{1}{\text{ft}^3\text{-°F}}$$

The characteristic length is the diameter of the duct.

$$L = (12\text{ in})\left(\frac{1\text{ ft}}{12\text{ in}}\right) = 1 \text{ ft}$$

The Grashof number is

$$\text{Gr} = L^3\left(\frac{\rho^2\beta g}{\mu^2}\right)(T_\infty - T_s)$$
$$= (1\text{ ft})^3\left(2.27 \times 10^6 \frac{1}{\text{ft}^3\text{-°F}}\right)(80°\text{F} - 70°\text{F})$$
$$= 2.27 \times 10^7$$
$$\text{PrGr} = (0.72)(2.27 \times 10^7) = 1.63 \times 10^7$$

From Table 35.3, the film coefficient for a horizontal cylinder is

$$h_o = (0.27)\left(\frac{T_\infty - T_s}{d}\right)^{0.25}$$
$$= (0.27)\left(\frac{80°\text{F} - 70°\text{F}}{1\text{ ft}}\right)^{0.25}$$
$$= 0.48 \text{ Btu/hr-ft}^2\text{-°F}$$

Neglecting the wall resistance, the overall film coefficient from Eq. 36.73 is

$$\frac{1}{U} = \frac{1}{h_o} + \frac{1}{h_i}$$

$$= \frac{1}{2.17 \dfrac{\text{Btu}}{\text{hr-ft}^2\text{-}°\text{F}}} + \frac{1}{0.48 \dfrac{\text{Btu}}{\text{hr-ft}^2\text{-}°\text{F}}}$$

$$= 2.544 \ \text{hr-ft}^2\text{-}°\text{F/Btu}$$

$$U = \frac{1}{2.544 \dfrac{\text{hr-ft}^2\text{-}°\text{F}}{\text{Btu}}} = 0.393 \ \text{Btu/hr-ft}^2\text{-}°\text{F}$$

The heat transfer due to convection is

$$Q_{\text{convection}} = U A_{\text{surface}}(T_\infty - T_{\text{bulk,air}})$$

$$= U(\pi d L)(T_\infty - T_{\text{bulk,air}})$$

$$= \left(0.393 \ \frac{\text{Btu}}{\text{hr-ft}^2\text{-}°\text{F}}\right)$$

$$\times \pi(1 \ \text{ft})(50 \ \text{ft})(80°\text{F} - 47.5°\text{F})$$

$$= 2006.3 \ \text{Btu/hr}$$

The heat transfer due to radiation is

$$Q_{\text{radiation}} = \sigma F_e F_a A_{\text{surface}}(T_\infty^4 - T_{\text{surface}}^4)$$

Assume the room and duct have an unobstructed view of each other. Then $F_a = 1.0$ and $F_e = \epsilon = 0.28$. The absolute temperatures are

$$T_\infty = 80°\text{F} + 460 = 540°\text{R}$$

$$T_{\text{surface}} = 70°\text{F} + 460 = 530°\text{R}$$

$$Q_{\text{radiation}} = \left(0.1713 \times 10^{-8} \ \frac{\text{Btu}}{\text{hr-ft}^2\text{-}°\text{R}^4}\right)(0.28)(1.0)$$

$$\times \pi(1 \ \text{ft})(50 \ \text{ft})\left[(540°\text{R})^4 - (530°\text{R})^4\right]$$

$$= 461.5 \ \text{Btu/hr}$$

The total heat transfer to the air is

$$Q_{\text{total}} = Q_{\text{convection}} + Q_{\text{radiation}}$$

$$= 2006.3 \ \frac{\text{Btu}}{\text{hr}} + 461.5 \ \frac{\text{Btu}}{\text{hr}}$$

$$= 2467.8 \ \text{Btu/hr}$$

At 47.5°F, the specific heat of air is approximately 0.240 Btu/lbm-°F. Since the heat transfer is known, the temperature of air leaving the duct can be calculated from

$$Q_{\text{total}} = \dot{m} c_p (T_{\text{air,out}} - T_{\text{air,in}})$$

$$T_{\text{air,out}} = T_{\text{air,in}} + \frac{Q_{\text{total}}}{\dot{m} c_p}$$

$$= 45°\text{F} + \frac{2467.8 \ \dfrac{\text{Btu}}{\text{hr}}}{\left(2357.1 \ \dfrac{\text{lbm}}{\text{hr}}\right)\left(0.24 \ \dfrac{\text{Btu}}{\text{lbm-}°\text{F}}\right)}$$

$$= \boxed{49.4°\text{F}}$$

This agrees with the engineer's estimate.

SI Solution

The absolute temperature of air entering the duct is $7°\text{C} + 273 = 280\text{K}$. From the ideal gas law, the density of air entering the duct is

$$\rho = \frac{p}{RT}$$

$$= \frac{(101.3 \ \text{kPa})\left(1000 \ \dfrac{\text{Pa}}{\text{kPa}}\right)}{\left(287.03 \ \dfrac{\text{J}}{\text{kg·K}}\right)(280\text{K})}$$

$$= 1.2604 \ \text{kg/m}^3$$

The mass flow rate of air entering the duct is

$$\dot{m} = \rho \dot{V} = \left(1.2604 \ \frac{\text{kg}}{\text{m}^3}\right)\left(0.25 \ \frac{\text{m}^3}{\text{s}}\right) = 0.3151 \ \text{kg/s}$$

The diameter of the duct is

$$d = (30 \ \text{cm})\left(\frac{1 \ \text{m}}{100 \ \text{cm}}\right) = 0.30 \ \text{m}$$

The velocity of air entering the duct is

$$\text{v} = \frac{\dot{V}}{A_{\text{flow}}} = \frac{0.25 \ \dfrac{\text{m}^3}{\text{s}}}{\left(\dfrac{\pi}{4}\right)(0.30 \ \text{m})^2} = 3.537 \ \text{m/s}$$

To calculate the initial film coefficients, estimate the temperatures based on the claim. The film coefficients are not highly sensitive to small temperature differences.

$$T_{\text{bulk,air}} = \left(\tfrac{1}{2}\right)(T_{\text{air,in}} + T_{\text{air,out}})$$

$$= \left(\tfrac{1}{2}\right)(7°\text{C} + 10°\text{C}) = 8.5°\text{C}$$

$$T_{\text{surface}} = 20°\text{C} \quad [\text{estimate}]$$

The film coefficient for air flowing inside the duct is given from Eq. 36.40 (independent of temperature).

$$h_i \approx \frac{(3.52)(\text{v}_{\text{m/s}})^{0.8}}{(d_\text{m})^{0.2}}$$

$$= \frac{(3.52)\left(3.537 \ \dfrac{\text{m}}{\text{s}}\right)^{0.8}}{(0.30 \ \text{m})^{0.2}} = 12.3 \ \text{W/m}^2\text{·}°\text{C}$$

For natural convection on the outside of the duct, estimate the film coefficient.

$$T_{\text{film}} = \left(\tfrac{1}{2}\right)(T_{\text{surface}} + T_\infty)$$

$$= \left(\tfrac{1}{2}\right)(20°\text{C} + 27°\text{C}) = 23.5°\text{C}$$

Heat Transfer

From App. 35.D, the properties of air at 23.5°C are

$$Pr = 0.709$$

$$\frac{g\beta\rho^2}{\mu^2} = 1.43 \times 10^8 \; \frac{1}{K \cdot m^3}$$

The characteristic length, L, is the diameter of the duct, which is 0.30 m. The Grashof number is

$$Gr = L^3 \left(\frac{\rho^2 \beta g}{\mu^2} \right) (T_\infty - T_{surface})$$

$$= (0.30 \text{ m})^3 \left(1.43 \times 10^8 \; \frac{1}{K \cdot m^3} \right) (27°C - 20°C)$$

$$= 2.70 \times 10^7$$

$$PrGr = (0.709)(2.70 \times 10^7) = 1.9 \times 10^7$$

From Table 35.3, the film coefficient for a horizontal cylinder is

$$h_o \approx (1.32) \left(\frac{T_\infty - T_{surface}}{d} \right)^{0.25}$$

$$= (1.32) \left(\frac{27°C - 20°C}{0.30 \text{ m}} \right)^{0.25} = 2.90 \text{ W/m}^2 \cdot \text{K}$$

Neglecting the wall resistance, the overall film coefficient from Eq. 37.63 is

$$\frac{1}{U} = \frac{1}{h_o} + \frac{1}{h_i}$$

$$= \frac{1}{12.3 \; \frac{W}{m^2 \cdot K}} + \frac{1}{2.90 \; \frac{W}{m^2 \cdot K}} = 0.426 \text{ m}^2 \cdot \text{K/W}$$

$$U = \frac{1}{0.426 \; \frac{m^2 \cdot K}{W}} = 2.35 \text{ W/m}^2 \cdot \text{K}$$

The heat transfer due to convection is

$$Q_{convection} = U A_{surface} (T_\infty - T_{bulk,air})$$

$$= U \pi d L (T_\infty - T_{bulk,air})$$

$$= \left(2.35 \; \frac{W}{m^2 \cdot K} \right) \pi (0.30 \text{ m})(15 \text{ m})$$

$$\times (27°C - 8.5°C)$$

$$= 614.6 \text{ W}$$

The heat transfer due to radiation is

$$Q_{radiation} = \sigma F_e F_a A_{surface} \left(T_\infty^4 - T_{surface}^4 \right)$$

Assume the room and duct have an unobstructed view of each other. Then $F_a = 1.0$ and $F_e = \epsilon = 0.28$. The absolute temperatures are

$$T_\infty = 27°C + 273 = 300K$$

$$T_{surface} = 20°C + 273 = 293K$$

$$Q_{radiation} = \left(5.67 \times 10^{-8} \; \frac{W}{m^2 \cdot K^4} \right) (0.28)(1)\pi$$

$$\times (0.30 \text{ m})(15 \text{ m}) \left[(300K)^4 - (293K)^4 \right]$$

$$= 163.8 \text{ W}$$

The total heat transfer to the air is

$$Q_{total} = Q_{convection} + Q_{radiation}$$

$$= 614.6 \text{ W} + 163.8 \text{ W} = 778.4 \text{ W}$$

At 8.5°C, the specific heat of air is

$$\left(1.0048 \; \frac{kJ}{kg \cdot K} \right) \left(1000 \; \frac{J}{kJ} \right) = 1004.8 \text{ J/kg} \cdot \text{K}$$

Since the heat transfer is known, the temperature of air leaving the duct can be calculated by

$$Q_{total} = \dot{m} c_p (T_{air,out} - T_{air,in})$$

$$T_{air,out} = T_{air,in} + \frac{Q_{total}}{\dot{m} c_p}$$

$$= 7°C + \frac{778.4 \text{ W}}{\left(0.3151 \; \frac{kg}{s} \right) \left(1004.8 \; \frac{J}{kg \cdot K} \right)}$$

$$= \boxed{9.5°C}$$

This agrees with the engineer's estimate.

5. *Customary U.S. Solution*

(a) The absolute temperature of entering air is

$$500°F + 460 = 960°R$$

The absolute pressure of entering air is

$$25 \text{ psig} + 14.7 \text{ psi} = 39.7 \text{ psia}$$

The density of air entering, from the ideal gas law, is

$$\rho = \frac{p}{RT}$$

$$= \frac{\left(39.7 \; \frac{lbf}{in^2} \right) \left(144 \; \frac{in^2}{ft^2} \right)}{\left(53.35 \; \frac{ft\text{-}lbf}{lbm\text{-}°R} \right) (960°R)} = 0.1116 \text{ lbm/ft}^3$$

The mass flow rate of entering air is

$$\dot{m} = \rho \dot{V} = \left(0.1116 \; \frac{lbm}{ft^3} \right) \left(200 \; \frac{ft^3}{min} \right) \left(60 \; \frac{min}{hr} \right)$$

$$= 1339.2 \text{ lbm/hr}$$

At low pressures, the air enthalpy is found from air tables (App. 24.F).

The absolute temperature of leaving air is

$$350°F + 460 = 810°R$$

From App. 24.F,

$$h_1 = 231.06 \text{ Btu/lbm at } 960°R$$
$$h_2 = 194.25 \text{ Btu/lbm at } 810°R$$

The heat loss is

$$
\begin{aligned}
Q &= \dot{m}(h_1 - h_2) \\
&= \left(1339.2 \ \frac{\text{lbm}}{\text{hr}}\right)\left(231.06 \ \frac{\text{Btu}}{\text{lbm}} - 194.25 \ \frac{\text{Btu}}{\text{lbm}}\right) \\
&= 49{,}296 \text{ Btu/hr}
\end{aligned}
$$

Assuming midpoint pipe surface temperature,

$$\left(\tfrac{1}{2}\right)(T_{\text{in}} + T_{\text{out}}) = \left(\tfrac{1}{2}\right)(500°F + 350°F) = 425°F$$

Since the heat loss is known, the overall heat transfer coefficient can be determined from

$$
Q = UA\Delta T = U(\pi dL)\Delta T
$$
$$
U = \frac{Q}{(\pi dL)\Delta T}
$$
$$
= \frac{49{,}296 \ \dfrac{\text{Btu}}{\text{hr}}}{\pi(4.25 \text{ in})\left(\dfrac{1 \text{ ft}}{12 \text{ in}}\right)(35 \text{ ft})(425°F - 70°F)}
$$
$$
= \boxed{3.57 \text{ Btu/hr-ft}^2\text{-}°F}
$$

(b) To calculate the overall heat transfer coefficient, disregard the pipe thermal resistance and the inside film coefficient (small compared with outside film and radiation).

Work with the midpoint pipe temperature of 425°F.

The absolute temperatures are

$$T_1 = 425°F + 460 = 885°R$$
$$T_2 = 70°F + 460 = 530°R$$

For radiation heat loss, assume $F_a = 1$. For 500°F enamel paint of any color,

$$F_e = \epsilon \approx 0.9$$
$$
\begin{aligned}
\frac{Q_{\text{net}}}{A} &= E_{\text{net}} = \sigma F_e F_a \left(T_1^4 - T_s^4\right) \\
&= \left(0.1713 \times 10^{-8} \ \frac{\text{Btu}}{\text{hr-ft}^2\text{-}°R^4}\right) \\
&\quad \times (0.9)(1.0)\left[(885°R)^4 - (530°R)^4\right] \\
&= 824.1 \text{ Btu/hr}
\end{aligned}
$$

From Eq. 37.2, the radiant heat transfer coefficient is

$$
h_{\text{radiation}} = \frac{E_{\text{net}}}{T_1 - T_2} = \frac{824.1 \ \dfrac{\text{Btu}}{\text{hr}}}{885°R - 530°R}
$$
$$
= 2.32 \text{ Btu/hr-ft}^2\text{-}°F
$$

For the outside film coefficient, evaluate the film at the pipe midpoint. The film temperature is

$$T_f = \left(\tfrac{1}{2}\right)(425°F + 70°F) = 247.5°F$$

From App. 35.C,

$$\text{Pr} = 0.72$$
$$\frac{g\beta\rho^2}{\mu^2} = 0.657 \times 10^6 \ \frac{1}{\text{ft}^3\text{-}°F}$$

The characteristic length, L, is $d_o = 4.25$ in. The Grashof number is

$$
\begin{aligned}
\text{Gr} &= L^3 \left(\frac{\rho^2 \beta g}{\mu^2}\right)\Delta T \\
&= (4.25 \text{ in})^3 \left(\frac{1 \text{ ft}}{12 \text{ in}}\right)^3 \left(0.657 \times 10^6 \ \frac{1}{\text{ft}^3\text{-}°F}\right) \\
&\quad \times (425°F - 70°F) \\
&= 1.04 \times 10^7 \\
\text{PrGr} &= (0.72)(1.04 \times 10^7) = 7.5 \times 10^6
\end{aligned}
$$

From Table 35.3, the film coefficient for a horizontal cylinder is

$$
\begin{aligned}
h_o &= (0.27)\left(\frac{\Delta T}{d}\right)^{0.25} \\
&= (0.27)\left(\frac{425°F - 70°F}{(4.25 \text{ in})\left(\dfrac{1 \text{ ft}}{12 \text{ in}}\right)}\right)^{0.25} \\
&= 1.52 \text{ Btu/hr-ft}^2\text{-}°F
\end{aligned}
$$

The overall film coefficient is

$$
\begin{aligned}
U &= h_{\text{total}} = h_{\text{radiation}} + h_o \\
&= 2.32 \ \frac{\text{Btu}}{\text{hr-ft}^2\text{-}°F} + 1.52 \ \frac{\text{Btu}}{\text{hr-ft}^2\text{-}°F} \\
&= \boxed{3.84 \text{ Btu/hr-ft}^2\text{-}°F}
\end{aligned}
$$

This is not too far from the actual value.

Heat Transfer

(c) • The internal film coefficient was disregarded.

• The emissivity could be lower due to dirt on the outside of the duct.

• h_r and h_o are not really additive.

• Pipe thermal resistance was disregarded.

• The midpoint calculations should be replaced with integration along the length.

SI Solution

(a) The absolute temperature of entering air is

$$260°C + 273 = 533K$$

The absolute pressure of entering air is

$$170 \text{ kPa} + 101.3 \text{ kPa} = 271.3 \text{ kPa}$$

The density of air entering, from the ideal gas law, is

$$\rho = \frac{p}{RT} = \frac{(271.3 \text{ kPa})\left(1000 \frac{\text{Pa}}{\text{kPa}}\right)}{\left(287.03 \frac{\text{J}}{\text{kg·K}}\right)(533K)}$$

$$= 1.773 \text{ kg/m}^3$$

The mass flow rate of entering air is

$$\dot{m} = \rho\dot{V} = \left(1.773 \frac{\text{kg}}{\text{m}^3}\right)\left(0.1 \frac{\text{m}^3}{\text{s}}\right) = 0.1773 \text{ kg/s}$$

At low pressure, the air enthalpy is found from air tables. The absolute temperature of leaving air is

$$180°C + 273 = 453K$$

From App. 24.S,

$$h_1 = 537.09 \text{ kJ/kg at } 533K$$

$$h_2 = 454.87 \text{ kJ/kg at } 453K$$

The heat loss is

$$Q = \dot{m}(h_1 - h_2)$$

$$= \left(0.1773 \frac{\text{kg}}{\text{s}}\right)\left(537.09 \frac{\text{kJ}}{\text{kg}} - 454.87 \frac{\text{kJ}}{\text{kg}}\right)$$

$$\times \left(1000 \frac{\text{W}}{\text{kW}}\right)$$

$$= 14\,578 \text{ W}$$

Assume the midpoint pipe surface temperature.

$$\left(\tfrac{1}{2}\right)(T_{\text{in}} - T_{\text{out}}) = \left(\tfrac{1}{2}\right)(260°C + 180°C) = 220°C$$

Since the heat loss is known, the overall heat transfer coefficient can be determined from

$$Q = UA\Delta T = U(\pi dL)\Delta T$$

$$U = \frac{Q}{(\pi dL)\Delta T}$$

$$= \frac{14\,578 \text{ W}}{\pi(10.8 \text{ cm})\left(\frac{1 \text{ m}}{100 \text{ cm}}\right)(10 \text{ m})(220°C - 20°C)}$$

$$= \boxed{21.5 \text{ W/m}^2\text{·K}}$$

(b) From the Customary U.S. Solution, work with the midpoint pipe temperature of 220°C.

The absolute temperatures are

$$T_1 = 220°C + 273 = 493K$$

$$T_2 = 20°C + 273 = 293K$$

For radiation heat loss, assume $F_a = 1$. For 260°C enamel paint of any color,

$$F_e = \epsilon \approx 0.9$$

From Eq. 37.21, the radiant heat transfer coefficient is

$$h_r = \frac{\sigma F_a F_e \left(T_1^4 - T_2^4\right)}{T_1 - T_2}$$

$$= \frac{\left(5.67 \times 10^{-8} \frac{\text{W}}{\text{m}^2\text{·K}^4}\right)(1)(0.9)}{493K - 293K}$$

$$\quad \times [(493K)^4 - (293K)^4]$$

$$= 13.2 \text{ W/m}^2\text{·K}$$

For the outside film coefficient, evaluate the film at the pipe midpoint. The film temperature is

$$T_f = \left(\tfrac{1}{2}\right)(220°C + 20°C) = 120°C$$

From App. 35.D, at 120°C,

$$\text{Pr} \approx 0.692$$

$$\frac{g\beta\rho^2}{\mu^2} = 0.528 \times 10^8 \frac{1}{\text{K·m}^3}$$

The characteristic length is

$$L = \text{outside diameter} = (10.8 \text{ cm})\left(\frac{1 \text{ m}}{100 \text{ cm}}\right)$$

$$= 0.108 \text{ m}$$

The Grashof number is

$$\text{Gr} = L^3 \left(\frac{\rho^2 g\beta}{\mu^2}\right)\Delta T$$

$$= (0.108 \text{ m})^3 \left(0.528 \times 10^8 \frac{1}{\text{K·m}^3}\right)$$

$$\quad \times (220°C - 20°C)$$

$$= 1.33 \times 10^7$$

$$\text{PrGr} = (0.692)(1.33 \times 10^7) = 9.20 \times 10^6$$

From Table 35.3, the film coefficient for a horizontal cylinder is

$$h_o = (1.32)\left(\frac{\Delta T}{d}\right)^{0.25}$$

$$= (1.32)\left(\frac{220°C - 20°C}{0.108 \text{ m}}\right)^{0.25}$$

$$= 8.66 \text{ W/m}^2\text{·K}$$

The overall film coefficient is

$$U = h_{\text{total}} = h_r + h_o = 13.2 \ \frac{\text{W}}{\text{m}^2\text{·K}} + 8.66 \ \frac{\text{W}}{\text{m}^2\text{·K}}$$

$$= \boxed{21.86 \text{ W/m}^2\text{·K}}$$

This solution is almost the same as the actual value.

(c) See the Customary U.S. Solution.

6. *Customary U.S. Solution*

(a) Heat is lost from the top and sides by radiation and convection. The absolute temperature of the surroundings is

$$75°F + 460 = 535°R$$

$$A_{\text{sides}} = \pi d L = \pi(0.75 \text{ in})(1.5 \text{ in})\left(\frac{1 \text{ ft}}{12 \text{ in}}\right)^2$$

$$= 0.0245 \text{ ft}^2$$

$$A_{\text{top}} = \frac{\pi}{4}d^2 = \left(\frac{\pi}{4}\right)(0.75 \text{ in})^2\left(\frac{1 \text{ ft}}{12 \text{ in}}\right)^2$$

$$= 0.003068 \text{ ft}^2$$

$$Q_{\text{total}} = Q_{\text{convection}} + Q_{\text{radiation}}$$
$$= h_{\text{sides}}A_{\text{sides}}(T_s - T_\infty) + h_{\text{top}}A_{\text{top}}(T_s - T_\infty)$$
$$+ \sigma F_e F_a (A_{\text{sides}} + A_{\text{top}})(T_s^4 - T_\infty^4) \quad [\text{Eq. 1}]$$

For the first approximation of T_s, assume $h_{\text{sides}} = h_{\text{top}}$ = 1.65 Btu/hr-ft²-°F, $F_a = 1$, and $F_e = \epsilon = 0.65$.

$$(5.0 \text{ W})\left(\frac{3.412 \ \frac{\text{Btu}}{\text{hr}}}{1 \text{ W}}\right) = \left(1.65 \ \frac{\text{Btu}}{\text{hr-ft}^2\text{-°F}}\right)$$

$$\times (0.0245 \text{ ft}^2)(T_s - 535°R)$$

$$+ \left(1.65 \ \frac{\text{Btu}}{\text{hr-ft}^2\text{-°F}}\right)$$

$$\times (0.003068 \text{ ft}^2)(T_s - 535°R)$$

$$+ \left(0.1713 \times 10^{-8} \ \frac{\text{Btu}}{\text{hr-ft}^2\text{-°R}^4}\right)$$

$$\times (0.65)(1)(0.0245 \text{ ft}^2$$

$$+ 0.003068 \text{ ft}^2)$$

$$\times \left(T_s^4 - (535°R)^4\right)$$

By trial and error, $T_s \approx 750°R$.

For natural convection on the outside, estimate the film temperature.

$$T_{\text{film}} = \left(\tfrac{1}{2}\right)(T_s + T_\infty) = \left(\tfrac{1}{2}\right)(750°R + 535°R)$$

$$= 642.5°R \quad (182.5°F)$$

From App. 35.C, the properties of air at 182.5°F are

$$\text{Pr} \approx 0.72$$

$$\frac{g\beta\rho^2}{\mu^2} = 1.01 \times 10^6 \ \frac{1}{\text{ft}^3\text{-°F}}$$

For the sides, the characteristic length is 1.5 in. The Grashof number is

$$\text{Gr} = L^3\left(\frac{\rho^2\beta g}{\mu^2}\right)(T_s - T_\infty)$$

$$= (1.5 \text{ in})^3\left(\frac{1 \text{ ft}}{12 \text{ in}}\right)^3\left(1.01 \times 10^6 \ \frac{1}{\text{ft}^3\text{-°F}}\right)$$

$$\times (750°R - 535°R)$$

$$= 4.24 \times 10^5$$

$$\text{PrGr} = (0.72)(4.24 \times 10^5) = 3.05 \times 10^5$$

From Table 35.3, the film coefficient for a vertical surface is

$$h_{\text{sides}} = (0.29)\left(\frac{T_s - T_\infty}{L}\right)^{0.25}$$

$$= (0.29)\left(\frac{750°R - 535°R}{(1.5 \text{ in})\left(\frac{1 \text{ ft}}{12 \text{ in}}\right)}\right)^{0.25}$$

$$= 1.87 \text{ Btu/hr-ft}^2\text{-°F}$$

For the top, the characteristic length is 0.75 in, so

$$\text{Gr} = (0.75 \text{ in})^3\left(\frac{1 \text{ ft}}{12 \text{ in}}\right)^3\left(1.01 \times 10^6 \ \frac{1}{\text{ft}^3\text{-°F}}\right)$$

$$\times (750°R - 535°R)$$

$$= 5.30 \times 10^4$$

$$\text{PrGr} = (0.72)(5.30 \times 10^4) = 3.8 \times 10^4$$

From Table 35.3, the film coefficient for a horizontal surface is

$$h_{\text{top}} = (0.27)\left(\frac{T_s - T_\infty}{L}\right)^{0.25}$$

$$= (0.27)\left(\frac{750°R - 535°R}{(0.75 \text{ in})\left(\frac{1 \text{ ft}}{12 \text{ in}}\right)}\right)^{0.25}$$

$$= 2.07 \text{ Btu/hr-ft}^2\text{-°F}$$

Substituting the calculated values of h_{top} and h_{sides} into Eq. 1 gives

$$Q_{total} = (5.0\ \text{W}) \left(\frac{3.412\ \frac{\text{Btu}}{\text{hr}}}{1\ \text{W}} \right)$$

$$= \left(1.87\ \frac{\text{Btu}}{\text{hr-ft}^2\text{-}°\text{F}} \right) (0.0245\ \text{ft}^2)(T_s - 535°\text{R})$$

$$+ \left(2.07\ \frac{\text{Btu}}{\text{hr-ft}^2\text{-}°\text{F}} \right) (0.003068\ \text{ft}^2)(T_s - 535°\text{R})$$

$$+ \left(0.1713 \times 10^{-8}\ \frac{\text{Btu}}{\text{hr-ft}^2\text{-}°\text{R}^4} \right) (0.65)(1)$$

$$\times (0.0245\ \text{ft}^2 + 0.003068\ \text{ft}^2)\left(T_s^4 - (535°\text{R})^4 \right)$$

By trial and error, $T_s \approx \boxed{736°\text{R}.}$

(b) Substituting $T_s = 736°\text{R}$ in the preceding equation,

$$Q_{total} = 9.209\ \frac{\text{Btu}}{\text{hr}} + 1.277\ \frac{\text{Btu}}{\text{hr}} + 6.492\ \frac{\text{Btu}}{\text{hr}}$$

$$= 16.98\ \text{Btu/hr}$$

$$\frac{Q_{convection}}{Q_{total}} = \frac{9.209\ \frac{\text{Btu}}{\text{hr}} + 1.277\ \frac{\text{Btu}}{\text{hr}}}{16.98\ \frac{\text{Btu}}{\text{hr}}}$$

$$= \boxed{0.618\ \ (61.8\%)}$$

$$\frac{Q_{radiation}}{Q_{total}} = \frac{6.492\ \frac{\text{Btu}}{\text{hr}}}{16.98\ \frac{\text{Btu}}{\text{hr}}} = \boxed{0.382\ \ (38.2\%)}$$

SI Solution

(a) Heat is lost from the top and sides by radiation and convection.

The absolute temperature of the surrounding is

$$24°\text{C} + 273 = 297\text{K}$$

$$A_{sides} = \pi dL = \pi(19\ \text{mm})(38\ \text{mm}) \left(\frac{1\ \text{m}}{1000\ \text{mm}} \right)^2$$

$$= 0.00227\ \text{m}^2$$

$$A_{top} = \frac{\pi}{4} d^2 = \left(\frac{\pi}{4} \right) (19\ \text{mm})^2 \left(\frac{1\ \text{m}}{1000\ \text{mm}} \right)^2$$

$$= 0.000284\ \text{m}^2$$

$$Q_{total} = Q_{convection} + Q_{radiation}$$

$$= h_{sides} A_{sides}(T_s - T_\infty) + h_{top} A_{top}(T_s - T_\infty)$$

$$+ \sigma F_e F_a (A_{sides} + A_{top})(T_s^4 - T_\infty^4) \quad [\text{Eq. 1}]$$

For a first approximation of T_s, assume $h_{sides} = h_{top} = 9.4\ \text{W/m}^2\text{·K}$, $F_a = 1$, and $F_e = \epsilon = 0.65$.

$$5.0\ \text{W} = \left(9.4\ \frac{\text{W}}{\text{m}^2\text{·K}} \right) (0.00227\ \text{m}^2)(T_s - 297\text{K})$$

$$+ \left(9.4\ \frac{\text{W}}{\text{m}^2\text{·K}} \right) (0.000284\ \text{m}^2)(T_s - 297\text{K})$$

$$+ \left(5.67 \times 10^{-8}\ \frac{\text{W}}{\text{m}^2\text{·K}^4} \right) (0.65)(1)$$

$$\times (0.00227\ \text{m}^2 + 0.000284\ \text{m}^2)$$

$$\times \left(T_s^4 - (297\text{K})^4 \right)$$

By trial and error, $T_s = 416.75\ \text{K}$.

For natural convection on the outside, estimate the film temperature.

$$T_{film} = \left(\tfrac{1}{2} \right)(T_s + T_\infty) = \left(\tfrac{1}{2} \right)(416.75\text{K} + 297\text{K})$$

$$= 356.9\text{K} \quad (83.9°\text{C})$$

From App. 35.D, the properties of air at 83.9°C are

$$\text{Pr} \approx 0.697$$

$$\frac{g\beta\rho^2}{\mu^2} \approx 0.616 \times 10^8\ \frac{1}{\text{K·m}^3}$$

For the sides, the characteristic length is 38 mm.

$$\text{Gr} = (38\ \text{mm})^3 \left(\frac{1\ \text{m}}{1000\ \text{mm}} \right)^3 \left(0.616 \times 10^8\ \frac{1}{\text{K·m}^3} \right)$$

$$\times (416.75\text{K} - 297\text{K})$$

$$= 4.048 \times 10^5$$

$$\text{PrGr} = (0.697)(4.048 \times 10^5) = 2.82 \times 10^5$$

For the top, the characteristic length is 19 mm.

$$\text{Gr} = (19\ \text{mm})^3 \left(\frac{1\ \text{m}}{1000\ \text{mm}} \right)^3 \left(0.616 \times 10^8\ \frac{1}{\text{K·m}^3} \right)$$

$$\times (416.75\text{K} - 297\text{K})$$

$$= 5.06 \times 10^4$$

$$\text{PrGr} = (0.697)(5.06 \times 10^4) = 3.53 \times 10^4$$

From Table 35.3, the film coefficient for a horizontal surface is

$$h_{top} = (1.32) \left(\frac{T_s - T_\infty}{L} \right)^{0.25}$$

$$= (1.32) \left(\frac{416.75\text{K} - 297\text{K}}{(19\ \text{mm}) \left(\frac{1\ \text{m}}{1000\ \text{mm}} \right)} \right)^{0.25}$$

$$= 11.76\ \text{W/m}^2\text{·K}$$

From Table 35.3, the film coefficient for a vertical surface is

$$h_{\text{sides}} = (1.37)\left(\frac{416.75\text{K} - 297\text{K}}{(38\text{ mm})\left(\frac{1\text{ m}}{1000\text{ mm}}\right)}\right)^{0.25}$$

$$= 10.26 \text{ W/m}^2\cdot\text{K}$$

Using the calculated values of h_{top} and h_{sides} into Eq. 1,

$$Q_{\text{total}} = 5 \text{ W}$$
$$= \left(10.26 \frac{\text{W}}{\text{m}^2\cdot\text{K}}\right)(0.00227 \text{ m}^2)(T_s - 297\text{K})$$
$$+ \left(11.76 \frac{\text{W}}{\text{m}^2\cdot\text{K}}\right)(0.000284 \text{ m}^2)(T_s - 297\text{K})$$
$$+ \left(5.67 \times 10^{-8} \frac{\text{W}}{\text{m}^2\cdot\text{K}^4}\right)(0.65)(1)$$
$$\times (0.00227 \text{ m}^2 + 0.000284 \text{ m}^2)$$
$$\times (T_s^4 - (297\text{K})^4)$$

By trial and error, $T_s = \boxed{411\text{K.}}$

(b) Substitute $T_s = 411\text{K}$ into the preceding equation.

$$Q_{\text{total}} = 2.655 \text{ W} + 0.381 \text{ W} + 1.953 \text{ W}$$
$$= 4.989 \text{ W}$$

$$\frac{Q_{\text{convection}}}{Q_{\text{total}}} = \frac{2.655 \text{ W} + 0.381 \text{ W}}{4.989 \text{ W}} = \boxed{0.609 \ (60.9\%)}$$

$$\frac{Q_{\text{radiation}}}{Q_{\text{total}}} = \frac{1.953 \text{ W}}{4.989 \text{ W}} = \boxed{0.391 \ (39.1\%)}$$

7. *Customary U.S. Solution*

The film coefficient on the probe is

$$h = \frac{0.024 G^{0.8}}{D^{0.4}}$$

$$= \frac{(0.024)\left(3480 \frac{\text{lbm}}{\text{hr-ft}^2}\right)^{0.8}}{\left((0.5\text{ in})\left(\frac{1\text{ ft}}{12\text{ in}}\right)\right)^{0.4}} = 58.3 \text{ Btu/hr-ft}^2\text{-}°\text{F}$$

The absolute temperature of the walls is

$$T_{\text{walls}} = 600°\text{F} + 460 = 1060°\text{R}$$

Neglect conduction and the insignificant kinetic energy loss. The thermocouple gains heat through radiation from the walls and loses heat through convection to the gas.

$$Q_{\text{convection}} = AE_{\text{radiation}}$$
$$hA(T_{\text{probe}} - T_{\text{gas}}) = A\sigma\epsilon(T_{\text{walls}}^4 - T_{\text{probe}}^4)$$
$$h(T_{\text{probe}} - T_{\text{gas}}) = \sigma\epsilon(T_{\text{walls}}^4 - T_{\text{probe}}^4)$$

(a) If the actual gas temperature is $300°\text{F} + 460 = 760°\text{R}$,

$$\left(58.3 \frac{\text{Btu}}{\text{hr-ft}^2\text{-}°\text{F}}\right)$$
$$\times (T_{\text{probe}} - 760°\text{R}) = \left(0.1713 \times 10^{-8} \frac{\text{Btu}}{\text{hr-ft}^2\text{-}°\text{R}^4}\right)$$
$$\times (0.8)\left((1060°\text{R})^4 - T_{\text{probe}}^4\right)$$
$$(1.37 \times 10^{-9})T_{\text{probe}}^4$$
$$+ (58.3)T_{\text{probe}} = 46{,}038$$

By trial and error, $T_{\text{probe}} = \boxed{781°\text{R.}}$

(b) If $T_{\text{probe}} = 300°\text{F} + 460 = 760°\text{R}$,

$$\left(58.3 \frac{\text{Btu}}{\text{hr-ft}^2\text{-}°\text{F}}\right)$$
$$\times (760°\text{R} - T_{\text{gas}}) = \left(0.1713 \times 10^{-8} \frac{\text{Btu}}{\text{hr-ft}^2\text{-}°\text{R}^4}\right)$$
$$\times (0.8)\left((1060°\text{R})^4 - (760°\text{R})^4\right)$$
$$T_{\text{gas}} = \boxed{738.2°\text{R}}$$

SI Solution

The film coefficient on the probe is

$$h = \frac{2.9 G^{0.8}}{D^{0.4}}$$

$$= \frac{(2.9)\left(4.7 \frac{\text{kg}}{\text{s}\cdot\text{m}^2}\right)^{0.8}}{(13\text{ mm})^{0.4}\left(\frac{1\text{ m}}{1000\text{ mm}}\right)^{0.4}} = 56.82 \text{ W/m}^2\cdot\text{K}$$

The absolute temperature of the walls is

$$T_{\text{walls}} = 315°\text{C} + 273 = 588\text{K}$$

Neglecting conduction and the insignificant kinetic energy loss, the thermocouple gains heat through radiation from the walls and loses heat through convection to the gas.

$$\frac{Q_{\text{convection}}}{A} = E_{\text{radiation}}$$
$$h(T_{\text{probe}} - T_{\text{gas}}) = \sigma\epsilon(T_{\text{walls}}^4 - T_{\text{probe}}^4)$$

(a) If the actual gas temperature is $150°C + 273 = 423K$,

$$\left(56.82\ \frac{W}{m^2 \cdot K}\right)$$
$$\times (T_{probe} - 423K) = \left(5.67 \times 10^{-8}\ \frac{W}{m^2 \cdot K^4}\right)(0.8)$$
$$\times [(588K)^4 - T_{probe}^4]$$

$$(4.536 \times 10^{-8})T_{probe}^4$$
$$+(56.82)T_{probe} = 29\,457$$

By trial and error, $T_{probe} = \boxed{477K.}$

(b) If $T_{probe} = 150°C + 273 = 423K$,

$$\left(56.82\ \frac{W}{m^2 \cdot K}\right)$$
$$\times (423K - T_{gas}) = \left(5.67 \times 10^{-8}\ \frac{W}{m^2 \cdot K^4}\right)(0.8)$$
$$\times [(588K)^4 - (423K)^4]$$
$$T_{gas} = \boxed{353.1K}$$

38 Psychrometrics

1. Customary U.S. Solution

Locate the intersection of 80°F dry bulb and 67°F wet bulb on the psychrometric chart (App. 38.A). Read the value of humidity and enthalpy.

$$\omega = 0.0112 \text{ lbm moisture/lbm dry air}$$

$$h = 31.5 \text{ Btu/lbm dry air}$$

c_p is gravimetrically weighted. c_p for air is 0.240 Btu/lbm-°F, and c_p for steam is approximately 0.40 Btu/lbm-°F.

$$G_{\text{air}} = \frac{1}{1 + 0.0112} = 0.989$$

$$G_{\text{steam}} = \frac{0.0112}{1 + 0.0112} = 0.011$$

$$
\begin{aligned}
c_{p,\text{mixture}} &= G_{\text{air}}c_{p,\text{air}} + G_{\text{steam}}c_{p,\text{steam}} \\
&= (0.989)\left(0.240 \, \frac{\text{Btu}}{\text{lbm-°F}}\right) \\
&\quad + (0.011)\left(0.40 \, \frac{\text{Btu}}{\text{lbm-°F}}\right) \\
&= \boxed{0.242 \text{ Btu/lbm-°F}}
\end{aligned}
$$

SI Solution

Locate the intersection of 27°C dry bulb and 19°C wet bulb on the psychrometric chart (App. 38.B). Read the value of humidity and enthalpy.

$$
\begin{aligned}
\omega &= \left(10.5 \, \frac{\text{g}}{\text{kg dry air}}\right)\left(\frac{1 \text{ kg}}{1000 \text{ g}}\right) \\
&= 0.0105 \text{ kg/kg dry air}
\end{aligned}
$$

$$h = 53.9 \text{ kJ/kg dry air}$$

c_p is gravimetrically weighted. c_p for air is 1.0048 kJ/kg·K, and c_p for steam is approximately 1.675 kJ/kg·K.

$$G_{\text{air}} = \frac{1}{1 + 0.0105} = 0.990$$

$$G_{\text{steam}} = \frac{0.0105}{1 + 0.0105} = 0.010$$

$$
\begin{aligned}
c_{p,\text{mixture}} &= G_{\text{air}}c_{p,\text{air}} + G_{\text{air}}c_{p,\text{steam}} \\
&= (0.990)\left(1.0048 \, \frac{\text{kJ}}{\text{kg·K}}\right) \\
&\quad + (0.010)\left(1.675 \, \frac{\text{kJ}}{\text{kg·K}}\right) \\
&= \boxed{1.0115 \text{ kJ/kg·K}}
\end{aligned}
$$

2.

$$
\begin{aligned}
\text{BF}_{n \text{ rows}} &= (\text{BF}_{1 \text{ row}})^n \\
&= \left(\tfrac{1}{3}\right)^4 = 0.0123
\end{aligned}
$$

3.

Customary U.S. Solution

(a) Locate the two points on the psychrometric chart and draw a line between them.

Reading from the chart (specific volumes),

$$v_{\text{A}} = 13.0 \text{ ft}^3/\text{lbm}$$

$$v_{\text{B}} = 13.7 \text{ ft}^3/\text{lbm}$$

The density at each point is

$$\rho_{\text{A}} = \frac{1}{v_{\text{A}}} = \frac{1}{13.0 \, \frac{\text{ft}^3}{\text{lbm}}} = 0.0769 \text{ lbm/ft}^3$$

$$\rho_{\text{B}} = \frac{1}{v_{\text{B}}} = \frac{1}{13.7 \, \frac{\text{ft}^3}{\text{lbm}}} = 0.0730 \text{ lbm/ft}^3$$

The mass flow at each point is

$$\dot{m}_A = \rho_A \dot{V}_A = \left(0.0769 \ \frac{\text{lbm}}{\text{ft}^3}\right)\left(1000 \ \frac{\text{ft}^3}{\text{min}}\right)$$
$$= 76.9 \ \text{lbm/min}$$

$$\dot{m}_B = \rho_B \dot{V}_B = \left(0.0730 \ \frac{\text{lbm}}{\text{ft}^3}\right)\left(1500 \ \frac{\text{ft}^3}{\text{min}}\right)$$
$$= 109.5 \ \text{lbm/min}$$

The gravimetric fraction of flow A is

$$\frac{76.9 \ \dfrac{\text{lbm}}{\text{min}}}{76.9 \ \dfrac{\text{lbm}}{\text{min}} + 109.5 \ \dfrac{\text{lbm}}{\text{min}}} = 0.413$$

Since the scales are all linear,

$$0.413 = \frac{T_B - T_C}{T_B - T_A}$$
$$T_C = T_B - (0.413)(T_B - T_A)$$
$$= 76°\text{F} - (0.413)(76°\text{F} - 50°\text{F})$$
$$= \boxed{65.3°\text{F}}$$

(b) $\omega = \boxed{0.0082 \ \text{lbm moisture/lbm dry air}}$

(c) $T_{\text{dp}} = \boxed{51°\text{F}}$

SI Solution

(a) Locate the two points on the psychrometric chart and draw a line between them.

Reading from the chart (specific volumes),

$$v_A = 0.813 \ \text{m}^3/\text{kg dry air}$$
$$v_B = 0.856 \ \text{m}^3/\text{kg dry air}$$

The density at each point is

$$\rho_A = \frac{1}{v_A} = \frac{1}{0.813 \ \dfrac{\text{m}^3}{\text{kg}}} = 1.23 \ \text{kg/m}^3$$

$$\rho_B = \frac{1}{v_B} = \frac{1}{0.856 \ \dfrac{\text{m}^3}{\text{kg}}} = 1.17 \ \text{kg/m}^3$$

The mass flow at each point is

$$\dot{m}_A = \rho_A \dot{V}_A = \left(1.23 \ \frac{\text{kg}}{\text{m}^3}\right)\left(0.5 \ \frac{\text{m}^3}{\text{s}}\right) = 0.615 \ \text{kg/s}$$

$$\dot{m}_B = \rho_B \dot{V}_B = \left(1.17 \ \frac{\text{kg}}{\text{m}^3}\right)\left(0.75 \ \frac{\text{m}^3}{\text{s}}\right) = 0.878 \ \text{kg/s}$$

The gravimetric fraction of flow A is

$$\frac{0.615 \ \dfrac{\text{kg}}{\text{s}}}{0.615 \ \dfrac{\text{kg}}{\text{s}} + 0.878 \ \dfrac{\text{kg}}{\text{s}}} = 0.412$$

Since the scales are linear,

$$0.412 = \frac{T_B - T_C}{T_B - T_A}$$
$$T_C = T_B - (0.412)(T_B - T_A)$$
$$= 24°\text{C} - (0.412)(24°\text{C} - 10°\text{C})$$
$$= \boxed{18.2°\text{C}}$$

(b) $\omega = \left(8.0 \ \dfrac{\text{g}}{\text{kg dry air}}\right)\left(\dfrac{1 \ \text{kg}}{1000 \ \text{g}}\right)$

$$= \boxed{0.008 \ \text{kg/kg dry air}}$$

(c) $T_{\text{dp}} = \boxed{10.6°\text{C}}$

4. *Customary U.S. Solution*

From Eq. 38.24, the bypass factor is

$$\text{BF} = 1 - \eta_{\text{coil}}$$
$$= 1 - 0.70 = 0.30$$

From Eq. 38.34, the dry-bulb temperature of air leaving the washer can be determined.

$$\text{BF} = \frac{T_{\text{db,in}} - T_{\text{db,out}}}{T_{\text{db,in}} - T_{\text{wb,in}}}$$

$$0.70 = \frac{60°\text{F} - T_{\text{db,out}}}{60°\text{F} - 45°\text{F}} = \boxed{49.5°\text{F}}$$

SI Solution

From Eq. 38.24, the bypass factor is

$$\text{BF} = 1 - \eta_{\text{coil}}$$
$$= 1 - 0.70 = 0.30$$

From Eq. 38.34, the dry-bulb temperature of air leaving the washer can be determined.

$$\text{BF} = \frac{T_{\text{db,in}} - T_{\text{db,out}}}{T_{\text{db,in}} - T_{\text{wb,in}}}$$

$$0.70 = \frac{16°\text{C} - T_{\text{db,out}}}{16°\text{C} - 7°\text{C}} = \boxed{9.7°\text{C}}$$

5. *Customary U.S. Solution*

(a) Refer to the psychrometric chart (App. 38.A).

At point 1, properties of air at $T_{\text{db}} = 95°F$ and $T_{\text{wb}} = 75°F$ are

$$\omega_1 = 0.0141 \text{ lbm moisture/lbm air}$$
$$h_1 = 38.6 \text{ Btu/lbm air} - 0.2 \text{ Btu/lbm air}$$
$$= 38.4 \text{ lbm air}$$
$$v_1 = 14.3 \text{ ft}^3/\text{lbm air}$$

At point 2, properties of air at $T_{\text{db}} = 85°F$ and 90% relative humidity are

$$\omega_2 = 0.0237 \text{ lbm moisture/lbm air}$$
$$h_2 = 46.6 \text{ Btu/lbm air}$$

The enthalpy change is

$$\frac{h_2 - h_1}{v_1} = \frac{46.6 \ \dfrac{\text{Btu}}{\text{lbm air}} - 38.4 \ \dfrac{\text{Btu}}{\text{lbm air}}}{14.3 \ \dfrac{\text{ft}^3}{\text{lbm air}}}$$

$$= \boxed{0.573 \text{ Btu/ft}^3 \text{ air}}$$

(b) The moisture added is

$$\frac{\omega_2 - \omega_1}{v_1} = \frac{0.0237 \ \dfrac{\text{lbm moisture}}{\text{lbm air}} - 0.0141 \ \dfrac{\text{lbm moisture}}{\text{lbm air}}}{14.3 \ \dfrac{\text{ft}^3}{\text{lbm air}}}$$

$$= \boxed{6.71 \times 10^{-4} \text{ lbm/ft}^3 \text{ air}}$$

SI Solution

(a) Refer to the psychrometric chart (App. 38.B).

At point 1, properties of air at $T_{\text{db}} = 35°C$ and $T_{\text{wb}} = 24°C$ are

$$\omega_1 = 14.3 \text{ g/kg air}$$
$$h_1 = 71.8 \text{ kJ/kg air}$$
$$v_1 = 0.8893 \text{ m}^3/\text{kg air}$$

At point 2, properties of air at $T_{\text{db}} = 29°C$ and 90% relative humidity are

$$\omega_2 = 23.1 \text{ g/kg air}$$
$$h_2 = 88 \text{ kJ/kg air}$$

The enthalpy change is

$$\frac{h_2 - h_1}{v_1} = \frac{88 \ \dfrac{\text{kJ}}{\text{kg air}} - 71.8 \ \dfrac{\text{kJ}}{\text{kg air}}}{0.8893 \ \dfrac{\text{m}^3}{\text{kg air}}}$$

$$= \boxed{18.2 \text{ kJ/m}^3 \text{ air}}$$

(b) The moisture added is

$$\frac{\omega_2 - \omega_1}{v_1} = \frac{\left[\left(23.1 \ \dfrac{\text{g}}{\text{kg air}}\right) - \left(14.3 \ \dfrac{\text{kg}}{\text{kg air}}\right)\right] \times \left(\dfrac{1 \text{ kg}}{1000 \text{ g}}\right)}{0.8893 \ \dfrac{\text{m}^3}{\text{kg air}}}$$

$$= \boxed{9.90 \times 10^{-3} \text{ kg/m}^3 \text{ air}}$$

6.

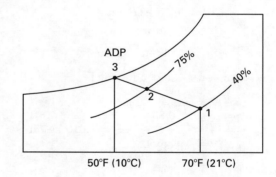

Customary U.S. Solution

(a) Refer to the psychrometric chart (App. 38.A).

At point 1, properties of air at $T_{\text{db}} = 70°F$ and $\phi = 40\%$ are

$$h_1 = 23.6 \text{ Btu/lbm air}$$
$$\omega_1 = 0.00623 \text{ lbm moisture/lbm air}$$
$$v_1 = 13.48 \text{ ft}^3/\text{lbm air}$$

The mass flow rate of incoming air is

$$\dot{m}_{a,1} = \frac{\dot{V}_1}{v_1} = \frac{1800 \ \dfrac{\text{ft}^3}{\text{min}}}{13.48 \ \dfrac{\text{ft}^3}{\text{lbm air}}} = 133.53 \text{ lbm air/min}$$

Locate point 1 on the psychrometric chart.

Locate point 3 as 50°F saturated condition (water being sprayed) on the psychrometric chart.

Draw a line from point 1 to point 3. The intersection of this line with 75% relative humidity defines point 2 as

$$h_2 = 21.4 \text{ Btu/lbm air}$$
$$\omega_2 = 0.0072 \text{ lbm moisture/lbm air}$$
$$T_{db,2} = 56°F$$
$$T_{wb,2} = 51.8°F$$

(b) The moisture (water) added is

$$\dot{m}_w = \dot{m}_{a,1}(\omega_2 - \omega_1)$$
$$= \left(133.53 \frac{\text{lbm air}}{\text{min}}\right)\left(0.0072 \frac{\text{lbm moisture}}{\text{lbm air}}\right.$$
$$\left. - 0.00625 \frac{\text{lbm moisture}}{\text{lbm air}}\right)$$
$$= \boxed{0.127 \text{ lbm/min}}$$

SI Solution

(a) Refer to the psychrometric chart (App. 38.B).

At point 1, properties of air at $T_{db} = 21°C$ and $\phi = 40\%$ are
$$h_1 = 36.75 \text{ kJ/kg air}$$
$$\omega_1 = 6.2 \text{ g moisture/kg air}$$
$$v_1 = 0.842 \text{ m}^3/\text{kg air}$$

The mass flow rate of incoming air is

$$\dot{m}_{a,1} = \frac{\dot{V}_1}{v_1} = \frac{0.85 \frac{\text{m}^3}{\text{s}}}{0.842 \frac{\text{m}^3}{\text{kg air}}} = 1.010 \text{ kg air/s}$$

Locate point 1 on the psychrometric chart.

Locate point 3 as 10°C saturated condition (water being sprayed) on the psychrometric chart.

Draw a line from point 1 to point 3. The intersection of this line with 75% relative humidity defines point 2 as

$$T_{2,db} = 14.7°C$$
$$h_2 = 34.1 \text{ kJ/kg air}$$
$$\omega_2 = 7.6 \text{ g moisture/kg air}$$

(b) The water added is

$$\dot{m}_w = \dot{m}_{a,1}(\omega_2 - \omega_1)$$
$$= \left(1.010 \frac{\text{kg air}}{\text{s}}\right)\left(7.6 \frac{\text{g moisture}}{\text{kg air}} - 6.2 \frac{\text{g moisture}}{\text{kg air}}\right)$$
$$\times \left(\frac{1 \text{ kg}}{1000 \text{ g}}\right)$$
$$= \boxed{0.00141 \text{ kg/s}}$$

7. *Customary U.S. Solution*

From Prob. 6,

$$\omega_1 = 0.00623 \text{ lbm moisture/lbm air}$$
$$h_1 = 23.6 \text{ Btu/lbm air}$$
$$\dot{m}_{a,1} = 133.53 \text{ lbm air/min}$$

From the steam table (App. 24.B) for 1 atm steam, $h_{steam} = 1150.5 \text{ Btu/lbm}$.

From the conservation of energy equation (Eq. 38.32),

$$\dot{m}_{a,1}h_1 + \dot{m}_{steam}h_{steam} = \dot{m}_{a,1}h_2$$
$$\left(133.53 \frac{\text{lbm air}}{\text{min}}\right)\left(23.6 \frac{\text{Btu}}{\text{lbm air}}\right)$$
$$+ \dot{m}_{steam}\left(1150.5 \frac{\text{Btu}}{\text{lbm}}\right) = \left(133.53 \frac{\text{lbm air}}{\text{min}}\right)h_2$$
[Eq. 1]

From conservation of mass for the water (Eq. 38.33),

$$\dot{m}_{a,1}\omega_1 + \dot{m}_{steam} = \dot{m}_{a,2}\omega_2$$
$$\left(133.53 \frac{\text{lbm air}}{\text{min}}\right)\left(0.00623 \frac{\text{lbm moisture}}{\text{lbm air}}\right)$$
$$+ \dot{m}_{steam} = \left(133.53 \frac{\text{lbm air}}{\text{min}}\right)\omega_2 \quad \text{[Eq. 2]}$$

Since no single relationship exists between ω_2, $\dot{m}_{steam}$, and h_2, a trial and error solution is required. Once $\dot{m}_{steam}$ is selected, ω_2 and h_2 can be found from Eq. 1 and Eq. 2 as

$$h_2 = (8.616)\dot{m}_{steam} + 23.6$$
$$\omega_2 = 0.00623 + 0.00749\dot{m}_{steam}$$

Once h_2 and ω_2 are known, the relative humidity can be determined from the psychrometric chart. Continue the process until a relative humidity of 75% is achieved.

$\dot{m}_{steam}$ $\left(\frac{\text{lbm}}{\text{min}}\right)$	ω_2 $\left(\frac{\text{lbm moisture}}{\text{lbm air}}\right)$	h_2 $\left(\frac{\text{Btu}}{\text{lbm air}}\right)$	ϕ_2 (%)
0.3	0.00848	26.18	53
0.4	0.00923	27.05	58
0.5	0.00998	27.91	62
0.6	0.01072	28.77	66
0.7	0.01147	29.63	70
0.8	0.01222	30.49	74
0.82	0.01237	30.67	74.8
0.83	0.01245	30.75	75.3
0.825	0.01241	30.71	75.0

$$\dot{m}_{\text{steam}} = 0.825 \text{ lbm/min}$$
$$\omega_2 = 0.01241 \text{ lbm moisture/lbm air}$$
$$h_2 = 30.71 \text{ Btu/lbm air}$$
$$T_{\text{db}} = 71.5°\text{F}$$
$$T_{\text{wb}} = 65.9°\text{F}$$

$$\dot{m}_{\text{steam}} = 0.0056 \text{ kg/s}$$
$$\omega_2 = \left(0.0117 \frac{\text{kg moisture}}{\text{kg air}}\right)\left(1000 \frac{\text{g}}{\text{kg}}\right)$$
$$= 11.7 \text{ g moisture/kg air}$$
$$T_{\text{db}} = 21.3°\text{C}$$
$$T_{\text{wb}} = 18.2°\text{C}$$

SI Solution

From Prob. 6,

$$\omega_1 = 6.2 \text{ g moisture/kg air}$$
$$h_1 = 36.75 \text{ kJ/kg air}$$
$$\dot{m}_{a,1} = 1.010 \text{ kg air/s}$$

From the steam table (App. 24.O), for 1 atm steam, $h_{\text{steam}} = 2675.5 \text{ kJ/kg}$.

From the conservation of energy equation (Eq. 38.32),

$$\dot{m}_{a,1}h_1 + \dot{m}_{\text{steam}}h_{\text{steam}} = \dot{m}_{a,1}h_2$$
$$\left(1.010 \frac{\text{kg air}}{\text{s}}\right)\left(36.75 \frac{\text{kJ}}{\text{kg air}}\right)$$
$$+ \dot{m}_{\text{steam}}\left(2675.5 \frac{\text{kJ}}{\text{kg}}\right) = \left(1.010 \frac{\text{kg air}}{\text{s}}\right)h_2$$

[Eq. 1]

From conservation of mass of water (Eq. 38.33),

$$\dot{m}_{a,1}\omega_1 + \dot{m}_{\text{steam}} = \dot{m}_{a,2}\omega_2$$
$$\left(1.010 \frac{\text{kg air}}{\text{s}}\right)\left(6.2 \frac{\text{g moisture}}{\text{kg air}}\right)\left(\frac{1 \text{ kg}}{1000 \text{ kg}}\right)$$
$$+ m_{\text{steam}} = \left(1.010 \frac{\text{kg air}}{\text{s}}\right)\omega_2$$

[Eq. 2]

Since no single relationship exists between ω_2, $\dot{m}_{\text{steam}}$, and h_2, a trial and error solution is required. Once $\dot{m}_{\text{steam}}$ is selected, ω_2 and h_2 can be found from Eq. 1 and Eq. 2 as

$$h_2 = 36.75 + 2649.0\dot{m}_{\text{steam}}$$
$$\omega_2 = 0.0062 + 0.99\dot{m}_{\text{steam}}$$

Once h_2 and ω_2 are known, the relative humidity can be determined from the psychrometric chart. Continue the process until a relative humidity of 75% is achieved.

$\dot{m}_{\text{steam}}$ $\left(\frac{\text{kg}}{\text{s}}\right)$	ω_2 $\left(\frac{\text{kg moisture}}{\text{kg air}}\right)$	h_2 $\left(\frac{\text{kJ}}{\text{kg air}}\right)$	ϕ_2 (%)
0.005	0.0112	50.00	69.5
0.0055	0.0116	51.32	74.5
0.0056	0.0117	51.58	75.0

8. *Customary U.S. Solution*

From the psychrometric chart (App. 38.A), for incoming air at 65°F and 55% relative humidity, $\omega_1 = 0.0072$ lbm moisture/lbm air.

With sensible heating as a limiting factor, calculate the mass flow rate of air entering the theater from Eq. 38.26 (ventilation rate).

$$\dot{q} = \dot{m}_a(c_{p,\text{air}} + \omega c_{p,\text{moisture}})(T_2 - T_1)$$
$$500{,}000 \frac{\text{Btu}}{\text{hr}} = \dot{m}_a\left[0.240 \frac{\text{Btu}}{\text{lbm-°F}}\right.$$
$$+ \left(0.0072 \frac{\text{lbm moisture}}{\text{lbm air}}\right)$$
$$\left. \times \left(0.444 \frac{\text{Btu}}{\text{lbm-°F}}\right)\right](75°\text{F} - 65°\text{F})$$
$$\dot{m}_a = 2.056 \times 10^5 \text{ lbm air/hr}$$

Assume that this air absorbs all the moisture. Then, the final humidity ratio is given by

$$\dot{m}_w = \dot{m}_a(\omega_2 - \omega_1)$$
$$\omega_2 = \left(\frac{\dot{m}_w}{\dot{m}_a}\right) + \omega_1$$
$$= \frac{175 \frac{\text{lbm moisture}}{\text{hr}}}{2.056 \times 10^5 \frac{\text{lbm air}}{\text{hr}}} + 0.0072 \frac{\text{lbm moisture}}{\text{lbm air}}$$
$$= 0.00805 \text{ lbm moisture/lbm air}$$

The final conditions are

$$T_{\text{db}} = 75°\text{F} \quad \text{[given]}$$
$$\omega_2 = 0.00805 \text{ lbm moisture/lbm air}$$

From the psychrometric chart (App. 38.A), the relative humidity is 44%. This is below 60%.

SI Solution

From the psychrometric chart (App. 38.B), for incoming air at 18°C and 55% relative humidity, $\omega_1 = 7.1$ g moisture/kg air.

With sensible heating as a limiting factor, calculate the mass flow rate of air entering the theater from Eq. 38.26 (ventilation rate).

$$\dot{q} = \dot{m}_a (c_{p,\text{air}} + \omega c_{p,\text{moisture}})$$
$$\times (T_2 - T_1)$$

$$(150\,\text{kW})\left(1000\,\frac{\text{W}}{\text{kW}}\right) = \dot{m}_a \left[\left(1.005\,\frac{\text{kJ}}{\text{kg·°C}}\right)\left(1000\,\frac{\text{J}}{\text{kJ}}\right)\right.$$
$$+ \left(1.805\,\frac{\text{kJ}}{\text{kg·°C}}\right)\left(1000\,\frac{\text{J}}{\text{kJ}}\right)$$
$$\left.\times \left(7.1\,\frac{\text{g moisture}}{\text{kg air}}\right)\left(\frac{1\,\text{kg}}{1000\,\text{g}}\right)\right]$$
$$\times (24°\text{C} - 18°\text{C})$$

$$\dot{m}_a = 24.56\,\text{kg/s}$$

Assume that this air absorbs all the moisture. Then, the final humidity ratio is given by

$$\dot{m}_w = \dot{m}_a (\omega_2 - \omega_1)$$
$$\omega_2 = \frac{\dot{m}_w}{\dot{m}_a} + \omega_1$$
$$= \frac{\left(80\,\frac{\text{kg}}{\text{h}}\right)\left(\frac{1\,\text{h}}{3600\,\text{s}}\right)}{24.56\,\frac{\text{kg}}{\text{s}}}$$
$$+ \left(7.0\,\frac{\text{g moisture}}{\text{kg air}}\right)\left(\frac{1\,\text{kg}}{1000\,\text{g}}\right)$$
$$= 0.00790\,\text{kg moisture/kg air}$$

The final conditions are

$$T_{\text{db}} = 24°\text{C}$$
$$\omega_2 = \left(0.00790\,\frac{\text{kg moisture}}{\text{kg air}}\right)\left(1000\,\frac{\text{g}}{\text{kg}}\right)$$
$$= 7.9\,\text{g moisture/kg air}$$

From the psychrometric chart (App. 38.B), the relative humidity is 44%. This is below 60%.

9.

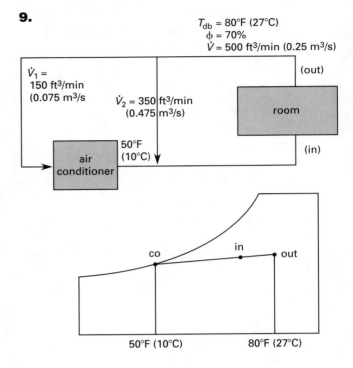

Customary U.S. Solution

Locate point (out) ($T_{\text{db}} = 80°\text{F}$ and $\phi = 70\%$) and point (co) (saturated at 50°F) on the psychrometric chart. At point (out) from App. 38.A,

$$v_{\text{out}} = 13.95\,\text{ft}^3/\text{lbm air}$$
$$h_{\text{out}} = 36.2\,\text{Btu/lbm air}$$

At point (co), $h_{\text{co}} = 20.3$ Btu/lbm air.

The air mass flow rate through the air conditioner is

$$\dot{m}_1 = \frac{\dot{V}_1}{v_1} = \frac{\dot{V}_1}{v_{\text{out}}} = \frac{150\,\frac{\text{ft}^3}{\text{min}}}{13.95\,\frac{\text{ft}^3}{\text{lbm air}}}$$
$$= 10.75\,\text{lbm air/min}$$

The mass flow rate of the bypass air is

$$\dot{m}_2 = \frac{\dot{V}_2}{v} = \frac{350\,\frac{\text{ft}^3}{\text{min}}}{13.95\,\frac{\text{ft}^3}{\text{lbm air}}} = 25.09\,\text{lbm air/min}$$

The percentage of bypass air is

$$x = \frac{25.09\,\frac{\text{lbm air}}{\text{min}}}{10.75\,\frac{\text{lbm air}}{\text{min}} + 25.09\,\frac{\text{lbm air}}{\text{min}}} = 0.70\ \ (70\%)$$

Using the lever rule and the fact that all of the temperature scales are linear,

$$T_{\rm db,in} = T_{\rm co} + (0.70)(T_{\rm out} - T_{\rm co})$$
$$= 50°{\rm F} + (0.70)(80°{\rm F} - 50°{\rm F})$$
$$= 71°{\rm F}$$

At that point,

$$T_{\rm db,in} = 71°{\rm F}$$
$$\omega_{\rm in} = 0.0132 \text{ lbm moisture/lbm air}$$
$$\phi_{\rm in} = 81\%$$

The air conditioner capacity is given by

$$\dot{Q} = \dot{m}_{\rm air}(h_{t,2} - h_{t,1}) = \dot{m}_1(h_{\rm out} - h_{\rm co})$$
$$= \left(10.75 \ \frac{\text{lbm air}}{\text{min}}\right)\left(36.2 \ \frac{\text{Btu}}{\text{lbm air}} - 20.3 \ \frac{\text{Btu}}{\text{lbm air}}\right)$$
$$\times \left(\frac{1 \text{ ton}}{200 \ \frac{\text{Btu}}{\text{min}}}\right)$$
$$= \boxed{0.85 \text{ ton}}$$

SI Solution

Locate point (out) ($T_{\rm db} = 27°{\rm C}$, $\phi = 70\%$) and point (co) (saturated at $10°{\rm C}$) on the psychrometric chart. At point (out) from App. 38.B,

$$v_{\rm out} = 0.872 \text{ m}^3/\text{kg air}$$
$$h_{\rm out} = 67.3 \text{ kJ/kg air}$$

At point (co) from App. 38.B, $h_{\rm co} = 29.26$ kJ/kg air.

At mass flow rate through the air conditioner,

$$\dot{m}_1 = \frac{\dot{V}_1}{v} = \frac{0.075 \ \frac{\text{m}^3}{\text{s}}}{0.872 \ \frac{\text{m}^3}{\text{kg air}}} = 0.0860 \text{ kg air/s}$$

The flow rate of bypass air is

$$\dot{m}_2 = \frac{\dot{V}_2}{v} = \frac{0.175 \ \frac{\text{m}^3}{\text{s}}}{0.872 \ \frac{\text{m}^3}{\text{kg air}}} = 0.2007 \text{ kg air/s}$$

The percentage bypass air is

$$x = \frac{0.2007 \ \frac{\text{kg air}}{\text{s}}}{0.0860 \ \frac{\text{kg air}}{\text{s}} + 0.2007 \ \frac{\text{kg air}}{\text{s}}}$$
$$= 0.70 \ (70\%)$$

Using the lever rule and the fact that all of the temperature scales are linear,

$$T_{\rm db,in} = T_{\rm co} + (0.70)(T_{\rm out} - T_{\rm co})$$
$$= 10°{\rm C} + (0.70)(27°{\rm C} - 10°{\rm C})$$
$$= 21.9°{\rm C}$$

At that point,

$$T_{\rm db,in} = 21.9°{\rm C}$$
$$\omega_{\rm in} = 13.4 \text{ g moisture/kg air}$$
$$\phi_{\rm in} = 81\%$$

The air conditioner capacity is given by

$$\dot{Q} = \dot{m}_{\rm air}(h_{t,2} - h_{t,1}) = \dot{m}_1(h_{\rm out} - h_{\rm co})$$
$$= \left(0.0860 \ \frac{\text{kg air}}{\text{s}}\right)\left(67.3 \ \frac{\text{kJ}}{\text{kg air}} - 29.26 \ \frac{\text{kJ}}{\text{kg air}}\right)$$
$$\times \left(0.2843 \ \frac{\text{ton}}{\text{kW}}\right)$$
$$= \boxed{0.93 \text{ ton}}$$

10.

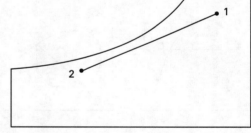

Customary U.S. Solution

(a) At point 1, from the psychrometric chart (App. 38.A) at $T_{\rm db} = 95°{\rm F}$ and $\phi = 70\%$,

$$\boxed{\begin{array}{l} h_1 = 50.7 \text{ Btu/lbm air} \\ v_1 = 14.56 \text{ ft}^3/\text{lbm air} \\ \omega_1 = 0.0253 \text{ lbm water/lbm air} \end{array}}$$

At point 2, from the psychrometric chart (App. 38.A) at $T_{\rm db} = 60°{\rm F}$ and $\phi = 95\%$,

$$\boxed{\begin{array}{l} h_2 = 25.8 \text{ Btu/lbm air} \\ \omega_2 = 0.0105 \text{ lbm water/lbm air} \end{array}}$$

(b) The air mass flow rate is

$$\dot{m}_a = \frac{\dot{V}}{v_1} = \frac{5000 \ \frac{\text{ft}^3}{\text{min}}}{14.56 \ \frac{\text{ft}^3}{\text{lbm air}}} = 343.4 \text{ lbm air/min}$$

From Eq. 38.27, the water removed is

$$\dot{m}_w = \dot{m}_a(\omega_1 - \omega_2)$$
$$= \left(343.4 \ \frac{\text{lbm air}}{\text{min}}\right)$$
$$\times \left(0.0253 \ \frac{\text{lbm water}}{\text{lbm air}} - 0.0105 \ \frac{\text{lbm water}}{\text{lbm air}}\right)$$
$$= \boxed{5.08 \ \text{lbm water/min}}$$

(c) From Eq. 38.28, the quantity of heat removed is

$$\dot{q} = \dot{m}_a(h_1 - h_2)$$
$$= \left(343.4 \ \frac{\text{lbm air}}{\text{min}}\right)\left(50.7 \ \frac{\text{Btu}}{\text{lbm air}} - 25.8 \ \frac{\text{Btu}}{\text{lbm air}}\right)$$
$$= \boxed{8551 \ \text{Btu/min}}$$

(d) Considering an R-12 refrigeration cycle operating at saturated condition at 100°F, the T-s and h-s diagrams are as follows.

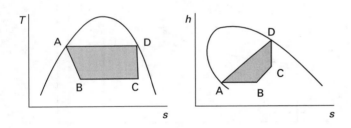

Use App. 24.G for saturated conditions.

(e) At A,

$$T = 100°\text{F} \quad [\text{given}]$$
$$p = p_{\text{sat}} \text{ at } 100°\text{F} = 131.6 \text{ psia}$$
$$h_\text{A} = h_f \text{ at } 100°\text{F} = 31.16 \text{ Btu/lbm}$$
$$s_\text{A} = s_f \text{ at } 100°\text{F} = 0.06316 \text{ Btu/lbm-°R}$$
$$v_\text{A} = v_f \text{ at } 100°\text{F} = 0.0127 \text{ ft}^3/\text{lbm}$$

At point B,

$$T = 50°\text{F} \quad [\text{given}]$$
$$p = p_{\text{sat}} \text{ at } 50°\text{F} = 61.39 \text{ psia}$$
$$h_\text{B} = h_a = 31.16 \text{ Btu/lbm}$$

$$h_{f,\text{B}} = 19.27 \text{ Btu/lbm}$$
$$h_{fg,\text{B}} = 64.51 \text{ Btu/lbm}$$
$$x = \frac{h_\text{B} - h_{f,\text{B}}}{h_{fg,\text{B}}}$$
$$= \frac{31.16 \ \dfrac{\text{Btu}}{\text{lbm}} - 19.27 \ \dfrac{\text{Btu}}{\text{lbm}}}{64.51 \ \dfrac{\text{Btu}}{\text{lbm}}}$$
$$= 0.184$$
$$s_\text{B} = s_{f,\text{B}} + x s_{fg,\text{B}}$$
$$= 0.04126 \ \frac{\text{Btu}}{\text{lbm-°R}}$$
$$\quad + (0.184)\left(0.12659 \ \frac{\text{Btu}}{\text{lbm-°R}}\right)$$
$$= 0.06455 \text{ Btu/lbm-°R}$$
$$v_\text{B} = v_{f,\text{B}} + x(v_g - v_f)$$
$$= 0.0118 \ \frac{\text{ft}^3}{\text{lbm}}$$
$$\quad + (0.184)\left(0.673 \ \frac{\text{ft}^3}{\text{lbm}} - 0.0118 \ \frac{\text{ft}^3}{\text{lbm}}\right)$$
$$= 0.1335 \text{ ft}^3/\text{lbm}$$

At point D,

$$T = 100°\text{F} \quad [\text{given}]$$
$$p = p_{\text{sat}} \text{ at } 100°\text{F} = 131.6 \text{ psia}$$
$$h_\text{D} = h_g \text{ at } 100°\text{F} = 88.62 \text{ Btu/lbm}$$
$$s_\text{D} = s_g \text{ at } 100°\text{F} = 0.16584 \text{ Btu/lbm-°R}$$
$$v_\text{D} = v_g \text{ at } 100°\text{F} = 0.319 \text{ ft}^3/\text{lbm}$$

At point C,

$$T = 50°\text{F} \quad [\text{given}]$$
$$p = p_{\text{sat}} \text{ at } 50°\text{F} = 61.39 \text{ psia}$$
$$s_\text{C} = s_\text{D} = 0.16584 \text{ Btu/lbm-°R}$$
$$s_{f,\text{C}} = 0.04126 \text{ Btu/lbm-°R}$$
$$s_{fg,\text{C}} = 0.12659 \text{ Btu/lbm-°R}$$
$$x = \frac{s_\text{C} - s_{f,\text{C}}}{s_{fg,\text{C}}}$$
$$= \frac{0.16584 \ \dfrac{\text{Btu}}{\text{lbm-°R}} - 0.04126 \ \dfrac{\text{Btu}}{\text{lbm-°R}}}{0.12659 \ \dfrac{\text{Btu}}{\text{lbm-°R}}}$$
$$= 0.984$$

$$h_C = h_{f,C} + x h_{fg,C}$$

$$= 19.27 \ \frac{\text{Btu}}{\text{lbm}} + (0.984)\left(64.51 \ \frac{\text{Btu}}{\text{lbm}}\right)$$

$$= 82.75 \ \text{Btu/lbm}$$

$$v_C = v_{f,C} + x(v_{g,C} - v_{f,C})$$

$$= 0.0118 \ \frac{\text{ft}^3}{\text{lbm}}$$

$$+ (0.984)\left(0.673 \ \frac{\text{ft}^3}{\text{lbm}} - 0.0118 \ \frac{\text{ft}^3}{\text{lbm}}\right)$$

$$= \boxed{0.662 \ \text{ft}^3/\text{lbm}}$$

SI Solution

(a) The psychrometric chart is shown in the Customary U.S. Solution. At point 1, from the psychrometric chart (App. 38.B) at $T_{\text{db}} = 35°\text{C}$ and $\phi = 70\%$,

$$\boxed{\begin{aligned} h_1 &= 99.9 \ \text{kJ/kg air} \\ v_1 &= 0.91 \ \text{m}^3/\text{kg air} \\ \omega_1 &= \left(25.3 \ \frac{\text{g moisture}}{\text{kg air}}\right)\left(\frac{1 \ \text{kg}}{1000 \ \text{g}}\right) \\ &= 0.0253 \ \text{kg moisture/kg air} \end{aligned}}$$

At point 2, from the psychrometric chart (App. 38.B) at $T_{\text{db}} = 16°\text{C}$ and $\phi = 95\%$,

$$\boxed{\begin{aligned} h_2 &= 43.4 \ \text{kJ/kg air} \\ \omega_2 &= \left(10.8 \ \frac{\text{g moisture}}{\text{kg air}}\right)\left(\frac{1 \ \text{kg}}{1000 \ \text{g}}\right) \\ &= 0.0108 \ \text{kg moisture/kg air} \end{aligned}}$$

(b) The air mass flow rate is

$$\dot{m}_a = \frac{\dot{V}_1}{v_1} = \frac{\dot{V}_1}{v_{\text{out}}} = \frac{2.36 \ \frac{\text{m}^3}{\text{s}}}{0.91 \ \frac{\text{m}^3}{\text{kg air}}} = 2.593 \ \text{kg air/s}$$

The water removed from Eq. 38.27 is

$$\dot{m}_w = \dot{m}_a(\omega_1 - \omega_2)$$

$$= \left(2.593 \ \frac{\text{kg air}}{\text{s}}\right)\left(0.0253 \ \frac{\text{kg moisture}}{\text{kg air}}\right.$$

$$\left. - \ 0.0108 \ \frac{\text{kg moisture}}{\text{kg air}}\right)$$

$$= \boxed{0.0376 \ \text{kg moisture/s}}$$

(c) From Eq. 38.28, the quantity of heat removed is

$$\dot{q} = \dot{m}_a(h_1 - h_2)$$

$$= \left(2.593 \ \frac{\text{kg air}}{\text{s}}\right)\left(99.9 \ \frac{\text{kJ}}{\text{kg air}} - 43.4 \ \frac{\text{kJ}}{\text{kg air}}\right)$$

$$= \boxed{146.5 \ \text{kW}}$$

(d) The T-s and h-s diagrams are shown in the Customary U.S. Solution.

(e) Use App. 24.T for saturated conditions.

At point A,

$$T = 38°\text{C} \quad \text{[given]}$$

$$p = p_{\text{sat}} \text{ at } 38°\text{C} = 0.91324 \ \text{MPa}$$

$$h_A = h_f \text{ at } 38°\text{C} = 237.23 \ \text{kJ/kg}$$

$$s_A = s_f \text{ at } 38°\text{C} = 1.1259 \ \text{kJ/kg·°C}$$

$$v_A = v_f \text{ at } 38°\text{C} = \frac{1}{\rho_f} = \frac{1}{1261.9 \ \frac{\text{kg}}{\text{m}^3}}$$

$$= 0.0007925 \ \text{m}^3/\text{kg}$$

At point B,

$$T = 10°\text{C} \quad \text{[given]}$$

$$p = p_{\text{sat}} \text{ at } 10°\text{C} = 0.42356 \ \text{MPa}$$

$$h_B = h_A = 237.23 \ \text{kJ/kg}$$

$$h_{f,B} = 209.48 \ \text{kJ/kg}$$

$$h_{g,B} = 356.79 \ \text{kJ/kg}$$

$$x = \frac{h_B - h_{f,B}}{h_{g,B} - h_{f,B}} = \frac{237.23 \ \frac{\text{kJ}}{\text{kg}} - 209.48 \ \frac{\text{kJ}}{\text{kg}}}{356.79 \ \frac{\text{kJ}}{\text{kg}} - 209.48 \ \frac{\text{kJ}}{\text{kg}}}$$

$$= 0.188$$

$$s_B = s_{f,B} + x(s_{g,B} - s_{f,B})$$

$$= 1.0338 \ \frac{\text{kJ}}{\text{kg·K}}$$

$$+ (0.188)\left(1.5541 \ \frac{\text{kJ}}{\text{kg·K}} - 1.0338 \ \frac{\text{kJ}}{\text{kg·K}}\right)$$

$$= 1.1316 \ \text{kJ/kg·K}$$

$$v_B = v_{f,B} + x(v_{g,B} - v_{f,B})$$

$$v_{f,B} = \frac{1}{\rho_{f,B}} = \frac{1}{1363.0 \ \frac{\text{kg}}{\text{m}^3}} = 0.0007337 \ \text{m}^3/\text{kg}$$

$$v_{g,B} = 0.04119 \ \text{m}^3/\text{kg}$$

$$v_B = 0.0007337 \ \frac{\text{m}^3}{\text{kg}}$$

$$+ (0.188)\left(0.04119 \ \frac{\text{m}^3}{\text{kg}} - 0.0007337 \ \frac{\text{m}^3}{\text{kg}}\right)$$

$$= 0.008339 \ \text{m}^3/\text{kg}$$

At point D,

$$T = 38°\text{C} \quad \text{[given]}$$

$$p = p_{\text{sat}} \text{ at } 38°\text{C} = 0.42356 \ \text{MPa}$$

$$h_D = h_g \text{ at } 38°\text{C} = 367.95 \ \text{kJ/kg}$$

$$s_D = s_g \text{ at } 38°\text{C} = 1.5461 \ \text{kJ/kg·K}$$

$$v_D = v_g \text{ at } 38°\text{C} = 0.01931 \ \text{m}^3/\text{kg}$$

HVAC

At point C,

$$T = 10°C$$

$$p = p_{sat} \text{ at } 10°C = 0.42356 \text{ MPa}$$

$$s_C = s_D = 1.5461 \text{ kJ/kg·K}$$

$$s_{f,C} = 1.0338 \text{ kJ/kg·K}$$

$$s_{g,C} = 1.5541 \text{ kJ/kg·K}$$

$$x = \frac{s_C - s_{f,C}}{s_{g,C} - s_{f,C}} = \frac{1.5461 \frac{\text{kJ}}{\text{kg·K}} - 1.0338 \frac{\text{kJ}}{\text{kg·K}}}{1.5541 \frac{\text{kJ}}{\text{kg·K}} - 1.0338 \frac{\text{kJ}}{\text{kg·K}}}$$

$$= 0.985$$

$$h_C = h_{f,C} + x(h_{g,C} - h_{f,C})$$

$$= 209.48 \frac{\text{kJ}}{\text{kg}} + (0.985)\left(356.79 \frac{\text{kJ}}{\text{kg}} - 209.48 \frac{\text{kJ}}{\text{kg}}\right)$$

$$= 354.58 \text{ kJ/kg}$$

$$v_C = v_{f,C} + x(v_{g,C} - v_{f,C})$$

$$v_{g,C} = 0.04119 \text{ m}^3/\text{kg}$$

$$v_C = 0.0007337 \frac{\text{m}^3}{\text{kg}}$$

$$+ (0.985)\left(0.04119 \frac{\text{m}^3}{\text{kg}} - 0.0007337 \frac{\text{m}^3}{\text{kg}}\right)$$

$$= \boxed{0.04058 \text{ m}^3/\text{kg}}$$

11. *Customary U.S. Solution*

(a) The saturation pressure at 200°F from App. 24.A is $p_{sat,1} = 11.529$ psia.

Since air is saturated (100% relative humidity), the water vapor pressure is equal to the saturation pressure.

$$p_{w,1} = p_{sat,1} = 11.529 \text{ psia}$$

The partial pressure of the air is

$$p_{a,1} = p_1 - p_{w,1} = 25 \text{ psia} - 11.529 \text{ psia}$$

$$= 13.471 \text{ psia}$$

From Table 24.7, the specific gas constants are

$$R_w = 85.78 \text{ ft-lbf/lbm-°R}$$

$$R_{air} = 53.35 \text{ ft-lbf/lbm-°R}$$

The mass of water vapor from the ideal gas law is

$$\dot{m}_{w,1} = \frac{p_{w,1}\dot{V}}{R_w T}$$

$$= \frac{\left(11.529 \frac{\text{lbf}}{\text{in}^2}\right)\left(144 \frac{\text{in}^2}{\text{ft}^2}\right)\left(1500 \frac{\text{ft}^3}{\text{min}}\right)}{\left(85.78 \frac{\text{ft-lbf}}{\text{lbm-°R}}\right)(200°F + 460)}$$

$$= 43.99 \text{ lbm/min water}$$

The mass of air from the ideal gas law is

$$\dot{m}_{a,1} = \frac{p_{a,1}\dot{V}}{R_{air}T}$$

$$= \frac{\left(13.471 \frac{\text{lbf}}{\text{in}^2}\right)\left(144 \frac{\text{in}^2}{\text{ft}^2}\right)\left(1500 \frac{\text{ft}^3}{\text{min}}\right)}{\left(53.35 \frac{\text{ft-lbf}}{\text{lbm-°R}}\right)(200°F + 460)}$$

$$= 82.64 \text{ lbm/min air}$$

The humidity ratio is

$$\omega_1 = \frac{\dot{m}_{w,1}}{\dot{m}_{a,1}} = \frac{43.99 \frac{\text{lbm water}}{\text{min}}}{82.64 \frac{\text{lbm air}}{\text{min}}}$$

$$= 0.532 \text{ lbm water/lbm air}$$

Since it is a constant pressure, constant moisture drying process, mole fractions and partial pressures do not change.

$$p_{w,2} = p_{w,1} = 11.529 \text{ psia}$$

The saturation pressure at 400°F from App. 24.A is $p_{sat,2} = 247.1$ psia.

The relative humidity at state 2 is

$$\phi_2 = \frac{p_{w,2}}{p_{sat,2}} = \frac{11.529 \text{ psia}}{247.1 \text{ psia}} = \boxed{0.0467 \ (4.67\%)}$$

(b) The specific humidity remains constant.

$$\omega_2 = \omega_1 = \boxed{0.532 \text{ lbm water/lbm air}}$$

(c) The heat required consists of two parts.

Obtain enthalpy for air from App. 24.F.

The absolute temperatures are

$$T_1 = 200°F + 460 = 660°R$$

$$T_2 = 400°F + 460 = 860°R$$

$$h_1 = 157.92 \text{ Btu/lbm}$$

$$h_2 = 206.46 \text{ Btu/lbm}$$

The heat absorbed by the air is

$$q_1 = h_2 - h_1 = 206.46 \frac{\text{Btu}}{\text{lbm}} - 157.92 \frac{\text{Btu}}{\text{lbm}}$$

$$= 48.54 \text{ Btu/lbm dry air}$$

(There will be a small error if constant specific heat is used instead.)

For water, use the Mollier diagram. From App. 24.E, h_1 at 200°F and 11.529 psia is 1146 Btu/lbm (almost saturated).

Follow a constant pressure curve up to 400°F.

$$h_2 = 1240 \text{ Btu/lbm}$$

(There will be a small error if Eq. 38.19(b) is used instead.)

The heat absorbed by the steam is

$$
\begin{aligned}
q_2 &= m_w(h_2 - h_1) \\
&= \left(0.532 \, \frac{\text{lbm water}}{\text{lbm air}}\right)\left(1240 \, \frac{\text{Btu}}{\text{lbm}} - 1146 \, \frac{\text{Btu}}{\text{lbm}}\right) \\
&= 50.01 \text{ Btu/lbm air}
\end{aligned}
$$

The total heat absorbed is

$$
q_{\text{total}} = q_1 + q_2 = 48.54 \, \frac{\text{Btu}}{\text{lbm air}} + 50.01 \, \frac{\text{Btu}}{\text{lbm air}}
$$

$$\boxed{= 98.55 \text{ Btu/lbm air}}$$

(d) The dew point is the temperature at which water starts to condense out in a constant pressure process. Following the constant pressure line back to the saturation line, $\boxed{T_{\text{dp}} = 200°\text{F}.}$

SI Solution

(a) From App. 24.N, the saturation pressure at 93°C is

$$p_{\text{sat},1} = (0.7879 \text{ bar})\left(100 \, \frac{\text{kPa}}{\text{bar}}\right) = 78.79 \text{ kPa}$$

Since air is saturated (100% relative humidity), water vapor pressure is equal to saturation pressure.

$$p_{w,1} = p_{\text{sat},1} = 78.79 \text{ kPa}$$

The partial pressure of air is

$$p_{a,1} = p_1 - p_{w,1} = 170 \text{ kPa} - 78.79 \text{ kPa} = 91.21 \text{ kPa}$$

From Table 24.7, the specific gas constants are

$$R_w = 461.50 \text{ J/kg·K}$$
$$R_{\text{air}} = 287.03 \text{ J/kg·K}$$

The mass of water vapor from the ideal gas law is

$$
\begin{aligned}
\dot{m}_{w,1} &= \frac{p_{w,1}\dot{V}}{R_w T} \\
&= \frac{(78.79 \text{ kPa})\left(1000 \, \frac{\text{Pa}}{\text{kPa}}\right)\left(0.71 \, \frac{\text{m}^3}{\text{s}}\right)}{\left(461.50 \, \frac{\text{J}}{\text{kg·K}}\right)(93°\text{C} + 273)} \\
&= 0.3312 \text{ kg/s water}
\end{aligned}
$$

The mass of air from the ideal gas law is

$$
\begin{aligned}
\dot{m}_{a,1} &= \frac{p_{a,1}\dot{V}}{R_{\text{air}} T} \\
&= \frac{(91.21 \text{ kPa})\left(1000 \, \frac{\text{Pa}}{\text{kPa}}\right)\left(0.71 \, \frac{\text{m}^3}{\text{s}}\right)}{\left(287.03 \, \frac{\text{J}}{\text{kg·K}}\right)(93°\text{C} + 273)} \\
&= 0.6164 \text{ kg/s air}
\end{aligned}
$$

The humidity ratio is

$$
\omega_1 = \frac{\dot{m}_{w,1}}{\dot{m}_{a,1}} = \frac{0.3312 \, \dfrac{\text{kg water}}{\text{s}}}{0.6164 \, \dfrac{\text{kg air}}{\text{s}}}
$$

$$= 0.537 \text{ kg water/kg air}$$

Since it is a constant pressure, constant moisture drying process, mole fractions and partial pressure do not change.

$$p_{w,2} = p_{w,1} = 78.79 \text{ kPa}$$

The saturation pressure at 204°C from App. 24.N is

$$p_{\text{sat},2} = (16.95 \text{ bar})\left(100 \, \frac{\text{kPa}}{\text{bar}}\right) = 1695 \text{ kPa}$$

The relative humidity at state 2 is

$$\phi_2 = \frac{p_{w,2}}{p_{\text{sat},2}} = \frac{78.79 \text{ kPa}}{1695 \text{ kPa}} = \boxed{0.0465 \ \ (4.65\%)}$$

(b) The specific humidity remains constant.

$$\omega_2 = \omega_1 = \boxed{0.537 \text{ kg water/kg air}}$$

(c) The heat required consists of two parts.

Obtain enthalpy for air from App. 24.S.

The absolute temperatures are

$$
\begin{aligned}
T_1 &= 93°\text{C} + 273 = 366\text{K} \\
T_2 &= 204°\text{C} + 273 = 477\text{K} \\
h_1 &= 366.63 \text{ kJ/kg} \\
h_2 &= 479.42 \text{ kJ/kg}
\end{aligned}
$$

The heat absorbed by air is

$$
\begin{aligned}
q_1 &= h_2 - h_1 = 479.42 \, \frac{\text{kJ}}{\text{kg}} - 366.63 \, \frac{\text{kJ}}{\text{kg}} \\
&= 112.79 \text{ kJ/kg air}
\end{aligned}
$$

(There will be a small error if constant specific heat is used instead.)

HVAC

For water use the Mollier diagram. From App. 24.R, h_1 at 93°C and 78.79 kPa is 2670 kJ/kg (almost saturated).

Follow a constant pressure curve up to 204°C.

$$h_2 = 2890 \text{ kJ/kg}$$

(There will be a small error if Eq. 38.19(a) is used instead.)

The heat absorbed by steam is

$$q_2 = m_w(h_2 - h_1)$$
$$= \left(0.537 \, \frac{\text{kg water}}{\text{kg air}}\right)\left(2890 \, \frac{\text{kJ}}{\text{kg}} - 2670 \, \frac{\text{kJ}}{\text{kg}}\right)$$
$$= 118.14 \text{ kJ/kg air}$$

The total heat absorbed is

$$q_{\text{total}} = q_1 + q_2$$
$$= 112.79 \, \frac{\text{kJ}}{\text{kg air}} + 118.14 \, \frac{\text{kJ}}{\text{kg air}}$$
$$= \boxed{230.93 \text{ kJ/kg air}}$$

(d) The dew point is the temperature at which water starts to condense out in a constant pressure process. Following the constant pressure line back to the saturation line, $\boxed{T_{\text{dp}} \approx 93°\text{C.}}$

12. *Customary U.S. Solution*

(a) The absolute air temperatures are

$$T_1 = 800°\text{F} + 460 = 1260°\text{R}$$
$$T_2 = 350°\text{F} + 460 = 810°\text{R}$$

At low pressures, use air tables. From App. 24.F,

$$h_1 = 306.65 \text{ Btu/lbm}$$
$$h_2 = 194.25 \text{ Btu/lbm}$$

From App. 24.A, the enthalpy of water at 80°F is $h_{w,1} = 48.09$ Btu/lbm.

From Eq. 38.19(b), the enthalpy of steam at 350°F is

$$h_{w,2} \approx \left(0.444 \, \frac{\text{Btu}}{\text{lbm-°F}}\right)(350°\text{F}) + 1061 \, \frac{\text{Btu}}{\text{lbm}}$$
$$= 1216.4 \text{ Btu/lbm}$$

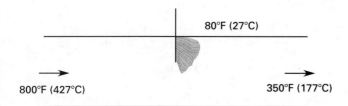

Air temperature is reduced from 800°F to 350°F, and this energy is used to change water at 80°F to steam at 350°F. From the energy balance equation,

$$\dot{m}_w(h_{w,2} - h_{w,1}) = \dot{m}_a(h_1 - h_2)$$
$$\dot{m}_w = \frac{\dot{m}_a(h_1 - h_2)}{h_{w,2} - h_{w,1}}$$
$$= \frac{\left(410 \, \frac{\text{lbm}}{\text{hr}}\right)\left(306.65 \, \frac{\text{Btu}}{\text{lbm}} - 194.25 \, \frac{\text{Btu}}{\text{lbm}}\right)}{1216.4 \, \frac{\text{Btu}}{\text{lbm}} - 48.09 \, \frac{\text{Btu}}{\text{lbm}}}$$
$$= \boxed{39.4 \text{ lbm/hr water}}$$

(b) The number of moles of water evaporated (in the air mixture) is

$$\dot{n}_w = \frac{39.4 \, \frac{\text{lbm}}{\text{hr}}}{18.016 \, \frac{\text{lbm}}{\text{lbmol}}} = 2.19 \text{ lbmol/hr}$$

The number of moles of air at the exit in the mixture is

$$\dot{n}_a = \frac{410 \, \frac{\text{lbm}}{\text{hr}}}{28.967 \, \frac{\text{lbm}}{\text{lbmol}}} = 14.15 \text{ lbmol/hr}$$

The mole fraction of water in the mixture is

$$x_w = \frac{\dot{n}_w}{\dot{n}_a + \dot{n}_w}$$
$$= \frac{2.19 \, \frac{\text{lbmol}}{\text{hr}}}{14.15 \, \frac{\text{lbmol}}{\text{hr}} + 2.19 \, \frac{\text{lbmol}}{\text{hr}}} = 0.134$$

Partial pressure of water vapor is

$$p_w = x(p_{\text{chamber}}) = (0.134)(20 \text{ psia}) = 2.68 \text{ psia}$$

From App. 24.A, the saturation pressure at 350 is $p_{\text{sat}} = 134.53$ psia.

The relative humidity is

$$\phi = \frac{p_w}{p_{\text{sat}}} = \frac{2.68 \text{ psia}}{134.53 \text{ psia}} = \boxed{0.020 \quad (2.0\%)}$$

SI Solution

(a) The absolute temperatures are

$$T_1 = 427°\text{C} + 273 = 700\text{K}$$
$$T_2 = 177°\text{C} + 273 = 450\text{K}$$

Air tables can be used at low pressures. From App. 24.S,

$$h_1 = 713.27 \text{ kJ/kg}$$
$$h_2 = 451.80 \text{ kJ/kg}$$

From App. 24.N, the enthalpy of water at 27°C is $h_{w,1} = 113.25$ kJ/kg.

From Eq. 38.19(a), the enthalpy of steam at 177°C is

$$h_{w,2} = \left(1.805 \frac{\text{kJ}}{\text{kg·°C}}\right)(177°\text{C}) + 2501 \frac{\text{kJ}}{\text{kg}}$$
$$= 2820.5 \text{ kJ/kg}$$

Air temperature is reduced from 427°C to 177°C, and this energy is used to change water at 27°C to steam at 177°C. From the energy balance equation,

$$\dot{m}_w = \frac{\dot{m}_a(h_1 - h_2)}{h_{w,2} - h_{w,1}}$$
$$= \frac{\left(0.052 \frac{\text{kg}}{\text{s}}\right)\left(713.27 \frac{\text{kJ}}{\text{kg}} - 451.80 \frac{\text{kJ}}{\text{kg}}\right)}{2820.5 \frac{\text{kJ}}{\text{kg}} - 113.25 \frac{\text{kJ}}{\text{kg}}}$$
$$= \boxed{0.00502 \text{ kg/s}}$$

(b) The number of moles of water evaporated (in the air mixture) is

$$\dot{n}_w = \frac{0.00502 \frac{\text{kg}}{\text{s}}}{18.016 \frac{\text{kg}}{\text{kmol}}} = 2.79 \times 10^{-4} \text{ kmol/s}$$

The number of moles of air in the mixture at the exit is

$$\dot{n}_a = \frac{0.052 \frac{\text{kg}}{\text{s}}}{28.967 \frac{\text{kg}}{\text{kmol}}} = 1.80 \times 10^{-3} \text{ kmol/s}$$

The mole fraction of water in the mixture is

$$x_w = \frac{\dot{n}_w}{\dot{n}_a + \dot{n}_w}$$
$$= \frac{2.79 \times 10^{-4} \frac{\text{kmol}}{\text{s}}}{1.80 \times 10^{-3} \frac{\text{kmol}}{\text{s}} + 2.79 \times 10^{-4} \frac{\text{kmol}}{\text{s}}}$$
$$= 0.134$$

The partial pressure of water vapor is

$$p_w = x p_{\text{chamber}} = (0.134)(140 \text{ kPa})$$
$$= 18.76 \text{ kPa}$$

From App. 24.N, the saturation pressure at 177°C is

$$p_{\text{sat}} = (9.389 \text{ bar})\left(100 \frac{\text{kPa}}{\text{bar}}\right) = 938.9 \text{ kPa}$$

The relative humidity is

$$\phi = \frac{p_w}{p_{\text{sat}}} = \frac{18.76 \text{ kPa}}{938.9 \text{ kPa}} = \boxed{0.020 \ (2.0\%)}$$

13. *Customary U.S. Solution*

(a) The cooled water flow rate is given by

$$Q = \dot{m}_w c_p \Delta T$$
$$1 \times 10^6 \text{ Btu} = \dot{m}_w \left(1.0 \frac{\text{Btu}}{\text{lbm-°F}}\right)(120°\text{F} - 110°\text{F})$$
$$\dot{m}_w = 1 \times 10^5 \text{ lbm/hr}$$

From the psychrometric chart (App. 38.A), for air in at $T_{\text{db}} = 91°$F and $\phi = 60\%$,

$$h_{\text{in}} \approx 42.7 \text{ Btu/lbm}$$
$$\omega_{\text{in}} = 0.0190 \text{ lbm moisture/lbm air}$$

For air out, the normal psychrometric chart (offscale) cannot be used, so use Eq. 38.11 to find the humidity ratio and Eqs. 38.17, 38.18(b), and 38.19(b) to calculate the enthalpy of air. (App. 38.D could also be used as a simpler solution.)

From App. 24.A, the saturated steam pressure at 100°F is 0.9503 psia.

From Eq. 38.1,

$$p_a = p - p_w = 14.696 \text{ psia} - 0.9503 \text{ psia}$$
$$= 13.7457 \text{ psia}$$

From Eq. 38.11, the humidity ratio for air out is

$$\phi = 1.608\omega_{\text{out}}\left(\frac{p_a}{p_{\text{sat}}}\right)$$
$$0.82 = 1.608\omega_{\text{out}}\left(\frac{13.7457 \text{ psia}}{0.9503 \text{ psia}}\right)$$
$$\omega_{\text{out}} = 0.0353 \text{ lbm moisture/lbm air}$$

From Eqs. 38.17, 38.18(b), and 38.19(b), the enthalpy of air out is

$$h_2 = h_a + \omega_2 h_w$$
$$= \left(0.240 \frac{\text{Btu}}{\text{lbm-°F}}\right) T_{2,°\text{F}} + \omega_2$$
$$\times \left[\left(0.444 \frac{\text{Btu}}{\text{lbm-°F}}\right) T_{2,°\text{F}} + 1061 \frac{\text{Btu}}{\text{lbm}}\right]$$
$$= \left(0.240 \frac{\text{Btu}}{\text{lbm-°F}}\right)(100°\text{F})$$
$$+ \left(0.0353 \frac{\text{lbm moisture}}{\text{lbm air}}\right)\left[\left(0.444 \frac{\text{Btu}}{\text{lbm-°F}}\right)\right.$$
$$\times (100°\text{F}) + 1061 \left.\frac{\text{Btu}}{\text{lbm}}\right]$$
$$= 63.02 \text{ Btu/lbm air}$$

The mass flow rate of air can be determined from Eq. 38.26.

$$q = \dot{m}_a(h_2 - h_1)$$

$$\dot{m}_{\text{air}} = \frac{q}{h_2 - h_1} = \frac{1 \times 10^6 \ \dfrac{\text{Btu}}{\text{hr}}}{63.02 \ \dfrac{\text{Btu}}{\text{lbm air}} - 42.7 \ \dfrac{\text{Btu}}{\text{lbm air}}}$$

$$= \boxed{4.921 \times 10^4 \ \text{lbm air/hr}}$$

(b) From conservation of water vapor,

$$\omega_1 \dot{m}_{\text{air}} + \dot{m}_{\text{make-up}} = \omega_2 \dot{m}_{\text{air}}$$
$$\dot{m}_{\text{make-up}} = \dot{m}_{\text{air}}(\omega_{\text{out}} - \omega_{\text{in}})$$

$$= \left(4.921 \times 10^4 \ \frac{\text{lbm air}}{\text{hr}}\right)$$
$$\times \left(0.0353 \ \frac{\text{lbm moisture}}{\text{lbm air}} - 0.0191 \ \frac{\text{lbm moisture}}{\text{lbm air}}\right)$$

$$= \boxed{797 \ \text{lbm water/hr}}$$

SI Solution

(a) The cooled water flow rate is given by

$$Q = \dot{m}_w c_p \Delta T$$
$$290 \ \text{kW} = \dot{m}_w \left(4.187 \ \frac{\text{kJ}}{\text{kg} \cdot {}^\circ\text{C}}\right)(49^\circ\text{C} - 43^\circ\text{C})$$
$$\dot{m}_w = 11.54 \ \text{kg/s}$$

From the psychrometric chart (App. 38.B), for air in at $T_{\text{db}} = 33^\circ\text{C}$ and $\phi = 60\%$,

$$h_{\text{in}} = 82.3 \ \text{kJ/kg air}$$
$$\omega_{\text{in}} = \left(19.2 \ \frac{\text{g moisture}}{\text{kg air}}\right)\left(\frac{1 \ \text{kg}}{1000 \ \text{g}}\right)$$
$$= 0.0192 \ \text{kg moisture/kg air}$$

For air out, the psychrometric chart (off scale) cannot be used, so use Eq. 38.11 to find the humidity ratio and Eqs. 38.17, 38.18(a), and 38.19(a) to calculate enthalpy of air.

From App. 24.N, the saturated steam pressure at 38°C is 0.06632 bars.

From Eq. 38.1,

$$p_a = p - p_w = 1 \ \text{bar} - 0.06632 \ \text{bar}$$
$$= 0.93368 \ \text{bar}$$

From Eq. 38.11, the humidity ratio for air out is

$$\phi = 1.608\omega_{\text{out}}\left(\frac{p_a}{p_{\text{sat}}}\right)$$
$$0.82 = 1.608\omega_{\text{out}}\left(\frac{0.93368 \ \text{bar}}{0.06632 \ \text{bar}}\right)$$
$$\omega_{\text{out}} = 0.0362 \ \text{kg moisture/kg air}$$

From Eqs. 38.17, 38.18(a), and 38.19(a), the enthalpy of air out is

$$h_2 = h_a + \omega_2 h_w$$
$$= \left(1.005 \ \frac{\text{kJ}}{\text{kg} \cdot {}^\circ\text{C}}\right) T_{{}^\circ\text{C}}$$
$$\quad + \omega_{\text{out}}\left[\left(1.805 \ \frac{\text{kJ}}{\text{kg} \cdot {}^\circ\text{C}}\right)T_{{}^\circ\text{C}} + 2501 \ \frac{\text{kJ}}{\text{kg}}\right]$$
$$= \left(1.005 \ \frac{\text{kJ}}{\text{kg} \cdot {}^\circ\text{C}}\right)(38^\circ\text{C}) + \left(0.0362 \ \frac{\text{kg moisture}}{\text{kg air}}\right)$$
$$\quad \times \left[\left(1.805 \ \frac{\text{kJ}}{\text{kg} \cdot {}^\circ\text{C}}\right)(38^\circ\text{C}) + 2501 \ \frac{\text{kJ}}{\text{kg}}\right]$$
$$= 131.2 \ \text{kJ/kg air}$$

The mass flow rate of air can be determined from Eq. 38.26.

$$q = \dot{m}_a(h_2 - h_1)$$
$$\dot{m}_{\text{air}} = \frac{q}{h_2 - h_1} = \frac{290 \ \text{kW}}{131.2 \ \dfrac{\text{kJ}}{\text{kg air}} - 82.3 \ \dfrac{\text{kJ}}{\text{kg air}}}$$

$$= \boxed{5.930 \ \text{kg air/s}}$$

(b) From conservation of water vapor,

$$\omega_1 \dot{m}_{\text{air}} + \dot{m}_{\text{make-up}} = \omega_2 \dot{m}_{\text{air}}$$
$$\dot{m}_{\text{make-up}} = \dot{m}_{\text{air}}(\omega_{\text{out}} - \omega_{\text{in}})$$

$$= \left(5.930 \ \frac{\text{kg air}}{\text{s}}\right)$$
$$\times \left(0.0362 \ \frac{\text{kg moisture}}{\text{kg air}} - 0.0192 \ \frac{\text{kg moisture}}{\text{kg air}}\right)$$

$$= \boxed{0.101 \ \text{kg water/s}}$$

39 Ventilation

1. *Customary U.S. Solution*

(a) The office volume is

$$V = (60 \text{ ft})(95 \text{ ft})(10 \text{ ft}) = 57{,}000 \text{ ft}^3$$

Based on six air changes per hour, the flow rate is

$$\dot{V} = \left(57{,}000 \, \frac{\text{ft}^3}{\text{air change}}\right) \left(6 \, \frac{\text{air changes}}{\text{hr}}\right) \left(\frac{1 \text{ hr}}{60 \text{ min}}\right)$$

$$= \boxed{5700 \text{ ft}^3/\text{min}}$$

(b) For preferred ventilation based on Sec. 2, Chap. 39, "Ventilation Standards," assume the following.

- The ventilation rate for a nonsmoking area is 20 ft^3/min.

- The ventilation rate for a smoking area ranges from 30 to 60 ft^3/min, with an average value of 45 ft^3/min.

The preferred ventilation rate is

$$\dot{V} = \left(\tfrac{1}{2}\right)(45 \text{ persons}) \left(\frac{20 \, \frac{\text{ft}^3}{\text{min}}}{1 \text{ person}}\right)$$

$$+ \left(\tfrac{1}{2}\right)(45 \text{ persons}) \left(\frac{45 \, \frac{\text{ft}^3}{\text{min}}}{1 \text{ person}}\right)$$

$$= \boxed{1463 \text{ ft}^3/\text{min}}$$

SI Solution

(a) The office volume is

$$(18 \text{ m})(29 \text{ m})(3 \text{ m}) = 1566 \text{ m}^3$$

Based on six air changes per hour, the flow rate is

$$\dot{V} = \left(1566 \, \frac{\text{m}^3}{\text{air change}}\right) \left(6 \, \frac{\text{air changes}}{\text{h}}\right) \left(\frac{1 \text{ h}}{60 \text{ min}}\right)$$

$$= \boxed{156.6 \text{ m}^3/\text{min}}$$

(b) For preferred ventilation based on Sec. 2, Chap. 39, "Ventilation Standards," assume the following.

- The ventilation rate for a nonsmoking area is 0.57 m^3/min.

- The ventilation rate for a smoking area ranges from 0.84 to 1.68 m^3/min, with an average value of 1.26 m^3/min.

The preferred ventilation rate is

$$\dot{V} = \left(\tfrac{1}{2}\right)(45 \text{ persons}) \left(\frac{0.57 \, \frac{\text{m}^3}{\text{min}}}{1 \text{ person}}\right)$$

$$+ \left(\tfrac{1}{2}\right)(45 \text{ persons}) \left(\frac{1.26 \, \frac{\text{m}^3}{\text{min}}}{1 \text{ person}}\right)$$

$$= \boxed{41.2 \text{ m}^3/\text{min}}$$

2. From Eq. 39.12(b), the ventilation rate required is

$$\dot{V}_{\text{cfm}} = \frac{(4.03 \times 10^8) K (\text{SG}) R_{\text{pints/min}}}{(\text{MW}) \text{TLV}_{\text{ppm}}}$$

For the methanol,

$$\dot{V}_{\text{cfm}} = \frac{(4.03 \times 10^8)(6)(0.792) \left(2 \, \frac{\text{pints}}{\text{h}}\right) \left(\frac{1 \text{ h}}{60 \text{ min}}\right)}{(32.04)(200 \text{ ppm})}$$

$$= 9962 \text{ ft}^3/\text{min}$$

For the methylene chloride,

$$\dot{V}_{\text{cfm}} = \frac{(4.03 \times 10^8)(6)(1.336) \left(2 \, \frac{\text{pints}}{\text{hr}}\right) \left(\frac{1 \text{ hr}}{60 \text{ min}}\right)}{(84.94)(500 \text{ ppm})}$$

$$= 2535 \text{ ft}^3/\text{min}$$

The total ventilation rate is

$$9962 \, \frac{\text{ft}^3}{\text{min}} + 2535 \, \frac{\text{ft}^3}{\text{min}} = \boxed{12{,}497 \text{ ft}^3/\text{min}}$$

HVAC

3. *Customary U.S. Solution*

(a) The total ventilation rate is

$$\dot{V} = \left(\frac{60 \ \frac{\text{ft}^3}{\text{min}}}{1 \ \text{person}}\right)(4500 \ \text{persons})\left(60 \ \frac{\text{min}}{\text{hr}}\right)$$

$$= 1.62 \times 10^7 \ \text{ft}^3/\text{hr}$$

The absolute temperature of outside air is

$$T = 0°\text{F} + 460 = 460°\text{R}$$

From the ideal gas law, the density of outside air is

$$\rho = \frac{p}{RT} = \frac{\left(14.6 \ \frac{\text{lbf}}{\text{in}^2}\right)\left(144 \ \frac{\text{in}^2}{\text{ft}^2}\right)}{\left(53.35 \ \frac{\text{ft-lbf}}{\text{lbm-}°\text{R}}\right)(460°\text{R})}$$

$$= 0.08567 \ \text{lbm/ft}^3$$

The mass flow rate is

$$\dot{m} = \dot{V}\rho = \left(1.62 \times 10^7 \ \frac{\text{ft}^3}{\text{hr}}\right)\left(0.08567 \ \frac{\text{lbm}}{\text{ft}^3}\right)$$

$$= 1.388 \times 10^6 \ \text{lbm/hr}$$

Assume no latent heat (no moisture) at 0°F.

From Table 39.1, the sensible heat generated by each person seated in the theater is 225 Btu/hr. Therefore,

$$Q_{\text{in from people}} = \left(225 \ \frac{\frac{\text{Btu}}{\text{hr}}}{\text{person}}\right)(4500 \ \text{persons})$$

$$= 1.01 \times 10^6 \ \text{Btu/hr}$$

The air leaves the auditorium at 70°F. From App. 35.C, the specific heat is 0.240 Btu/lbm-°F (remains fairly constant). Since Q is known, the air temperature entering the auditorium can be calculated by

$$Q = \dot{m}c_p(T_{\text{out,air}} - T_{\text{in,air}})$$

$$T_{\text{in,air}} = T_{\text{out,air}} - \frac{Q}{\dot{m}c_p}$$

$$= 70°\text{F} - \frac{1.01 \times 10^6 \ \frac{\text{Btu}}{\text{hr}}}{\left(1.388 \times 10^6 \ \frac{\text{lbm}}{\text{hr}}\right)\left(0.240 \ \frac{\text{Btu}}{\text{lbm-}°\text{F}}\right)}$$

$$= \boxed{67.0°\text{F}}$$

(b) The heat needed to heat dry ventilation air from 0°F to 67°F is

$$Q = \dot{m}c_p\Delta T$$

$$= \left(1.388 \times 10^6 \ \frac{\text{lbm}}{\text{hr}}\right)\left(0.240 \ \frac{\text{Btu}}{\text{lbm-}°\text{F}}\right)(67°\text{F} - 0°\text{F})$$

$$= 2.23 \times 10^7 \ \text{Btu/hr}$$

(c) Since 2.23×10^7 Btu/hr $> 1.25 \times 10^6$, the furnace is too small.

SI Solution

(a) The total ventilation rate is

$$\dot{V} = \left(\frac{1.68 \ \frac{\text{m}^3}{\text{min}}}{\text{person}}\right)(4500 \ \text{persons})\left(60 \ \frac{\text{min}}{\text{h}}\right)$$

$$= 4.54 \times 10^5 \ \text{m}^3/\text{h}$$

The absolute temperature of outside air is

$$T = -18°\text{C} + 273 = 255\text{K}$$

From the ideal gas law, the density of outside air is

$$\rho = \frac{p}{RT} = \frac{(100.6 \ \text{kPa})\left(1000 \ \frac{\text{Pa}}{\text{kPa}}\right)}{\left(287.03 \ \frac{\text{J}}{\text{kg·K}}\right)(255\text{K})}$$

$$= 1.374 \ \text{kg/m}^3$$

The mass flow rate is

$$\dot{m} = \rho\dot{V} = \left(1.374 \ \frac{\text{kg}}{\text{m}^3}\right)\left(4.54 \times 10^5 \ \frac{\text{m}^3}{\text{h}}\right)$$

$$= 6.238 \times 10^5 \ \text{kg/h}$$

Assume no latent heat (no moisture) at −18°C.

From Table 39.1 and the table footnote, the sensible heat generated by people seated in the theater is

$$\left(225 \ \frac{\text{Btu}}{\text{h}}\right)\left(0.293 \ \frac{\text{W}}{\frac{\text{Btu}}{\text{h}}}\right) = 65.93 \ \text{W}$$

Therefore,

$$Q_{\text{in from people}} = \left(65.93 \ \frac{\text{W}}{\text{persons}}\right)(4500 \ \text{persons})$$

$$\times \left(\frac{1 \ \text{kW}}{1000 \ \text{W}}\right)$$

$$= 296.7 \ \text{kW}$$

The air leaves the auditorium at 21°C. From App. 35.D, the specific heat ≈ 1.0048 kJ/kg·K (remains fairly constant). The air temperature entering the auditorium can be found from known Q as

$$Q = \dot{m}c_p(T_{\text{out,air}} - T_{\text{in,air}})$$

$$T_{\text{in,air}} = T_{\text{out,air}} - \frac{Q}{\dot{m}c_p}$$

$$= 21°\text{C} - \frac{296.7 \ \text{kW}}{\left(6.238 \times 10^5 \ \frac{\text{kg}}{\text{h}}\right)}$$

$$\times \left(\frac{1 \ \text{h}}{3600 \ \text{s}}\right)\left(1.0048 \ \frac{\text{kJ}}{\text{kg·K}}\right)$$

$$= \boxed{19.3°\text{C}}$$

(b) The heat needed to heat dry ventilation air from $-18°C$ to $19.3°C$ is

$$Q = \dot{m}c_p\Delta T$$
$$= \left(6.238 \times 10^5 \ \frac{kg}{h}\right)\left(\frac{1\ h}{3600\ s}\right)\left(1.0048\ \frac{kJ}{kg\cdot K}\right)$$
$$\times \left(19.3°C - (-18°C)\right)$$
$$= 6494\ kW$$

(c) Since 6494 kW > 370 kW, the furnace is too small.

4.

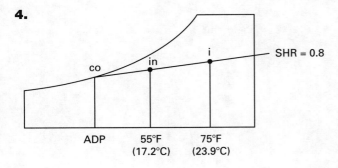

Customary U.S. Solution

(a) From Eq. 38.22, the sensible heat factor is

$$SHR = \frac{q_s}{q_t} = \frac{q_s}{q_s + q_l}$$
$$= \frac{200{,}000\ \frac{Btu}{hr}}{200{,}000\ \frac{Btu}{hr} + 50{,}000\ \frac{Btu}{hr}}$$
$$= 0.8$$

Locate the point i for design conditions of 75°F dry bulb and 50% relative humidity. Draw a condition line with a slope of 0.8 through point i.

$$ADP = 50.8°F$$
$$T_w = ADP$$
$$T_{db,in} = 75°F - 20°F = 55°F$$

From Eq. 39.6(b), the volumetric flow rate of air entering the room is

$$\dot{V}_{in,cfm} = \frac{\dot{q}_{s,Btu/hr}}{\left(1.08\ \frac{Btu\text{-}min}{ft^3\text{-}hr\text{-}°F}\right)(T_{i,°F} - T_{in,°F})}$$
$$= \frac{200{,}000\ \frac{Btu}{hr}}{\left(1.08\ \frac{Btu\text{-}min}{ft^3\text{-}hr\text{-}°F}\right)(75°F - 55°F)}$$
$$= 9259\ ft^3/min$$

This is a mixing problem.

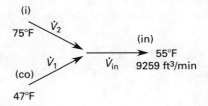

Using the lever rule, and since the temperature scales are all linear, the fraction of air passing through the conditioner is

$$\frac{T_i - T_{in}}{T_i - T_{co}} = \frac{75°F - 55°F}{75°F - 50.8°F} = 0.826$$
$$\dot{V}_1 = (0.826)\left(9259\ \frac{ft^3}{min}\right) = \boxed{7648\ ft^3/min}$$

SI Solution

(a) From Eq. 38.22, the sensible heat factor is

$$SHR = \frac{q_s}{q_s + q_l} = \frac{60\ kW}{60\ kW + 15\ kW} = 0.8$$

Locate the point i for design conditions of 23.9°C dry bulb and 50% relative humidity. Draw a condition line with a slope of 0.8 through point i.

$$ADP = 10°C$$
$$T_w = ADP$$
$$T_{db,in} = 23.9°C - 6.7°C = 17.2°C$$

From Eq. 39.6(a),

$$\dot{V}_{in,m^3/min} = \frac{\dot{q}_{s,kW}}{\left(0.02\ \frac{kJ\cdot min}{m^3\cdot s\cdot°C}\right)(T_{i,°C} - T_{in,°C})}$$
$$= \frac{60\ kW}{\left(0.02\ \frac{kJ\text{-}min}{m^3\cdot s\cdot°C}\right)(23.9°C - 17.2°C)}$$
$$= 447.8\ m^3/min$$

This is a mixing problem.

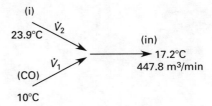

Using the lever rule, and since the temperature scales are all linear, the fraction of air passing through the conditioner is

$$\frac{T_i - T_{\text{in}}}{T_i - T_{\text{co}}} = \frac{23.9°\text{C} - 17.2°\text{C}}{23.9°\text{C} - 10°\text{C}}$$

$$= 0.482$$

$$\dot{V}_1 = (0.482) \left(447.8 \ \frac{\text{m}^3}{\text{min}} \right)$$

$$= \boxed{215.8 \ \text{m}^3/\text{min}}$$

40 Heating Load

1. Customary U.S. Solution

Based on Sec. 10, Chap. 40, for fluorescent lights, the rated wattage should be increased by 20–25% to account for ballast heating. Since the lights are pendant-mounted on chain from the ceiling, most of this heat enters the conditioned space. Assume rated wattage increases by 20%. From Eq. 40.7(b), the internal heat gain due to lights (SF = 1.2) is

$$\dot{q}_{lights} = \left(3413 \ \frac{Btu}{kW\text{-}hr}\right)(SF)\left(\frac{P}{\eta}\right)$$

$$\eta = 1 \quad \text{[given]}$$

$$\dot{q}_{lights} = \left(3413 \ \frac{Btu}{kW\text{-}hr}\right)(1.2)$$

$$\times \left(\frac{(12{,}000 \ W)\left(\frac{1 \ kW}{1000 \ W}\right)}{1}\right)$$

$$= 4.9147 \times 10^4 \ Btu/hr$$

From Eq. 40.7(b), the internal heat gain due to motors (SF = 0.8) is

$$\dot{q}_{motors} = \left(2545 \ \frac{Btu}{hr\text{-}hp}\right)(SF)\left(\frac{P}{\eta}\right)$$

$$\eta = 0.90 \quad \text{[given]}$$

$$\dot{q}_{motors} = (12 \ motors)\left(2545 \ \frac{Btu}{hr\text{-}hp}\right)(0.8)\left(\frac{10 \ hp}{0.90}\right)$$

$$= 2.7147 \times 10^5 \ Btu/hr$$

$$\dot{q}_{total} = \dot{q}_{lights} + \dot{q}_{motors}$$

$$= 4.9147 \times 10^4 \ \frac{Btu}{hr} + 2.7147 \times 10^5 \ \frac{Btu}{hr}$$

$$= \boxed{3.206 \times 10^5 \ Btu/hr}$$

SI Solution

Based on the Customary U.S. Solution, SF = 1.2 for lights. From Eq. 40.7(a), the internal heat gain due to lights is

$$\eta = 1 \quad \text{[given]}$$

$$\dot{q}_{lights} = (SF)\left(\frac{P}{\eta}\right)$$

$$= (1.2)\left(\frac{(12\,000 \ W)\left(\frac{1 \ kW}{1000 \ W}\right)}{1}\right)$$

$$= 14.4 \ kW$$

From Eq. 40.7(a), the internal heat gain due to motors (12 motors) is

$$\dot{q}_{motors} = \left(0.7457 \ \frac{kW}{hp}\right)(SF)\left(\frac{P}{\eta}\right)$$

$$SF = 0.8 \quad \text{[given]}$$

$$\eta = 0.90 \quad \text{[given]}$$

$$\dot{q}_{motors} = (12 \ motors)\left(0.7457 \ \frac{kW}{hp}\right)(0.8)\left(\frac{10 \ hp}{0.90}\right)$$

$$= 79.5 \ kW$$

$$\dot{q}_{total} = \dot{q}_{lights} + \dot{q}_{motors}$$

$$= 14.4 \ kW + 79.5 \ kW$$

$$= \boxed{93.9 \ kW}$$

2. Customary U.S. Solution

From Eq. 40.10(b), the fuel consumption (in gal/heating season) is

$$\frac{\left(24 \ \frac{hr}{day}\right)\dot{q}_{Btu/hr}(DD)}{(T_i - T_o)(HV_{Btu/gal})\eta_{furnace}}$$

$$= \frac{\left(24 \ \frac{hr}{day}\right)\left(3.5 \times 10^6 \ \frac{Btu}{hr}\right)(4772°F\text{-days})}{(70°F - 0°F)\left(153{,}600 \ \frac{Btu}{gal}\right)(0.70)}$$

$$= 53{,}260 \ gal$$

The total cost of 53,260 gal fuel at $0.15/gal is

$$(53{,}260 \ gal)\left(\frac{\$0.15}{gal}\right) = \boxed{\$7989}$$

SI Solution

$$HV_{kJ/L} = \left(42\,800\ \frac{MJ}{m^3}\right)\left(\frac{1000\ kJ}{1\ MJ}\right)\left(\frac{1\ m^3}{1000\ L}\right)$$

$$= 42\,800\ kJ/L$$

From Eq. 40.10(a), fuel consumption (in L/heating season) is

$$\frac{\left(86\,400\ \frac{s}{day}\right)\dot{q}(DD)}{(T_c - T_o)(HV)\eta_{furnace}}$$

$$= \frac{\left(86\,400\ \frac{s}{day}\right)(1\ MW)\left(\frac{1000\ kW}{1\ MW}\right)}{(21.1°C - (-17.8°C))\left(42\,800\ \frac{kJ}{L}\right)(0.70)}$$

$$= 196\,531\ L$$

The total cost at \$0.034/L is

$$(196\,531\ L)\left(\frac{\$0.034}{L}\right) = \boxed{\$6682}$$

3. *Customary U.S. Solution*

From Table 40.3, the surface film coefficient for outside air (horizontal, heat flow up, 15 mph) is $h_o = 6$ Btu/ft²-hr-°F. The film thermal resistance is

$$R_1 = \frac{1}{h_o} = \frac{1}{6\ \frac{Btu}{ft^2\text{-}hr\text{-}°F}} = 0.167\ ft^2\text{-}hr\text{-}°F/Btu$$

From App. 40.A, for roof insulation, the thermal resistance per inch is 2.78 ft²-°F-hr/Btu-in.

$$R_2 = \left(2.78\ \frac{ft^2\text{-}°F\text{-}hr}{Btu\text{-}in}\right)(1.5\ in) = 4.17\ ft^2\text{-}hr\text{-}°F/Btu$$

From App. 40.A, the thermal resistance per inch for soft wood is 1.25 ft²-°F-hr/Btu-in.

$$R_3 = \left(1.25\ \frac{ft^2\text{-}°F\text{-}hr}{Btu\text{-}in}\right)(3\ in) = 3.75\ ft^2\text{-}°F\text{-}hr/Btu$$

For the space between soft wood and an acoustic ceiling, the effective surface emissivity from Eq. 40.4 is

$$E = \frac{1}{\frac{1}{\epsilon_1} + \frac{1}{\epsilon_2} - 1}$$

$$\epsilon_1 = \epsilon_{wood} = 0.90\quad [Sec.\ 6]$$

$$\epsilon_2 = \epsilon_{paper} = 0.95\quad [used\ for\ acoustic\ tile]$$

$$E = \frac{1}{\frac{1}{0.90} + \frac{1}{0.95} - 1} = 0.86$$

From Table 40.2, the thermal conductance of 4 in planar air space at $E = 0.86$ is approximately 0.81 Btu/hr-ft²-°F. The thermal resistance is

$$R_4 = \frac{1}{0.81\ \frac{Btu}{ft^2\text{-}hr\text{-}°F}} = 1.235\ ft^2\text{-}hr\text{-}°F/Btu$$

From App. 40.A, the thermal resistance for 3/4 in acoustical tile is $R_5 = 1.78$ ft²-°F-hr/Btu.

From Table 40.3, the surface film coefficient for inside air (v = 0) (horizontal, heat flow up) is $h_i = 1.63$ Btu/ft²-hr-°F. The film thermal resistance is

$$R_6 = \frac{1}{h_i} = \frac{1}{1.63\ \frac{Btu}{ft^2\text{-}hr\text{-}°F}} = 0.613\ ft^2\text{-}hr\text{-}°F/Btu$$

The total resistance is

$$R_{total} = R_1 + R_2 + R_3 + R_4 + R_5 + R_6$$

$$= 0.167\ \frac{ft^2\text{-}hr\text{-}°F}{Btu} + 4.17\ \frac{ft^2\text{-}hr\text{-}°F}{Btu}$$

$$+ 3.75\ \frac{ft^2\text{-}hr\text{-}°F}{Btu} + 1.235\ \frac{ft^2\text{-}hr\text{-}°F}{Btu}$$

$$+ 1.78\ \frac{ft^2\text{-}hr\text{-}°F}{Btu} + 0.613\ \frac{ft^2\text{-}hr\text{-}°F}{Btu}$$

$$= 11.72\ ft^2\text{-}hr\text{-}°F/Btu$$

The overall coefficient of heat transfer is

$$U = \frac{1}{R_{total}} = \frac{1}{11.72\ \frac{ft^2\text{-}hr\text{-}°F}{Btu}}$$

$$= \boxed{0.0853\ Btu/ft^2\text{-}hr\text{-}°F}$$

SI Solution

From Table 40.3, the surface film coefficient for outside air (horizontal, heat flow up) at 15 mph is $h_o = 34.1$ W/m²·°C. The film thermal resistance is

$$R_1 = \frac{1}{h_o} = \frac{1}{34.1\ \frac{W}{m^2\text{·}°C}} = 0.0293\ m^2\text{·}°C/W$$

From App. 40.A for roof insulation, the thermal resistance per inch is 2.78 ft²-°F-hr/Btu-in.

$$R_2 = \left(2.78\ \frac{ft^2\text{-}°F\text{-}hr}{Btu\text{-}in}\right)\left(6.93\ \frac{\frac{m\text{·}°C}{W}}{\frac{ft^2\text{-}°F\text{-}hr}{Btu\text{-}in}}\right)$$

$$\times (38\ mm)\left(\frac{1\ m}{1000\ mm}\right)$$

$$= 0.732\ m^2\text{·}°C/W$$

From App. 40.A, the thermal resistance per inch for soft wood is 1.25 ft²-°F-hr/Btu-in.

$$R_3 = \left(1.25 \ \frac{\text{ft}^2\text{-}°\text{F-hr}}{\text{Btu-in}}\right)\left(6.93 \ \frac{\frac{\text{m}\cdot°\text{C}}{\text{W}}}{\frac{\text{ft}^2\text{-}°\text{F-hr}}{\text{Btu-in}}}\right)$$
$$\times (76 \text{ mm})\left(\frac{1 \text{ m}}{1000 \text{ mm}}\right)$$
$$= 0.658 \text{ m}^2\cdot°\text{C/W}$$

From the Customary U.S. Solution, the effective surface emissivity between soft wood and an acoustic ceiling is $E = 0.86$.

From Table 40.2, the thermal conductance of 100 mm planar air space at $E = 0.86$ is approximately 4.6 W/m²·°C. The thermal resistance is

$$R_4 = \frac{1}{4.6 \ \frac{\text{W}}{\text{m}^2\cdot°\text{C}}} = 0.217 \text{ m}^2\cdot°\text{C/W}$$

From App. 40.A, the thermal resistance for 19 mm (³/₄ in) acoustical tile is

$$R_5 = \left(1.78 \ \frac{\text{ft}^2\text{-}°\text{F-hr}}{\text{Btu-in}}\right)\left(0.176 \ \frac{\frac{\text{m}^2\cdot°\text{C}}{\text{W}}}{\frac{\text{ft}^2\text{-}°\text{F-hr}}{\text{Btu}}}\right)$$
$$= 0.313 \text{ m}^2\cdot°\text{C/W}$$

From Table 40.3, the surface film coefficient for inside air (v = 0) (horizontal, heat flow up) is $h_i = 9.26$ W/m²·°C. The film thermal resistance is

$$R_6 = \frac{1}{h_i} = \frac{1}{9.26 \ \frac{\text{W}}{\text{m}^2\cdot°\text{C}}} = 0.108 \text{ m}^2\cdot°\text{C/W}$$

The total resistance is

$$R_\text{total} = R_1 + R_2 + R_3 + R_4 + R_5 + R_6$$
$$= 0.0293 \ \frac{\text{m}^2\cdot°\text{C}}{\text{W}} + 0.732 \ \frac{\text{m}^2\cdot°\text{C}}{\text{W}}$$
$$+ 0.658 \ \frac{\text{m}^2\cdot°\text{C}}{\text{W}} + 0.217 \ \frac{\text{m}^2\cdot°\text{C}}{\text{W}}$$
$$+ 0.313 \ \frac{\text{m}^2\cdot°\text{C}}{\text{W}} + 0.108 \ \frac{\text{m}^2\cdot°\text{C}}{\text{W}}$$
$$= 2.057 \text{ m}^2\cdot°\text{C/W}$$

The overall coefficient of heat transfer is

$$U = \frac{1}{R_\text{total}} = \frac{1}{2.057 \ \frac{\text{m}^2\cdot°\text{C}}{\text{W}}} = \boxed{0.486 \text{ W/m}^2\cdot°\text{C}}$$

4. *Customary U.S. Solution*

From Eq. 40.5, the heat loss from the slab is

$$\dot{q} = pF(T_i - T_o)$$

The slab edge coefficient is given as $F = 0.55$ Btu/ft-hr-°F.

The perimeter is

$$p = 12 \text{ ft} + 12 \text{ ft} \quad \text{[2 edges only]}$$
$$= 24 \text{ ft}$$
$$\dot{q} = (24 \text{ ft})\left(0.55 \ \frac{\text{Btu}}{\text{ft-hr-}°\text{F}}\right)(70°\text{F} - (-10°\text{F}))$$
$$= \boxed{1056 \text{ Btu/hr}}$$

SI Solution

From Eq. 40.5, the heat loss from the slab is

$$\dot{q} = pF(T_i - T_o)$$

The slab edge coefficient is given as $F = 0.95$ W/m·°C.

The perimeter is

$$p = 3.6 \text{ m} + 3.6 \text{ m} \quad \text{[2 edges only]}$$
$$= 7.2 \text{ m}$$
$$\dot{q} = (7.2 \text{ m})\left(0.95 \ \frac{\text{W}}{\text{m}\cdot°\text{C}}\right)(21.1°\text{C} - (-23.3°\text{C}))$$
$$= \boxed{303.7 \text{ W}}$$

5.

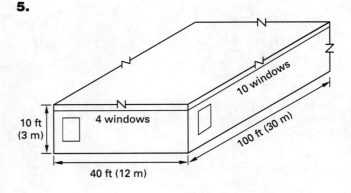

Customary U.S. Solution

For three unshared walls, the total exposed (walls + windows) area is

$$(10 \text{ ft})(40 \text{ ft} + 100 \text{ ft} + 100 \text{ ft}) = 2400 \text{ ft}^2$$

- There are two windows per 20 ft.

- The number of windows for a 40 ft wall is 4.

- The number of windows for each 100 ft wall is 10.

- The total number of windows is

$$4 + 10 + 10 = 24$$

- The total window area is

$$(24)(4 \text{ ft})(6 \text{ ft}) = 576 \text{ ft}^2$$

- The total wall area is

$$2400 \text{ ft}^2 - 576 \text{ ft}^2 = 1824 \text{ ft}^2$$

From Table 40.3, the outside film coefficient for 15 mph wind is $h_o = 6.00$ Btu/hr-ft^2-°F.

From Table 40.3, the inside film coefficient for still air (horizontal, heat flow up) is $h_i = 1.63$ Btu/ft^2-hr-°F.

The overall coefficient of heat transfer for the wall is

$$U_{\text{wall}} = \cfrac{1}{\cfrac{1}{h_o} + \cfrac{1}{h_{\text{wall}}} + \cfrac{1}{h_i}}$$

$$= \cfrac{1}{\cfrac{1}{6.00 \, \cfrac{\text{Btu}}{\text{hr-ft}^2\text{-°F}}} + \cfrac{1}{0.2 \, \cfrac{\text{Btu}}{\text{ft}^2\text{-hr-°F}}} + \cfrac{1}{1.63 \, \cfrac{\text{Btu}}{\text{ft}^2\text{-hr-°F}}}}$$

$$= 0.173 \text{ Btu/hr-ft}^2\text{-°F}$$

The heat loss from the wall is

$$\dot{q}_{\text{wall}} = U_{\text{wall}} A_{\text{wall}} \Delta T$$

$$= \left(0.173 \, \frac{\text{Btu}}{\text{hr-ft}^2\text{-°F}}\right)(1824 \text{ ft}^2)(70\text{°F} - (-10\text{°F}))$$

$$= 25{,}244 \text{ Btu/hr}$$

From App. 40.A, for double, vertical ($^1/_4$ in air space) glass windows, the thermal resistance is 1.63 ft^2-°F-hr/Btu.

$$U_{\text{windows}} = \frac{1}{1.63 \, \dfrac{\text{ft}^2\text{-°F-hr}}{\text{Btu}}} = 0.613 \text{ Btu/ft}^2\text{-°F-hr}$$

The heat loss from the windows is

$$\dot{q}_{\text{windows}} = U_{\text{windows}} A_{\text{windows}} \Delta T$$

$$= \left(0.613 \, \frac{\text{Btu}}{\text{ft}^2\text{-°F-hr}}\right)(576 \text{ ft}^2)$$

$$\times (70\text{°F} - (-10\text{°F}))$$

$$= 28{,}247 \text{ Btu/hr}$$

From Eq. 39.1, the infiltration flow rate is

$$\dot{V} = BL$$

The crack coefficient is given as $B = 32$ ft^3/hr-ft.

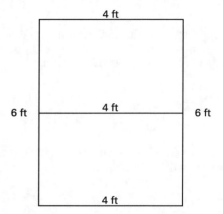

For double-hung windows, the crack length is

$$\text{L} = 4 \text{ ft} + 4 \text{ ft} + 4 \text{ ft} + 6 \text{ ft} + 6 \text{ ft}$$

$$= 24 \text{ ft}$$

$$\dot{V} = \left(32 \, \frac{\text{ft}^3}{\text{hr-ft}}\right)(24 \text{ ft})$$

$$= 768 \text{ ft}^3/\text{hr per window}$$

For 24 windows,

$$\dot{V} = (24)\left(768 \, \frac{\text{ft}^3}{\text{hr}}\right) = 18{,}432 \text{ ft}^3/\text{hr}$$

For atmospheric air, assume $\rho = 0.076$ lbm/ft^3 and $c_p = 0.24$ Btu/lbm-°F.

The mass flow rate of infiltrated air is

$$\dot{m} = \rho \dot{V} = \left(0.075 \, \frac{\text{lbm}}{\text{ft}^3}\right)\left(18{,}432 \, \frac{\text{ft}^3}{\text{hr}}\right)$$

$$= 1382.4 \text{ lbm/hr}$$

The heat loss due to infiltration is

$$\dot{q}_{\text{infiltration}} = \dot{m} c_p \Delta T$$

$$= \left(1382.4 \, \frac{\text{lbm}}{\text{hr}}\right)\left(0.24 \, \frac{\text{Btu}}{\text{lbm-°F}}\right)$$

$$\times (70\text{°F} - (-10\text{°F}))$$

$$= 26{,}542 \text{ Btu/hr}$$

The total heat loss is

$$\dot{q}_{\text{total}} = \dot{q}_{\text{wall}} + \dot{q}_{\text{windows}} + \dot{q}_{\text{infiltration}}$$

$$= 25{,}244 \ \frac{\text{Btu}}{\text{hr}} + 28{,}247 \ \frac{\text{Btu}}{\text{hr}} + 26{,}542 \ \frac{\text{Btu}}{\text{hr}}$$

$$= \boxed{80{,}033 \ \text{Btu/hr}}$$

SI Solution

For three unshared walls, the total exposed (walls + windows) area is

$$(3 \ \text{m})(12 \ \text{m} + 30 \ \text{m} + 30 \ \text{m}) = 216 \ \text{m}^2$$

For 24 windows (from the Customary U.S. Solution), the total window area is

$$(24)(1.2 \ \text{m})(1.8 \ \text{m}) = 51.8 \ \text{m}^2$$

The total wall area is

$$216 \ \text{m}^2 - 51.8 \ \text{m}^2 = 164.2 \ \text{m}^2$$

From Table 40.3, the outside film coefficient for 15 mph wind is $h_o = 34.1 \ \text{W/m}^2\text{·}°\text{C}$.

From Table 40.3, the inside film coefficient for still air (horizontal, heat flow up) is $h_i = 9.26 \ \text{W/m}^2\text{·}°\text{C}$.

The overall coefficient of heat transfer for the wall is

$$U_{\text{wall}} = \cfrac{1}{\cfrac{1}{h_o} + \cfrac{1}{h_{\text{wall}}} + \cfrac{1}{h_i}}$$

$$= \cfrac{1}{\cfrac{1}{34.1 \ \frac{\text{W}}{\text{m}^2\text{·}°\text{C}}} + \cfrac{1}{1.1 \ \frac{\text{W}}{\text{m}^2\text{·}°\text{C}}} + \cfrac{1}{9.26 \ \frac{\text{W}}{\text{m}^2\text{·}°\text{C}}}}$$

$$= 0.956 \ \text{W/m}^2\text{·}°\text{C}$$

The heat loss from the wall is

$$\dot{q}_{\text{wall}} = U_{\text{wall}} A_{\text{wall}} \Delta T$$

$$= \left(0.956 \ \frac{\text{W}}{\text{m}^2\text{·}°\text{C}}\right)(164.2 \ \text{m}^2)$$

$$\times \ (21.1°\text{C} - (-23.3°\text{C}))$$

$$= 6970 \ \text{W}$$

From the Customary U.S. Solution,

$$U_{\text{windows}} = \left(0.613 \ \frac{\text{Btu}}{\text{ft}^2\text{-}°\text{F-hr}}\right)\left(5.68 \ \cfrac{\frac{\text{W}}{\text{m}^2\text{·}°\text{C}}}{\frac{\text{Btu}}{\text{ft}^2\text{-}°\text{F-hr}}}\right)$$

$$= 3.48 \ \text{W/m}^2\text{·}°\text{C}$$

The heat loss from the windows is

$$\dot{q}_{\text{windows}} = U_{\text{windows}} A_{\text{windows}} \Delta T$$

$$= \left(3.48 \ \frac{\text{W}}{\text{m}^2\text{·}°\text{C}}\right)(51.8 \ \text{m}^2)$$

$$\times \ (21.1°\text{C} - (-23.3°\text{C}))$$

$$= 8004 \ \text{W}$$

From Eq. 39.1, the infiltration flow rate is

$$\dot{V} = BL$$

The crack coefficient is given as $B = 3.0 \ \text{m}^3/\text{h·m}$.

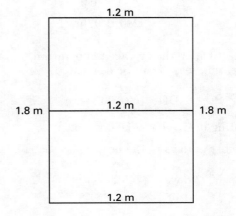

For double-hung windows, the crack length is

$$L = 1.2 \ \text{m} + 1.2 \ \text{m} + 1.2 \ \text{m} + 1.8 \ \text{m} + 1.8 \ \text{m}$$

$$= 7.2 \ \text{m}$$

$$\dot{V} = \left(3.0 \ \frac{\text{m}^3}{\text{h·m}}\right)(7.2 \ \text{m}) = 21.6 \ \text{m}^2/\text{h per window}$$

For 24 windows,

$$\dot{V} = (24)\left(21.6 \ \frac{\text{m}^3}{\text{h}}\right) = 518.4 \ \text{m}^3/\text{h}$$

For atmospheric air, assume $\rho = 1.20 \ \text{kg/m}^3$ and $c_p = 1.005 \ \text{kJ/kg·}°\text{C}$.

The mass flow rate of infiltrated air is

$$\dot{m} = \rho \dot{V} = \left(1.2 \ \frac{\text{kg}}{\text{m}^3}\right)\left(518.4 \ \frac{\text{m}^3}{\text{h}}\right)$$

$$= 622.1 \ \text{kg/h}$$

The heat loss due to infiltration is

$$\dot{q}_{\text{infiltration}} = \dot{m} c_p \Delta T$$

$$= \left(622.1 \ \frac{\text{kg}}{\text{h}}\right)\left(1.005 \ \frac{\text{kJ}}{\text{kg·}°\text{C}}\right)\left(1000 \ \frac{\text{J}}{\text{kg}}\right)$$

$$\times \left(\frac{1 \ \text{h}}{3600 \ \text{s}}\right)(21.1°\text{C} - (-23.3°\text{C}))$$

$$= 7711 \ \text{W}$$

The total heat loss is

$$\dot{q}_{\text{total}} = \dot{q}_{\text{wall}} + \dot{q}_{\text{windows}} + \dot{q}_{\text{infiltration}}$$
$$= 6970 \text{ W} + 8004 \text{ W} + 7711 \text{ W}$$
$$= \boxed{22\,685 \text{ W} \quad (22.7 \text{ kW})}$$

6. *Customary U.S. Solution*

The heat loss per degree of temperature difference is

$$\frac{\dot{q}}{\Delta T} = \frac{650{,}000 \ \dfrac{\text{Btu}}{\text{hr}}}{70°\text{F} - 0°\text{F}}$$
$$= 9286 \text{ Btu/hr-°F}$$

From Eq. 40.9(b), the average temperature, $\overline{\overline{T}}$, over the entire heating season can be calculated.

$$\text{DD} = N(65°\text{F} - \overline{\overline{T}})$$

The heating degree days, DD, are 5252.

The number of days in the heating season, N, is 245.

$$5252 \text{ days} = (245 \text{ days})(65°\text{F} - \overline{\overline{T}})$$
$$\overline{\overline{T}} = 43.56°\text{F}$$

The period between 8:30 A.M. and 5:30 P.M. is 9 hr. For this period, the temperature in the building is 70°F. For the remaining 15 hr, the temperature in the building is 50°F. The total winter heat loss is

$$(245 \text{ days}) \left(9286 \ \dfrac{\text{Btu}}{\text{hr-°F}} \right)$$
$$\times \left[\left(9 \ \dfrac{\text{hr}}{\text{day}} \right)(70°\text{F} - 43.56°\text{F}) \right.$$
$$\left. + \left(15 \ \dfrac{\text{hr}}{\text{day}} \right)(50°\text{F} - 43.56°\text{F}) \right]$$
$$= 7.61 \times 10^8 \text{ Btu}$$

The fuel consumption is

$$\frac{7.61 \times 10^8 \text{ Btu}}{\left(13{,}000 \ \dfrac{\text{Btu}}{\text{lbm}} \right)(0.70)} = \boxed{83{,}626 \text{ lbm/yr}}$$

SI Solution

The heat loss per degree of temperature difference is

$$\frac{\dot{q}}{\Delta T} = \frac{(0.19 \text{ MW}) \left(10^6 \ \dfrac{\text{W}}{\text{MW}} \right)}{21.1°\text{C} - (-17.8°\text{C})}$$
$$= 4884 \text{ W/°C}$$

From Eq. 40.9(a), the average temperature, $\overline{\overline{T}}$, over the entire heating season can be calculated.

$$\text{DD} = N(18°\text{C} - \overline{\overline{T}})$$

The heating Kelvin degree days, DD, are 2918 K·days.

The number of days in the entire heating season, N, is 245.

$$2918 \text{ days} = (245 \text{ days})(18°\text{C} - \overline{\overline{T}})$$
$$\overline{\overline{T}} = 6.09°\text{C}$$

The period between 8:30 A.M. and 5:30 P.M. is 9 h. For this period, the temperature in the building is 21.1°C. For the remaining 15 h, the temperature in the building is 10°C. The total winter heat loss is

$$(245 \text{ days}) \left(4884 \ \dfrac{\text{W}}{°\text{C}} \right)$$
$$\times \left[\left(9 \ \dfrac{\text{h}}{\text{day}} \right)\left(3600 \ \dfrac{\text{s}}{\text{h}} \right)(21.1°\text{C} - 6.09°\text{C}) \right.$$
$$\left. + \left(15 \ \dfrac{\text{h}}{\text{day}} \right)\left(3600 \ \dfrac{\text{s}}{\text{h}} \right)(10°\text{C} - 6.09°\text{C}) \right] \left(\dfrac{1 \text{ MJ}}{10^6 \text{ J}} \right)$$
$$= 8.345 \times 10^5 \text{ MJ}$$

The fuel consumption is

$$\frac{8.345 \times 10^5 \text{ MJ}}{\left(30.2 \ \dfrac{\text{MJ}}{\text{kg}} \right)(0.70)} = \boxed{39\,475 \text{ kg/yr}}$$

7. *Customary U.S. Solution*

The heat loss per degree of temperature difference is

$$\frac{\dot{q}}{\Delta T} = \frac{200{,}000 \ \dfrac{\text{Btu}}{\text{hr}}}{70°\text{F} - 0°\text{F}} = 2857 \text{ Btu/hr-°F}$$

From Eq. 40.9(b), the average temperature, $\overline{\overline{T}}$, over the entire heating season can be calculated.

$$\text{DD} = N(65°\text{F} - \overline{\overline{T}})$$

The heating degree days, DD, are 4200.

The number of days in the heating season, N, is 210.

$$4200 \text{ days} = (210 \text{ days})(65°\text{F} - \overline{\overline{T}})$$
$$\overline{\overline{T}} = 45°\text{F}$$

The total original winter heat loss based on 70°F inside is

$$(210 \text{ days}) \left(24 \ \dfrac{\text{hr}}{\text{day}} \right) \left(2857 \ \dfrac{\text{Btu}}{\text{hr-°F}} \right)$$
$$\times (70°\text{F} - 45°\text{F}) = 3.60 \times 10^8 \text{ Btu}$$

The reduced heat loss based on 68°F inside is

$$(210 \text{ days})\left(24 \ \frac{\text{hr}}{\text{day}}\right)\left(2857 \ \frac{\text{Btu}}{\text{hr-°F}}\right)$$
$$\times (68°F - 45°F) = 3.31 \times 10^8 \text{ Btu}$$

The reduction is

$$\frac{3.60 \times 10^8 \text{ Btu} - 3.31 \times 10^8 \text{ Btu}}{3.60 \times 10^8 \text{ Btu}} = \boxed{0.081 \ (8.1\%)}$$

SI Solution

Since the problem only concerns the percentage reduction in heat loss, determine only the average temperature, $\overline{T}$, as all other parameters except inside temperature remain constant.

From Eq. 40.9(a), the average temperature, $\overline{\overline{T}}$, over the entire heating season can be calculated.

$$DD = N(18°C - \overline{\overline{T}})$$

The heating Kelvin degree days, DD, are 2333 K·days.

The number of days in the entire heating season, N, is 210.

$$2333 \text{ days} = (210 \text{ days})(18°C - \overline{\overline{T}})$$
$$\overline{\overline{T}} = 6.89°C$$

The reduction is

$$\frac{\Delta T_{\text{original}} - \Delta T_{\text{reduced}}}{\Delta T_{\text{original}}}$$

$$\Delta T_{\text{original}} = 21.1°C - 6.89°C = 14.21°C$$
$$\Delta T_{\text{reduced}} = 20°C - 6.89°C = 13.11°C$$

The reduction is

$$\frac{14.21°C - 13.11°C}{14.21°C} = \boxed{0.077 \ (7.7\%)}$$

8. *Customary U.S. Solution*

With air at 70°F, $c_p = 0.240$ Btu/lbm-°F and $\rho = 0.075$ lbm/ft^3. The energy saved during one air change (ventilation) for 12°F set back is

$$\dot{q}_{\text{air}} = mc_p\Delta T$$
$$= (801,000 \text{ ft}^3)\left(0.075 \ \frac{\text{lbm}}{\text{ft}^3}\right)\left(0.240 \ \frac{\text{Btu}}{\text{lbm-°F}}\right)(12°F)$$
$$= 173,016 \text{ Btu/air change}$$

Since the number of air changes is also reduced by half, then on an hourly basis,

$$\dot{q}_{\text{air/hr}} = \left(173,016 \ \frac{\text{Btu}}{\text{air change}}\right)\left(\frac{\frac{1}{2} \text{ air change}}{\text{hr}}\right)$$
$$= 86,508 \text{ Btu/hr}$$

The savings due to reduced heat losses from the roof, floor, and walls (for 12°F set back) is

$$\dot{q} = UA\Delta T$$
$$= \left[\left(0.15 \ \frac{\text{Btu}}{\text{ft}^2\text{-hr-°F}}\right)(11,040 \text{ ft}^2) + \left(1.13 \ \frac{\text{Btu}}{\text{ft}^2\text{-hr-°F}}\right)\right.$$
$$\times (2760 \text{ ft}^2) + \left(0.05 \ \frac{\text{Btu}}{\text{ft}^2\text{-hr-°F}}\right)(26,700 \text{ ft}^2)$$
$$+ \left.\left(1.5 \ \frac{\text{Btu}}{\text{ft-hr-°F}}\right)(690 \text{ ft})\right](12°F)$$
$$= 85,738 \text{ Btu/hr}$$

During an entire week, the building is occupied from 8:00 A.M. to 6:00 P.M. (for 10 hr) and is unoccupied 14 hr each day for 5 days, and it is unoccupied 24 hr each day for 2 days (over the weekend).

The unoccupied time for a 21-week period over a year is

$$t = \left(14 \ \frac{\text{hr}}{\text{day}}\right)\left(5 \ \frac{\text{days}}{\text{wk}}\right)\left(21 \ \frac{\text{wk}}{\text{yr}}\right)$$
$$+ \left(24 \ \frac{\text{hr}}{\text{day}}\right)\left(2 \ \frac{\text{days}}{\text{wk}}\right)\left(21 \ \frac{\text{wk}}{\text{yr}}\right)$$
$$= 2478 \text{ hr/yr}$$

The energy saved per year is

$$\dot{q}_{\text{saved/yr}} = \frac{(\dot{q}_{\text{air/hr}} + \dot{q})t}{\eta_{\text{furnace}}}$$
$$= \frac{\left(86,508 \ \frac{\text{Btu}}{\text{hr}} + 85,738 \ \frac{\text{Btu}}{\text{hr}}\right)\left(2478 \ \frac{\text{hr}}{\text{yr}}\right)}{0.75}$$
$$= (5.691 \times 10^8 \text{ Btu})\left(\frac{1 \text{ therm}}{100,000 \text{ Btu}}\right)$$
$$= 5691 \text{ therms}$$

The cost savings is

$$(5691 \text{ therms})\left(\frac{\$0.25}{\text{therm}}\right) = \boxed{\$1423}$$

SI Solution

With air at 21°C, $c_p = 1.005$ kJ/kg·°C and $\rho = 1.2$ kg/m^3. The energy saved during one air change (ventilation) for 6.7°C set back is

$$\dot{q}_{\text{air}} = mc_p\Delta T$$
$$= (22\,700 \text{ m}^3)\left(1.2 \ \frac{\text{kg}}{\text{m}^3}\right)\left(1.005 \ \frac{\text{kJ}}{\text{kg·°C}}\right)$$
$$\times \left(1000 \ \frac{\text{J}}{\text{kJ}}\right)(6.7°C)$$
$$= 1.834 \times 10^8 \text{ J/air change}$$

HVAC

Since the number of changes is also reduced by one-half, then on an hourly basis,

$$
\dot{q}_{\text{air/hr}} = \left(1.834 \times 10^8 \ \frac{\text{J}}{\text{air change}} \right) \left(\frac{\frac{1}{2} \ \text{air change}}{\text{h}} \right)
$$
$$
\times \left(\frac{1 \ \text{h}}{3600 \ \text{s}} \right)
$$
$$
= 25\,472 \ \text{W}
$$

The savings due to reduced heat losses from the roof, floor, and walls for 6.7°C set back is

$$
\dot{q} = UA\Delta T
$$
$$
= \left[\left(0.85 \ \frac{\text{W}}{\text{m}^2 \cdot {}^\circ\text{C}} \right) (993 \ \text{m}^2) \right.
$$
$$
+ \left(6.42 \ \frac{\text{W}}{\text{m}^2 \cdot {}^\circ\text{C}} \right) (260 \ \text{m}^2)
$$
$$
+ \left(0.3 \ \frac{\text{W}}{\text{m}^2 \cdot {}^\circ\text{C}} \right) (2480 \ \text{m}^2)
$$
$$
\left. + \left(2.6 \ \frac{\text{W}}{\text{m} \cdot {}^\circ\text{C}} \right) (210 \ \text{m}) \right] (6.7 \ {}^\circ\text{C})
$$
$$
= 25\,482 \ \text{W}
$$

From the Customary U.S. Solution, the unoccupied time per year is 2478 h/yr.

The energy saved per year is

$$
\dot{q}_{\text{saved/yr}} = \left(\frac{\dot{q}_{\text{air/h}} + \dot{q}}{\eta_{\text{furnace}}} \right) t
$$
$$
= \left(\frac{25\,472 \ \text{W} + 25\,482 \ \text{W}}{0.75} \right) \left(2478 \ \frac{\text{h}}{\text{yr}} \right)
$$
$$
\times \left(3600 \ \frac{\text{s}}{\text{h}} \right) \left(\frac{1 \ \text{MJ}}{10^6 \ \text{J}} \right) \left(\frac{1 \ \text{therm}}{105.506 \ \text{MJ}} \right)
$$
$$
= 5744 \ \text{therms}
$$

The cost savings is

$$
(5744 \ \text{therms}) \left(\frac{\$0.25}{\text{therm}} \right) = \boxed{\$1436}
$$

41 Cooling Load

1. *Customary U.S. Solution*

(a) This is a standard bypass problem.

The indoor conditions are

$$T_i = 75°F$$

$$\phi_i = 50\%$$

The outdoor conditions are

$$T_{o,\text{db}} = 90°F$$

$$T_{o,\text{wb}} = 76°F$$

The ventilation rate is 2000 ft^3/min.

The loads are

$$q_s = 200{,}000 \text{ Btu/hr}$$

$$q_l = 450{,}000 \text{ gr/hr}$$

To find the sensible heat ratio, q_l must be expressed in Btu/hr.

From the psychrometric chart (App. 38.A), for the room conditions, $\omega = 0.0095$ lbm moisture/lbm dry air.

From Eq. 38.7,

$$\omega = (0.622)\left(\frac{p_w}{p_a}\right)$$

$$= (0.622)\left(\frac{p_w}{p - p_w}\right)$$

$$0.0095 \, \frac{\text{lbm moisture}}{\text{lbm dry air}} = (0.622)\left(\frac{p_{w,\text{psia}}}{14.7 \text{ psia} - p_{w,\text{psia}}}\right)$$

$$p_w = 0.22 \text{ psia}$$

From steam tables (App. 24.A), for 0.22 psia,

$$h_{fg} = 1062 \text{ Btu/lbm}$$

$$q_l = \left(450{,}000 \, \frac{\text{gr}}{\text{hr}}\right)\left(\frac{1 \text{ lbm}}{7000 \text{ gr}}\right)\left(1062 \, \frac{\text{Btu}}{\text{lbm}}\right)$$

$$= 68{,}271 \text{ Btu/hr}$$

From Eq. 38.22, the sensible heat ratio is

$$\text{SHR} = \frac{q_s}{q_s + q_l} = \frac{200{,}000 \, \frac{\text{lbm}}{\text{hr}}}{200{,}000 \, \frac{\text{lbm}}{\text{hr}} + 68{,}271 \, \frac{\text{lbm}}{\text{hr}}}$$

$$= 0.75$$

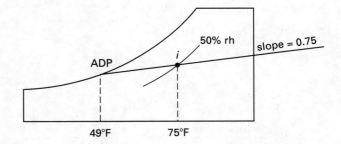

Locate 75°F and 50% relative humidity on the psychrometric chart (App. 38.A). Draw a line with a slope of 0.75 through this point.

The left-hand intersection shows ADP = 49°F. Since the air leaves the conditioner saturated,

$$\text{BF}_{\text{coil}} = 0$$

$$T_{\text{co}} = \boxed{49°F}$$

(b) Calculate the air flow through the room from Eq. 41.9(b).

$$\dot{V}_{\text{in}} = \frac{\dot{q}_{s,\text{Btu/hr}}}{\left(1.08 \, \frac{\text{Btu-min}}{\text{ft}^3\text{-hr}}\right)(T_i - T_{\text{in}})}$$

$$\dot{V}_{\text{in,cfm}} = \frac{200{,}000 \, \frac{\text{Btu}}{\text{hr}}}{\left(1.08 \, \frac{\text{Btu-min}}{\text{ft}^3\text{-hr}}\right)(75°F - 58°F)}$$

$$= \boxed{10{,}893 \text{ ft}^3/\text{min}}$$

(c) Since $T_{\text{in}} = 58°F$, locate this dry-bulb temperature on the condition line. Reading from the chart (App. 38.A),

$$\omega_{\text{in}} = \boxed{0.0081 \text{ lbm/lbm}}$$

SI Solution

(a) The indoor conditions are

$$T_i = 23.9°C$$

$$\phi_i = 50\%$$

The outdoor conditions are

$$T_{o,\text{db}} = 32.2°C$$

$$T_{o,\text{wb}} = 24.4°C$$

HVAC

The ventilation rate is 940 L/s.

The loads are

$$q_s = 58.6 \text{ kW}$$

$$q_l = 29 \text{ kg/h}$$

To find the sensible heat ratio, q_l must be expressed in kW.

From the psychrometric chart (App. 38.B), for the room conditions, $\omega \approx 9.3$ g moisture/kg dry air (9.3×10^{-3} kg moisture/kg dry air).

From Eq. 38.7,

$$\omega = (0.622)\left(\frac{p_w}{p_a}\right)$$

$$= (0.622)\left(\frac{p_w}{p - p_w}\right)$$

$$9.3 \times 10^{-3} \frac{\text{kg moisture}}{\text{kg dry air}} = (0.622)\left(\frac{p_w}{101.3 \text{ kPa} - p_w}\right)$$

$$p_w = 1.49 \text{ kPa}$$

From steam tables (App. 24.N), for 1.49 kPa,

$$h_{fg} = 2470.7 \text{ kJ/kg}$$

$$q_l = \left(29 \frac{\text{kg}}{\text{h}}\right)\left(\frac{1 \text{ h}}{3600 \text{ s}}\right)\left(2470.7 \frac{\text{kJ}}{\text{kg}}\right) = 19.9 \text{ kW}$$

From Eq. 38.22, the sensible heat ratio is

$$\text{SHR} = \frac{q_s}{q_s + q_l} = \frac{58.6 \text{ kW}}{58.6 \text{ kW} + 19.9 \text{ kW}}$$

$$= 0.75$$

Locate 23.9°C and 50% relative humidity on the psychrometric chart (Fig. 38.B). Draw a line with a slope of 0.75 through this point.

The left-hand intersection shows ADP = 9°C. Since the air leaves the conditioner saturated,

$$\text{BF}_{\text{coil}} = 0$$

$$T_{\text{co}} = \boxed{9°\text{C}}$$

(b) Calculate the air flow through the room from Eq. 41.9(a).

$$\dot{V}_{\text{in,L/s}} = \frac{\dot{q}_{s,\text{W}}}{\left(1.20 \frac{\text{W·s}}{\text{L·°C}}\right)(T_i - T_{\text{in}})}$$

$$= \frac{(58.6 \text{ kW})\left(1000 \frac{\text{W}}{\text{kW}}\right)}{\left(1.20 \frac{\text{W·s}}{\text{L·°C}}\right)(23.9°\text{C} - 14.4°\text{C})}$$

$$= \boxed{5140 \text{ L/s}}$$

(c) Since $T_{\text{in}} = 14.4°\text{C}$, locate this dry-bulb temperature on the condition line. Reading from the chart (38.B),

$$\omega_{\text{in}} = \boxed{8.1 \text{ g/kg dry air}}$$

2. *step 1:* Determine thermal resistances for walls, roof, and windows.

For walls:

Assume 2 in furring to be 2 in air space.

From Eq. 40.4, the effective space emissivity is

$$\frac{1}{E} = \frac{1}{\epsilon_1} + \frac{1}{\epsilon_2} - 1$$

$$= \frac{1}{0.96} + \frac{1}{0.95} - 1$$

$$E = 0.91$$

From Table 40.2, for vertical air space orientation, the thermal conductance (by extrapolating) is

$$C = \frac{1}{1.07 \frac{\text{Btu}}{\text{hr-ft}^2\text{-°F}}}$$

$$= 0.93 \text{ hr-ft}^2\text{-°F/Btu}$$

Use App. 40.A.

type of construction	$R, \dfrac{\text{ft}^2\text{-°F-hr}}{\text{Btu}}$	notes
	walls	
4 in brick spacing	0.44	
3 in concrete block	0.40	
1 in mineral wool	3.85	value given per in
2 in furring	0.93	see calculation above
3/8 in drywall gypsum	0.34	0.45 for 1/2 is given
1/2 in plaster (sand aggregate)	0.09	
surface outside (Table 40.3)	0.25	assume 7 1/2 mph air speed
surface inside (Table 40.3)	0.68	still air, $U = 1.46 \dfrac{\text{Btu}}{\text{ft}^2\text{-°F-hr}}$

roof

type of construction	$R, \dfrac{\text{ft}^2\text{-}°\text{F-hr}}{\text{Btu}}$	notes
4 in concrete	0.32	sand aggregate
2 in insulation	5.56	2.28/in
felt	0.06	
1 in air gap	0.87	$\epsilon = 0.90$ for buildup material
$^1\!/_2$ in accoustical ceiling tile	1.19	
surface outside (Table 40.3)	0.25	assume $7^1\!/_2$ mph air speed and downward heat flow $\sim$ upward heat flow
surface inside (Table 40.3)	0.93	still air, $U = 1.08 \dfrac{\text{Btu}}{\text{ft}^2\text{-}°\text{F-hr}}$

windows

type of construction	$R, \dfrac{\text{ft}^2\text{-}°\text{F-hr}}{\text{Btu}}$	notes
$^1\!/_4$ in thick, single glazing	0.66	without shades, $R = 0.88 \dfrac{\text{ft}^2\text{-}°\text{F-hr}}{\text{Btu}}$
cream colored venetian shades, no exterior shades		assume shading factor of 0.75

step 2: Determine the overall heat transfer coefficient for walls, roof, and windows using Eq. 40.3.

$$U = \frac{1}{\sum R_i}$$

For the walls,

$$U = \cfrac{1}{0.25\,\dfrac{\text{ft}^2\text{-}°\text{F-hr}}{\text{Btu}} + 0.44\,\dfrac{\text{ft}^2\text{-}°\text{F-hr}}{\text{Btu}} + 0.40\,\dfrac{\text{ft}^2\text{-}°\text{F-hr}}{\text{Btu}} + 3.85\,\dfrac{\text{ft}^2\text{-}°\text{F-hr}}{\text{Btu}} + 0.93\,\dfrac{\text{ft}^2\text{-}°\text{F-hr}}{\text{Btu}} + 0.34\,\dfrac{\text{ft}^2\text{-}°\text{F-hr}}{\text{Btu}} + 0.09\,\dfrac{\text{ft}^2\text{-}°\text{F-hr}}{\text{Btu}} + 0.68\,\dfrac{\text{ft}^2\text{-}°\text{F-hr}}{\text{Btu}}}$$

$$= 0.143\ \text{Btu/ft}^2\text{-}°\text{F-hr}$$

The cooling load is calculated from the equivalent temperature differences for the walls and roof. Tables of these values are not common; they are now often incorporated directly into HVAC computer application databases. Results from the remainder of this problem will vary with the temperature differences used.

Assume the following equivalent temperature differences for 4 in brick face walls at 4 P.M.

facing east: $\Delta T = 20°\text{F}$

facing west: $\Delta T = 20°\text{F}$

facing south: $\Delta T = 28°\text{F}$

facing north: $\Delta T = 17°\text{F}$

For 4 in brick facing at 4 P.M.,

$$\begin{aligned}
Q_{\text{walls}} &= \left(0.143\ \frac{\text{Btu}}{\text{ft}^2\text{-}°\text{F-hr}}\right)[(1600\ \text{ft}^2)(17°\text{F}) \\
&\quad + (1400\ \text{ft}^2)(28°\text{F}) + (1500\ \text{ft}^2)(20°\text{F}) \\
&\quad + (1400\ \text{ft}^2)(20°\text{F})] \\
&= 17{,}789\ \text{Btu/hr}
\end{aligned}$$

For the roof,

$$U = \cfrac{1}{0.25\,\dfrac{\text{ft}^2\text{-}°\text{F-hr}}{\text{Btu}} + 0.32\,\dfrac{\text{ft}^2\text{-}°\text{F-hr}}{\text{Btu}} + 5.56\,\dfrac{\text{ft}^2\text{-}°\text{F-hr}}{\text{Btu}} + 0.06\,\dfrac{\text{ft}^2\text{-}°\text{F-hr}}{\text{Btu}} + 0.87\,\dfrac{\text{ft}^2\text{-}°\text{F-hr}}{\text{Btu}} + 1.19\,\dfrac{\text{ft}^2\text{-}°\text{F-hr}}{\text{Btu}} + 0.93\,\dfrac{\text{ft}^2\text{-}°\text{F-hr}}{\text{Btu}}}$$

$$= 0.109\ \text{Btu/ft}^2\text{-}°\text{F-hr}$$

Assume an equivalent temperature difference for 4 in concrete roof at 4 P.M. $= 74°\text{F}$. Therefore,

$$\begin{aligned}
Q_{\text{roof}} &= \left(0.109\ \frac{\text{Btu}}{\text{ft}^2\text{-}°\text{F-hr}}\right)(6000\ \text{ft}^2)(74°\text{F}) \\
&= 48{,}396\ \text{Btu/hr}
\end{aligned}$$

For the windows:

Since all windows facing east will receive no direct sunlight at 4 P.M., consider $\Delta T = 95°\text{F} - 78°\text{F}$.

$$\begin{aligned}
Q_{\text{windows}} &= \left(\cfrac{1}{0.66\,\dfrac{\text{ft}^2\text{-}°\text{F-hr}}{\text{Btu}}}\right)(100\ \text{ft}^2)(95°\text{F} - 78°\text{F}) \\
&= 2576\ \text{Btu/hr}
\end{aligned}$$

The total sensible transmission load (at 4 P.M.) is

$$\begin{aligned}
Q_{\text{total}} &= 17{,}789\ \frac{\text{Btu}}{\text{hr}} + 48{,}396\ \frac{\text{Btu}}{\text{hr}} + 2576\ \frac{\text{Btu}}{\text{hr}} \\
&= 68{,}761\ \text{Btu/hr}
\end{aligned}$$

HVAC

This may not be the peak load. Since Q_{walls} and Q_{roof} are the major contributors and ΔT equivalent temperature differences are maximum between 4 P.M. and 6 P.M., the peak cooling load will be maximum somewhere between 4 P.M. and 6 P.M. Consider Q_{walls} and Q_{roof} for 6 P.M.

At 6 P.M., the equivalent temperature differences for 4 in brick facing are assumed as

$$\text{facing east: } \Delta T = 22°\text{F}$$
$$\text{facing west: } \Delta T = 35°\text{F}$$
$$\text{facing south: } \Delta T = 28°\text{F}$$
$$\text{facing north: } \Delta T = 20°\text{F}$$

$$
\begin{aligned}
Q_{\text{walls}} = & \left(0.143 \ \frac{\text{Btu}}{\text{ft}^2\text{-}°\text{F-hr}} \right) \Big[(1600 \ \text{ft}^2)(20°\text{F}) \\
& + (1400 \ \text{ft}^2)(28°\text{F}) + (1500 \ \text{ft}^2)(22°\text{F}) \\
& + (1400 \ \text{ft}^2)(35°\text{F}) \Big] \\
= & \ 21{,}908 \ \text{Btu/hr}
\end{aligned}
$$

Assume the equivalent temperature difference for a 4 in concrete roof at 6 P.M. is 68°F.

$$
\begin{aligned}
Q_{\text{roof}} &= \left(0.109 \ \frac{\text{Btu}}{\text{ft}^2\text{-}°\text{F-hr}} \right) (6000 \ \text{ft}^2)(68°\text{F}) \\
&= 44{,}880 \ \text{Btu/hr}
\end{aligned}
$$

The total sensible transmission load at 6 P.M. is

$$
\begin{aligned}
Q_{\text{total}} &= 21{,}908 \ \frac{\text{Btu}}{\text{hr}} + 44{,}472 \ \frac{\text{Btu}}{\text{hr}} + 2576 \ \frac{\text{Btu}}{\text{hr}} \\
&= 68{,}956 \ \text{Btu/hr}
\end{aligned}
$$

This is very close to the 4 P.M. load.

An SI solution of this problem is not supported by this book.

43 Determinate Statics

---

1. *Customary U.S. Solution*

Use Eq. 43.67 to relate the midpoint sag, S, to the constant c.

$$S = c\left(\cosh\left(\frac{a}{c}\right) - 1\right)$$

$$10\text{ ft} = c\left(\cosh\left(\frac{50\text{ ft}}{c}\right) - 1\right)$$

Solve by trial and error.

$$c = 126.6\text{ ft}$$

(a) Use Eq. 43.69 to find the midpoint tension.

$$H = wc = \left(2\,\frac{\text{lbm}}{\text{ft}}\right)\left(\frac{32.2\,\frac{\text{ft-lbf}}{\text{lbm-sec}^2}}{32.2\,\frac{\text{ft}}{\text{sec}^2}}\right)(126.6\text{ ft})$$

$$= \boxed{253.2\text{ lbf}}$$

(b) Use Eq. 43.71 to find the maximum tension.

$$T = wy = w(c + S)$$

$$= \left(2\,\frac{\text{lbm}}{\text{ft}}\right)\left(\frac{32.2\,\frac{\text{ft-lbf}}{\text{lbm-sec}^2}}{32.2\,\frac{\text{ft}}{\text{sec}^2}}\right)(126.6\text{ ft} + 10\text{ ft})$$

$$= \boxed{273.2\text{ lbf}}$$

(c) From $T = wy$,

$$y = \frac{T}{w} = \frac{500\text{ lbf}}{2\,\frac{\text{lbf}}{\text{ft}}} = 250\text{ ft}\quad\text{[at right support]}$$

$$250\text{ ft} = c\left(\cosh\left(\frac{50\text{ ft}}{c}\right)\right)$$

By trial and error, $c = 245$ ft.

Substitute into Eq. 43.67.

$$S = c\left(\cosh\left(\frac{a}{c}\right) - 1\right)$$

$$= \left(245\,\frac{\text{ft}}{\text{sec}}\right)\left(\cosh\left(\frac{50\text{ ft}}{245\,\frac{\text{ft}}{\text{sec}}}\right) - 1\right)$$

$$= \boxed{5.12\text{ ft}}$$

SI Solution

Use Eq. 43.67 to relate the midpoint sag, S, to the constant c.

$$S = c\left(\cosh\left(\frac{a}{c}\right) - 1\right)$$

$$3\text{ m} = c\left(\cosh\left(\frac{15\text{ m}}{c}\right) - 1\right)$$

Solve by trial and error.

$$c = 38.0\text{ m}$$

(a) Use Eq. 43.69 to find the midpoint tension.

$$H = wc = mgc = \left(3\,\frac{\text{kg}}{\text{m}}\right)\left(9.81\,\frac{\text{m}}{\text{s}^2}\right)(38.0\text{ m})$$

$$= \boxed{1118.3\text{ N}}$$

(b) Use Eq. 43.71 to find the maximum tension.

$$T = wy = w(c + S) = mg(c + S)$$

$$= \left(3\,\frac{\text{kg}}{\text{m}}\right)\left(9.81\,\frac{\text{m}}{\text{s}^2}\right)(38.0\text{ m} + 3.0\text{ m})$$

$$= \boxed{1127.1\text{ N}}$$

(c) From $T = wy$,

$$y = \frac{T}{w} = \frac{2200\text{ N}}{\left(3\,\frac{\text{kg}}{\text{m}}\right)\left(9.81\,\frac{\text{m}}{\text{s}^2}\right)}$$

$$= 74.75\text{ m}\quad\text{[at right support]}$$

$$74.75\text{ m} = c\left(\cosh\left(\frac{15\text{ m}}{c}\right)\right)$$

By trial and error, $c = 73.2$ ft.

Substitute into Eq. 43.67.

$$S = c\left(\cosh\left(\frac{a}{c}\right) - 1\right)$$

$$= (73.72\text{ m})\left(\cosh\left(\frac{15\text{ m}}{73.2\text{ m·s}}\right) - 1\right)$$

$$= \boxed{1.54\text{ m}}$$

2. *step 1:* Draw the tripod with the origin at the apex.

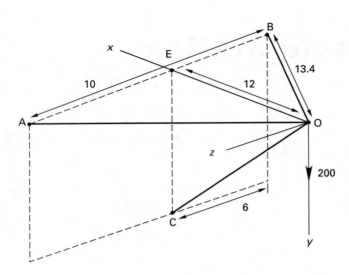

step 2: By inspection, the force components are $F_x = 0$, $F_y = 200$, and $F_z = 0$.

step 3: First, from triangle EBO, length BE is

$$BE = \sqrt{(13.4 \text{ units})^2 - (12 \text{ units})^2} = 5.96 \text{ units}$$
$$[\text{say } 6 \text{ units}]$$

The (x, y, z) coordinates of the three support points are

$$\begin{array}{l} \text{point A}-(12, 0, 4) \\ \text{point B}-(12, 0, -6) \\ \text{point C}-(12, 9, 0) \end{array}$$

step 4: Find the lengths of the legs.

$$\begin{aligned} AO &= \sqrt{x^2 + y^2 + z^2} \\ &= \sqrt{(12 \text{ units})^2 + (0 \text{ units})^2 + (4 \text{ units})^2} \\ &= 12.65 \text{ units} \\ BO &= \sqrt{x^2 + y^2 + z^2} \\ &= \sqrt{(12 \text{ units})^2 + (0 \text{ units})^2 + (-6 \text{ units})^2} \\ &= 13.4 \text{ units} \\ CO &= \sqrt{x^2 + y^2 + z^2} \\ &= \sqrt{(12 \text{ units})^2 + (9 \text{ units})^2 + (0 \text{ units})^2} \\ &= 15.0 \text{ units} \end{aligned}$$

step 5: Use Eqs. 43.75, 43.76, and 43.77 to find the direction cosines for each leg.

For leg AO,

$$\cos \theta_{A,x} = \frac{x_A}{AO} = \frac{12 \text{ units}}{12.65 \text{ units}} = 0.949$$

$$\cos \theta_{A,y} = \frac{y_A}{AO} = \frac{0 \text{ units}}{12.65 \text{ units}} = 0$$

$$\cos \theta_{A,z} = \frac{z_A}{AO} = \frac{4 \text{ units}}{12.65 \text{ units}} = 0.316$$

For leg BO,

$$\cos \theta_{B,x} = \frac{x_B}{BO} = \frac{12 \text{ units}}{13.4 \text{ units}} = 0.896$$

$$\cos \theta_{B,y} = \frac{y_B}{BO} = \frac{0 \text{ units}}{13.4 \text{ units}} = 0$$

$$\cos \theta_{B,z} = \frac{z_B}{BO} = \frac{-6 \text{ units}}{13.4 \text{ units}} = -0.448$$

For leg CO,

$$\cos \theta_{C,x} = \frac{x_C}{CO} = \frac{12 \text{ units}}{15.0 \text{ units}} = 0.80$$

$$\cos \theta_{C,y} = \frac{y_C}{CO} = \frac{9 \text{ units}}{15.0 \text{ units}} = 0.60$$

$$\cos \theta_{C,z} = \frac{z_C}{CO} = \frac{0 \text{ units}}{15.0 \text{ units}} = 0$$

steps 6 and 7: Substitute Eqs. 43.78, 43.79, and 43.80 into equilibrium Eqs. 43.81, 43.82, and 43.83.

$$F_A \cos \theta_{A,x} + F_B \cos \theta_{B,x} + F_C \cos \theta_{C,x} + F_x = 0$$
$$F_A \cos \theta_{A,y} + F_B \cos \theta_{B,y} + F_C \cos \theta_{C,y} + F_y = 0$$
$$F_A \cos \theta_{A,z} + F_B \cos \theta_{B,z} + F_C \cos \theta_{C,z} + F_z = 0$$
$$0.949 F_A + 0.896 F_B + 0.80 F_C + 0 = 0$$
$$0 F_A + 0 F_B + 0.60 F_C + 200 = 0$$
$$0.316 F_A - 0.448 F_B + 0 F_C + 0 = 0$$

Solve the three equations simultaneously.

$$\boxed{\begin{array}{l} F_A = -333.3 \quad (C) \\ F_B = 118.9 \quad (T) \\ F_C = 168.6 \quad (T) \end{array}}$$

3. First, find the vertical reaction at point D.

$$\sum M_C = (CD)D_y - (AF)(8000) + (AC)(1600) = 0$$
$$6D_y - (6)(8000) + (16)(1600) = 0$$

Solve for $D_y = 3733.3$.

The free-body diagram of pin D is as follows.

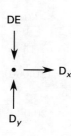

$$\sum F_y = D_y - DE = 0$$

Therefore,

$$DE = D_y = \boxed{3733.3 \quad (C)}$$

4. *step 1:* Move the origin to the apex of the tripod. Call this point O.

step 2: By inspection, the force components are $F_x = 1200$, $F_y = 0$, and $F_z = 0$.

step 3: The (x, y, z) coordinates of the three support points are

$$\begin{aligned}\text{point A} &- (5, -12, 0) \\ \text{point B} &- (0, -8, -8) \\ \text{point C} &- (-4, -7, 6)\end{aligned}$$

step 4: Find the lengths of the legs.

$$\begin{aligned}AO &= \sqrt{x^2 + y^2 + z^2} = \sqrt{(5)^2 + (-12)^2 + (0)^2} \\ &= 13.0\end{aligned}$$

$$\begin{aligned}BO &= \sqrt{x^2 + y^2 + z^2} = \sqrt{(0)^2 + (-8)^2 + (-8)^2} \\ &= 11.31\end{aligned}$$

$$\begin{aligned}CO &= \sqrt{x^2 + y^2 + z^2} = \sqrt{(-4)^2 + (-7)^2 + (6)^2} \\ &= 10.05\end{aligned}$$

step 5: Use Eqs. 43.75, 43.76, and 43.77 to find the direction cosines for each leg.

For leg AO,

$$\cos\theta_{A,x} = \frac{x_A}{AO} = \frac{5}{13.0} = 0.385$$

$$\cos\theta_{A,y} = \frac{y_A}{AO} = \frac{-12}{13.0} = -0.923$$

$$\cos\theta_{A,z} = \frac{z_A}{AO} = \frac{0}{13.0} = 0$$

For leg BO,

$$\cos\theta_{B,x} = \frac{x_B}{BO} = \frac{0}{11.31} = 0$$

$$\cos\theta_{B,y} = \frac{y_B}{BO} = \frac{-8}{11.31} = -0.707$$

$$\cos\theta_{B,z} = \frac{z_B}{BO} = \frac{-8}{11.31} = -0.707$$

For leg CO,

$$\cos\theta_{C,x} = \frac{x_C}{CO} = \frac{-4}{10.05} = -0.398$$

$$\cos\theta_{C,y} = \frac{y_C}{CO} = \frac{-7}{10.05} = -0.697$$

$$\cos\theta_{C,z} = \frac{z_C}{CO} = \frac{6}{10.05} = 0.597$$

steps 6 and 7: Substitute Eqs. 43.78, 43.79, and 43.80 into equilibrium Eqs. 43.81, 43.82, and 43.83.

$$F_A \cos\theta_{A,x} + F_B \cos\theta_{B,x} + F_C \cos\theta_{C,x} + F_x = 0$$
$$F_A \cos\theta_{A,y} + F_B \cos\theta_{B,y} + F_C \cos\theta_{C,y} + F_y = 0$$
$$F_A \cos\theta_{A,z} + F_B \cos\theta_{B,z} + F_C \cos\theta_{C,z} + F_z = 0$$
$$0.385 F_A + 0 F_B - 0.398 F_C + 1200 = 0$$
$$-0.923 F_A - 0.707 F_B - 0.697 F_C + 0 = 0$$
$$0 F_A - 0.707 F_B + 0.597 F_C + 0 = 0$$

Solve the three equations simultaneously.

$$\boxed{\begin{aligned} F_A &= -1793 \quad (C) \\ F_B &= 1080 \quad (T) \\ F_C &= 1279 \quad (T) \end{aligned}}$$

5. First, find the vertical reactions.

$$\sum F_y = A_y + L_y - (5)(4000) - (5)(60{,}000) = 0$$

By symmetry, $A_y = L_y$.

$$2A_y = (5)(4000) + (5)(60{,}000)$$
$$A_y = 160{,}000$$
$$L_y = 160{,}000$$

(a) For DE, make a cut in members BD and DE.

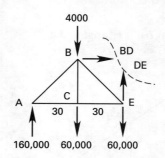

$$\sum F_y = 160{,}000 - 60{,}000 - 60{,}000 + DE - 4000 = 0$$
$$DE = -36{,}000 \quad (C)$$

(b) For HJ, make a cut in members HJ, HI, and GI.

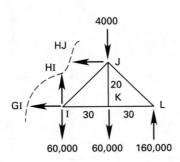

$$\sum M_I = (160,000)(60) - (60,000)(30)$$
$$- (4000)(30) + HJ(20)$$
$$= 0$$

$$HJ = \boxed{-384,000 \quad (C)}$$

6. First, consider a free-body diagram at point O in the x-y plane.

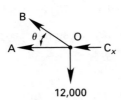

θ is obtained from triangle AOB.

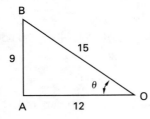

C_x is obtained from triangle AOC.

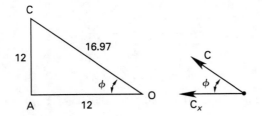

Equilibrium in the x-y plane at point O is $\sum F_y = 0$,

$$B \sin \theta = 12,000$$
$$B = \frac{12,000}{\sin \theta} = \frac{12,000}{\dfrac{9}{15}} = 20,000$$
$$B_x = B \cos \theta = (20,000)\left(\frac{12}{15}\right) = 16,000$$
$$B_y = B \sin \theta = (20,000)\left(\frac{9}{15}\right) = 12,000$$

Since BO is in the x-y plane, $B_z = 0$.

Next, consider a free-body diagram at point O in the x-z plane.

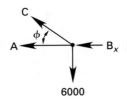

$\sum F_x = 0$:

$$A + B_x + C \cos \phi = 0$$
$$A + C \cos \phi = -B_x = -B \cos \theta$$
$$= (-20,000)\left(\frac{12}{15}\right)$$
$$= -16,000$$

$\sum F_y = 0$:

$$C \sin \phi = 6000$$
$$C = \frac{6000}{\sin \phi}$$
$$= \frac{6000}{\dfrac{12}{16.97}} = 8485$$

Thus,

$$A = -C \cos \phi - 16,000$$
$$= (-8485)\left(\frac{12}{16.97}\right) - 16,000$$
$$= -22,000$$

Since AO is on the x-axis,

$$A_x = -22,000$$
$$A_y = 0$$
$$A_z = 0$$

Solve for C reactions.

$$C_x = C \cos \phi = (8485)\left(\frac{12}{16.97}\right) = 6000$$
$$C_z = C \sin \phi = (8485)\left(\frac{12}{16.97}\right) = 6000$$

Since CO is in the x-z plane, $C_y = 0$.

7. *Customary U.S. Solution*

First, find the amount of thermal expansion. From Table 49.2, the coefficient of thermal expansion for steel is 6.5×10^{-6} $1/°F$.

$$\delta = \alpha L_o (T_2 - T_1)$$
$$= \left(6.5 \times 10^{-6}\ \frac{1}{°F}\right) (1\ \text{mi}) \left(5280\ \frac{\text{ft}}{\text{mi}}\right)$$
$$\times (99.14°F - 70°F)$$
$$= 1.000085\ \text{ft} \approx 1\ \text{ft}$$

For thermal expansion, assume the distributed load is uniform along the length of the rail. This resembles the case of a cable under its own weight. From the parabolic cable figure (Fig. 43.18), when the distance S is small relative to distance a, the problem can be solved by using the parabolic equation, Eq. 43.57.

$$L \approx a \left[1 + \left(\frac{2}{3}\right)\left(\frac{S}{a}\right)^2 - \left(\frac{2}{5}\right)\left(\frac{S}{a}\right)^4 \right]$$

$$\frac{5280\ \text{ft} + 1\ \text{ft}}{2} \approx (2640\ \text{ft}) \left[1 + \left(\frac{2}{3}\right)\left(\frac{S}{2640\ \text{ft}}\right)^2 \right.$$
$$\left. - \left(\frac{2}{5}\right)\left(\frac{S}{2640\ \text{ft}}\right)^4 \right]$$

Using trial and error, $S \approx \boxed{44.5\ \text{ft.}}$

SI Solution

First, find the amount of thermal expansion. From Table 49.2, the coefficient of thermal expansion for steel is 11.7×10^{-6} $1/°C$.

$$\delta = \alpha L_o (T_2 - T_1)$$
$$= \left(11.7 \times 10^{-6}\ \frac{1}{°C}\right) (1.6\ \text{km}) \left(1000\ \frac{\text{m}}{\text{km}}\right)$$
$$\times (37.30°C - 21.11°C)$$
$$= 0.30308\ \text{m} \approx 0.30\ \text{m}$$

For thermal expansion, assume the distributed load is uniform along the length of the rail. This resembles the case of a cable under its own weight. From the parabolic cable figure (Fig. 43.18), when distance S is small relative to distance a, the problem can be solved by using the parabolic equation, Eq. 43.57.

$$L \approx a \left[1 + \left(\frac{2}{3}\right)\left(\frac{S}{a}\right)^2 - \left(\frac{2}{5}\right)\left(\frac{S}{a}\right)^4 \right]$$

$$\frac{1600\ \text{m} + 0.3\ \text{m}}{2} \approx (800\ \text{m}) \left[1 + \left(\frac{2}{3}\right)\left(\frac{S}{800\ \text{m}}\right)^2 \right.$$
$$\left. - \left(\frac{2}{5}\right)\left(\frac{S}{800\ \text{m}}\right)^4 \right]$$

Using trial and error, $S \approx \boxed{13.6\ \text{m.}}$

Statics

45 Engineering Materials

1. The vinyl chloride mer is

$$
\begin{array}{ccc}
\text{H} & & \text{H} \\
| & & | \\
\text{C} & = & \text{C} \\
| & & | \\
\text{H} & & \text{Cl}
\end{array}
$$

With 20% efficiency, 5 molecules of HCl per PVC molecule are required to supply each end Cl atom. This is the same as 5 mol HCl per mole PVC. Using Avogadro's number of 6.022×10^{23} molecules per mole, the number of molecules of HCl per gram of PVC is

$$
\frac{\left(5 \; \dfrac{\text{mol HCl}}{\text{mol PVC}}\right)\left(6.022 \times 10^{23} \; \dfrac{\text{molecules}}{\text{mol}}\right)}{7000 \; \dfrac{\text{g}}{\text{mol}}}
$$

$$
= \boxed{4.30 \times 10^{20} \text{ molecules HCl/gram PVC}}
$$

2. The molecular weight of hydrogen peroxide, H_2O_2, is

$$
(2)\left(1 \; \frac{\text{g}}{\text{mol}}\right) + (2)\left(16 \; \frac{\text{g}}{\text{mol}}\right) = 34 \text{ g/mol}
$$

The weight of H_2O_2 is

$$
(10 \text{ mL})\left(1 \; \frac{\text{g}}{\text{mL}}\right) = 10 \text{ g}
$$

The number of H_2O_2 molecules in a 0.2% solution is

$$
\frac{(10 \text{ g})\left(\dfrac{0.2\%}{100\%}\right)\left(6.022 \times 10^{23} \; \dfrac{\text{molecules}}{\text{mol}}\right)}{34 \; \dfrac{\text{g}}{\text{mol}}}
$$

$$
= 3.54 \times 10^{20} \text{ molecules}
$$

The molecular weight of ethylene, C_2H_4, is

$$
(2)\left(12 \; \frac{\text{g}}{\text{mol}}\right) + (4)\left(1 \; \frac{\text{g}}{\text{mol}}\right) = 28 \text{ g/mol}
$$

The number of ethylene molecules is

$$
\frac{(12 \text{ g})\left(6.022 \times 10^{23} \; \dfrac{\text{molecules}}{\text{mol}}\right)}{28 \; \dfrac{\text{g}}{\text{mol}}}
$$

$$
= 2.58 \times 10^{23} \text{ molecules}
$$

Since it takes one H_2O_2 molecule (i.e., $2OH^-$ radicals) to stabilize a polyethylene molecule, there are 3.54×10^{20} polymers.

The degree of polymerization is

$$
\text{DP} = \frac{2.58 \times 10^{23} \; C_2H_4 \text{ molecules}}{3.54 \times 10^{20} \text{ polymers}} = \boxed{729}
$$

46 Material Properties and Testing

1. *Customary U.S. Solution*

The fractional reduction in diameter is

$$\nu e = (0.3)\left(0.020 \ \frac{\text{in}}{\text{in}}\right) = 0.006$$

(a) From Eq. 46.5, the true stress is

$$\sigma = \frac{F}{A_o(1-\nu e)^2} = \left(\frac{F_o}{A_o}\right)\left(\frac{1}{(1-\nu e)^2}\right)$$
$$= \left(20{,}000 \ \frac{\text{lbf}}{\text{in}^2}\right)\left(\frac{1}{(1-0.006)^2}\right)$$
$$= \boxed{20{,}242 \ \text{lbf/in}^2}$$

(b) From Eq. 46.6, the true strain is

$$\epsilon = \ln(1+e) = \ln(1+0.020) = \boxed{0.0198 \ \text{in/in}}$$

SI Solution

The fractional reduction in diameter is

$$\nu e = (0.3)\left(0.200 \ \frac{\text{mm}}{\text{mm}}\right) = 0.06$$

(a) From Eq. 46.5, the true stress is

$$\sigma = \frac{F}{A_o(1-\nu e)^2} = \left(\frac{F}{A_o}\right)\left(\frac{1}{(1-\nu e)^2}\right)$$
$$= (140 \ \text{MPa})\left(\frac{1}{(1-0.06)^2}\right)$$
$$= \boxed{158.4 \ \text{MPa}}$$

(b) From Eq. 46.6, the true strain is

$$\epsilon = \ln(1+e) = \ln(1+0.200) = \boxed{0.182 \ \text{mm/mm}}$$

2. *Customary U.S. Solution*

(a) Extend a line from the 0.5% offset strain value parallel to the linear portion of the curve.

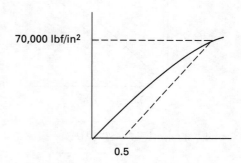

The 0.5% yield strength is $\boxed{70{,}000 \ \text{lbf/in}^2}$.

(b) At the elastic limit, the stress is 60,000 lbf/in² and the percent strain is 2. The elastic modulus is

$$E = \frac{\text{stress}}{\text{strain}} = \frac{60{,}000 \ \dfrac{\text{lbf}}{\text{in}^2}}{0.02}$$
$$= \boxed{3 \times 10^6 \ \text{lbf/in}^2}$$

(c) The ultimate strength is the highest point of the curve. This value is $\boxed{80{,}000 \ \text{lbf/in}^2}$.

(d) The fracture strength is at the end of the curve. This value is $\boxed{70{,}000 \ \text{lbf/in}^2}$.

(e) The percent elongation at fracture is determined by extending a straight line down from the fracture point. This gives a value of $\boxed{8\%}$.

(f) From Eq. 46.21, the shear modulus is

$$G = \frac{E}{(2)(1+\nu)} = \frac{3 \times 10^6 \ \dfrac{\text{lbf}}{\text{in}^2}}{(2)(1+0.3)}$$
$$= \boxed{1.15 \times 10^6 \ \text{lbf/in}^2}$$

Materials

(g) The toughness is the area under the stress-strain curve. Divide the area into squares of 20 ksi × 1%. There are about 25.5 squares covered.

$$(25.5)\left(20{,}000\ \frac{\text{lbf}}{\text{in}^2}\right)\left(0.01\ \frac{\text{in}}{\text{in}}\right) = \boxed{5100\ \text{in-lbf/in}^3}$$

SI Solution

(a) Extend a line from the 0.5% offset strain value parallel to the linear portion of the curve.

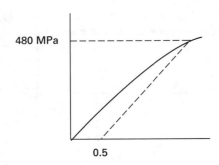

The 0.5% yield strength is $\boxed{480\ \text{MPa.}}$

(b) At the elastic limit, the stress is 410 MPa and the percent strain is 2. The elastic modulus is

$$E = \frac{\text{stress}}{\text{strain}} = \frac{410\ \text{MPa}}{(0.02)\left(1000\ \dfrac{\text{MPa}}{\text{GPa}}\right)}$$

$$= \boxed{20.5\ \text{GPa}}$$

(c) The ultimate strength is the highest point of the curve. This value is $\boxed{550\ \text{MPa.}}$

(d) The fracture strength is at the end of the curve. This value is $\boxed{480\ \text{MPa.}}$

(e) The percent elongation at fracture is determined by extending a straight line down from the fracture point. This gives a value of $\boxed{8\%.}$

(f) From Eq. 46.21, the shear modulus is

$$G = \frac{E}{(2)(1+\nu)} = \frac{20.5\ \text{GPa}}{(2)(1+0.3)}$$

$$= \boxed{7.88\ \text{GPa}}$$

(g) The toughness is the area under the stress-strain curve. Divide the area into squares of 137.5 MPa × 1%. There are about 25.5 squares covered.

$$(25.5)(137.5\ \text{MPa})\left(0.01\ \frac{\text{m}}{\text{m}}\right) = \boxed{35\ \text{MJ/m}^3}$$

3. *Customary U.S. Solution*

Use the reduction in area as the measure of ductility. From Eq. 46.12,

$$\text{ductility} = \text{reduction in area} = \frac{A_o - A_f}{A_o}$$

$$= \frac{4.0\ \text{in}^2 - 3.42\ \text{in}^2}{4.0\ \text{in}^2} = \boxed{0.145}$$

SI Solution

Use the reduction in area as the measure of ductility. From Eq. 46.12,

$$\text{ductility} = \text{reduction in area} = \frac{A_o - A_f}{A_o}$$

$$= \frac{25\ \text{cm}^2 - 22\ \text{cm}^2}{25\ \text{cm}^2} = \boxed{0.12}$$

4. Plot the data and draw a straight line. Disregard the first and last data points, as these represent primary and tertiary creep, respectively.

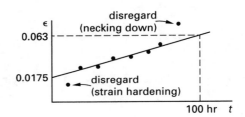

$$\text{creep rate} = \frac{0.063 - 0.0175}{100\ \text{hr}}$$

$$= \boxed{0.000455\ \frac{1}{\text{hr}}}$$

47 Thermal Treatment of Metals

1. (a) For temperature T_1, the equilibrium diagram is

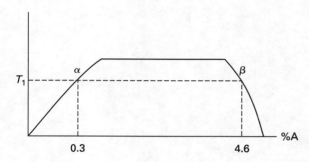

From the diagram, solid α is $\boxed{0.3\% \text{ A.}}$

The %B for solid α is

$$\%B = 100\% - 0.3\% = \boxed{97.7\%}$$

For solid β,

$$\%A = \boxed{4.6\%}$$

$$\%B = 100\% - 4.6\% = \boxed{95.4\%}$$

(b) For temperature T_2, the equilibrium diagram is

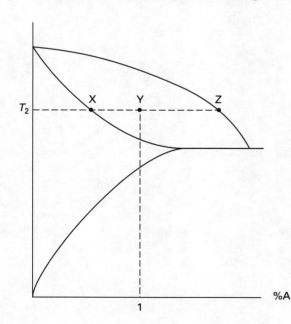

From the diagram, the following distances are measured.

The distance from point X to point Y is 9 mm.

The distance from point X to point Z is 21 mm.

From Eq. 47.2, the percent liquid is

$$\left(\frac{XY}{XZ}\right)(100\%) = \left(\frac{9 \text{ mm}}{21 \text{ mm}}\right)(100\%) = \boxed{42.9\%}$$

From Eq. 47.1, the percent solid is

$$100\% - \text{percent liquid} = 100\% - 42.9\% = \boxed{57.1\%}$$

2. (a) Since 2011 aluminum is a nonferrous substance, it does not readily form allotropes and thus its properties cannot be changed by the controlled cooling in an annealing process.

(b) The procedures for precipitation hardening of 2011 aluminum are

1. precipitation

2. rapid quenching

3. artificial aging

48 Properties of Areas

1. The area is divided into three basic shapes.

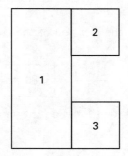

First, calculate the areas of the basic shapes.
$$A_1 = (4)(8) = 32 \text{ units}^2$$
$$A_2 = (4)(2) = 8 \text{ units}^2$$
$$A_3 = (4)(2) = 8 \text{ units}^2$$

Next, find the x-components of the centroids of the basic shapes.
$$x_{c1} = 2 \text{ units}$$
$$x_{c2} = 6 \text{ units}$$
$$x_{c3} = 6 \text{ units}$$

Finally, use Eq. 48.5.
$$x_c = \frac{\sum_i A_i x_{ci}}{\sum A_i} = \frac{(32)(2) + (8)(6) + (8)(6)}{32 + 8 + 8}$$
$$= \boxed{3.33 \text{ units}}$$

2. *Customary U.S. Solution*

The parabolic shape is
$$f(x) = 300\sqrt{\frac{x}{3}}$$

First, use Eq. 48.3 to find the concentrated load given by the area.
$$A = \int f(x)dx = \int_0^3 300\sqrt{\frac{x}{3}}dx = \left(\frac{300}{\sqrt{3}}\right)\left[\frac{x^{\frac{3}{2}}}{\frac{3}{2}}\right]_0^3$$
$$= \left(\frac{300}{\left(\frac{3}{2}\right)\sqrt{3}}\right)\left(3^{\frac{3}{2}} - 0^{\frac{3}{2}}\right) = \boxed{600 \text{ lbf}}$$

From Eq. 48.4,
$$dA = f(x)dx = 300\sqrt{\frac{x}{3}}$$

Finally, use Eq. 48.1 to find the location x_c of the concentrated load from the left end.

$$x_c = \frac{\int x dx}{A} = \frac{1}{600 \text{ lbf}}\int_0^3 300x\sqrt{\frac{x}{3}}dx$$
$$= \frac{300}{600\sqrt{3}}\int_0^3 x^{\frac{3}{2}}dx = \left(\frac{300}{600\sqrt{3}}\right)\left[\frac{x^{\frac{5}{2}}}{\frac{5}{2}}\right]_0^3$$
$$= \left(\frac{300}{600\sqrt{3}\left(\frac{5}{2}\right)}\right)\left(3^{\frac{5}{2}} - 0^{\frac{5}{2}}\right) = \boxed{1.8 \text{ ft}}$$

Alternate solution for the parabola:

$$A = \frac{2bh}{3} = \frac{(2)(300 \text{ lbf})(3 \text{ ft})}{3}$$
$$= \boxed{600 \text{ lbf}}$$

The centroid is located at

$$\frac{3h}{5} = \frac{(3)(3 \text{ ft})}{5} = \boxed{1.8 \text{ ft}}$$

The concentrated load for the triangular shape is the area from App. 48.A.

$$A = \frac{bh}{2} = \frac{\left(700 \dfrac{\text{lbf}}{\text{ft}} - 300 \dfrac{\text{lbf}}{\text{ft}}\right)(8 \text{ ft})}{2}$$
$$= \boxed{1600 \text{ lbf}}$$

From App. 48.A, the location of the concentrated load from the right end is

$$\frac{h}{3} = \frac{8 \text{ ft}}{3} = \boxed{2.67 \text{ ft}}$$

The concentrated load for the rectangular shape is the area from App. 48.A.

$$A = bh = \left(300 \; \frac{\text{lbf}}{\text{ft}}\right)(8 \text{ ft})$$

$$= \boxed{2400 \text{ lbf}}$$

From App. 48.A, the location of the concentrated load from the right end is

$$\frac{h}{2} = \frac{8 \text{ ft}}{2} = \boxed{4 \text{ ft}}$$

SI Solution

The parabolic shape is

$$f(x) = 4000\sqrt{x}$$

First, use Eq. 48.3 to find the concentrated load given by the area.

$$A = \int f(x)dx = \int_0^1 4000\sqrt{x}\,dx = \left[\frac{4000 \; x^{\frac{3}{2}}}{\frac{3}{2}}\right]_0^1$$

$$= \left(\frac{4000}{\frac{3}{2}}\right)\left(1^{\frac{3}{2}} - 0^{\frac{3}{2}}\right) = \boxed{2666.7 \text{ N}}$$

[first concentrated load]

From Eq. 48.4,

$$dA = f(x)dx = 4000\sqrt{x}\,dx$$

Finally, use Eq. 48.1 to find the location, x_c, of the concentrated load from the left end.

$$x_c = \frac{\int x \, dA}{A} = \frac{1}{2666.7 \text{ N}} \int_0^1 4000x\sqrt{x}\,dx$$

$$= \frac{4000}{2666.7} \int_0^1 x^{\frac{3}{2}}dx = \left(\frac{4000}{2666.7}\right)\left[\frac{x^{\frac{5}{2}}}{\frac{5}{2}}\right]_0^1$$

$$= \left(\frac{4000}{2666.7}\right)\left(\frac{1^{\frac{5}{2}} - 0^{\frac{5}{2}}}{\frac{5}{2}}\right) = \boxed{0.60 \text{ m}} \quad \text{[location]}$$

Alternate solution for the parabola:

$$A = \frac{2bh}{3} = \frac{(2)\left(4000 \; \frac{\text{N}}{\text{m}}\right)(1 \text{ m})}{3}$$

$$= \boxed{2666.7 \text{ N}}$$

The centroid is located at

$$\frac{3h}{5} = \frac{(3)(1 \text{ m})}{5} = \boxed{0.6 \text{ m}}$$

The concentrated load for the triangular shape is the area from App. 48.A.

$$A = \frac{bh}{2} = \frac{\left(10\,000 \; \frac{\text{N}}{\text{m}} - 4000 \; \frac{\text{N}}{\text{m}}\right)(2.5 \text{ m})}{2}$$

$$= \boxed{7500 \text{ N}} \quad \text{[second concentrated load]}$$

From App. 48.A, the location of the concentrated load from the right end is

$$\frac{h}{3} = \frac{2.5 \text{ m}}{3} = \boxed{0.83 \text{ m}}$$

The concentrated load for the rectangular shape is the area from App. 48.A.

$$A = bh = \left(4000 \; \frac{\text{N}}{\text{m}}\right)(2.5 \text{ m})$$

$$= \boxed{10\,000 \text{ N}} \quad \text{[third concentrated load]}$$

From App. 48.A, the location of the concentrated load from the right end is

$$\frac{h}{2} = \frac{2.5 \text{ m}}{2} = \boxed{1.25 \text{ m}}$$

3. The area is divided into three basic shapes.

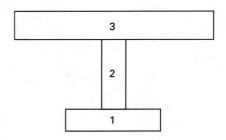

First, calculate the areas of the basic shapes.

$$A_1 = (4)(1) = 4 \text{ units}^2$$
$$A_2 = (2)(12) = 24 \text{ units}^2$$
$$A_3 = (6)(0.5) = 3 \text{ units}^2$$

Next, find the y-components of the centroids of the basic shapes.

$$y_{c1} = 0.5 \text{ unit}$$
$$y_{c2} = 7 \text{ units}$$
$$y_{c3} = 13.25 \text{ units}$$

From Eq. 48.6, the centroid of the area is

$$y_c = \frac{\sum_i A_i y_{ci}}{A_i} = \frac{(4)(0.5) + (24)(7) + (3)(13.25)}{4 + 24 + 3}$$
$$= 6.77 \text{ units}$$

From App. 48.A, the moment of inertia of basic shape 1 about its own centroid is

$$I_{cx1} = \frac{bh^3}{12} = \frac{(4)(1)^3}{12} = 0.33 \text{ units}^4$$

The moment of inertia of basic shape 2 about its own centroid is

$$I_{cx2} = \frac{bh^3}{12} = \frac{(2)(12)^3}{12} = 288 \text{ units}^4$$

The moment of inertia of basic shape 3 about its own centroid is

$$I_{cx3} = \frac{bh^3}{12} = \frac{(6)(0.5)^3}{12} = 0.063 \text{ units}^4$$

From the parallel axis theorem, Eq. 48.20, the moment of inertia of basic shape 1 about the centroidal axis of the section is

$$I_{x1} = I_{cx1} + A_1 d_1^2 = 0.33 + (4)(6.77 - 0.5)^2$$
$$= 157.6 \text{ units}^4$$

The moment of inertia of basic shape 2 about the centroidal axis of the section is

$$I_{x2} = I_{cx2} + A_2 d_2^2 = 288 + (24)(7.0 - 6.77)^2$$
$$= 289.3 \text{ units}^4$$

The moment of inertia of basic shape 3 about the centroidal axis of the section is

$$I_{x3} = I_{cx3} + A_3 d_3^2 = 0.063 + (3)(13.25 - 6.77)^2$$
$$= 126.0 \text{ units}^4$$

The total moment of inertia about the centroidal axis of the section is

$$I_x = I_{x1} + I_{x2} + I_{x3}$$
$$= 157.6 \text{ units}^4 + 289.3 \text{ units}^4 + 126.0 \text{ units}^4$$
$$= \boxed{572.9 \text{ units}^4}$$

49 Strength of Materials

1. *Customary U.S. Solution*

First, determine the reactions. The uniform load can be assumed to be concentrated at the center of the beam.

Sum the moments about A.

$$(100 \text{ lbf})(2 \text{ ft}) + (80 \text{ lbf})(14 \text{ ft})$$

$$+ \left(20 \text{ } \frac{\text{lbm}}{\text{ft}}\right) \left(\frac{32.2 \text{ } \frac{\text{ft}}{\text{sec}^2}}{32.2 \text{ } \frac{\text{lbm-ft}}{\text{lbf-sec}^2}}\right)$$

$$\times (14 \text{ ft})(7 \text{ ft}) - R(12 \text{ ft}) = 0$$

$$R = 273.3 \text{ lbf}$$

Sum the forces in the vertical direction.

$$L + 273.3 \text{ lbf} = 100 \text{ lbf} + 80 \text{ lbf}$$

$$+ \left(20 \text{ } \frac{\text{lbm}}{\text{ft}}\right) \left(\frac{32.2 \text{ } \frac{\text{ft}}{\text{sec}^2}}{32.2 \text{ } \frac{\text{lbm-ft}}{\text{lbf-sec}^2}}\right)(14 \text{ ft})$$

$$L = 186.7 \text{ lbf}$$

The shear diagram starts at +186.7 lbf at the left reaction and decreases linearly at a rate of 20 lbf/ft to 146.7 lbf at point B. The concentrated load reduces the shear to 46.7 lbf. The shear then decreases linearly at a rate of 20 lbf/ft to point C. Measuring x from the left, the shear line goes through zero at

$$x = 2 \text{ ft} + \frac{46.7 \text{ lbf}}{20 \text{ } \frac{\text{lbf}}{\text{ft}}} = 4.3 \text{ ft}$$

The shear at the right of the beam at point D is 80 lbf and increases linearly at a rate of 20 lbf/ft to 120 lbf at point C. The reaction R at point C decreases the shear to −153.3 lbf. This is sufficient to draw the shear diagram.

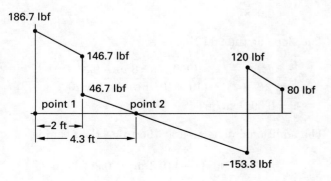

(a) From the shear diagram, the maximum moment occurs when the shear is zero. Call this point 2. The moment at the left reaction is zero. Call this point 1. Use Eq. 49.27.

$$M_2 = M_1 + \int_{x_1}^{x_2} V \, dx$$

The integral is the area under the curve from $x_1 = 0$ to $x_2 = 4.3$ ft.

$$M_2 = 0 + (146.7 \text{ lbf})(2 \text{ ft})$$

$$+ \left(\tfrac{1}{2}\right)(186.7 \text{ lbf} - 146.7 \text{ lbf})(2 \text{ ft})$$

$$+ \left(\tfrac{1}{2}\right)(46.7 \text{ lbf})(4.3 \text{ ft} - 2 \text{ ft})$$

$$= \boxed{387.1 \text{ ft-lbf}}$$

(b) From the shear diagram, the maximum shear is

$$\boxed{186.7 \text{ lbf.}}$$

SI Solution

First, determine the reactions. The uniform load can be assumed to be concentrated at the center of the beam.

Sum the moments about A.

$$(450 \text{ N})(0.6 \text{ m}) + (350 \text{ N})(4.2 \text{ m})$$

$$+ \left(30 \text{ } \frac{\text{kg}}{\text{m}}\right)(4.2 \text{ m})\left(9.81 \text{ } \frac{\text{N}}{\text{kg}}\right)(2.1 \text{ m})$$

$$-R(3.6 \text{ m}) = 0$$

$$R = 1204.4 \text{ N}$$

Sum the forces in the vertical direction.

$$L + 1204.4 \text{ N} = 450 \text{ N} + 350 \text{ N}$$

$$+ \left(30 \text{ } \frac{\text{kg}}{\text{m}}\right)(4.2 \text{ m})\left(9.81 \text{ } \frac{\text{N}}{\text{kg}}\right)$$

$$L = 831.7 \text{ N}$$

The shear diagram starts at +831.7 N at the left reaction and decreases linearly at a rate of 294.3 N/m to 655.1 N at point B. The concentrated load reduces the shear to 205.1 N. The shear then decreases linearly at a rate of 294.3 N/m to point C. Measuring x from the left, the shear line goes through zero at

$$x = 0.6 \text{ m} + \frac{205.1 \text{ N}}{294.3 \text{ } \frac{\text{N}}{\text{m}}} = 1.3 \text{ m}$$

Materials

The shear at the right of the beam at point D is 350 N and increases linearly at a rate of 294.3 N/m to 703.2 N at point C. The reaction R at point C decreases the shear to −501.2 N. This is sufficient to draw the shear diagram.

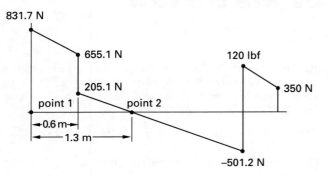

(a) From the shear diagram, the maximum moment occurs when the shear = 0. Call this point 2. The moment at the left reaction = 0. Call this point 1.

Use Eq. 49.27.

$$M_2 = M_1 + \int_{x_1}^{x_2} V \, dx$$

The integral is the area under the curve from $x_1 = 0$ to $x_2 = 1.3$ m.

$$
\begin{aligned}
M_2 = {} & 0 + (655.1 \text{ N})(0.6 \text{ m}) \\
& + \left(\tfrac{1}{2}\right)(831.7 \text{ N} - 655.1 \text{ N})(0.6 \text{ m}) \\
& + \left(\tfrac{1}{2}\right)(205.1 \text{ N})(1.3 \text{ m} - 0.6 \text{ m}) \\
= {} & \boxed{517.8 \text{ N·m}}
\end{aligned}
$$

(b) From the shear diagram, the maximum shear is

$$\boxed{831.7 \text{ N.}}$$

2. *Customary U.S. Solution*

First, the moment of inertia of the beam cross section is

$$I = \frac{bh^3}{12} = \frac{(6 \text{ in})(4 \text{ in})^3}{12} = 32 \text{ in}^4$$

From case 1 in App. 49.A, the deflection of the 200 lbf load is

$$y_1 = \frac{PL^3}{3EI} = \frac{(200 \text{ lbf})(72 \text{ in} - 12 \text{ in})^3}{(3)\left(1.5 \times 10^6 \dfrac{\text{lbf}}{\text{in}^2}\right)(32 \text{ in}^4)}$$

$$= 0.30 \text{ in}$$

The slope at the 200 lbf load is

$$\theta = \frac{PL^2}{2EI} = \frac{(200 \text{ lbf})(72 \text{ in} - 12 \text{ in})^2}{(2)\left(1.5 \times 10^6 \dfrac{\text{lbf}}{\text{in}^2}\right)(32 \text{ in}^4)}$$

$$= 0.0075 \text{ in/in}$$

The additional deflection at the tip of the beam is

$$y_{1'} = \left(0.0075 \, \frac{\text{in}}{\text{in}}\right)(12 \text{ in}) = 0.09 \text{ in}$$

From case 1 in App. 49.A, the deflection at the 120 lbf load is

$$y_2 = \frac{PL^3}{3EI} = \frac{(120 \text{ lbf})(72 \text{ in} - 24 \text{ in})^3}{(3)\left(1.5 \times 10^6 \dfrac{\text{lbf}}{\text{in}^2}\right)(32 \text{ in}^4)}$$

$$= 0.0922 \text{ in}$$

The slope at the 120 lbf load is

$$\theta_2 = \frac{PL^2}{2EI} = \frac{(120 \text{ lbf})(72 \text{ in} - 24 \text{ in})^2}{(2)\left(1.5 \times 10^6 \dfrac{\text{lbf}}{\text{in}^2}\right)(32 \text{ in}^4)}$$

$$= 0.00288 \text{ in/in}$$

The additional deflection at the tip of the beam is

$$y_{2'} = \left(0.00288 \, \frac{\text{in}}{\text{in}}\right)(24 \text{ in}) = 0.0691 \text{ in}$$

The total deflection is the sum of the preceding four parts.

$$
\begin{aligned}
y_{\text{tip}} &= y_1 + y_{1'} + y_2 + y_{2'} \\
&= 0.30 \text{ in} + 0.09 \text{ in} + 0.0922 \text{ in} + 0.0691 \text{ in} \\
&= \boxed{0.5513 \text{ in}}
\end{aligned}
$$

SI Solution

First, the moment of inertia of the beam cross section is

$$I = \frac{bh^3}{12} = \frac{(0.15 \text{ m})(0.10 \text{ m})^3}{12} = 1.25 \times 10^{-5} \text{ m}^4$$

From case 1 in App. 49.A, the deflection at the 900 N load is

$$y_1 = \frac{PL^3}{3EI} = \frac{(900 \text{ N})(1.8 \text{ m} - 0.3 \text{ m})^3}{(3)(10 \times 10^9 \text{ Pa})(1.25 \times 10^{-5} \text{ m}^4)}$$

$$= 0.0081 \text{ m}$$

The slope at the 900 N load is

$$\theta_1 = \frac{PL^2}{2EI} = \frac{(900 \text{ N})(1.8 \text{ m} - 0.3 \text{ m})^2}{(2)(10 \times 10^9 \text{ Pa})(1.25 \times 10^{-5} \text{ m}^4)}$$

$$= 0.0081 \text{ m/m}$$

The additional deflection at the tip of the beam is

$$y_{1'} = \left(0.0081 \, \frac{\text{m}}{\text{m}}\right)(0.3 \text{ m}) = 0.00243 \text{ m}$$

From case 1 in App. 49.A, the deflection at the 530 N load is

$$y_2 = \frac{PL^3}{3EI} = \frac{(530 \text{ N})(1.8 \text{ m} - 0.6 \text{ m})^3}{(3)(10 \times 10^9 \text{ Pa})(1.25 \times 10^{-5} \text{ m}^4)}$$
$$= 0.00244 \text{ m}$$

The slope at the 530 N load is

$$\theta_2 = \frac{PL^2}{2EI} = \frac{(530 \text{ N})(1.8 \text{ m} - 0.6 \text{ m})^2}{(2)(10 \times 10^9 \text{ Pa})(1.25 \times 10^{-5} \text{ m}^4)}$$
$$= 0.00305 \text{ m/m}$$

The additional deflection at the tip of the beam is

$$y_{2'} = \left(0.00305 \frac{\text{m}}{\text{m}}\right)(0.6 \text{ m}) = 0.00183 \text{ m}$$

The total deflection is the sum of the preceding four parts.

$$y_{\text{tip}} = y_1 + y_{1'} + y_2 + y_{2'}$$
$$= 0.0081 \text{ m} + 0.00243 \text{ m} + 0.00244 \text{ m} + 0.00305 \text{ m}$$
$$= \boxed{0.0160 \text{ m}}$$

3. *Customary U.S. Solution*

Use Eq. 49.9 to find the amount of expansion for an unconstrained beam.

$$\Delta L = \alpha L_o (T_2 - T_1)$$
$$= \left(6.5 \times 10^{-6} \frac{1}{\text{°F}}\right)(200 \text{ ft})\left(12 \frac{\text{in}}{\text{ft}}\right)$$
$$\times (110\text{°F} - 40\text{°F})$$
$$= 1.092 \text{ in}$$

The constrained length is

$$\Delta L_c = 1.092 \text{ in} - 0.5 \text{ in} = 0.592 \text{ in}$$

From Eq. 49.14, the thermal strain is

$$\epsilon_{\text{th}} = \frac{\Delta L_c}{L_o + 0.5 \text{ in}} = \frac{0.592 \text{ in}}{2400 \text{ in} + 0.5 \text{ in}}$$
$$= 2.466 \times 10^{-4} \text{ in/in}$$

From Eq. 49.15, the compressive thermal stress is

$$\sigma_{\text{th}} = E\epsilon_{\text{th}} = \left(30 \times 10^6 \frac{\text{lbf}}{\text{in}^2}\right)(2.466 \times 10^{-4})$$
$$= \boxed{7398 \text{ lbf/in}^2}$$

SI Solution

Use Eq. 49.9 to find the amount of expansion for an unconstrained beam.

$$\Delta L = \alpha L_o (T_2 - T_1)$$
$$= \left(1.2 \times 10^{-5} \frac{1}{\text{°C}}\right)(60 \text{ m})(43\text{°C} - 4\text{°C})$$
$$= 0.02808 \text{ m}$$

The constrained length is

$$\Delta L_c = 0.02808 \text{ m} - 0.012 \text{ m} = 0.01608 \text{ m}$$

From Eq. 49.14, the thermal strain is

$$\epsilon_{\text{th}} = \frac{\Delta L_c}{L_o + 0.012 \text{ m}} = \frac{0.01608 \text{ m}}{60 \text{ m} + 0.012 \text{ m}}$$
$$= 0.000268 \text{ m/m}$$

From Eq. 49.15, the compressive thermal stress is

$$\sigma_{\text{th}} = E\epsilon_{\text{th}} = (20 \times 10^{10} \text{ Pa})\left(0.000268 \frac{\text{m}}{\text{m}}\right)$$
$$= \boxed{5.36 \times 10^7 \text{ Pa}}$$

4. *Customary U.S. Solution*

First, the cross-sectional area of the rod is

$$A = \frac{\pi d^2}{4}$$

From Eq. 49.4, the unstretched length of the rod is

$$L_o = \frac{\delta E A}{F} = \frac{(0.158 \text{ in})\left(2.9 \times 10^7 \frac{\text{lbf}}{\text{in}^2}\right)\left(\frac{\pi}{4}\right)(1 \text{ in})^2}{15{,}000 \text{ lbf}}$$
$$= 239.913 \text{ in}$$

The total length of the rod is

$$L = L_o + \delta = 239.913 + 0.158 = \boxed{240.071 \text{ in}}$$

SI Solution

First, the cross-sectional area of the rod is

$$A = \frac{\pi d^2}{4}$$

From Eq. 49.4, the unstretched length of the rod is

$$L_o = \frac{\delta E A}{F}$$
$$= \frac{(0.004 \text{ m})\left(20 \times 10^{10} \frac{\text{N}}{\text{m}^2}\right)\left(\frac{\pi}{4}\right)(0.025 \text{ m})^2}{67 \times 10^3 \text{ N}}$$
$$= 5.861 \text{ m}$$

Materials

The total length of the rod is

$$L = L_o + \delta = 5.861 \text{ m} + 0.004 \text{ m} = \boxed{5.865 \text{ m}}$$

5. *Customary U.S. Solution*

First, find the properties of the shaft cross section. The area is

$$A = \frac{\pi d^2}{4} = \frac{\pi (3 \text{ in})^2}{4} = 7.07 \text{ in}^2$$

The moment of inertia is

$$I_c = \frac{\pi r^4}{4} = \frac{\pi \left(\frac{3 \text{ in}}{2}\right)^4}{4} = 3.98 \text{ in}^4$$

The polar moment of inertia is

$$J = \frac{\pi r^4}{2} = \frac{\pi \left(\frac{3 \text{ in}}{2}\right)^4}{2} = 7.95 \text{ in}^4$$

The moment at the bearing face due to the pulley weight is

$$M_y = (600 \text{ lbm}) \left(\frac{32.2 \frac{\text{ft}}{\text{sec}^2}}{32.2 \frac{\text{lbm-ft}}{\text{lbf-sec}^2}} \right) (8 \text{ in}) = 4800 \text{ in-lbf}$$

From Eq. 49.37, the maximum bending stress at the extreme fiber on the y-axis is

$$\sigma_y = \frac{M_y c}{I_c} = \frac{(4800 \text{ in-lbf}) \left(\frac{3 \text{ in}}{2}\right)}{3.98 \text{ in}^4} = 1809 \text{ lbf/in}^2$$

The moment at the bearing face due to the belt tensions is

$$M_z = (1500 \text{ lbf} + 350 \text{ lbf})(8 \text{ in}) = 14{,}800 \text{ in-lbf}$$

From Eq. 49.37, the maximum bending stress at the extreme fiber on the z-axis is

$$\sigma_z = \frac{M_z c}{I_c} = \frac{(14{,}800 \text{ in-lbf}) \left(\frac{3 \text{ in}}{2}\right)}{3.98 \text{ in}^4}$$
$$= 5578 \text{ lbf/in}^2$$

The maximum resultant bending stress at the extreme fiber between the preceding two points is

$$\sigma_R = \sqrt{\sigma_y^2 + \sigma_z^2}$$
$$= \sqrt{\left(1809 \frac{\text{lbf}}{\text{in}^2}\right)^2 + \left(5578 \frac{\text{lbf}}{\text{in}^2}\right)^2}$$
$$= 5864 \text{ lbf/in}^2$$

The net torque from the belt tensions is

$$T = (1500 \text{ lbf} - 350 \text{ lbf})(16 \text{ in}) = 18{,}400 \text{ in-lbf}$$

The maximum torsional shear stress at the extreme fiber is

$$\tau = \frac{Tc}{J} = \frac{(18{,}400 \text{ in-lbf}) \left(\frac{3 \text{ in}}{2}\right)}{7.95 \text{ in}^4}$$
$$= 3472 \text{ lbf/in}^2$$

The direct shear stress is zero at the surface of the shaft. Use Eqs. 49.19 and 49.20 to find the maximum stress in the shaft.

$$\sigma_1 = \frac{\sigma_R}{2} + \frac{1}{2}\sqrt{\sigma_R^2 + (2\tau)^2}$$
$$= \frac{5864 \frac{\text{lbf}}{\text{in}^2}}{2}$$
$$+ \frac{1}{2}\sqrt{\left(5864 \frac{\text{lbf}}{\text{in}^2}\right)^2 + \left((2)\left(3472 \frac{\text{lbf}}{\text{in}^2}\right)\right)^2}$$
$$= \boxed{7476 \text{ lbf/in}^2}$$

SI Solution

First, find the properties of the shaft cross section. The area is

$$A = \frac{\pi d^2}{4} = \frac{\pi (0.075 \text{ m})^2}{4} = 4.42 \times 10^{-3} \text{ m}^2$$

The moment of inertia is

$$I_c = \frac{\pi r^4}{4} = \frac{\pi \left(\frac{0.075 \text{ m}}{2}\right)^4}{4} = 1.55 \times 10^{-6} \text{ m}^4$$

The polar moment of inertia is

$$J = \frac{\pi r^4}{2} = \frac{\pi \left(\frac{0.075 \text{ m}}{2}\right)^4}{2} = 3.11 \times 10^{-6} \text{ m}^4$$

The moment at the bearing face due to the pulley weight is

$$M_y = (270 \text{ kg}) \left(9.81 \frac{\text{m}}{\text{s}^2}\right)(0.2 \text{ m}) = 529.74 \text{ N·m}$$

From Eq. 49.37, the maximum bending stress at the extreme fiber on the y-axis is

$$\sigma_y = \frac{M_y c}{I_c} = \frac{(529.74 \text{ N·m}) \left(\frac{0.075 \text{ m}}{2}\right)}{1.55 \times 10^{-6} \text{ m}^4}$$
$$= 1.282 \times 10^7 \text{ Pa}$$

The moment at the bearing face due to the belt tensions is

$$M_z = (6.7 \times 10^3 \text{ N} + 1.6 \times 10^3 \text{ N})(0.2 \text{ m}) = 1660 \text{ N·m}$$

From Eq. 49.37, the maximum bending stress at the extreme fiber on the z-axis is

$$\sigma_z = \frac{M_z c}{I_c}$$

$$= \frac{(1660 \text{ N·m}) \left(\dfrac{0.075 \text{ m}}{2} \right)}{1.55 \times 10^{-6} \text{ m}^4}$$

$$= 4.016 \times 10^7 \text{ Pa}$$

The maximum resultant bending stress at the extreme fiber between the preceding two points is

$$\sigma_R = \sqrt{\sigma_y^2 + \sigma_z^2}$$

$$= \sqrt{(1.282 \times 10^7 \text{ Pa})^2 + (4.016 \times 10^7 \text{ Pa})^2}$$

$$= 4.216 \times 10^7 \text{ Pa}$$

The net torque from the belt tensions is

$$T = (6.7 \times 10^3 \text{ N} - 1.6 \times 10^3 \text{ N})(0.40 \text{ m}) = 2040 \text{ N·m}$$

The maximum torsional shear stress at the extreme fiber is

$$\tau = \frac{Tc}{J}$$

$$= \frac{(2040 \text{ N·m}) \left(\dfrac{0.075 \text{ m}}{2} \right)}{3.11 \times 10^{-6} \text{ m}^4}$$

$$= 2.460 \times 10^7 \text{ Pa}$$

The direct shear stress is zero at the surface of the shaft.

Use Eqs. 49.19 and 49.20 to find the maximum stress in the shaft.

$$\sigma_1 = \frac{\sigma_R}{2} + \frac{1}{2}\sqrt{\sigma_R^2 + (2\tau)^2}$$

$$= \frac{4.216 \times 10^7 \text{ Pa}}{2}$$

$$\quad + \frac{1}{2}\sqrt{\begin{array}{l}(4.216 \times 10^7 \text{ Pa})^2 \\ + ((2)(2.460 \times 10^7 \text{ Pa}))^2\end{array}}$$

$$= \boxed{5.35 \times 10^7 \text{ Pa} \quad (53.5 \text{ MPa})}$$

6. *Customary U.S. Solution*

First, find the properties of the rod cross section. The area is

$$A = \frac{\pi d^2}{4} = \frac{\pi (1 \text{ in})^2}{4} = 0.7854 \text{ in}^2$$

The moment of inertia is

$$J_c = \frac{\pi r^4}{4} = \frac{\pi \left(\dfrac{1.0 \text{ in}}{2} \right)^4}{4} = 0.04909 \text{ in}^4$$

The polar moment of inertia is

$$J = \frac{\pi r^4}{2} = \frac{\pi \left(\dfrac{1 \text{ in}}{2} \right)^2}{2} = 0.09817 \text{ in}^4$$

The moment at the chuck is

$$M = (60 \text{ lbf})(8 \text{ in}) = 480 \text{ in-lbf}$$

From Eq. 49.37, the maximum bending stress at the extreme fiber of the rod is

$$\sigma = \frac{Mc}{I_c} = \frac{(480 \text{ in-lbf}) \left(\dfrac{1.0 \text{ in}}{2} \right)}{0.04909 \text{ in}^4} = 4889 \text{ lbf/in}^2$$

The torque applied to the rod is

$$T = (60 \text{ lbf})(12 \text{ in}) = 720 \text{ in-lbf}$$

The maximum torsional shear stress at the extreme fiber of the rod is

$$\tau = \frac{Tc}{J} = \frac{(720 \text{ in-lbf}) \left(\dfrac{1.0 \text{ in}}{2} \right)}{0.09817 \text{ in}^4} = 3667 \text{ lbf/in}^2$$

The direct shear stress is zero at the surface of the rod.

(a) Use Eq. 49.20 to find the maximum shear stress in the rod.

$$\tau_1 = \frac{1}{2}\sqrt{\sigma^2 + (2\tau)^2}$$

$$= \frac{1}{2}\sqrt{\left(4889 \, \frac{\text{lbf}}{\text{in}^2} \right)^2 + \left((2)\left(3667 \, \frac{\text{lbf}}{\text{in}^2} \right) \right)^2}$$

$$= \boxed{4407 \text{ lbf/in}^2}$$

(b) Use Eq. 49.19 to find the maximum normal stress in the rod.

$$\sigma_1 = \frac{\sigma}{2} + \tau_1$$

$$= \frac{4889 \, \dfrac{\text{lbf}}{\text{in}^2}}{2} + 4407 \, \frac{\text{lbf}}{\text{in}^2}$$

$$= \boxed{6852 \text{ lbf/in}^2}$$

Materials

SI Solution

First, find the properties of the rod cross section. The area is

$$A = \frac{\pi d^2}{4} = \frac{\pi (0.025 \text{ m})^2}{4} = 4.909 \times 10^{-4} \text{ m}^2$$

The moment of inertia is

$$I_c = \frac{\pi r^4}{4} = \frac{\pi \left(\frac{0.025 \text{ m}}{2}\right)^4}{4} = 1.917 \times 10^{-8} \text{ m}^4$$

The polar moment of inertia is

$$J = \frac{\pi r^4}{2} = \frac{\pi \left(\frac{0.025 \text{ m}}{2}\right)^4}{2} = 3.835 \times 10^{-8} \text{ m}^4$$

The moment at the chuck is

$$M = (270 \text{ N})(0.2 \text{ m}) = 54 \text{ N·m}$$

From Eq. 49.37, the maximum bending stress at the extreme fiber of the rod is

$$\sigma = \frac{Mc}{I_c} = \frac{(54 \text{ N·m})\left(\frac{0.025 \text{ m}}{2}\right)}{1.917 \times 10^{-8} \text{ m}^4}$$

$$= 3.52 \times 10^7 \text{ Pa} \quad (35.2 \text{ MPa})$$

The torque applied to the rod is

$$T = (270 \text{ N})(0.3 \text{ m}) = 81 \text{ N·m}$$

The maximum torsional shear stress at the extreme fiber of the rod is

$$\tau = \frac{Tc}{J} = \frac{(81 \text{ N·m})\left(\frac{0.025 \text{ m}}{2}\right)}{3.835 \times 10^{-8} \text{ m}^4}$$

$$= 2.64 \times 10^7 \text{ Pa} \quad (26.4 \text{ MPa})$$

The direct shear stress is zero at the surface of the rod.

(a) Use Eq. 49.20 to find the maximum shear stress in the rod.

$$\tau_1 = \tfrac{1}{2}\sqrt{\sigma^2 + (2\tau)^2}$$

$$= \tfrac{1}{2}\sqrt{(35.2 \text{ MPa})^2 + ((2)(26.4 \text{ MPa}))^2}$$

$$= \boxed{31.7 \text{ MPa}}$$

(b) Use Eq. 49.19 to find the maximum normal stress in the rod.

$$\sigma_1 = \frac{\sigma}{2} + \tau_1$$

$$= \frac{35.2 \text{ MPa}}{2} + 31.7 \text{ MPa}$$

$$= \boxed{49.3 \text{ MPa}}$$

7. *Customary U.S. Solution*

The normal stress in the bar is

$$\sigma_x = \frac{F}{A} = \frac{-18{,}000 \text{ lbf}}{1.5 \text{ in}^2} = -12{,}000 \text{ lbf/in}^2$$

The shear stress in the bar is $\tau = 4000 \text{ lbf/in}^2$.

From Fig. 49.7, a plane inclined $+30°$ from the horizontal gives an angle θ of $60°$.

(a) From Eq. 49.17, the normal stress on the plane is

$$\sigma_\sigma = \frac{\sigma_x}{2} + \left(\frac{\sigma_x}{2}\right)(\cos 2\theta) + \tau \sin 2\theta$$

$$= \frac{-12{,}000 \frac{\text{lbf}}{\text{in}^2}}{2} + \frac{\left(-12{,}000 \frac{\text{lbf}}{\text{in}^2}\right)(\cos 120°)}{2}$$

$$+ \left(4000 \frac{\text{lbf}}{\text{in}^2}\right)(\sin 120°)$$

$$= \boxed{464 \text{ lbf/in}^2}$$

(b) From Eq. 49.18, the shear stress on the plane is

$$\tau_\theta = -\frac{\tau_x \sin 2\theta}{2} + \tau \cos 2\theta$$

$$= -\frac{\left(-12{,}000 \frac{\text{lbf}}{\text{in}^2}\right)(\sin 120°)}{2}$$

$$+ \left(4000 \frac{\text{lbf}}{\text{in}^2}\right)(\cos 120°)$$

$$= \boxed{3196 \text{ lbf/in}^2}$$

SI Solution

The normal stress in the bar is

$$\sigma_x = \frac{F}{A} = \frac{-80 \times 10^3 \text{ N}}{(9.7 \text{ cm}^2)\left(\frac{1 \text{ m}}{100 \text{ cm}}\right)^2}$$

$$= -8.247 \times 10^7 \text{ Pa} \quad (-82.5 \text{ MPa})$$

From Fig. 49.17, a plane inclined $+30°$ from the horizontal gives an angle θ of $60°$.

(a) From Eq. 49.17, the normal stress on the plane is

$$\sigma_\theta = \frac{\sigma_x}{2} + \left(\frac{\sigma_x}{2}\right)(\cos 2\theta) + \tau \sin 2\theta$$

$$= \frac{-82.5 \text{ MPa}}{2} + \frac{(-82.5 \text{ MPa})(\cos 120°)}{2}$$

$$+ (28 \text{ MPa})(\sin 120°)$$

$$= \boxed{3.62 \text{ MPa}}$$

(b) From Eq. 49.18, the shear stress on the plane is

$$\tau_\theta = -\frac{\sigma_x \sin 2\theta}{2} + \tau \cos 2\theta$$

$$= -\frac{(-82.4 \text{ MPa})(\sin 120°)}{2}$$

$$+ (28 \text{ MPa})(\cos 120°)$$

$$= \boxed{21.7 \text{ MPa}}$$

8. *Customary U.S. Solution*

First, find the properties of the handle cross section. The moment of inertia is

$$I_c = \frac{\pi r^4}{4} = \frac{\pi \left(\frac{0.625 \text{ in}}{2}\right)^4}{4} = 0.00749 \text{ in}^4$$

The polar moment of inertia is

$$J = \frac{\pi r^4}{2} = \frac{\pi \left(\frac{0.625 \text{ in}}{2}\right)^2}{2} = 0.01498 \text{ in}^4$$

The moment at section A-A is

$$M = (50 \text{ lbf})(14 \text{ in} + 3 \text{ in}) = 850 \text{ in-lbf}$$

From Eq. 49.37, the maximum bending stress at the extreme fiber at section A-A is

$$\sigma = \frac{Mc}{I_c} = \frac{(850 \text{ in-lbf})\left(\frac{0.625 \text{ in}}{2}\right)}{0.00749 \text{ in}^4} = 35,464 \text{ lbf/in}^2$$

The torque at section A-A is

$$T = (50 \text{ lbf})(3 \text{ in}) = 150 \text{ in-lbf}$$

The maximum torsional shear stress at the extreme fiber at section A-A is

$$\tau = \frac{Tc}{J} = \frac{(150 \text{ in-lbf})\left(\frac{0.625 \text{ in}}{2}\right)}{0.01498 \text{ in}^4} = 3129 \text{ lbf/in}^2$$

The direct shear at the extreme fiber is assumed to be small enough to be neglected.

(a) Use Eq. 49.20 to find the maximum shear stress at section A-A.

$$\tau_1 = \tfrac{1}{2}\sqrt{\sigma^2 + (2\tau)^2}$$

$$= \tfrac{1}{2}\sqrt{\left(35,464 \frac{\text{lbf}}{\text{in}^2}\right)^2 + \left((2)\left(3129 \frac{\text{lbf}}{\text{in}^2}\right)\right)^2}$$

$$= 18,006 \text{ lbf/in}^2$$

Use Eq. 49.19 to find the principal stresses.

$$\sigma_1 = \frac{\sigma}{2} + \tau_1$$

$$= \frac{35,464 \frac{\text{lbf}}{\text{in}^2}}{2} + 18,006 \frac{\text{lbf}}{\text{in}^2}$$

$$= \boxed{35,738 \text{ lbf/in}^2}$$

$$\sigma_2 = \frac{\sigma}{2} - \tau_1$$

$$= \frac{35,464 \frac{\text{lbf}}{\text{in}^2}}{2} - 18,006 \frac{\text{lbf}}{\text{in}^2}$$

$$= \boxed{-274 \text{ lbf/in}^2}$$

(b) From part (a), the maximum shear at section A-A is $\tau_1 = \boxed{18,006 \text{ lbf/in}^2.}$

SI Solution

First, find the properties of the handle cross section. The moment of inertia is

$$I_c = \frac{\pi r^4}{4} = \frac{\pi \left(\frac{0.016 \text{ m}}{2}\right)^4}{4} = 3.22 \times 10^{-9} \text{ m}^4$$

The polar moment of inertia is

$$J = \frac{\pi r^4}{2} = \frac{\pi \left(\frac{0.016 \text{ m}}{2}\right)^4}{2} = 6.43 \times 10^{-9} \text{ m}^4$$

The moment at section A-A is

$$M = (220 \text{ N})(0.355 \text{ m} + 0.075 \text{ m}) = 94.6 \text{ N·m}$$

From Eq. 49.37, the maximum bending stress at the extreme fiber at section A-A is

$$\sigma = \frac{Mc}{I_c} = \frac{(94.6 \text{ N·m})\left(\frac{0.016 \text{ m}}{2}\right)}{3.22 \times 10^{-9} \text{ m}^4}$$

$$= 2.35 \times 10^8 \text{ Pa} \quad (235 \text{ MPa})$$

The torque at section A-A is

$$T = (220 \text{ N})(0.075 \text{ m}) = 16.5 \text{ N·m}$$

The maximum torsional shear stress at the extreme fiber at section A-A is

$$\tau = \frac{Tc}{J} = \frac{(16.5 \text{ N·m})\left(\frac{0.016 \text{ m}}{2}\right)}{6.43 \times 10^{-9} \text{ m}^4}$$

$$= 2.05 \times 10^7 \text{ Pa} \quad (20.5 \text{ MPa})$$

The direct shear at the extreme fiber is assumed to be small enough to be neglected.

Materials

(a) Use Eq. 49.20 to find the maximum shear stress at section A-A.

$$\tau_1 = \tfrac{1}{2}\sqrt{\sigma^2 + (2\tau)^2}$$

$$= \tfrac{1}{2}\sqrt{(235 \text{ MPa})^2 + \left((2)\left((20.5 \text{ MPa})^2\right)\right)}$$

$$= 119.3 \text{ MPa}$$

Use Eq. 49.19 to find the principal stresses.

$$\sigma_1 = \frac{\sigma}{2} + \tau_1$$

$$= \frac{235 \text{ MPa}}{2} + 119.3 \text{ MPa}$$

$$= \boxed{237 \text{ MPa}}$$

$$\sigma_2 = \frac{\sigma}{2} - \tau_1$$

$$= \frac{235 \text{ MPa}}{2} - 119.3 \text{ MPa}$$

$$= \boxed{-1.8 \text{ MPa}}$$

(b) From part (a), the maximum shear at section A-A is $\tau_1 = \boxed{119.3 \text{ MPa.}}$

9. *Customary U.S. Solution*

(a) The moment of inertia of the brass tube annular cross section is

$$I_{\text{brass}} = \left(\frac{\pi}{4}\right)(r_o^4 - r_i^4)$$

$$= \left(\frac{\pi}{4}\right)\left(\left(\frac{2.0 \text{ in}}{2}\right)^4 - \left(\frac{1.0 \text{ in}}{2}\right)^4\right)$$

$$= 0.736 \text{ in}^4$$

The moment of inertia of the steel rod insert circular cross section is

$$I_{\text{steel}} = \frac{\pi r^4}{4} = \left(\frac{\pi}{4}\right)\left(\frac{1.0 \text{ in}}{2}\right)^4$$

$$= 0.0491 \text{ in}^4$$

The product EI for the brass tube is

$$E_{\text{brass}}I_{\text{brass}} = \left(1.5 \times 10^7 \frac{\text{lbf}}{\text{in}^2}\right)(0.736 \text{ in}^4)$$

$$= 1.104 \times 10^7 \text{ lbf-in}^2$$

The product EI for the steel rod insert is

$$E_{\text{steel}}I_{\text{steel}} = \left(2.9 \times 10^7 \frac{\text{lbf}}{\text{in}^2}\right)(0.0491 \text{ in}^4)$$

$$= 0.142 \times 10^7 \text{ lbf-in}^2$$

The total EI for the composite is

$$E_cI_c = E_{\text{brass}}I_{\text{brass}} + E_{\text{steel}}I_{\text{steel}}$$

$$= 1.104 \times 10^7 \text{ lbf-in}^2 + 0.142 \times 10^7 \text{ lbf-in}^2$$

$$= 1.246 \times 10^7 \text{ lbf-in}^2$$

From case 1 in App. 49.A, the tip deflection of the tube is

$$y_{\text{tip}} = \frac{PL^3}{3EI}$$

> Since the deflection is inversely proportional to EI, the suggestion of inserting a steel rod does have merit because the insert increases the EI product.

(b) The percent change in tip deflection is

$$\text{percent} = (100\%)\left(\frac{y_{\text{tip}_{\text{brass}}} - y_{\text{tip}_{\text{brass + steel}}}}{y_{\text{tip}_{\text{brass}}}}\right)$$

$$= (100\%)\left(\frac{\dfrac{PL^3}{3E_{\text{brass}}I_{\text{brass}}} - \dfrac{PL^3}{3E_cI_c}}{\dfrac{PL^3}{3E_{\text{brass}}I_{\text{brass}}}}\right)$$

Simplify.

$$\text{percent} = (100\%)\left(\frac{\dfrac{1}{E_{\text{brass}}I_{\text{brass}}} - \dfrac{1}{E_cI_c}}{\dfrac{1}{E_{\text{brass}}I_{\text{brass}}}}\right)$$

$$= (100\%)\left(\frac{\dfrac{1}{1.104 \times 10^7 \text{ lbf-in}^2} - \dfrac{1}{1.246 \times 10^7 \text{ lbf-in}^2}}{\dfrac{1}{1.104 \times 10^7 \text{ lbf-in}^2}}\right)$$

$$= \boxed{11.4\%}$$

SI Solution

(a) The moment of inertia of the brass tube annular cross section is

$$I_{\text{brass}} = \left(\frac{\pi}{4}\right)(r_o^4 - r_i^4)$$

$$= \left(\frac{\pi}{4}\right)\left(\left(\frac{0.050 \text{ m}}{2}\right)^4 - \left(\frac{0.025 \text{ m}}{2}\right)^4\right)$$

$$= 2.876 \times 10^{-7} \text{ m}^4$$

The moment of inertia of the steel rod insert circular cross section is

$$I_{\text{steel}} = \frac{\pi r^4}{4} = \left(\frac{\pi}{4}\right)\left(\frac{0.025 \text{ m}}{2}\right)^4$$

$$= 1.917 \times 10^{-8} \text{ m}^4$$

The product EI for the brass tube is

$$E_{\text{brass}}I_{\text{brass}} = \left(100 \times 10^9 \text{ Pa}\right)\left(2.876 \times 10^{-7} \text{ m}^4\right)$$
$$= 28\,760 \text{ N·m}^2$$

The product EI for the steel rod insert is

$$E_{\text{steel}}I_{\text{steel}} = \left(200 \times 10^9 \text{ Pa}\right)\left(1.917 \times 10^{-8} \text{ m}^4\right)$$
$$= 3834 \text{ N·m}^2$$

The total EI for the composite is

$$E_cI_c = E_{\text{brass}}I_{\text{brass}} + E_{\text{steel}}I_{\text{steel}}$$
$$= 28\,760 \text{ N·m}^2 + 3834 \text{ N·m}^2$$
$$= 32\,594 \text{ N·m}^2$$

From case 1 in App. 49.A, the tip deflection of the tube is

$$y_{\text{tip}} = \frac{PL^3}{3EI}$$

Since the deflection is inversely proportional to EI, the suggestion of inserting a steel rod does have merit because the insert increases the EI product.

(b) The percent change in tip deflection is

$$\text{percent} = (100\%)\left(\frac{y_{\text{tip}_{\text{brass}}} - y_{\text{tip}_{\text{brass}+\text{steel}}}}{y_{\text{tip}_{\text{brass}}}}\right)$$

$$= (100\%)\left(\frac{\dfrac{PL^3}{3E_{\text{brass}}I_{\text{brass}}} - \dfrac{PL^3}{3E_cI_c}}{\dfrac{PL^3}{3E_{\text{brass}}I_{\text{brass}}}}\right)$$

Simplify.

$$\text{percent} = (100\%)\left(\frac{\dfrac{1}{E_{\text{brass}}I_{\text{brass}}} - \dfrac{1}{E_cI_c}}{\dfrac{1}{E_{\text{brass}}I_{\text{brass}}}}\right)$$

$$= (100\%)\left(\frac{\dfrac{1}{28\,760 \text{ N·m}^2} - \dfrac{1}{32\,594 \text{ N·m}^2}}{\dfrac{1}{28\,760 \text{ N·m}^2}}\right)$$

$$= \boxed{11.8\%}$$

10. *Customary U.S. Solution*

The centroidal moment of inertia of the shaft is

$$J = \left(\frac{\pi}{4}\right)r^4 = \left(\frac{\pi}{4}\right)\left(\frac{2 \text{ in}}{2}\right)^4 = 0.7854 \text{ in}^4$$

Although the stress is probably greatest at the fillet toe, it is difficult to specify exactly where the greatest stress occurs. By common convention, it is assumed to occur at the shoulder.

The moment at the shoulder is

$$M = Fd$$

$$= m\left(\frac{g}{g_c}\right)d = (2500 \text{ lbm})\left(\frac{32.2 \dfrac{\text{ft}}{\text{sec}^2}}{32.2 \dfrac{\text{ft-lbm}}{\text{lbf-sec}^2}}\right)(4 \text{ in})$$

$$= 10{,}000 \text{ in-lbf}$$

Use App. 49.B, Fig. (c).

$$\frac{r}{d} = \frac{\frac{5}{16} \text{ in}}{2 \text{ in}} = 0.156$$
$$\frac{D}{d} = \frac{3 \text{ in}}{2 \text{ in}} = 1.5$$

From App. 49.B, the stress concentration factor is approximately 1.5.

The bending stress is

$$\sigma = K\left(\frac{Mc}{I}\right) = \frac{(1.5)(10{,}000 \text{ in-lbf})\left(\dfrac{2 \text{ in}}{2}\right)}{0.7854 \text{ in}^4}$$

$$= \boxed{19{,}099 \text{ lbf/in}^2}$$

(Note that shear stress is zero where bending stress is maximum.)

SI Solution

The centroidal moment of inertia of the shaft is

$$J = \left(\frac{\pi}{4}\right)r^4 = \left(\frac{\pi}{4}\right)\left(\frac{50 \text{ mm}}{(2)\left(1000 \dfrac{\text{mm}}{\text{m}}\right)}\right)^4$$

$$= 3.068 \times 10^{-7} \text{ m}^4$$

Although the stress is probably greatest at the fillet toe, it is difficult to specify exactly where the greatest stress occurs. By common convention, it is assumed to occur at the shoulder.

The moment at the shoulder is

$$M = Fd = mgd = (1100 \text{ kg})\left(9.81 \dfrac{\text{m}}{\text{s}^2}\right)\left(\frac{100 \text{ mm}}{1000 \dfrac{\text{mm}}{\text{m}}}\right)$$

$$= 1079 \text{ N·m}$$

Materials

Use App. 49.B, Fig. (c).

$$\frac{r}{d} = \frac{8 \text{ mm}}{50 \text{ mm}} = 0.16$$

$$\frac{D}{d} = \frac{75 \text{ mm}}{50 \text{ mm}} = 1.5$$

From App. 49.B, the stress concentration factor is approximately 1.5.

The bending stress is

$$\sigma = K\left(\frac{Mc}{I}\right)$$

$$= \frac{(1.5)(1079 \text{ N·m})\left(\dfrac{50 \text{ mm}}{(2)\left(1000 \dfrac{\text{mm}}{\text{m}}\right)}\right)}{3.068 \times 10^{-7} \text{ m}^4}$$

$$= \boxed{1.319 \times 10^8 \text{ Pa} \quad (132 \text{ MPa})}$$

11. *Customary U.S. Solution*

First, determine an equivalent aluminum area for the steel. The ratio of equivalent aluminum area to steel area is the modulus of elasticity ratio.

$$\frac{30 \times 10^6 \ \dfrac{\text{lbf}}{\text{in}^2}}{10 \times 10^6 \ \dfrac{\text{lbf}}{\text{in}^2}} = 3$$

The equivalent aluminum width to replace the steel is

$$(1.5 \text{ in})(3) = 4.5 \text{ in}$$

The equivalent all-aluminum cross section is

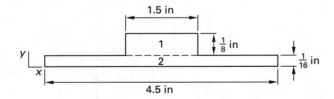

To find the centroid of the section, first calculate the areas of the basic shapes

$$A_1 = (1.5 \text{ in})\left(\tfrac{1}{8} \text{ in}\right) = 0.1875 \text{ in}^2$$

$$A_2 = (4.5 \text{ in})\left(\tfrac{1}{16} \text{ in}\right) = 0.28125 \text{ in}^2$$

Next, find the y-components of the centroids of the basic shapes.

$$y_{c1} = \tfrac{1}{16} \text{ in} + \left(\tfrac{1}{2}\right)\left(\tfrac{1}{8} \text{ in}\right) = 0.125 \text{ in}$$

$$y_{c2} = \frac{\tfrac{1}{16} \text{ in}}{2} = 0.03125 \text{ in}$$

The centroid of the section is

$$y_c = \frac{\displaystyle\sum_i A_i y_{ci}}{\displaystyle\sum A_i}$$

$$= \frac{(0.1875 \text{ in}^2)(0.125 \text{ in}) + (0.28125 \text{ in}^2)(0.03125 \text{ in})}{0.1875 \text{ in}^2 + 0.28125 \text{ in}^2}$$

$$= 0.06875 \text{ in}$$

The moment of inertia of basic shape 1 about its own centroid is

$$I_{cy1} = \frac{bh^3}{12} = \frac{(1.5 \text{ in})(0.125 \text{ in})^3}{12} = 2.441 \times 10^{-4} \text{ in}^4$$

The moment of inertia of basic shape 2 about its own centroid is

$$I_{cy2} = \frac{bh^3}{12} = \frac{(4.5 \text{ in})(0.0625 \text{ in})^3}{12} = 9.155 \times 10^{-5} \text{ in}^4$$

The distance from the centroid of basic shape 1 to the section centroid is

$$d_1 = y_{c1} - y_c = 0.125 \text{ in} - 0.06875 \text{ in} = 0.05625 \text{ in}$$

The distance from the centroid of basic shape 2 to the section centroid is

$$d_2 = y_c - y_{c2} = 0.06875 \text{ in} - 0.03125 \text{ in} = 0.0375 \text{ in}$$

From the parallel axis theorem, the moment of inertia of basic shape 1 about the centroid of the section is

$$I_{y1} = I_{yc1} + A_1 d_1^2$$
$$= 2.411 \times 10^{-4} \text{ in}^4 + (0.1875 \text{ in}^2)(0.05625 \text{ in})^2$$
$$= 8.344 \times 10^{-4} \text{ in}^4$$

The moment of inertia of basic shape 2 about the centroid of the section is

$$I_{y2} = I_{yc2} + A_2 d_2^2$$
$$= 9.155 \times 10^{-5} \text{ in}^2 + (0.28125 \text{ in}^2)(0.0375 \text{ in})^2$$
$$= 4.871 \times 10^{-4} \text{ in}^2$$

The total moment of inertia of the section about the centroid of the section is

$$I_y = I_{y1} + I_{y2} = 8.344 \times 10^{-4} \text{ in}^2 + 4.871 \times 10^{-4} \text{ in}^2$$

$$= \boxed{1.322 \times 10^{-3} \text{ in}^2}$$

SI Solution

First, determine an equivalent aluminum area for the steel. The ratio of equivalent aluminum area to steel area is the modulus of elasticity ratio.

$$\frac{20 \times 10^4 \text{ MPa}}{70 \times 10^3 \text{ MPa}} = 2.86$$

The equivalent aluminum width to replace the steel is

$$(38 \text{ mm})(2.86) = 108.7 \text{ mm}$$

The equivalent all-aluminum cross section is

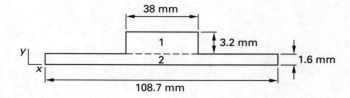

To find the centroid of the section, first calculate the areas of the basic shapes

$$A_1 = (38 \text{ mm})(3.2 \text{ mm}) = 121.6 \text{ mm}^2$$
$$A_2 = (108.7 \text{ mm})(1.6 \text{ mm}) = 173.9 \text{ mm}^2$$

Next, find the y-components of the centroids of the basic shapes.

$$y_{c1} = 1.6 \text{ mm} + \left(\tfrac{1}{2}\right)(3.2 \text{ mm}) = 3.2 \text{ mm}$$
$$y_{c2} = \frac{1.6 \text{ mm}}{2} = 0.8 \text{ mm}$$

The centroid of the section is

$$\begin{aligned}
y_c &= \frac{\sum\limits_{i} A_i y_{ci}}{\sum A_i} \\
&= \frac{(121.6 \text{ mm}^2)(3.2 \text{ mm}) + (173.9 \text{ mm}^2)(0.8 \text{ mm})}{121.6 \text{ mm}^2 + 173.9 \text{ mm}^2} \\
&= 1.79 \text{ mm}
\end{aligned}$$

The moment of inertia of basic shape 1 about its own centroid is

$$I_{cy1} = \frac{bh^3}{12} = \frac{(38 \text{ mm})(3.2 \text{ mm})^3}{12} = 103.77 \text{ mm}^4$$

The moment of inertia of basic shape 2 about its own centroid is

$$I_{cy2} = \frac{bh^3}{12} = \frac{(108.7 \text{ mm})(1.6 \text{ mm})^3}{12} = 37.10 \text{ mm}^4$$

The distance from the centroid of basic shape 1 to the section centroid is

$$d_1 = y_{c1} - y_c = 3.2 \text{ mm} - 1.79 \text{ mm} = 1.41 \text{ mm}$$

The distance from the centroid of basic shape 2 to the section centroid is

$$d_2 = y_c - y_{c2} = 1.79 \text{ mm} - 0.8 \text{ mm} = 0.99 \text{ mm}$$

From the parallel axis theorem, the moment of inertia of basic shape 1 about the centroid of the section is

$$\begin{aligned}
I_{y1} &= I_{yc1} + A_1 d_1^2 \\
&= 103.77 \text{ mm}^4 + (121.6 \text{ mm}^2)(1.41 \text{ mm})^2 \\
&= 345.52 \text{ mm}^4
\end{aligned}$$

The moment of inertia of basic shape 2 about the centroid of the section is

$$\begin{aligned}
I_{y2} &= I_{yc2} + A_2 d_2^2 \\
&= 37.10 \text{ mm}^4 + (173.9 \text{ mm}^2)(0.99 \text{ mm})^2 \\
&= 207.54 \text{ mm}^4
\end{aligned}$$

The total moment of inertia of the section about the centroid of the section is

$$I_y = I_{y1} + I_{y2} = 345.52 \text{ mm}^4 + 207.54 \text{ mm}^4$$
$$\boxed{= 553.06 \text{ mm}^4}$$

50 Failure Theories

1. *Customary U.S. Solution*

Use the distortion energy failure theory. From Eq. 50.27, the yield strength in shear is

$$S_{ys} = 0.577 S_{yt} = (0.577)\left(73.9 \times 10^3 \, \frac{\text{lbf}}{\text{in}^2}\right)$$
$$= 42.64 \times 10^3 \, \text{lbf/in}^2$$

For a safety factor of 2.5, the maximum allowable shear stress is

$$\tau_{\max} = \frac{S_{ys}}{\text{FS}} = \frac{42.64 \times 10^3 \, \frac{\text{lbf}}{\text{in}^2}}{2.5}$$
$$= 17.06 \times 10^3 \, \text{lbf/in}^2$$

The total shear at the pin is

$$V = \frac{\text{shaft torque}}{\text{shaft radius}} = \frac{400 \text{ in-lbf}}{\dfrac{1.125 \text{ in}}{2}} = 711.1 \text{ lbf}$$

Since the pin is a round bar, the maximum shear stress in the pin is

$$\tau_{\max} = \frac{4V}{3A}$$

Solve for the required total pin area.

$$A = \frac{4V}{3\tau_{\max}} = \frac{(4)(711.1 \text{ lbf})}{(3)\left(17.06 \times 10^3 \, \dfrac{\text{lbf}}{\text{in}^2}\right)} = 0.05558 \text{ in}^2$$

Since two surfaces of the pin resist the shear,

$$A = (2)\left(\frac{\pi d^2}{4}\right) = \frac{\pi d^2}{2}$$

Solve for the pin diameter.

$$d = \sqrt{\frac{2A}{\pi}} = \sqrt{\frac{(2)(0.05558 \text{ in}^2)}{\pi}} = \boxed{0.188 \text{ in}}$$

SI Solution

Use the distortion energy failure theory. From Eq. 50.27, the yield strength in shear is

$$S_{ys} = 0.577 S_{yt} = (0.577)\left(510 \times 10^6 \text{ Pa}\right)$$
$$= 294.3 \times 10^6 \text{ Pa}$$

For a safety factor of 2.5, the maximum allowable shear stress is

$$\tau_{\max} = \frac{S_{ys}}{\text{FS}} = \frac{294.3 \times 10^6 \text{ Pa}}{2.5}$$
$$= 117.7 \times 10^6 \text{ Pa}$$

The total shear at the pin is

$$V = \frac{\text{shaft torque}}{\text{shaft radius}} = \frac{45 \text{ N·m}}{\dfrac{0.0286 \text{ m}}{2}} = 3146.9 \text{ N}$$

Since the pin is a round bar, the maximum shear stress in the pin is

$$\tau_{\max} = \frac{4V}{3A}$$

Solve for the required total pin area.

$$A = \frac{4V}{3\tau_{\max}} = \frac{(4)(3146.9 \text{ N})}{(3)\left(117.7 \times 10^6 \text{ Pa}\right)}$$
$$= 3.565 \times 10^{-5} \text{ m}^2$$

Since two surfaces of the pin resist the shear, the total pin area is

$$A = (2)\left(\frac{\pi d^2}{4}\right) = \frac{\pi d^2}{2}$$

Solve for the pin diameter.

$$d = \sqrt{\frac{2A}{\pi}} = \sqrt{\frac{(2)(3.565 \times 10^{-5} \text{ m}^2)}{\pi}} = \boxed{0.00476 \text{ m}}$$

2. *Customary U.S. Solution*

From Table 51.5, the tensile stress area for a $^5/_8$ in UNC bolt is $A = 0.226 \text{ in}^2$.

The maximum stress is

$$\sigma_{\max} = \frac{F_{\max}}{A} = \frac{8000 \text{ lbf}}{0.226 \text{ in}^2} = 35{,}398 \text{ lbf/in}^2$$

The minimum stress is

$$\sigma_{\min} = \frac{F_{\min}}{A} = \frac{1000 \text{ lbf}}{0.226 \text{ in}^2} = 4425 \text{ lbf/in}^2$$

From Eq. 50.28, the mean stress is

$$\sigma_m = \frac{\sigma_{max} + \sigma_{min}}{2} = \frac{35,398 \ \frac{lbf}{in^2} + 4425 \ \frac{lbf}{in^2}}{2}$$

$$= 19,912 \ lbf/in^2$$

From Eq. 50.30, the alternating stress is

$$\sigma_{alt} = \left(\tfrac{1}{2}\right)(\sigma_{max} - \sigma_{min})$$

$$= \left(\tfrac{1}{2}\right)\left(35,398 \ \frac{lbf}{in^2} - 4425 \ \frac{lbf}{in^2}\right)$$

$$= 15,487 \ lbf/in^2$$

From Sec. 51.11, the stress concentration factor for rolled threads is 2.2. Thus, the alternating stress is

$$\sigma_{alt} = \left(15,487 \ \frac{lbf}{in^2}\right)(2.2) = 34,071 \ lbf/in^2$$

Draw the Soderberg line and locate the (σ_m, σ_{alt}) point.

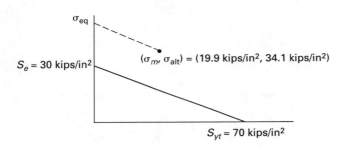

The Soderberg equivalent stress is

$$\sigma_{eq} = \sigma_{alt} + \left(\frac{S_e}{S_{yt}}\right)\sigma_m$$

$$= 34,071 \ \frac{lbf}{in^2} + \left(\frac{30,000 \ \frac{lbf}{in^2}}{70,000 \ \frac{lbf}{in^2}}\right)\left(19,912 \ \frac{lbf}{in^2}\right)$$

$$= 42,605 \ lbf/in^2$$

The factor of safety is

$$FS = \frac{S_e}{\sigma_{eq}} = \frac{30,000 \ \frac{lbf}{in^2}}{42,605 \ \frac{lbf}{in^2}} = \boxed{0.704}$$

SI Solution

From Table 51.5, the tensile stress area for a $^5/_8$ in UNC bolt is

$$A = (0.226 \ in^2)\left(\frac{1 \ m}{39.36 \ in}\right)^2 = 1.459 \times 10^{-4} \ m^2$$

The maximum stress is

$$\sigma_{max} = \frac{F_{max}}{A} = \frac{35\,000 \ N}{1.459 \times 10^{-4} \ m^2} = 239.89 \times 10^6 \ Pa$$

The minimum stress is

$$\sigma_{min} = \frac{F_{min}}{A} = \frac{4400 \ N}{1.459 \times 10^{-4} \ m^2} = 30.16 \times 10^6 \ Pa$$

From Eq. 50.28, the mean stress is

$$\sigma_m = \frac{\sigma_{max} + \sigma_{min}}{2}$$

$$= \frac{239.89 \times 10^6 \ Pa + 30.16 \times 10^6 \ Pa}{2}$$

$$= 135.03 \times 10^6 \ Pa \quad (135.03 \ MPa)$$

From Eq. 50.30, the alternating stress is

$$\sigma_{alt} = \left(\tfrac{1}{2}\right)(\sigma_{max} - \sigma_{min})$$

$$= \left(\tfrac{1}{2}\right)(239.89 \times 10^6 \ Pa - 30.16 \times 10^6 \ Pa)$$

$$= 104.87 \times 10^6 \ Pa \quad (104.87 \ MPa)$$

From Sec. 51.11, the stress concentration factor for rolled threads is 2.2. Thus the alternating stress is

$$\sigma_{alt} = (104.87 \ MPa)(2.2) = 230.71 \ MPa$$

Draw the Soderberg line and locate the (σ_m, σ_{alt}) point.

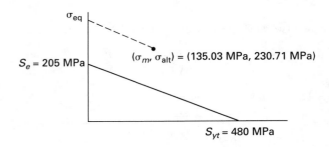

The Soderberg equivalent stress is

$$\sigma_{eq} = \sigma_{alt} + \left(\frac{S_e}{S_{yt}}\right)\sigma_m$$

$$= 230.71 \ MPa + \left(\frac{205 \ MPa}{480 \ MPa}\right)(135.03 \ MPa)$$

$$= 288.38 \ MPa$$

The factor of safety is

$$\text{FS} = \frac{S_e}{\sigma_{\text{eq}}} = \frac{205 \text{ MPa}}{288.38 \text{ MPa}} = \boxed{0.711}$$

From Eq. 50.26, the factor of safety for the spool is

$$\text{FS} = \frac{S_{yt}}{\sigma'} = \frac{19{,}000 \, \dfrac{\text{lbf}}{\text{in}^2}}{11{,}271 \, \dfrac{\text{lbf}}{\text{in}^2}} = \boxed{1.69}$$

3. *Customary U.S. Solution*

The spool is considered to be a thin-walled tube. Only the hoop stress and the longitudinal stress are significant.

The end disc area exposed to the 500 psi pressure is

$$A_e = \left(\frac{\pi}{4}\right)\left((2.0 \text{ in})^2 - (1.0 \text{ in})^2\right) = 2.356 \text{ in}^2$$

The longitudinal force produced by the 500 psig pressure is

$$F = pA_e = \left(500 \, \frac{\text{lbf}}{\text{in}^2}\right)(2.356 \text{ in}^2) = 1178 \text{ lbf}$$

The annular area of the tube is

$$\begin{aligned} A &= \left(\frac{\pi}{4}\right)(d_o^2 - d_i^2) \\ &= \left(\frac{\pi}{4}\right)\left((1.0 \text{ in})^2 - (1 \text{ in} - (2)(0.05 \text{ in}))^2\right) \\ &= 0.149 \text{ in}^2 \end{aligned}$$

The longitudinal stress in the tube is

$$\sigma_{\text{long}} = \frac{F}{A} = \frac{1178 \text{ lbf}}{0.149 \text{ in}^2} = 7906 \text{ lbf/in}^2$$

Since $d/t < 0.10$, this qualifies as a thin-walled cylinder.

The compressive hoop stress in the tube is

$$\begin{aligned} \sigma_{\text{hoop}} &= -\frac{pr_o}{t} = -\frac{\left(500 \, \dfrac{\text{lbf}}{\text{in}^2}\right)\left(\dfrac{1.0 \text{ in}}{2}\right)}{0.050 \text{ in}} \\ &= -5000 \text{ lbf/in}^2 \end{aligned}$$

The principal stresses are

$$\sigma_1 = \sigma_{\text{long}} = 7906 \text{ lbf/in}^2$$
$$\sigma_2 = \sigma_{\text{hoop}} = -5000 \text{ lbf/in}^2$$

For the distortion energy theory, use Eq. 50.23 to find the von Mises stress.

$$\begin{aligned} \sigma' &= \sqrt{\sigma_1^2 + \sigma_2^2 - \sigma_1\sigma_2} \\ &= \sqrt{\begin{array}{c} \left(7906 \, \dfrac{\text{lbf}}{\text{in}^2}\right)^2 + \left(-5000 \, \dfrac{\text{lbf}}{\text{in}^2}\right)^2 \\ - \left(7906 \, \dfrac{\text{lbf}}{\text{in}^2}\right)\left(-5000 \, \dfrac{\text{lbf}}{\text{in}^2}\right) \end{array}} \\ &= 11{,}271 \text{ lbf/in}^2 \end{aligned}$$

SI Solution

The spool is considered to be a thin-walled tube. Only the hoop stress and the longitudinal stress are significant.

The end disc area exposed to the 3.5 MPa pressure is

$$A_e = \left(\frac{\pi}{4}\right)\left((0.050 \text{ m})^2 - (0.025 \text{ m})^2\right) = 0.001473 \text{ m}^2$$

The longitudinal force produced by the 3.5 MPa pressure is

$$F = pA_e = \left(3.5 \times 10^6 \text{ Pa}\right)(0.001473 \text{ m}^2) = 5155.5 \text{ N}$$

The annular area of the tube is

$$\begin{aligned} A &= \left(\frac{\pi}{4}\right)(d_o^2 - d_i^2) \\ &= \left(\frac{\pi}{4}\right)\left((0.025 \text{ m})^2 - (0.025 \text{ m} - (2)(0.00125))^2\right) \\ &= 9.327 \times 10^{-5} \text{ m}^2 \end{aligned}$$

The longitudinal stress in the tube is

$$\sigma_{\text{long}} = \frac{F}{A} = \frac{5155.5 \text{ N}}{9.327 \times 10^{-5} \text{ m}^2} = 55.28 \times 10^6 \text{ Pa}$$

Since $d/t < 0.10$, this qualifies as a thin-walled cylinder.

The compressive hoop stress in the tube is

$$\begin{aligned} \sigma_{\text{hoop}} &= -\frac{pr_o}{t} = \frac{-\left(3.5 \times 10^6 \text{ Pa}\right)\left(\dfrac{0.025 \text{ m}}{2}\right)}{0.00125 \text{ m}} \\ &= -35.0 \times 10^6 \text{ Pa} \end{aligned}$$

The principal stresses are

$$\sigma_1 = \sigma_{\text{long}} = 55.28 \times 10^6 \text{ Pa} \quad (55.28 \text{ MPa})$$
$$\sigma_2 = \sigma_{\text{hoop}} = -35.0 \times 10^6 \text{ Pa} \quad (-35.0 \text{ MPa})$$

For the distortion energy theory, use Eq. 50.23 to find the von Mises stress.

$$\begin{aligned} \sigma' &= \sqrt{\sigma_1^2 + \sigma_2^2 - \sigma_1\sigma_2} \\ &= \sqrt{\begin{array}{c} (55.28 \text{ MPa})^2 + (-35.0 \text{ MPa})^2 \\ - (55.28 \text{ MPa})(-35.0 \text{ MPa}) \end{array}} \\ &= 78.84 \text{ MPa} \end{aligned}$$

Machine Design

From Eq. 50.26, the factor of safety for the spool is

$$\text{FS} = \frac{S_{yt}}{\sigma'} = \frac{130 \text{ MPa}}{78.84 \text{ MPa}} = \boxed{1.65}$$

4. *Customary U.S. Solution*

First find the portion of the pressure load, p, taken by the bolts.

The length of the bolt in tension is

$$L = 0.75 \text{ in} + 0.50 \text{ in} = 1.25 \text{ in}$$

The modulus of elasticity of cold-rolled bolts is $E = 30 \times 10^6 \text{ lbf/in}^2$.

The total bolt stiffness is

$$k_{\text{bolt}} = (6)\left(\frac{AE}{L}\right)$$

$$= \frac{(6)\left(\frac{\pi}{4}\right)(0.375 \text{ in})^2 \left(30 \times 10^6 \dfrac{\text{lbf}}{\text{in}^2}\right)}{1.25 \text{ in}}$$

$$= 1.590 \times 10^7 \text{ lbf/in}$$

The plate/vessel contact area is an annulus with an 8.5 in inside diameter and an 11.5 in outside diameter.

$$A = \left(\frac{\pi}{4}\right)\left((11.5 \text{ in})^2 - (8.5 \text{ in})^2\right) = 47.12 \text{ in}^2$$

The modulus of elasticity of the plate/vessel material is $E = 29 \times 10^6 \text{ lbf/in}^2$.

The plate/vessel stiffness is

$$k_{\text{plate/vessel}} = \frac{AE}{L} = \frac{(47.12 \text{ in}^2)\left(29 \times 10^6 \dfrac{\text{lbf}}{\text{in}^2}\right)}{1.25 \text{ in}}$$

$$= 1.093 \times 10^9 \text{ lbf/in}$$

Let x be the decimal portion of the pressure load, p, taken by the bolts. The increase in bolt length is

$$\delta_{\text{bolt}} = \frac{xp}{k_{\text{bolt}}}$$

The plate/vessel deformation is

$$\delta_{\text{plate/vessel}} = \frac{(1-x)p}{k_{\text{plate/vessel}}}$$

Set $\delta_{\text{bolt}} = \delta_{\text{plate/vessel}}$.

$$\frac{xp}{k_{\text{bolt}}} = \frac{(1-x)p}{k_{\text{plate/vessel}}}$$

Canceling p gives

$$\frac{x}{1.590 \times 10^7 \dfrac{\text{lbf}}{\text{in}^2}} = \frac{1-x}{1.093 \times 10^9 \dfrac{\text{lbf}}{\text{in}^2}}$$

$$x = 0.0143$$

Next, find the stresses in the bolts.

The end plate area exposed to pressure is

$$A_{\text{plate}} = \left(\frac{\pi}{4}\right)(8.5 \text{ in})^2 = 56.75 \text{ in}^2$$

The forces on the end plate are

$$F_{\max} = p_{\max} A_{\text{plate}} = \left(350 \frac{\text{lbf}}{\text{in}^2}\right)(56.75 \text{ in}^2)$$

$$= 19{,}863 \text{ lbf}$$

$$F_{\min} = p_{\min} A_{\text{plate}} = \left(50 \frac{\text{lbf}}{\text{in}^2}\right)(56.75 \text{ in}^2)$$

$$= 2838 \text{ lbf}$$

From Table 51.5, the stress area of a $^3/_8$-24 UNF bolt is $A = 0.0878 \text{ in}^2$.

For a preload, F_o, the maximum stress in each bolt is

$$\sigma_{\max} = \frac{F_o + \dfrac{xF_{\max}}{6}}{A}$$

$$= \frac{3700 \text{ lbf} + \dfrac{(0.0143)(19{,}863 \text{ lbf})}{6}}{0.0878}$$

$$= 42{,}680 \text{ lbf/in}^2$$

The minimum stress in each bolt is

$$\sigma_{\min} = \frac{F_o + \dfrac{xF_{\min}}{6}}{A}$$

$$= \frac{3700 \text{ lbf} + \dfrac{(0.0143)(2838 \text{ lbf})}{6}}{0.0878}$$

$$= 42{,}218 \text{ lbf/in}^2$$

From Eq. 50.28, the mean stress is

$$\sigma_m = \frac{\sigma_{\max} + \sigma_{\min}}{2} = \frac{42{,}680 \dfrac{\text{lbf}}{\text{in}^2} + 42{,}218 \dfrac{\text{lbf}}{\text{in}^2}}{2}$$

$$= 42{,}449 \text{ lbf/in}^2$$

For a thread stress concentration factor of 2, use Eq. 50.30 to find the alternating stress.

$$\sigma_{\text{alt}} = (2)\left(\frac{\sigma_{\max} - \sigma_{\min}}{2}\right) = \sigma_{\max} - \sigma_{\min}$$

$$= 42{,}680 \frac{\text{lbf}}{\text{in}^2} - 42{,}218 \frac{\text{lbf}}{\text{in}^2} = 462 \text{ lbf/in}^2$$

The endurance strength of the bolt is considered to be one-half the ultimate strength.

$$S'_e = 0.5 S_{ut} = (0.5)\left(110{,}000\ \frac{\text{lbf}}{\text{in}^2}\right) = 55{,}000\ \text{lbf/in}^2$$

Use the following endurance strength derating factors (from Shigley and Mischke, *Mechanical Engineering Design*).

      surface finish: $K_a = 0.72$
      size: $K_b = 0.85$
      reliability: $K_c = 0.90$

The new endurance strength of the bolt is

$$S_e = K_a K_b K_c S'_e = (0.72)(0.85)(0.90)\left(55{,}000\ \frac{\text{lbf}}{\text{in}^2}\right)$$

$$= 30{,}294\ \text{lbf/in}^2$$

Draw the Goodman line and locate the $(\sigma_m,\ \sigma_{\text{alt}})$ point.

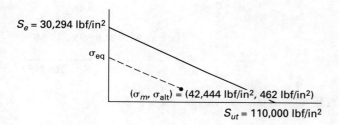

The Goodman equivalent stress is

$$\sigma_{\text{eq}} = \sigma_{\text{alt}} + \left(\frac{S_e}{S_{ut}}\right)\sigma_m$$

$$= 462\ \frac{\text{lbf}}{\text{in}^2} + \left(\frac{30{,}294\ \dfrac{\text{lbf}}{\text{in}^2}}{110{,}000\ \dfrac{\text{lbf}}{\text{in}^2}}\right)\left(42{,}449\ \frac{\text{lbf}}{\text{in}^2}\right)$$

$$= 12{,}152\ \text{lbf/in}^2$$

From Eq. 50.32, the factor of safety is

$$\text{FS} = \frac{S_e}{\sigma_{\text{eq}}} = \frac{30{,}294\ \dfrac{\text{lbf}}{\text{in}^2}}{12{,}152\ \dfrac{\text{lbf}}{\text{in}^2}} = \boxed{2.5}$$

SI Solution

First find the portion of the pressure load, p, taken by the bolts.

The length of the bolt in tension is

$$L = (19\ \text{mm} + 12\ \text{mm})\left(\frac{1\ \text{m}}{1000\ \text{mm}}\right) = 0.031\ \text{m}$$

The modulus of elasticity of cold-rolled bolts is $E = 20 \times 10^4$ MPa.

The total bolt stiffness is

$$k_{\text{bolt}} = (6)\left(\frac{AE}{L}\right)$$

$$= \frac{(6)\left(\dfrac{\pi}{4}\right)(0.0095\ \text{m})^2\left(20 \times 10^{10}\ \text{Pa}\right)}{0.031\ \text{m}}$$

$$= 2.744 \times 10^9\ \text{N/m}$$

The plate/vessel contact area is an annulus with a 215 mm inside diameter and a 290 mm outside diameter.

$$A = \left(\frac{\pi}{4}\right)\left((0.290\ \text{m})^2 - (0.215\ \text{m})^2\right) = 0.02975\ \text{m}^2$$

The modulus of elasticity of the plate/vessel material is $E = 19 \times 10^4$ MPa.

The plate/vessel stiffness is

$$k_{\text{plate/vessel}} = \frac{AE}{L} = \frac{(0.02975\ \text{m}^2)\left(19 \times 10^{10}\ \text{Pa}\right)}{0.031\ \text{m}}$$

$$= 1.823 \times 10^{11}\ \text{N/m}$$

Let x be the decimal portion of the pressure load, p, taken by the bolts. The increase in bolt length is

$$\delta_{\text{bolt}} = \frac{xp}{k_{\text{bolt}}}$$

The plate/vessel deformation is

$$\delta_{\text{plate/vessel}} = \frac{(1-x)p}{k_{\text{plate/vessel}}}$$

Set $\delta_{\text{bolt}} = \delta_{\text{plate/vessel}}$.

$$\frac{xp}{k_{\text{bolt}}} = \frac{(1-x)p}{k_{\text{plate/vessel}}}$$

Canceling p gives

$$\frac{x}{2.744 \times 10^9\ \dfrac{\text{N}}{\text{m}}} = \frac{1-x}{1.823 \times 10^{11}\ \dfrac{\text{N}}{\text{m}}}$$

$$x = 0.0148$$

Next, find the stresses in the bolts.

The end plate area exposed to pressure is

$$A_{\text{plate}} = \left(\frac{\pi}{4}\right)(0.215\ \text{m})^2 = 0.0363\ \text{m}^2$$

The forces on the end plate are

$$F_{\text{max}} = p_{\text{max}} A_{\text{plate}} = \left(2400 \times 10^3\ \text{Pa}\right)(0.0363\ \text{m}^2)$$

$$= 87.12 \times 10^3\ \text{N}$$

$$F_{\text{min}} = p_{\text{min}} A_{\text{plate}} = \left(340 \times 10^3\ \text{Pa}\right)(0.0363\ \text{m}^2)$$

$$= 12.34 \times 10^3\ \text{N}$$

From Table 51.15, the stress area of a $^3/_8$-24 UNF bolt is

$$A = (0.0878 \text{ in}^2)\left(\frac{1 \text{ m}}{39.36 \text{ in}}\right)^2 = 5.667 \times 10^{-5} \text{ m}^2$$

For a preload F_o, the maximum stress in each bolt is

$$\begin{aligned}\sigma_{\max} &= \frac{F_o + \dfrac{xF_{\max}}{6}}{A} \\ &= \frac{16.4 \times 10^3 \text{ N} + \dfrac{(0.0148)(87.12 \times 10^3 \text{ N})}{6}}{5.667 \times 10^{-5} \text{ m}^2} \\ &= 2.932 \times 10^8 \text{ Pa}\end{aligned}$$

The minimum stress in each bolt is

$$\begin{aligned}\sigma_{\min} &= \frac{F_o + \dfrac{xF_{\min}}{6}}{A} \\ &= \frac{16.4 \times 10^3 \text{ N} + \dfrac{(0.0148)(12.34 \times 10^3 \text{ N})}{6}}{5.667 \times 10^{-5} \text{ m}^2} \\ &= 2.899 \times 10^8 \text{ Pa}\end{aligned}$$

From Eq. 50.28, the mean stress is

$$\begin{aligned}\sigma_m &= \frac{\sigma_{\max} + \sigma_{\min}}{2} \\ &= \frac{2.932 \times 10^8 \text{ Pa} + 2.899 \times 10^8 \text{ Pa}}{2} \\ &= 2.916 \times 10^8 \text{ Pa} \quad (291.6 \text{ MPa})\end{aligned}$$

For a thread stress concentration factor of 2, use Eq. 50.36 to find the alternating stress.

$$\begin{aligned}\sigma_{\text{alt}} &= (2)\left(\frac{\sigma_{\max} - \sigma_{\min}}{2}\right) = \sigma_{\max} - \sigma_{\min} \\ &= 2.932 \times 10^8 \text{ Pa} - 2.899 \times 10^8 \text{ Pa} \\ &= 0.033 \times 10^8 \text{ Pa} \quad (3.5 \text{ MPa})\end{aligned}$$

The endurance strength of the bolt is considered to be one-half the ultimate strength.

$$S'_e = 0.5 S_{ut} = (0.5)(760 \text{ MPa}) = 380 \text{ MPa}$$

Use the following endurance strength derating factors (from Shigley and Mischke, *Mechanical Engineering Design*).

surface finish: $K_a = 0.72$
size: $K_b = 0.85$
reliability: $K_c = 0.90$

The new endurance strength of the bolt is

$$\begin{aligned}S_e &= K_a K_b K_c S'_e = (0.72)(0.85)(0.90)(380 \text{ MPa}) \\ &= 209.3 \text{ MPa}\end{aligned}$$

Draw the Goodman line and locate the $(\sigma_m, \sigma_{\text{alt}})$ point.

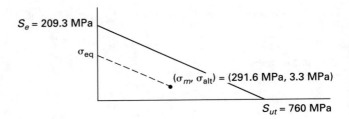

The Goodman equivalent stress is

$$\begin{aligned}\sigma_{\text{eq}} &= \sigma_{\text{alt}} + \left(\frac{S_e}{S_{ut}}\right)\sigma_m \\ &= 3.3 \text{ MPa} + \left(\frac{209.3 \text{ MPa}}{760 \text{ MPa}}\right)(291.6 \text{ MPa}) \\ &= 83.6 \text{ MPa}\end{aligned}$$

From Eq. 50.32, the factor of safety is

$$\text{FS} = \frac{S_e}{\sigma_{\text{eq}}} = \frac{209.3 \text{ MPa}}{83.6 \text{ MPa}} = \boxed{2.5}$$

51 Basic Machine Design

1. *Customary U.S. Solution*

The factor of safety is

$$\text{FS} = \frac{S_{yt}}{\sigma} = \frac{36{,}000 \ \frac{\text{lbf}}{\text{in}^2}}{8240 \ \frac{\text{lbf}}{\text{in}^2}} = \boxed{4.37}$$

SI Solution

The factor of safety is

$$\text{FS} = \frac{S_{yt}}{\sigma} = \frac{250 \ \text{MPa}}{57 \ \text{MPa}} = \boxed{4.39}$$

2. *Customary U.S. Solution*

The design load for a factor of safety of 2.5 is

$$F = (75{,}000 \ \text{lbf})(2.5) = 187{,}500 \ \text{lbf}$$

From Table 51.1, the theoretical end restraint coefficient for built-in ends is $C = 0.5$, and the minimum design value is 0.65.

From Eq. 51.3, the effective length of the column is

$$L' = CL = (0.65)(50 \ \text{ft})\left(12 \ \frac{\text{in}}{\text{ft}}\right) = 390 \ \text{in}$$

Set the design load equal to the Euler load F_e and use Eq. 51.1 to find the required moment of inertia.

$$I = \frac{F_e(L')^2}{\pi^2 E}$$

$$= \frac{(187{,}500 \ \text{lbf})(390 \ \text{in})^2}{\pi^2 \left(30 \times 10^6 \ \frac{\text{lbf}}{\text{in}^2}\right)} = \boxed{96.32 \ \text{in}^4}$$

SI Solution

The design load for a factor of safety of 2.5 is

$$F = (330 \times 10^3 \ \text{N})(2.5) = 825 \times 10^3 \ \text{N}$$

From Table 51.1, the theoretical end restraint coefficient for built-in ends is $C = 0.5$, and the minimum design value is 0.65.

From Eq. 51.3, the effective length of the column is

$$L' = CL = (0.65)(15 \ \text{m}) = 9.75 \ \text{m}$$

Set the design load equal to the Euler load F_e and use Eq. 51.1 to find the required moment of inertia.

$$I = \frac{F_e(L')^2}{\pi^2 E}$$

$$= \frac{(825 \times 10^3 \ \text{N})(9.75 \ \text{m})^2}{\pi^2 \left(20 \times 10^{10} \ \frac{\text{N}}{\text{m}^2}\right)} = \boxed{3.973 \times 10^{-5} \ \text{m}^4}$$

3. *Customary U.S. Solution*

The radius of gyration is

$$k = \sqrt{\frac{I}{A}} = \sqrt{\frac{350 \ \text{in}^4}{25.6 \ \text{in}^2}} = 3.70 \ \text{in}$$

The slenderness ratio is

$$\frac{L}{K} = \frac{(25 \ \text{ft})\left(12 \ \frac{\text{in}}{\text{ft}}\right)}{3.70 \ \text{in}} = 81.08$$

The total buckling load is

$$F = 100{,}000 \ \text{lbf} + 150{,}000 \ \text{lbf} = 250{,}000 \ \text{lbf}$$

From Eq. 51.9,

$$\phi = \left(\tfrac{1}{2}\right)\left(\frac{L}{K}\right)\sqrt{\frac{F}{AE}}$$

$$= \left(\tfrac{1}{2}\right)(81.08)\sqrt{\frac{250{,}000 \ \text{lbf}}{(25.6 \ \text{in}^2)\left(30 \times 10^6 \ \frac{\text{lbf}}{\text{in}^2}\right)}}$$

$$= 0.731 \ \text{rad}$$

The eccentricity is

$$e = \frac{M}{F} = \frac{(150{,}000 \ \text{lbf})(3.33 \ \text{in})}{250{,}000 \ \text{lbf}} = 2.0 \ \text{in}$$

From Eq. 51.8, the critical column stress is

$$\sigma_{\max} = \left(\frac{F}{A}\right)\left(1 + \left(\frac{ec}{k^2}\right)(\sec\phi)\right)$$

$$= \left(\frac{250,000 \text{ lbf}}{25.6 \text{ in}^2}\right)\left(1 + \left[\frac{(2.0 \text{ in})(7 \text{ in})}{(3.70 \text{ in})^2}\right.\right.$$

$$\left.\left.\times (\sec(0.567 \text{ rad}))\right]\right)$$

$$= 21,605 \text{ lbf/in}^2$$

The stress factor of safety for the column is

$$\text{FS} = \frac{S_y}{\sigma_{\max}} = \frac{36,000 \dfrac{\text{lbf}}{\text{in}^2}}{21,605 \dfrac{\text{lbf}}{\text{in}^2}} = \boxed{1.67}$$

SI Solution

The radius of gyration is

$$k = \sqrt{\frac{I}{A}} = \sqrt{\frac{14\,600 \text{ cm}^4}{165 \text{ cm}^2}} = 9.41 \text{ cm}$$

The slenderness ratio is

$$\frac{L}{k} = \frac{(7.5 \text{ m})\left(100 \dfrac{\text{cm}}{\text{m}}\right)}{9.41 \text{ cm}} = 79.70$$

The total buckling load is

$$F = 440 \text{ kN} + 660 \text{ kN} = (1100 \text{ kN})\left(1000 \dfrac{\text{N}}{\text{kN}}\right)$$

$$= 1.1 \times 10^6 \text{ N}$$

From Eq. 51.9,

$$\phi = \left(\tfrac{1}{2}\right)\left(\frac{L}{K}\right)\sqrt{\frac{F}{AE}}$$

$$= \left(\tfrac{1}{2}\right)(79.70)\sqrt{\frac{1.1 \times 10^6 \text{ N}}{\left(\dfrac{165 \text{ cm}^2}{\left(100 \dfrac{\text{cm}}{\text{m}}\right)^2}\right)\left(20 \times 10^{10} \dfrac{\text{N}}{\text{m}^2}\right)}}$$

$$= 0.728 \text{ rad}$$

The eccentricity is

$$e = \frac{M}{F} = \frac{(660 \text{ kN})(80 \text{ mm})}{1100 \text{ kN}} = 48 \text{ mm}$$

From Eq. 51.8, the critical column stress is

$$\sigma_{\max} = \left(\frac{F}{A}\right)\left(1 + \left(\frac{ec}{k^2}\right)(\sec\phi)\right)$$

$$= \left(\frac{1.1 \times 10^6 \text{ N}}{\dfrac{165 \text{ cm}^2}{\left(100 \dfrac{\text{cm}}{\text{m}}\right)^2}}\right)\left(1 + \left[\frac{(48 \text{ mm})(180 \text{ mm})}{(9.41 \text{ cm})^2\left(100 \dfrac{\text{mm}^2}{\text{cm}^2}\right)}\right.\right.$$

$$\left.\left.\times (\sec(0.728 \text{ rad}))\right]\right)\left(\frac{1 \text{ MPa}}{10^6 \text{ Pa}}\right)$$

$$= 153.8 \text{ MPa}$$

The stress factor of safety for the column is

$$\text{FS} = \frac{S_y}{\sigma_{\max}} = \frac{250 \text{ MPa}}{153.8 \text{ MPa}} = \boxed{1.63}$$

4. *Customary U.S. Solution*

The dimensions of the face are

$$a = (2 \text{ ft})\left(12 \dfrac{\text{in}}{\text{ft}}\right) = 24 \text{ in}$$

$$b = (2 \text{ ft})\left(12 \dfrac{\text{in}}{\text{ft}}\right) = 24 \text{ in}$$

The ratio of the side dimensions is

$$\frac{a}{b} = \frac{24 \text{ in}}{24 \text{ in}} = 1$$

The plate is considered to have built-in edges. From Table 51.7, the maximum stress is

$$\sigma_{\max} = \frac{C_3 p b^2}{t^2} = \frac{(0.308)\left(2 \dfrac{\text{lbf}}{\text{in}^2}\right)(24 \text{ in})^2}{(0.25 \text{ in})^2}$$

$$= 5677 \text{ lbf/in}^2$$

The factor of safety is

$$\text{FS} = \frac{S_y}{\sigma_{\max}} = \frac{36,000 \dfrac{\text{lbf}}{\text{in}^2}}{5677 \dfrac{\text{lbf}}{\text{in}^2}} = \boxed{6.34}$$

Machine Design

SI Solution

The dimensions of the face are $a = 60$ cm and $b = 60$ cm.

The ratio of the side dimensions is

$$\frac{a}{b} = \frac{60 \text{ cm}}{60 \text{ cm}} = 1$$

The plate is considered to have built-in edges. From Table 51.7, the maximum stress is

$$\sigma_{\max} = \frac{C_3 p b^2}{t^2}$$
$$= \frac{(0.308)(14 \text{ kPa}) \left((60 \text{ cm}) \left(\frac{1 \text{ m}}{100 \text{ cm}} \right) \right)^2}{\left(6.3 \text{ mm} \left(\frac{1 \text{ m}}{1000 \text{ mm}} \right) \right)^2 \left(1000 \frac{\text{kPa}}{\text{MPa}} \right)}$$
$$= 39.11 \text{ MPa}$$

The factor of safety is

$$\text{FS} = \frac{S_y}{\sigma_{\max}} = \frac{250 \text{ MPa}}{39.11 \text{ MPa}} = \boxed{6.39}$$

5. *Customary U.S. Solution*

The inside radius is

$$r_i = \frac{d_i}{2} = \frac{1.750 \text{ in}}{2} = 0.875 \text{ in}$$

From Table 51.2, the maximum stress is the circumferential stress at the inside radius. This is a normal stress.

$$\sigma_{ci} = \frac{(r_o^2 + r_i^2)p}{r_o^2 - r_i^2}$$
$$20{,}000 \ \frac{\text{lbf}}{\text{in}^2} = \frac{\left(r_o^2 + (0.875 \text{ in})^2 \right) \left(2000 \ \frac{\text{lbf}}{\text{in}^2} \right)}{r_o^2 - (0.875 \text{ in})^2}$$

Simplify.

$$(10) \left(r_o^2 - (0.875 \text{ in})^2 \right) = r_o^2 + (0.875 \text{ in})^2$$
$$r_o^2 = \frac{(11)(0.875 \text{ in})^2}{9}$$
$$r_o = 0.9673 \text{ in}$$

The required outside diameter is

$$d_o = 2r_o = (2)(0.9673 \text{ in}) = \boxed{1.935 \text{ in}}$$

SI Solution

The inside radius is

$$r_i = \frac{d_i}{2} = \frac{44.5 \text{ mm}}{2} = 22.25 \text{ mm}$$

From Table 51.2, the maximum stress is the circumferential stress at the inside radius. This is a normal stress.

$$\sigma_{ci} = \frac{(r_o^2 + r_i^2)p}{r_o^2 - r_i^2}$$
$$140 \text{ MPa} = \frac{\left(r_o^2 + (22.25 \text{ mm})^2 \right) (14 \text{ MPa})}{r_o^2 - (22.25 \text{ mm})^2}$$

Simplify.

$$(10) \left(r_o^2 - (22.25 \text{ mm})^2 \right) = r_o^2 + (22.25 \text{ mm})^2$$
$$r_o^2 = \frac{(11)(22.25 \text{ mm})^2}{9}$$
$$r_o = 24.598 \text{ mm}$$

The required outside diameter is

$$d_o = 2r_o = (2)(24.598 \text{ mm}) = \boxed{49.20 \text{ mm}}$$

6. *Customary U.S. Solution*

The inside radius is

$$r_i = \frac{0.742 \text{ in}}{2} = 0.371 \text{ in}$$

The outside radius is

$$r_o = \frac{1.486 \text{ in}}{2} = 0.743 \text{ in}$$

From Table 51.2, the maximum stress developed in the cylinder is the circumferential stress at the inside radius.

$$\sigma_{ci} = \frac{-2r_o^2 p}{r_o^2 - r_i^2} = \frac{(-2)(0.743 \text{ in})^2 \left(400 \ \frac{\text{lbf}}{\text{in}^2} \right)}{(0.743 \text{ in})^2 - (0.371 \text{ in})^2}$$
$$= \boxed{-1066 \text{ lbf/in}^2 \text{ (c)}}$$

SI Solution

The inside radius is

$$r_i = \frac{18.8 \text{ mm}}{2} = 9.4 \text{ mm}$$

The outside radius is

$$r_o = \frac{37.7 \text{ mm}}{2} = 18.85 \text{ mm}$$

From Table 51.2, the maximum stress developed in the cylinder is the circumferential stress at the inside radius.

$$\sigma_{ci} = \frac{-2r_o^2 p}{r_o^2 - r_i^2} = \frac{(-2)(18.85 \text{ mm})^2(2.8 \text{ MPa})}{(18.85 \text{ mm})^2 - (9.4 \text{ mm})^2}$$

$$= \boxed{-7.45 \text{ MPa (c)}}$$

7. *Customary U.S. Solution*

The inside diameter of the shell is

$$d_i = d_o - 2t = 16 \text{ in} - (2)(0.10 \text{ in}) = 15.8 \text{ in}$$

The polar moment of inertia is

$$J = \left(\frac{\pi}{32}\right)(d_o^4 - d_i^4) = \left(\frac{\pi}{32}\right)((16 \text{ in})^4 - (15.8 \text{ in})^4)$$

$$= 315.7 \text{ in}^4$$

The shear stress is

$$\tau = \frac{Tc}{J} = \frac{(400{,}000 \text{ in-lbf})(8 \text{ in})}{315.7 \text{ in}^4} = 10{,}136 \text{ lbf/in}^2$$

(b) The maximum shear stress is

$$\tau_{\max} = \sqrt{\left(\frac{\sigma}{2}\right)^2 + \tau^2}$$

$$= \sqrt{\left(\frac{40{,}000 \frac{\text{lbf}}{\text{in}^2}}{2}\right)^2 + \left(10{,}136 \frac{\text{lbf}}{\text{in}^2}\right)^2}$$

$$= \boxed{22{,}422 \text{ lbf/in}^2}$$

(a) The principal stresses are

$$\sigma_1 = \frac{\sigma}{2} + \tau_{\max}$$

$$= \frac{40{,}000 \frac{\text{lbf}}{\text{in}^2}}{2} + 22{,}422 \frac{\text{lbf}}{\text{in}^2}$$

$$= \boxed{42{,}422 \text{ lbf/in}^2}$$

$$\sigma_2 = \frac{\sigma}{2} - \tau_{\max}$$

$$= \frac{40{,}000 \frac{\text{lbf}}{\text{in}^2}}{2} - 22{,}422 \frac{\text{lbf}}{\text{in}^2}$$

$$= \boxed{-2422 \text{ lbf/in}^2}$$

SI Solution

The inside diameter of the shell is

$$d_i = d_o - 2t = 406 \text{ mm} - (2)(2.54 \text{ mm}) = 400.92 \text{ mm}$$

The polar moment of inertia is

$$J = \left(\frac{\pi}{32}\right)(d_o^4 - d_i^4)$$

$$= \left(\frac{\pi}{32}\right)((406 \text{ mm})^4 - (400.92 \text{ mm})^4)$$

$$\times \left(\frac{1 \text{ m}}{10^3 \text{ mm}}\right)^4$$

$$= 0.000131 \text{ m}^4$$

The shear stress is

$$\tau = \frac{Tc}{J} = \frac{(45 \text{ kN·m})(0.203 \text{ m})\left(1000 \frac{\text{N}}{\text{kN}}\right)}{0.000131 \text{ m}^4}$$

$$= 6.973 \times 10^6 \text{ Pa} \quad (69.73 \text{ MPa})$$

(b) The maximum shear stress is

$$\tau_{\max} = \sqrt{\frac{\sigma^2}{2} + \tau^2}$$

$$= \sqrt{\left(\frac{280 \text{ MPa}}{2}\right)^2 + (69.73 \text{ MPa})^2}$$

$$= \boxed{156.4 \text{ MPa}}$$

(a) The principal stresses are

$$\sigma_1 = \frac{\sigma}{2} + \tau_{\max}$$

$$= \frac{280 \text{ MPa}}{2} + 156.4 \text{ MPa} = \boxed{296.4 \text{ MPa}}$$

$$\sigma_2 = \frac{\sigma}{2} - \tau_{\max}$$

$$= \frac{280 \text{ MPa}}{2} - 156.4 \text{ MPa} = \boxed{-16.4 \text{ MPa}}$$

8. *Customary U.S. Solution*

For the jacket,

$$r_o = \frac{12 \text{ in}}{2} = 6 \text{ in}$$

$$r_i = \frac{7.75 \text{ in}}{2} = 3.875 \text{ in}$$

From Table 51.2, the highest stress is the circumferential stress at the inside surface.

$$\sigma_{ci} = \frac{(r_o^2 + r_i^2)p}{r_o^2 - r_i^2}$$

Set σ_{ci} equal to the maximum allowable stress.

$$18{,}000 \; \frac{\text{lbf}}{\text{in}^2} = \frac{\left((6 \text{ in})^2 + (3.875 \text{ in})^2\right) p}{(6 \text{ in})^2 - (3.875 \text{ in})^2}$$

$$p = 7404 \text{ lbf/in}^2$$

The radial stress at the inside surface is

$$\sigma_{ri} = -p = -7404 \text{ lbf/in}^2$$

From Eq. 51.18, the diametral strain is

$$\epsilon = \frac{\sigma_c - \nu(\sigma_r + \sigma_l)}{E}$$

$$= \frac{18{,}000 \; \frac{\text{lbf}}{\text{in}^2} - (0.3)\left(-7404 \; \frac{\text{lbf}}{\text{in}^2} + 0\right)}{3 \times 10^7 \; \frac{\text{lbf}}{\text{in}^2}}$$

$$= 6.7404 \times 10^{-4}$$

The diametral deflection is

$$\Delta d = \epsilon d_i = (6.7404 \times 10^{-4})(7.75 \text{ in}) = 0.00522 \text{ in}$$

For the tube,

$$r_o = \frac{7.75 \text{ in}}{2} = 3.875 \text{ in}$$

$$r_i = \frac{4.7 \text{ in}}{2} = 2.35 \text{ in}$$

The external pressure acting on the tube is the same as the radial stress at the inside surface of the jacket. Thus, $p = 7404 \text{ lbf/in}^2$.

From Table 51.2, the circumferential stress at the outside surface is

$$\sigma_{co} = \frac{-(r_o^2 + r_i^2)p}{r_o^2 - r_i^2}$$

$$= \frac{-\left((3.875 \text{ in})^2 + (2.35 \text{ in})^2\right)\left(7404 \; \frac{\text{lbf}}{\text{in}^2}\right)}{(3.875 \text{ in})^2 - (2.35 \text{ in})^2}$$

$$= -16{,}018 \text{ lbf/in}^2$$

The radial stress at the outside surface is

$$\sigma_{ro} = -p = -7404 \text{ lbf/in}^2$$

From Eq. 51.18, the diametral strain is

$$\epsilon = \frac{\sigma_c - \nu(\sigma_r + \sigma_l)}{E}$$

$$= \frac{-16{,}018 \; \frac{\text{lbf}}{\text{in}^2} - (0.3)\left(-7404 \; \frac{\text{lbf}}{\text{in}^2} + 0\right)}{3 \times 10^7 \; \frac{\text{lbf}}{\text{in}^2}}$$

$$= -4.599 \times 10^{-4}$$

The diametral deflection is

$$\Delta d = \epsilon d_o = (-4.599 \times 10^{-4})(7.75 \text{ in}) = -0.00356 \text{ in}$$

(a) The diametral interference is the sum of the magnitudes of the two deflections. From Eq. 51.20,

$$I_{\text{diametral}} = |\Delta d_{\text{jacket}}| + |\Delta d_{\text{tube}}|$$

$$= |0.00522 \text{ in}| + |-0.00356 \text{ in}|$$

$$= \boxed{0.00878 \text{ in}}$$

(b) The maximum circumferential stress in the jacket is at the inside surface.

$$\sigma_{\text{max}} = \sigma_{ci} = \boxed{18{,}000 \text{ lbf/in}^2}$$

(c) The minimum circumferential stress in the tube is at the outside surface.

$$\sigma_{\text{min}} = \sigma_{co} = \boxed{-16{,}018 \text{ lbf/in}^2}$$

SI Solution

For the jacket,

$$r_o = \frac{300 \text{ mm}}{2} = 150 \text{ mm}$$

$$r_i = \frac{197 \text{ mm}}{2} = 98.5 \text{ mm}$$

From Table 51.2, the highest stress is the circumferential stress at the inside surface.

$$\sigma_{ci} = \frac{(r_o^2 + r_i^2)p}{r_o^2 - r_i^2}$$

Set σ_{ci} equal to the maximum allowable stress.

$$124 \text{ MPa} = \frac{\left((150 \text{ mm})^2 + (98.5 \text{ mm})^2\right) p}{(150 \text{ mm})^2 - (98.5 \text{ mm})^2}$$

$$p = 49.28 \text{ MPa}$$

The radial stress at the inside surface is

$$\sigma_{ri} = -p = -49.28 \text{ MPa}$$

From Eq. 51.18, the diametral strain is

$$\epsilon = \frac{\sigma_c - \nu(\sigma_r + \sigma_l)}{E}$$

$$= \frac{124 \text{ MPa} - (0.3)(-49.28 \text{ MPa} + 0)}{(204 \text{ GPa})\left(1000 \; \frac{\text{MPa}}{\text{GPa}}\right)}$$

$$= 6.803 \times 10^{-4}$$

The diametral deflection is

$$\Delta d = \epsilon d_i = (6.803 \times 10^{-4})(197 \text{ mm}) = 0.1340 \text{ mm}$$

For the tube,

$$r_o = \frac{197 \text{ mm}}{2} = 98.5 \text{ mm}$$

$$r_i = \frac{119 \text{ mm}}{2} = 59.5 \text{ mm}$$

The external pressure acting on the tube is the same as the radial stress at the inside surface of the jacket. Thus, $p = 49.28$ MPa.

From Table 51.2, the circumferential stress at the outside surface is

$$\sigma_{co} = \frac{-(r_o^2 + r_i^2)p}{r_o^2 - r_i^2}$$

$$= \frac{-\left((98.5 \text{ mm})^2 + (59.5 \text{ mm})^2\right)(49.28 \text{ MPa})}{(98.5 \text{ m})^2 - (59.5 \text{ mm})^2}$$

$$= -105.91 \text{ MPa}$$

The radial stress at the outside surface is

$$\sigma_{ro} = -p = -49.28 \text{ MPa}$$

From Eq. 51.18, the diametral strain is

$$\epsilon = \frac{\sigma_c - \nu(\sigma_r + \sigma_l)}{E}$$

$$= \frac{-105.91 \text{ MPa} - (0.3)(-49.28 \text{ MPa} - 0)}{(204 \text{ GPa})\left(1000 \frac{\text{MPa}}{\text{GPa}}\right)}$$

$$= -4.467 \times 10^{-4}$$

The diametral deflection is

$$\Delta d = \epsilon d_o = \left(-4.467 \times 10^{-4}\right)(197 \text{ mm}) = -0.0880 \text{ mm}$$

(a) The diametral interface is the sum of the magnitudes of the two deflections. From Eq. 51.20,

$$I_{\text{diametral}} = |\Delta d_{\text{jacket}}| + |\Delta d_{\text{tube}}|$$

$$= |0.1340 \text{ mm}| + |-0.0880 \text{ mm}|$$

$$= \boxed{0.222 \text{ mm}}$$

(b) The maximum circumferential stress in the jacket is at the inside surface.

$$\sigma_{\max} = \sigma_{ci} = \boxed{124 \text{ MPa}}$$

(c) The minimum circumferential stress in the tube is at the outside surface.

$$\sigma_{\min} = \sigma_{co} = \boxed{-105.91 \text{ MPa}}$$

9. *Customary U.S. Solution*

For the inner cylinder,

$$r_o = \frac{4.7 \text{ in} - (2)(0.079 \text{ in})}{2} = 2.27 \text{ in}$$

$$r_i = 2.27 \text{ in} - 0.12 \text{ in} = 2.15 \text{ in}$$

From Table 51.2, the circumferential stress at the outside surface due to external pressure, p, is

$$\sigma_{co} = \frac{-(r_o^2 + r_i^2)p}{r_o^2 - r_i^2}$$

$$= \frac{-\left((2.27 \text{ in})^2 + (2.15 \text{ in})^2\right)p}{(2.27 \text{ in})^2 - (2.15 \text{ in})^2}$$

$$= -18.43p \text{ in lbf/in}^2$$

The radial stress in lbf/in^2 is $\sigma_{ro} = -p$.

From Eq. 51.18, the diametral deflection is

$$\Delta d_{\text{inner}} = \left(\frac{d}{E}\right)(\sigma_c - \nu(\sigma_r + \sigma_l))$$

$$= \frac{(4.54 \text{ in})\left(-18.43p - (0.3)(-p + 0)\right)}{3 \times 10^7 \frac{\text{lbf}}{\text{in}^2}}$$

$$= -27.437 \times 10^{-7}p \quad [\text{in in}]$$

For the outer cylinder,

$$r_o = \frac{4.7 \text{ in}}{2} = 2.35 \text{ in}$$

$$r_i = 2.35 \text{ in} - 0.079 \text{ in} = 2.27 \text{ in}$$

From Table 51.2, the circumferential stress at the inside surface due to internal pressure, p, is

$$\sigma_{ci} = \frac{(r_o^2 + r_i^2)p}{r_o^2 - r_i^2} = \frac{\left((2.35 \text{ in})^2 + (2.27 \text{ in})^2\right)p}{(2.35 \text{ in})^2 - (2.27 \text{ in})^2}$$

$$= 28.88p \quad [\text{in lbf/in}^2]$$

The radial stress in lbf/in^2 is $\sigma_{ri} = -p$.

From Eq. 51.18, the diametral deflection is

$$\Delta d_{\text{outer}} = \left(\frac{d}{E}\right)(\sigma_e - \nu(\sigma_r + \sigma_l))$$

$$= \frac{(4.54 \text{ in})(28.88p - (0.3)(-p + 0))}{3 \times 10^7 \frac{\text{lbf}}{\text{in}^2}}$$

$$= 44.159 \times 10^{-7}p \quad [\text{in in}]$$

From Eq. 51.20, the diametral interference is

$$I_{\text{diametral}} = |\Delta d_{\text{inner}}| + |\Delta d_{\text{outer}}|$$

$$0.012 \text{ in} = |27.437 \times 10^{-7}p| + |44.159 \times 10^{-7}p|$$

$$p = 1676 \text{ lbf/in}^2$$

The circumferential stress at the interface between the two cylinders is as follows.

For the inner cylinder,

$$\sigma_{co} = -18.43p$$

$$= (-18.43)\left(1676 \; \frac{\text{lbf}}{\text{in}^2}\right) = \boxed{-30{,}889 \; \text{lbf/in}^2}$$

For the outer cylinder,

$$\sigma_{ci} = 28.88p$$

$$= (28.88)\left(1676 \; \frac{\text{lbf}}{\text{in}^2}\right) = \boxed{48{,}403 \; \text{lbf/in}^2}$$

SI Solution

For the inner cylinder,

$$r_o = \frac{120 \text{ mm} - (2)(2 \text{ mm})}{2} = 58 \text{ mm}$$

$$r_i = 58 \text{ mm} - 3 \text{ mm} = 55 \text{ mm}$$

From Table 51.2, the circumferential stress at the outside surface due to external pressure, p, is

$$\sigma_{co} = \frac{-(r_o^2 + r_i^2)p}{r_o^2 - r_i^2}$$

$$= \frac{-\left((58 \text{ mm})^2 + (55 \text{ mm})^2\right)p}{(58 \text{ mm})^2 - (55 \text{ mm})^2}$$

$$= -18.85p \quad [\text{in MPa}]$$

The radial stress in MPa is $\sigma_{ro} = -p$.

From Eq. 51.18, the diametral deflection is

$$\Delta d_{\text{inner}} = \left(\frac{d}{E}\right)(\sigma_c - \nu(\sigma_r + \sigma_l))$$

$$= \frac{(116 \text{ mm})\left((-18.85p - (0.3)(-p+0))\right)}{(207 \text{ GPa})\left(1000 \; \frac{\text{MPa}}{\text{GPa}}\right)}$$

$$= -1.040 \times 10^{-2}p \quad [\text{in mm}]$$

For the outer cylinder,

$$r_o = \frac{120 \text{ mm}}{2} = 60 \text{ mm}$$

$$r_i = 60 \text{ mm} - 2 \text{ mm} = 58 \text{ mm}$$

From Table 51.2, the circumferential stress at the inside surface due to internal pressure, p, is

$$\sigma_{ci} = \frac{(r_o^2 + r_i^2)p}{r_o^2 - r_i^2} = \frac{\left((60 \text{ mm})^2 + (58 \text{ mm})^2\right)p}{(60 \text{ mm})^2 - (58 \text{ mm})^2}$$

$$= 29.51p \quad [\text{in MPa}]$$

The radial stress in MPa is $\sigma_{ri} = -p$.

From Eq. 51.18, the diametral deflection is

$$\Delta d_{\text{outer}} = \left(\frac{d}{E}\right)(\sigma_e - \nu(\sigma_r - \sigma_l))$$

$$= \frac{(116 \text{ mm})(29.51p - (0.3)(-p+0))}{(207 \text{ GPa})\left(1000 \; \frac{\text{MPa}}{\text{GPa}}\right)}$$

$$= 1.671 \times 10^{-2}p \quad [\text{in mm}]$$

From Eq. 51.20, the diametral interference is

$$I_{\text{diametral}} = |\Delta d_{\text{inner}}| + |\Delta d_{\text{outer}}|$$

$$0.3 \text{ mm} = |1.040 \times 10^{-2}p| + |1.671 \times 10^{-2}p|$$

$$p = 11.07 \text{ MPa}$$

The circumferential stress at the interface between the two cylinders is as follows.

For the inner cylinder,

$$\sigma_{co} = -18.85p$$

$$= (-18.85)(11.07 \text{ MPa}) = \boxed{-209 \text{ MPa}}$$

For the outer cylinder,

$$\sigma_{ci} = 29.51p$$

$$= (29.51)(11.07 \text{ MPa}) = \boxed{327 \text{ MPa}}$$

10. *Customary U.S. Solution*

The elongation in the unthreaded part of the bolt is

$$\delta_1 = \frac{\sigma_1 L_1}{E} = \frac{\left(40{,}000 \; \frac{\text{lbf}}{\text{in}^2}\right)(4.0 \text{ in} - 0.75 \text{ in})}{2.9 \times 10^7 \; \frac{\text{lbf}}{\text{in}^2}}$$

$$= 0.00448 \text{ in}$$

From Table 51.5, the stress area for a $3/4$-16 UNF bolt is $A_1 = 0.373 \text{ in}^2$.

The stress area for the threaded part of the bolt is

$$A_2 = \frac{\pi d^2}{4} = \frac{\pi (0.75 \text{ in})^2}{4} = 0.4418 \text{ in}^2$$

The stress in the threaded part of the bolt is

$$\sigma_2 = \sigma_1 \left(\frac{A_2}{A_1}\right) = \left(40{,}000 \; \frac{\text{lbf}}{\text{in}^2}\right)\left(\frac{0.4418 \text{ in}^2}{0.373 \text{ in}^2}\right)$$

$$= 47{,}378 \text{ lbf/in}^2$$

Assume half of the bolt in the nut contributes to elongation. The elongation in the threaded part of the bolt, including 3 threads in the nut, is

$$\delta_2 = \frac{\sigma_2 L_2}{E}$$

$$= \frac{\left(47{,}378 \; \frac{\text{lbf}}{\text{in}^2}\right) \times \left(0.75 \text{ in} + (3 \text{ threads})\left(\dfrac{1}{16 \; \frac{\text{threads}}{\text{in}}}\right)\right)}{2.9 \times 10^7 \; \frac{\text{lbf}}{\text{in}^2}}$$

$$= 0.00153 \text{ in}$$

The total stretch of the bolt is

$$\delta = \delta_1 + \delta_2 = 0.00448 \text{ in} + 0.00153 \text{ in} = \boxed{0.00601 \text{ in}}$$

SI Solution

The elongation in the unthreaded part of the bolt is

$$\delta_1 = \frac{\sigma_1 L_1}{E} = \frac{(280 \text{ MPa})(100 \text{ mm} - 19 \text{ mm})}{(200 \text{ GPa})\left(1000 \; \frac{\text{MPa}}{\text{GPa}}\right)}$$

$$= 0.1134 \text{ mm}$$

From Table 51.5, the stress area for a $^3/_4$-16 UNF bolt is

$$A_1 = (0.373 \text{ in}^2)\left(25.4 \; \frac{\text{mm}}{\text{in}}\right)^2 = 240.64 \text{ mm}^2$$

The stress area for the threaded part of the bolt is

$$A_2 = \frac{\pi d^2}{4} = \frac{\pi (19 \text{ mm})^2}{4} = 283.53 \text{ mm}^2$$

The stress in the threaded part of the bolt is

$$\sigma_2 = \sigma_1 \left(\frac{A_2}{A_1}\right) = (280 \text{ MPa})\left(\frac{283.53 \text{ mm}^2}{240.64 \text{ mm}^2}\right)$$

$$= 330 \text{ MPa}$$

Assume half of the bolt in the nut contributes to elongation.

$$\delta_2 = \frac{\sigma_2 L_2}{E}$$

$$= \frac{(330 \text{ MPa})\left(19 \text{ mm} + (3 \text{ threads}) \times \left(\dfrac{1}{16 \; \frac{\text{threads}}{\text{in}}}\right)\left(25.4 \; \frac{\text{mm}}{\text{in}}\right)\right)}{(200 \text{ GPa})\left(1000 \; \frac{\text{MPa}}{\text{GPa}}\right)}$$

$$= 0.0392 \text{ mm}$$

The total stretch of the bolt is

$$\delta = \delta_1 + \delta_2 = 0.1134 \text{ mm} + 0.0392 \text{ mm} = \boxed{0.1526 \text{ mm}}$$

11. *Customary U.S. Solution*

For the cast-iron hub,

$$r_o = \frac{12 \text{ in}}{2} = 6 \text{ in}$$

$$r_i = \frac{6 \text{ in}}{2} = 3 \text{ in}$$

From Table 51.2, the circumferential stress at the inside radius due to internal pressure, p, is

$$\sigma_{ci} = \frac{(r_o^2 + r_i^2)p}{r_o^2 - r_i^2}$$

The ultimate strength of cast iron is $S_{ut} = 30{,}000 \text{ lbf/in}^2$.

For cast iron, nonlinearity begins at approximately $^1/_6 S_{ut}$.

$$\sigma_{ci} = \frac{S_{ut}}{\text{FS}} = \frac{30{,}000 \; \frac{\text{lbf}}{\text{in}^2}}{6} = 5000 \text{ lbf/in}^2$$

The σ_{ci} relationship is

$$5000 \; \frac{\text{lbf}}{\text{in}^2} = \frac{\left((6 \text{ in})^2 + (3 \text{ in})^2\right)p}{(6 \text{ in})^2 - (3 \text{ in})^2}$$

$$p = 3000 \text{ lbf/in}^2$$

The radial stress is

$$\sigma_{ri} = -p = -3000 \text{ lbf/in}^2$$

From Eq. 51.18, the radial deflection is

$$\Delta r_{\text{outer}} = \frac{r\left(\sigma_c - \nu(\sigma_r + \sigma_l)\right)}{E}$$

$$= \frac{(3 \text{ in})\left(5000 \; \frac{\text{lbf}}{\text{in}^2} - (0.27)\left(-3000 \; \frac{\text{lbf}}{\text{in}^2} + 0\right)\right)}{1.45 \times 10^7 \; \frac{\text{lbf}}{\text{in}^2}}$$

$$= 1.202 \times 10^{-3} \text{ in}$$

For the steel shaft,

$$r_o = \frac{6 \text{ in}}{2} = 3 \text{ in}$$

$$r_i = 0$$

From Table 51.2, the circumferential stress at the outside radius due to external pressure, p, is

$$\sigma_{co} = \frac{-(r_o^2 + r_i^2)p}{r_o^2 - r_i^2}$$

$$= \frac{((3 \text{ in})^2 + (0)^2)\left(3000 \, \dfrac{\text{lbf}}{\text{in}^2}\right)}{(3 \text{ in})^2 - (0)^2}$$

$$= -3000 \text{ lbf/in}^2$$

The radial stress is

$$\sigma_{ro} = -p = -3000 \text{ lbf/in}^2$$

From Eq. 51.18, the radial deflection is

$$\Delta r_{\text{inner}} = \frac{r(\sigma_c - \nu(\sigma_r + \sigma_l))}{E}$$

$$= \frac{(3 \text{ in})\left(-3000 \, \dfrac{\text{lbf}}{\text{in}^2}\right.}{\left. - (0.30)\left(-3000 \, \dfrac{\text{lbf}}{\text{in}^2} + 0\right)\right)}{2.9 \times 10^7 \, \dfrac{\text{lbf}}{\text{in}^2}}$$

$$= -2.172 \times 10^{-4} \text{ in}$$

From Eq. 51.20, the radial interference is

$$I_{\text{radial}} = |\Delta r_{\text{inner}}| + |\Delta r_{\text{outer}}|$$

$$= |-2.172 \times 10^{-4} \text{ in}| + |1.202 \times 10^{-3} \text{ in}|$$

$$= \boxed{1.419 \times 10^{-3} \text{ in}}$$

SI Solution

For the cast-iron hub,

$$r_o = \frac{300 \text{ mm}}{2} = 150 \text{ mm}$$

$$r_i = \frac{150 \text{ mm}}{2} = 75 \text{ mm}$$

From Table 51.2, the circumferential stress at the inside radius due to internal pressure, p, is

$$\sigma_{ci} = \frac{(r_o^2 + r_i^2)p}{r_o^2 - r_i^2}$$

The ultimate strength of cast iron is $S_{ut} = 210$ MPa.

For cast iron, nonlinearity begins at approximately $^1/_6 S_{ut}$.

$$\sigma_{ci} = \frac{S_{ut}}{\text{FS}} = \frac{210 \text{ MPa}}{6} = 35 \text{ MPa}$$

The σ_{ci} relationship is

$$35 \text{ MPa} = \frac{((150 \text{ mm})^2 + (75 \text{ mm})^2)p}{(150 \text{ mm})^2 - (75 \text{ mm})^2}$$

$$p = 21 \text{ MPa}$$

The radial stress is

$$\sigma_{ri} = -p = -21 \text{ MPa}$$

From Eq. 51.18, the radial deflection is

$$\Delta r_{\text{outer}} = \frac{r(\sigma_c - \nu(\sigma_r + \sigma_l))}{E}$$

$$= \frac{(75 \text{ mm})(35 \text{ MPa} - (0.27)(-21 \text{ MPa} + 0))}{(100 \text{ GPa})\left(1000 \, \dfrac{\text{MPa}}{\text{GPa}}\right)}$$

$$= 0.03050 \text{ mm}$$

For the steel shaft,

$$r_o = \frac{150 \text{ mm}}{2} = 75 \text{ mm}$$

$$r_i = 0$$

From Table 51.2, the circumferential stress at the outside radius due to external pressure, p, is

$$\sigma_{co} = \frac{-(r_o^2 + r_i^2)p}{r_o^2 - r_i^2}$$

$$= \frac{-((75 \text{ mm})^2 + (0)^2)(21 \text{ MPa})}{(75 \text{ mm})^2 - (0)^2}$$

$$= -21 \text{ MPa}$$

The radial stress is

$$\sigma_{ro} = -p = -21 \text{ MPa}$$

From Eq. 51.18, the radial deflection is

$$\Delta r_{\text{inner}} = \frac{r(\sigma_c - \nu(\sigma_r + \sigma_l))}{E}$$

$$= \frac{(75 \text{ mm})\left(-21 \text{ MPa}\right.}{\left. - (0.30)(-21 \text{ MPa} + 0)\right)}{(200 \text{ GPa})\left(1000 \, \dfrac{\text{MPa}}{\text{GPa}}\right)}$$

$$= -0.00551 \text{ mm}$$

From Eq. 51.20, the radial interference is

$$I_{\text{radial}} = |\Delta r_{\text{inner}}| + |\Delta r_{\text{outer}}|$$

$$= |-0.00551 \text{ mm}| + |0.03050 \text{ mm}|$$

$$= \boxed{0.03601 \text{ mm}}$$

12. *Customary U.S. Solution*

First, find the properties of the bolt area. For an equilateral triangular layout, the distance from the centroid of the bolt group to each bolt is

$$l = \left(\tfrac{2}{3}\right)(9 \text{ in}) = 6 \text{ in}$$

The area of each bolt is

$$A = \frac{\pi d^2}{4} = \frac{\pi (0.75 \text{ in})^2}{4} = 0.442 \text{ in}^2$$

The polar moment of inertia of a bolt about the centroid is

$$J = Al^2 = (0.442 \text{ in}^2)(6 \text{ in})^2 = 15.91 \text{ in}^4$$

The vertical shear load at each bolt is

$$F_v = \frac{F}{3} = 0.333F \quad [\text{in lbf}]$$

The moment applied to each bolt is

$$M = \frac{(20 \text{ in})F}{3} = 6.67F \quad [\text{in in-lbf}]$$

The vertical shear stress in each bolt is

$$\tau_v = \frac{F_v}{A} = \frac{0.333F}{0.442 \text{ in}^2} = 0.753F \quad [\text{in lbf/in}^2]$$

The torsional shear stress in each bolt is

$$\tau = \frac{Ml}{J} = \frac{(6.67F)(6 \text{ in})}{15.91 \text{ in}^4} = 2.52F \quad [\text{in lbf/in}^2]$$

The most highly stressed bolt is the right-most bolt. The shear stress configuration is

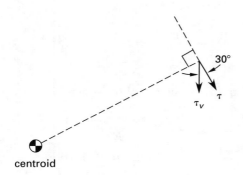

centroid

The stresses are combined to find the maximum stress.

$$\tau_{\text{max}} = \sqrt{(\tau \sin 30°)^2 + (\tau_v + \tau \cos 30°)^2}$$

$$15{,}000 \ \frac{\text{lbf}}{\text{in}^2} = \sqrt{\begin{array}{l}\left((2.52F)(\sin 30°)\right)^2 \\ + \left(0.753F + (2.52F)(\cos 30°)\right)^2\end{array}}$$

$$= 3.19F$$

$$F = \boxed{4702 \text{ lbf}}$$

SI Solution

First, find the properties of the bolt area. For an equilateral triangular layout, the distance from the centroid of the bolt group to each bolt is

$$l = \left(\tfrac{2}{3}\right)(230 \text{ mm}) = 153 \text{ mm}$$

The area of each bolt is

$$A = \frac{\pi d^2}{4} = \frac{\pi (19 \text{ mm})^2 \left(\dfrac{1 \text{ m}}{10^3 \text{ mm}}\right)^2}{4} = 2.835 \times 10^{-4} \text{ m}^2$$

The polar moment of inertia of a bolt about the centroid is

$$J = Al^2 = (2.835 \times 10^{-4} \text{ m}^2)(0.153 \text{ m})^2$$
$$= 6.636 \times 10^{-6} \text{ m}^4$$

The vertical shear load at each bolt is

$$F_v = \frac{F}{3} = 0.333F \quad [\text{in N}]$$

The moment applied to each bolt is

$$M = \frac{(0.5 \text{ m})F}{3} = 0.167F \text{ N·m}$$

The vertical shear stress in each bolt is

$$\tau_v = \frac{F_v}{A} = \frac{0.333F}{2.835 \times 10^{-4} \text{ m}^2} = 1.1746 \times 10^3 F \quad [\text{in N/m}^2]$$

The torsional shear stress in each bolt is

$$\tau = \frac{Ml}{J} = \frac{(0.167F)(0.15 \text{ m})}{6.636 \times 10^{-6} \text{ m}^4}$$
$$= 3.775 \times 10^3 F \quad [\text{in N/m}^2]$$

The most highly stressed bolt is the right-most bolt. The shear stress configuration is

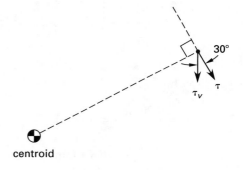

centroid

The stresses are combined to find the maximum stress.

$$\tau_{\text{max}} = \sqrt{(\tau \sin 30°)^2 + (\tau_v + \tau \cos 30°)^2}$$

$$(100 \text{ MPa}) \times \left(1000 \ \frac{\text{kPa}}{\text{MPa}}\right) = \sqrt{\begin{array}{l}\left((3.775 \times 10^3 F)(\sin 30°)\right)^2 \\ + \left(1.1746 \times 10^3 F \right. \\ \left. + (3.775 \times 10^3 F)(\cos 30°)\right)^2\end{array}}$$

$$= 4.83 \times 10^3 F \quad [\text{in N/m}^2]$$

$$F = \boxed{20.7 \text{ kN}}$$

13. *Customary U.S. Solution*

The fillet weld consists of three basic shapes, each with a throat size of t.

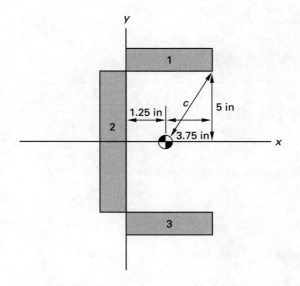

First, find the centroid.

By inspection, $y_c = 0$.

The areas of the basic shapes are

$$A_1 = 5t \quad [\text{in in}^2]$$
$$A_2 = 10t \quad [\text{in in}^2]$$
$$A_3 = 5t \quad [\text{in in}^2]$$

The x-components of the centroids of the basic shapes are

$$x_{c1} = \frac{5 \text{ in}}{2} = 2.5 \text{ in}$$
$$x_{c2} = -\frac{t}{2} = 0 \quad [\text{for small } t]$$
$$x_{c3} = \frac{5 \text{ in}}{2} = 2.5 \text{ in}$$
$$x_c = \frac{\sum_i A_i x_{ci}}{A_i}$$
$$= \frac{(5t)(2.5 \text{ in}) + (10t)(0) + (5t)(2.5 \text{ in})}{5t + 10t + 5t}$$
$$= 1.25 \text{ in}$$

Next, find the centroidal moments of inertia.

The moments of inertia of basic shape 1 about its own centroid are

$$I_{cx1} = \frac{bh^3}{12} = \frac{(5 \text{ in})t^3}{12} = 0.417t^3 \quad [\text{in in}^4]$$
$$I_{cy1} = \frac{bh^3}{12} = \frac{t(5 \text{ in})^3}{12} = 10.417t \quad [\text{in in}^4]$$

The moments of inertia of basic shape 2 about its own centroid are

$$I_{cx2} = \frac{bh^3}{12} = \frac{t(10 \text{ in})^3}{12} = 83.333t \quad [\text{in in}^4]$$
$$I_{cy2} = \frac{bh^3}{12} = \frac{(10 \text{ in})t^3}{12} = 0.833t^3 \quad [\text{in in}^4]$$

The moments of inertia of basic shape 3 about its own centroid are the same as for basic shape 1.

$$I_{cx3} = I_{cx1} = 0.417t^3 \quad [\text{in in}^4]$$
$$I_{cy3} = I_{cy1} = 10.417t \quad [\text{in in}^4]$$

From the parallel axis theorem, the moments of inertia of basic shape 1 about the centroidal axis of the section are

$$I_{x1} = I_{cx1} + A_1 d_1^2 = 0.417t^3 + (5t)(5 \text{ in})^2$$
$$= 0.417t^3 + 125t$$
$$I_{y1} = I_{cy1} + A_1 d_1^2$$
$$= 10.417t + 5t\left(\frac{5 \text{ in}}{2} - 1.25 \text{ in}\right)^2$$
$$= 18.23t \quad [\text{in in}^4]$$

The moments of inertia of basic shape 2 about the centroidal axis of the section are

$$I_{x2} = I_{cx2} + A_2 d_2^2 = 83.333t + (10t)(0)$$
$$= 83.333t \quad [\text{in in}^4]$$
$$I_{y2} = I_{cy2} + A_2 d_2^2 = 0.833t^3 + (10t)(1.25 \text{ in})^2$$
$$= 0.833t^3 + 15.625t$$

The moment of inertia of basic shape 3 about the centroidal axis of the section are the same as for basic shape 1.

$$I_{x3} = I_{x1} = 0.417t^3 + 125t$$
$$I_{y3} = I_{y1} = 18.23t \quad [\text{in in}^4]$$

The total moments of inertia about the centroidal axis of the section are

$$I_x = I_{x1} + I_{x2} + I_{x3}$$
$$= 0.417t^3 + 125t + 83.333t + 0.417t^3 + 125t$$
$$= 0.834t^3 + 333.33t$$
$$I_y = I_{y1} + I_{y2} + I_{y3}$$
$$= 18.23t + 0.833t^3 + 15.625t + 18.23t$$
$$= 0.833t^3 + 52.09t$$

Since t will be small and since the coefficient of the t^3 term is smaller than the coefficient of the t term, the higher-order t^3 term may be neglected.

$$I_x = 333.33t \quad [\text{in in}^4]$$
$$I_y = 52.09t \quad [\text{in in}^4]$$

The polar moment of inertia for the section is

$$J = I_x + I_y = 333.33t + 52.09t$$
$$= 385.42t \quad [\text{in in}^4]$$

The maximum shear stress will occur at the right-most point of basic shape 1 since this point is farthest from the centroid of the section.

This distance is

$$c = \sqrt{(5 \text{ in} - 1.25 \text{ in})^2 + \left(\frac{10 \text{ in}}{2}\right)^2}$$
$$= 6.25 \text{ in}$$

The applied moment is

$$M = Fd = (10,000 \text{ lbf})(12 \text{ in} + 5 \text{ in} - 1.25 \text{ in})$$
$$= 157,500 \text{ in-lbf}$$

The torsional shear stress is

$$\tau = \frac{Mc}{J} = \frac{(157,500 \text{ in-lbf})(6.25 \text{ in})}{385.42t} = \frac{2554.0}{t} \text{ lbf/in}^2$$

The shear stress is perpendicular to the line from the point to the centroid. The x and y components are shown on the figure.

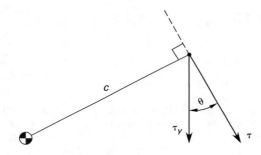

The angle θ is

$$\theta = 90° - \tan^{-1}\left(\frac{5 \text{ in} - 1.25 \text{ in}}{\frac{10 \text{ in}}{2}}\right) = 53.1°$$

$$\tau_x = \tau \sin\theta = \left(\frac{2554.0 \frac{\text{lbf}}{\text{in}^2}}{t}\right)(\sin 53.1°)$$

$$= \frac{2042.4}{t} \text{ lbf/in}^2$$

$$\tau_y = \tau \cos\theta = \left(\frac{2554.0 \frac{\text{lbf}}{\text{in}^2}}{t}\right)(\cos 53.1°)$$

$$= \frac{1553.5}{t} \text{ lbf/in}^2$$

The vertical shear stress due to the load is

$$\tau_{vy} = \frac{F}{\sum A_i} = \frac{10,000 \text{ lbf}}{5t + 10t + 5t}$$
$$= \frac{500}{t} \text{ lbf/in}^2$$

The resultant shear stress is

$$\tau = \sqrt{\tau_x^2 + (\tau_y + \tau_{vy})^2}$$
$$= \sqrt{\left(\frac{2042.4}{t}\right)^2 + \left(\frac{1553.5}{t} + \frac{500}{t}\right)^2}$$
$$= \frac{2896.2}{t} \text{ lbf/in}^2$$

For a maximum shear stress of 8000 lbf/in²,

$$8000 \frac{\text{lbf}}{\text{in}^2} = \frac{2896.2}{t} \text{ lbf/in}^2$$
$$t = 0.362 \text{ in}$$

From Eq. 51.42, the required weld size is

$$y = \frac{t}{0.707} = \frac{0.362 \text{ in}}{0.707} = \boxed{0.512 \text{ in}}$$

SI Solution

The fillet weld consists of three basic shapes, each with a throat size of t.

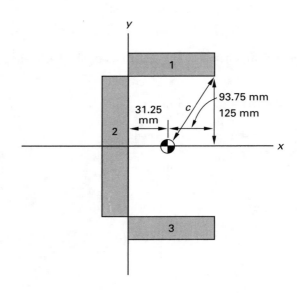

First, find the centroid.

By inspection, $y_c = 0$.

The areas of the basic shapes are

$$A_1 = 125t \quad [\text{in mm}^2]$$
$$A_2 = 250t \quad [\text{in mm}^2]$$
$$A_3 = 125t \quad [\text{in mm}^2]$$

The x-components of the centroids of the basic shapes are

$$x_{c1} = \frac{125 \text{ mm}}{2} = 62.5 \text{ mm}$$

$$x_{c2} = -\frac{t}{2} = 0 \quad [\text{for small } t]$$

$$x_{c3} = \frac{125 \text{ mm}}{2} = 62.5 \text{ mm}$$

$$x_c = \frac{\sum\limits_i A_i x_{ci}}{A_i}$$

$$= \frac{\begin{array}{c}(125t)(62.5 \text{ mm}) \\ +(250t)(0) + (125t)(62.5 \text{ mm})\end{array}}{125t + 250t + 125t}$$

$$= 31.25 \text{ mm}$$

Next, find the centroidal moments of inertia.

The moments of inertia of basic shape 1 about its own centroid are

$$I_{cx1} = \frac{bh^3}{12} = \frac{(125 \text{ mm})t^3}{12} = 10.42t^3 \quad [\text{in mm}^4]$$

$$I_{cy1} = \frac{bh^3}{12} = \frac{t(125 \text{ mm})^3}{12} = 162\,760t \quad [\text{in mm}^4]$$

The moments of inertia of basic shape 2 about its own centroid are

$$I_{cx2} = \frac{bh^3}{12} = \frac{t(250 \text{ mm})^3}{12} = 1\,302\,083t \quad [\text{in mm}^4]$$

$$I_{cy2} = \frac{bh^3}{12} = \frac{(250 \text{ mm})t^3}{12} = 20.83t^3 \quad [\text{in mm}^4]$$

The moments of inertia of basic shape 3 about its own centroid are the same as for basic shape 1.

$$I_{cx3} = I_{cx1} = 10.42t^3 \quad [\text{in mm}^4]$$

$$I_{cy3} = I_{cy1} = 162\,760t \quad [\text{in mm}^4]$$

From the parallel axis theorem, the moments of inertia of basic shape 1 about the centroidal axis of the section are

$$I_{x1} = I_{cx1} + A_1 d_1^2$$

$$= 10.42t^3 + (125t)(125 \text{ mm})^2$$

$$= 10.42t^3 + 1\,953\,125t$$

$$I_{y1} = I_{cy1} + A_1 d_1^2$$

$$= 162\,760t + (125t)\left(\frac{125 \text{ mm}}{2} - 31.25 \text{ mm}\right)^2$$

$$= 284\,830t \quad [\text{in mm}^4]$$

The moments of inertia of basic shape 2 about the centroidal axis of the section are

$$I_{x2} = I_{cx2} + A_2 d_2^2$$

$$= 1\,302\,083t + (250t)(0)^2$$

$$= 1\,302\,083t \quad [\text{in mm}^4]$$

$$I_{y2} = I_{cy2} + A_2 d_2^2$$

$$= 20.83t^3 + (250t)(31.25 \text{ mm})^2$$

$$= 20.83t^3 + 244\,140t$$

The moments of inertia of basic shape 3 about the centroidal axis of the section are the same as for basic shape 1.

$$I_{x3} = I_{x1} = 10.42t^3 + 1\,953\,125t$$

$$I_{y3} = I_{y1} = 284\,830t \quad [\text{in mm}^4]$$

The total moments of inertia about the centroidal axis of the section are

$$I_x = I_{x1} + I_{x2} + I_{x3}$$

$$= 10.42t^3 + 1\,953\,125t + 1\,302\,083t + 10.42t^3$$

$$\quad + 1\,953\,125t$$

$$= 20.84t^3 + 5\,208\,333t$$

$$I_y = I_{y1} + I_{y2} + I_{y3}$$

$$= 284\,830t + 20.83t^3 + 244\,140t$$

$$\quad + 284\,830t$$

$$= 20.83t^3 + 813\,800t$$

Since t will be small and since the coefficient of the t^3 term is smaller than the coefficient of the t term, the t^3 term may be neglected.

$$I_x = 5\,208\,333t \quad [\text{in mm}^4]$$

$$I_y = 813\,800t \quad [\text{in mm}^4]$$

The maximum shear stress will occur at the right-most point of basic shape 1 since this point is farthest from the centroid of the section.

The distance is

$$c = \sqrt{(125 \text{ mm} - 31.25 \text{ mm})^2 + \left(\frac{250 \text{ mm}}{2}\right)^2}$$

$$= 156.25 \text{ mm}$$

The polar moment of inertia for the section is

$$J = I_x + I_y = 5\,208\,333t + 813\,800t$$

$$= 6\,022\,133t \quad [\text{in mm}^4]$$

The applied moment is

$$M = Fd = (44 \text{ kN})(300 \text{ mm} + 125 \text{ mm} - 31.25 \text{ mm})$$

$$= 17\,325 \text{ kN·mm}$$

The torsional shear stress is

$$\tau = \frac{Mc}{J}$$
$$= \left(\frac{(17\,325 \text{ kN·mm})(156.25 \text{ mm})}{6\,022\,133t}\right)\left(10^3 \frac{\text{mm}}{\text{m}}\right)^2$$
$$\times \left(\frac{1 \text{ MPa}}{1000 \text{ kPa}}\right)$$
$$= \frac{449.5}{t} \text{ MPa}$$

The shear stress is perpendicular to the line from the point to the centroid. The x and y components are shown on the figure.

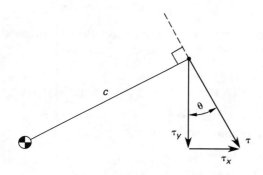

The angle θ is

$$\theta = 90° - \tan^{-1}\left(\frac{125 \text{ mm} - 31.25 \text{ mm}}{\frac{250 \text{ mm}}{2}}\right) = 53.1°$$

$$\tau_x = \tau \sin \theta = \left(\frac{449.5 \text{ MPa}}{t}\right)(\sin 53.1°)$$
$$= \frac{359.5 \text{ MPa}}{t}$$

$$\tau_y = \tau \cos \theta = \left(\frac{449.5 \text{ MPa}}{t}\right)(\cos 53.1°)$$
$$= \frac{269.9 \text{ MPa}}{t}$$

The vertical shear stress due to the load is

$$\tau_{vy} = \frac{F}{\sum A_i}$$
$$= \frac{(44 \text{ kN})\left(\frac{1 \text{ MPa}}{1000 \text{ kPa}}\right)}{(125t + 250t + 125t)\left(\frac{1 \text{ m}}{10^3 \text{ mm}}\right)^2}$$
$$= \frac{88.0}{t} \text{ MPa}$$

The resultant shear stress is

$$\tau = \sqrt{\tau_x^2 + (\tau_y + \tau_{vy})^2}$$
$$= \sqrt{\left(\frac{359.5}{t}\right)^2 + \left(\frac{269.9}{t} + \frac{88.0}{t}\right)^2}$$
$$= \frac{507.3}{t} \text{ MPa}$$

For a maximum shear stress of 55 MPa,

$$55 \text{ MPa} = \frac{507.3}{t} \text{ MPa}$$
$$t = 9.22 \text{ mm}$$

From Eq. 51.42, the required weld size is

$$y = \frac{t}{0.707} = \frac{9.22 \text{ mm}}{0.707} = \boxed{13.0 \text{ mm}}$$

14. *Customary U.S. Solution*

The rotational speed is

$$\omega = \frac{\left(3500 \frac{\text{rev}}{\text{min}}\right)\left(2\pi \frac{\text{rad}}{\text{rev}}\right)}{60 \frac{\text{sec}}{\text{min}}} = 366.5 \text{ rad/sec}$$

From Eq. 57.14, the tangential stress at the inside radius of the flywheel is

$$\sigma = \left(\frac{\rho\omega^2}{4g_c}\right)((3+\nu)r_o^2 + (1-\nu)r_i^2)$$
$$= \left(\frac{\left(0.283 \frac{\text{lbm}}{\text{in}^3}\right)\left(366.5 \frac{\text{rad}}{\text{sec}}\right)^2}{(4)\left(386 \frac{\text{in}}{\text{sec}^2}\right)}\right)$$
$$\times ((3+0.3)(8 \text{ in})^2 + (1-0.3)(1 \text{ in})^2)$$
$$= 5217 \text{ lbf/in}^2$$

The strain is

$$\epsilon = \frac{\sigma}{E} = \frac{5217 \frac{\text{lbf}}{\text{in}^2}}{2.9 \times 10^7 \frac{\text{lbf}}{\text{in}^2}} = 1.799 \times 10^{-4}$$

The change in the inner radius is

$$\Delta r = r\epsilon = (1 \text{ in})(1.799 \times 10^{-4}) = 1.799 \times 10^{-4} \text{ in}$$

Since the shaft and hub are both steel, the radial interference is obtained from Eq. 51.23.

$$I_{\text{radial}} = \left(\frac{2pr_{\text{shaft}}}{E}\right)\left(\frac{1}{1 - \left(\frac{r_{\text{shaft}}}{r_{o,\text{hub}}}\right)^2}\right)$$

$$= \left(\frac{(2)\left(1250\ \frac{\text{lbf}}{\text{in}^2}\right)(1\ \text{in})}{2.9 \times 10^7\ \frac{\text{lbf}}{\text{in}^2}}\right)\left(\frac{1}{1 - \left(\frac{1\ \text{in}}{8\ \text{in}}\right)^2}\right)$$

$$= 8.758 \times 10^{-5}\ \text{in}$$

The required initial interference is

$$I = \Delta r + I_{\text{radial}}$$
$$= 1.799 \times 10^{-4}\ \text{in} + 8.758 \times 10^{-5}\ \text{in}$$
$$= \boxed{2.67 \times 10^{-4}\ \text{in}}$$

SI Solution

The rotational speed is

$$\omega = \frac{\left(3500\ \frac{\text{rev}}{\text{min}}\right)\left(2\pi\ \frac{\text{rad}}{\text{rev}}\right)}{60\ \frac{\text{s}}{\text{min}}} = 366.5\ \text{rad/s}$$

From Eq. 57.14, the tangential stress at the inside radius of the flywheel is

$$\sigma = \left(\frac{\rho\omega}{4}\right)\left((3+\nu)r_o^2 + (1-\nu)r_i^2\right)$$

$$= \left(\frac{\left(7830\ \frac{\text{kg}}{\text{m}^3}\right)\left(366.5\ \frac{\text{rad}}{\text{s}}\right)^2}{4}\right)$$

$$\times \left((3+0.3)(0.203\ \text{m})^2 + (1-0.3)(0.025\ \text{m})^2\right)$$

$$= 35.87 \times 10^6\ \text{Pa}\quad (35.87\ \text{MPa})$$

The strain is

$$\epsilon = \frac{\sigma}{E} = \frac{35.87\ \text{MPa}}{(200\ \text{GPa})\left(1000\ \frac{\text{MPa}}{\text{GPa}}\right)} = 1.794 \times 10^{-4}$$

The change in inner radius is

$$\Delta r = r\epsilon = (25\ \text{mm})(1.794 \times 10^{-4})$$
$$= 44.85 \times 10^{-4}\ \text{mm}$$

Since the shaft and hub are both steel, the radial interference is obtained from Eq. 51.23.

$$I_{\text{radial}} = \left(\frac{2pr_{\text{shaft}}}{E}\right)\left(\frac{1}{1 - \left(\frac{r_{\text{shaft}}}{r_{o,\text{hub}}}\right)^2}\right)$$

$$= \left(\frac{(2)(8.6\ \text{MPa})(25\ \text{mm})}{(200\ \text{GPa})\left(1000\ \frac{\text{MPa}}{\text{GPa}}\right)}\right)$$

$$\times \left(\frac{1}{1 - \left(\frac{25\ \text{mm}}{203\ \text{mm}}\right)^2}\right)$$

$$= 21.83 \times 10^{-4}\ \text{mm}$$

The required initial interference is

$$I = \Delta r + I_{\text{radial}}$$
$$= 44.85 \times 10^{-4}\ \text{mm} + 21.83 \times 10^{-4}\ \text{mm}$$
$$= \boxed{6.67 \times 10^{-3}\ \text{mm}}$$

52 Advanced Machine Design

1. *Customary U.S. Solution*

Select a spring with a spring index of $C = 9$.

(a) From Eq. 52.10, the wire diameter is

$$
\begin{aligned}
d &= \frac{8FC^3 n_a}{G\delta} \\
&= \frac{(8)(50 \text{ lbf})(9)^3(12)}{\left(1.2 \times 10^7 \dfrac{\text{lbf}}{\text{in}^2}\right)(0.5 \text{ in})} \\
&= \boxed{0.583 \text{ in}}
\end{aligned}
$$

(b) From Eq. 52.8, the mean spring diameter is

$$
D = Cd = (9)(0.583 \text{ in}) = \boxed{5.247 \text{ in}}
$$

SI Solution

Select a spring with a spring index of $C = 9$.

(a) From Eq. 52.10, the wire diameter is

$$
\begin{aligned}
d &= \frac{8FC^3 n_a}{G\delta} \\
&= \left(\frac{(8)(220 \text{ N})(9)^3(12)}{(83 \times 10^9 \text{ Pa})(0.012 \text{ m})}\right)\left(1000 \frac{\text{mm}}{\text{m}}\right) \\
&= \boxed{15.45 \text{ mm}}
\end{aligned}
$$

(b) From Eq. 52.8, the mean spring diameter is

$$
D = Cd = (9)(15.45 \text{ mm}) = \boxed{139.1 \text{ mm}}
$$

2. *Customary U.S. Solution*

From Table 52.2, the ultimate tensile strength of ASTM A230 steel is selected for 0.15 in wire.

$$
S_{ut} = 205{,}000 \text{ lbf/in}^2
$$

From Table 52.3, the fatigue loading shear stress factor is 0.30. From Eq. 52.7, the maximum allowable shear stress is

$$
\begin{aligned}
\tau_{\max} &= \frac{(\text{factor})S_{ut}}{\text{FS}} = \frac{(0.3)\left(205{,}000 \dfrac{\text{lbf}}{\text{in}^2}\right)}{1.5} \\
&= 41{,}000 \text{ lbf/in}^2
\end{aligned}
$$

From Eq. 52.18, the Wahl correction factor is

$$
\begin{aligned}
W &= \frac{4C-1}{4C-4} + \frac{0.615}{C} \\
&= \frac{(4)(10)-1}{(4)(10)-4} + \frac{0.615}{10} = 1.145
\end{aligned}
$$

(a) From Eq. 52.14, the wire diameter is

$$
d = \sqrt{\frac{8FCW}{\pi\tau_{\max}}} = \sqrt{\frac{(8)(30 \text{ lbf})(10)(1.145)}{\pi\left(41{,}000 \dfrac{\text{lbf}}{\text{in}^2}\right)}}
$$

$$
= 0.146 \text{ in}
$$

Use W&M wire #9 with $d = \boxed{0.148 \text{ in.}}$

(b) From Eq. 52.2, the spring constant is

$$
k = \frac{F_1 - F_2}{\delta_1 - \delta_2} = \frac{30 \text{ lbf} - 20 \text{ lbf}}{0.3 \text{ in}} = \boxed{33.33 \text{ lbf/in}}
$$

(c) From Table 52.1, the shear modulus of ASTM A230 steel wire is $G = 11.5 \times 10^6 \text{ lbf/in}^2$.

From Eq. 52.12, the number of active coils is

$$
n_a = \frac{Gd}{8kC^3} = \frac{\left(11.5 \times 10^6 \dfrac{\text{lbf}}{\text{in}^2}\right)(0.148 \text{ in})}{(8)\left(33.33 \dfrac{\text{lbf}}{\text{in}}\right)(10)^3}
$$

$$
= \boxed{6.38}
$$

(d) From Table 52.4, the total number of coils for squared and ground ends is

$$
n_t = n_a + 2 = 6.38 + 2 = \boxed{8.38}
$$

(e) From Table 52.4, the solid height is

$$h_s = dn_t = (0.148 \text{ in})(8.38) = \boxed{1.24 \text{ in}}$$

(f) At solid height, the maximum shear stress is

$$\tau_{\text{max}} = (\text{factor})S_{ut} = (0.3)\left(205{,}000 \ \frac{\text{lbf}}{\text{in}^2}\right)$$

$$= 61{,}500 \text{ lbf/in}^2$$

From Eq. 52.14, the force at solid height is

$$F_s = \frac{\tau_{\text{max}}\pi d^2}{8CW} = \frac{\left(61{,}500 \ \dfrac{\text{lbf}}{\text{in}^2}\right)\pi(0.148 \text{ in})^2}{(8)(10)(1.145)}$$

$$= \boxed{46.20 \text{ lbf}}$$

(g) From Eq. 52.10, the deflection at solid height is

$$\delta_s = \frac{F_s}{k} = \frac{46.20 \text{ lbf}}{33.33 \ \dfrac{\text{lbf}}{\text{in}}} = \boxed{1.39 \text{ in}}$$

(h) From Eq. 52.15, the minimum free height is

$$h_f = h_s + \delta_s = 1.24 \text{ in} + 1.39 \text{ in} = \boxed{2.63 \text{ in}}$$

SI Solution

From Table 52.2, the ultimate tensile strength of ASTM A230 steel wire is selected for 3.8 mm wire.

$$S_{ut} = \left(205 \ \frac{\text{kips}}{\text{in}^2}\right)\left(6.9 \ \frac{\text{MPa}}{\frac{\text{kips}}{\text{in}^2}}\right) = 1414.5 \text{ MPa}$$

From Table 52.3, the fatigue loading shear stress factor is 0.30. From Eq. 52.7, the maximum allowable shear stress is

$$\tau_{\text{max}} = \frac{(\text{factor})S_{ut}}{\text{FS}} = \frac{(0.3)(1414.5 \text{ MPa})}{1.5}$$

$$= 282.9 \text{ MPa}$$

From Eq. 52.18, the Wahl correction factor is

$$W = \frac{4C - 1}{4C - 4} + \frac{0.615}{C}$$

$$= \frac{(4)(10) - 1}{(4)(10) - 4} + \frac{0.615}{10} = 1.145$$

(a) From Eq. 52.14, the wire diameter is

$$d = \sqrt{\frac{8FCW}{\pi\tau_{\text{max}}}} = \sqrt{\frac{(8)(150 \text{ N})(10)(1.145)}{\pi(282.9 \times 10^6 \text{ Pa})\left(\dfrac{1 \text{ m}}{10^3 \text{ mm}}\right)^2}}$$

$$= 3.93 \text{ mm}$$

Use W&M wire #8 with a diameter of

$$d = (0.162 \text{ in})\left(25.4 \ \frac{\text{mm}}{\text{in}}\right) = \boxed{4.115 \text{ mm}}$$

(b) From Eq. 52.2, the spring constant is

$$k = \frac{F_1 - F_2}{\delta_1 - \delta_2} = \frac{150 \text{ N} - 100 \text{ N}}{(8 \text{ mm})\left(\dfrac{1 \text{ m}}{10^3 \text{ mm}}\right)}$$

$$= \boxed{6.25 \times 10^3 \text{ N/m}}$$

(c) From Table 52.1, the shear modulus of ASTM A230 steel wire is

$$G = \left(11.5 \times 10^6 \ \frac{\text{lbf}}{\text{in}^2}\right)\left(6.89 \times 10^3 \ \frac{\text{Pa}}{\frac{\text{lbf}}{\text{in}^2}}\right)$$

$$= 79.2 \times 10^9 \text{ Pa}$$

From Eq. 52.12, the number of active coils is

$$n_a = \frac{Gd}{8kC^3} = \frac{(79.2 \times 10^9 \text{ Pa})(4.115 \text{ mm})\left(\dfrac{1 \text{ m}}{10^3 \text{ mm}}\right)}{(8)\left(6.25 \times 10^3 \ \dfrac{\text{N}}{\text{m}}\right)(10)^3}$$

$$= \boxed{6.52}$$

(d) From Table 52.4, the total number of coils for squared and ground ends is

$$n_t = n_a + 2 = 6.52 + 2 = \boxed{8.52}$$

(e) From Table 52.4, the solid height is

$$h_s = dn_t = (4.115 \text{ mm})(8.52) = \boxed{35.06 \text{ mm}}$$

(f) At solid height, the maximum shear stress is

$$\tau_{\text{max}} = (\text{factor})S_{ut} = (0.3)(1414.5 \text{ MPa}) = 424.4 \text{ MPa}$$

From Eq. 52.14, the force at solid height is

$$F_s = \frac{\tau_{max}\pi d^2}{8CW}$$

$$= \frac{(424.4 \text{ MPa})\pi(4.115 \text{ mm})^2 \times \left(\frac{1 \text{ m}}{10^3 \text{ mm}}\right)^2 \left(10^6 \frac{\text{Pa}}{\text{MPa}}\right)}{(8)(10)(1.145)}$$

$$= \boxed{246.5 \text{ N}}$$

(g) From Eq. 52.10, the deflection at solid height is

$$\delta_s = \frac{F_s}{k} = \left(\frac{246.5 \text{ N}}{6.25 \times 10^3 \frac{\text{N}}{\text{m}}}\right)\left(1000 \frac{\text{mm}}{\text{m}}\right)$$

$$= \boxed{39.44 \text{ mm}}$$

(h) From Eq. 52.15, the minimum free height is

$$h_f = h_s + \delta_s = 35.06 \text{ mm} + 39.44 \text{ mm} = \boxed{74.5 \text{ mm}}$$

3. *Customary U.S. Solution*

The potential energy absorbed is

$$\text{PE} = \frac{mg\Delta h}{g_c}$$

$$= \frac{(700 \text{ lbm})\left(32.2 \frac{\text{ft}}{\text{sec}^2}\right)(46 \text{ in} + 10 \text{ in})}{32.2 \frac{\text{ft-lbm}}{\text{lbf-sec}^2}}$$

$$= 39{,}200 \text{ in-lbf}$$

The work done by the spring is equal to the potential energy.

$$W = \tfrac{1}{2}k\delta^2 = \text{PE}$$

$$k = \frac{2(\text{PE})}{\delta^2} = \frac{(2)(39{,}200 \text{ in-lbf})}{(10 \text{ in})^2} = 784 \text{ lbf/in}$$

The equivalent spring force is

$$F = k\delta = \left(784 \frac{\text{lbf}}{\text{in}}\right)(10 \text{ in}) = 7840 \text{ lbf}$$

From Eq. 52.13, the Wahl correction factor is

$$W = \frac{4C-1}{4C-4} + \frac{0.615}{C} = \frac{(4)(7)-1}{(4)(7)-4} + \frac{0.615}{7} = 1.213$$

(a) From Eq. 52.14, the wire diameter is

$$d = \sqrt{\frac{8FCW}{\pi\tau_{allowable}}} = \sqrt{\frac{(8)(7840 \text{ lbf})(7)(1.213)}{\pi\left(50{,}000 \frac{\text{lbf}}{\text{in}^2}\right)}}$$

$$= \boxed{1.84 \text{ in}}$$

(b) From Eq. 52.8, the mean coil diameter is

$$D = Cd = (7)(1.84 \text{ in}) = \boxed{12.88 \text{ in}}$$

(c) From Eq. 52.12, the number of active coils is

$$n_a = \frac{Gd}{8kC^3} = \frac{\left(1.2 \times 10^7 \frac{\text{lbf}}{\text{in}^2}\right)(1.84 \text{ in})}{(8)\left(784 \frac{\text{lbf}}{\text{in}}\right)(7)^3}$$

$$= \boxed{10.3}$$

SI Solution

The potential energy absorbed is

$$\text{PE} = mg\Delta h = (320 \text{ kg})\left(9.81 \frac{\text{m}}{\text{s}^2}\right)(1.2 \text{ m} + 0.26 \text{ m})$$

$$= 4583 \text{ J}$$

The work done by the spring is equal to the potential energy.

$$W_k = \tfrac{1}{2}k\delta^2 = \text{PE}$$

$$k = \frac{2(\text{PE})}{\delta^2} = \frac{(2)(4583 \text{ J})}{(0.26 \text{ m})^2} = 135\,592 \text{ N/m}$$

The equivalent spring force is

$$F = k\delta = \left(135\,592 \frac{\text{N}}{\text{m}}\right)(0.26 \text{ m}) = 35\,254 \text{ N}$$

From Eq. 52.13, the Wahl correction factor is

$$W = \frac{4C-1}{4C-4} + \frac{0.615}{C} = \frac{(4)(7)-1}{(4)(7)-4} + \frac{0.615}{7} = 1.213$$

(a) From Eq. 52.14, the wire diameter is

$$d = \sqrt{\frac{8FCW}{\pi\tau_{allowable}}} = \sqrt{\frac{(8)(35\,254 \text{ N})(7)(1.213)}{\pi(350 \times 10^6 \text{ Pa})\left(\frac{1 \text{ m}}{10^3 \text{ mm}}\right)^2}}$$

$$= \boxed{46.7 \text{ mm}}$$

(b) From Eq. 52.8, the mean coil diameter is

$$D = Cd = (7)(46.7 \text{ mm}) = \boxed{327 \text{ mm}}$$

(c) From Eq. 52.12, the number of active coils is

$$n_a = \frac{Gd}{8kC^3} = \frac{(83 \times 10^9 \text{ Pa})(46.7 \text{ mm})\left(\frac{1 \text{ m}}{10^3 \text{ mm}}\right)}{(8)\left(135\,592 \frac{\text{N}}{\text{m}}\right)(7)^3}$$

$$= \boxed{10.4}$$

4. *Customary U.S. Solution*

The moment of inertia of the beam cross section is

$$I = \frac{bh^3}{12} = \frac{(6 \text{ in})h^3}{12} = 0.5h^3 \quad [\text{in in}^4]$$

The section modulus is

$$\frac{I}{c} = \frac{0.5h^3}{\frac{h}{2}} = h^2 \quad [\text{in in}^3]$$

From Table 52.1, the modulus of elasticity for a steel spring is $E = 30 \times 10^6 \text{ lbf/in}^2$.

(a) The tip deflection is

$$y = \frac{FL^3}{3EI} = \frac{FL^3}{3E(0.5)h^3}$$

$$h = \left(\frac{FL^3}{1.5yE}\right)^{\frac{1}{3}}$$

$$= \left(\frac{(800 \text{ lbf})(24 \text{ in})^3}{(1.5 \text{ in})(1.0 \text{ in})\left(30 \times 10^6 \frac{\text{lbf}}{\text{in}^2}\right)}\right)^{\frac{1}{3}}$$

$$= \boxed{0.627 \text{ in}}$$

The width-thickness ratio is

$$\frac{w}{t} = \frac{6.0 \text{ in}}{0.627 \text{ in}} \approx 9.6$$

Since $w/t < 10$, this is not a wide beam.

(b) The moment at the fixed end is

$$M = FL = (800 \text{ lbf})(24 \text{ in}) = 19{,}200 \text{ in-lbf}$$

The bending stress is

$$\sigma = \frac{M}{\frac{I}{c}} = \frac{M}{h^2}$$

$$h = \sqrt{\frac{M}{\sigma}}$$

$$= \sqrt{\frac{19{,}200 \text{ in-lbf}}{(1.0 \text{ in})\left(50{,}000 \frac{\text{lbf}}{\text{in}^2}\right)}}$$

$$= \boxed{0.620 \text{ in}}$$

SI Solution

The moment of inertia of the beam cross section is

$$I = \frac{bh^3}{12} = \frac{(150 \text{ mm})h^3}{12} = 12.5h^3 \quad [\text{in mm}^4]$$

The section modulus is

$$\frac{I}{c} = \frac{12.5h^3}{\frac{h}{2}} = 25h^2 \quad [\text{in mm}^3]$$

From Table 52.1, the modulus of elasticity for a steel spring is

$$E = \left(30 \times 10^6 \frac{\text{lbf}}{\text{in}^2}\right)\left(6.89 \times 10^3 \frac{\text{Pa}}{\frac{\text{lbf}}{\text{in}^2}}\right)$$

$$= 206.7 \times 10^9 \text{ Pa}$$

(a) The tip deflection is

$$y = \frac{FL^3}{3EI} = \frac{FL^3}{3E(12.5)h^3}$$

$$h = \left(\frac{FL^3}{37.5yE}\right)^{\frac{1}{3}}$$

$$= \left(\frac{(3.5 \text{ kN})\left(1000 \frac{\text{N}}{\text{kN}}\right)(610 \text{ mm})^3}{(37.5)(25 \text{ mm})} \times (206.7 \times 10^9 \text{ Pa})\left(\frac{1 \text{ m}}{10^3 \text{ mm}}\right)^2\right)^{\frac{1}{3}}$$

$$= \boxed{16.0 \text{ mm}}$$

The width-thickness ratio is

$$\frac{w}{t} = \frac{150 \text{ mm}}{16} \approx 9.4$$

Since $w/t < 10$, this is not a wide beam.

(b) The moment at the fixed end is

$$M = FL = \frac{(3.5 \text{ kN})\left(1000\ \frac{\text{N}}{\text{kN}}\right)(610 \text{ mm})}{1000\ \frac{\text{mm}}{\text{m}}}$$

$$= \boxed{2.135 \times 10^3 \text{ N·m}}$$

The bending stress is

$$\sigma = \frac{M}{\frac{I}{c}} = \frac{M}{25h^2}$$

$$h = \sqrt{\frac{M}{25\sigma}}$$

$$= \sqrt{\frac{2.135 \times 10^3 \text{ N·m}}{(25 \text{ mm})(345 \text{ MPa})\left(10^6\ \frac{\text{Pa}}{\text{MPa}}\right)\left(\frac{1 \text{ m}}{10^3 \text{ mm}}\right)}}$$

$$= \boxed{15.7 \text{ mm}}$$

5. The maximum speed ratio is

$$\frac{N_{\max}}{N_{\min}} = \frac{96 \text{ teeth}}{12 \text{ teeth}} = 8$$

(a) For three stages,

$$(8)^3 = 512$$

Since this is less than 600, $\boxed{\text{four stages are required.}}$

$$\text{check: } (8)^4 = 4096$$

(b) The approximate gear ratio for each stage should be

$$(600)^{\frac{1}{4}} = 4.95$$

Select 12 teeth for the pinion gears for the first three stages. Let the first three stages be

$$\frac{N_1}{12 \text{ teeth}} = 5$$

$$\frac{N_2}{12 \text{ teeth}} = 5$$

$$\frac{N_3}{12 \text{ teeth}} = 5$$

$$N_1 = 60 \text{ teeth}$$
$$N_2 = 60 \text{ teeth}$$
$$N_3 = 60 \text{ teeth}$$

The fourth stage is obtained from

$$\left(\frac{60 \text{ teeth}}{12 \text{ teeth}}\right)\left(\frac{60 \text{ teeth}}{12 \text{ teeth}}\right)\left(\frac{60 \text{ teeth}}{12 \text{ teeth}}\right)R_4 = 600$$

$$R_4 = 4.8$$

Select 15 teeth for the pinion of stage 4.

$$N_4 = R_4 15 = (4.8)(15) = 72 \text{ teeth}$$

The four-stage gear train would have four pairs of gears with the following numbers of teeth.

$$\frac{12}{60}, \frac{12}{60}, \frac{12}{60}, \frac{15}{72}$$

6. *Customary U.S. Solution*

(a) Let gear 1 be the gear and gear 2 be the pinion.

$$\frac{d_1}{2} + \frac{d_2}{2} = \text{center distance} = 15 \text{ in}$$

From Eq. 52.39,

$$\frac{d_1}{d_2} = \frac{n_2}{n_1} = \frac{1200 \text{ rpm}}{270 \text{ rpm}} = 4.44$$

Solving these two equations simultaneously gives

$$d_1 = \boxed{24.49 \text{ in}}$$

$$d_2 = \boxed{5.51 \text{ in}}$$

(b) From Eq. 52.31, the pitch circle velocity is

$$v_t = \pi d_1 n_1$$

$$= \pi(24.49 \text{ in})\left(\frac{1 \text{ ft}}{12 \text{ in}}\right)(270 \text{ rpm})$$

$$= 1731 \text{ ft/min}$$

From Eq. 52.46, the transmitted load is

$$F_t = \frac{P_{\text{hp}}\left(33,000\ \frac{\text{ft-lbf}}{\text{hp-min}}\right)}{v_t}$$

$$= \frac{(550 \text{ hp})\left(33,000\ \frac{\text{ft-lbf}}{\text{hp-min}}\right)}{1731\ \frac{\text{ft}}{\text{min}}}$$

$$= 10,485 \text{ lbf}$$

The allowable bending stress for the pinion is

$$\sigma_a = \frac{S_e}{\text{FS}} = \frac{90,000\ \frac{\text{lbf}}{\text{in}^2}}{3} = 30,000 \text{ lbf/in}^2$$

From Eq. 52.62, the Barth speed factor is

$$k_d = \frac{a}{a + v_t} = \frac{600 \ \dfrac{\text{ft}}{\text{min}}}{600 \ \dfrac{\text{ft}}{\text{min}} + 1731 \ \dfrac{\text{ft}}{\text{min}}} = 0.257$$

Select a pinion width of $w = 6$ in and an approximate form factor of $Y = 0.3$.

From Eq. 52.61, the diametral pitch is

$$P = \frac{k_d \sigma_a w Y}{F_t}$$

$$= \frac{(0.257)\left(30{,}000 \ \dfrac{\text{lbf}}{\text{in}^2}\right)(6 \text{ in})(0.3)}{10{,}485 \text{ lbf}}$$

$$= 1.32 \ \frac{1}{\text{in}}$$

Use a standard diametral pitch of $\boxed{1.50 \ 1/\text{in.}}$

(c) The number of teeth on the pinion is

$$N_2 = P d_2 = \left(1.50 \ \frac{1}{\text{in}}\right)(5.51 \text{ in}) = 8.27 \text{ teeth}$$

$$[\text{say 8 teeth}]$$

The number of teeth on the gear is

$$N_1 = P d_1 = \left(1.50 \ \frac{1}{\text{in}}\right)(24.49 \text{ in}) = 36.7$$

$$[\text{say 36 teeth}]$$

For a $14^1/_2°$, 36-tooth gear, the form factor is $Y = 0.33$. The allowable bending stress for the gear is

$$\sigma_a = \frac{S_e}{\text{FS}} = \frac{50{,}000 \ \dfrac{\text{lbf}}{\text{in}^2}}{3} = 16{,}667 \text{ lbf/in}^2$$

From Eq. 52.61, the face width of the gear is

$$w = \frac{P F_t}{k_d \sigma_a Y}$$

$$= \frac{\left(1.5 \ \dfrac{1}{\text{in}}\right)(10{,}485 \text{ lbf})}{(0.257)\left(16{,}667 \ \dfrac{\text{lbf}}{\text{in}^2}\right)(0.33)}$$

$$= 11.1 \text{ in}$$

For a $14^1/_2°$, eight-tooth gear, the form factor is $Y \approx 0.2$. The allowable bending stress for the pinion is

$$\sigma_a = \frac{90{,}000 \ \dfrac{\text{lbf}}{\text{in}^2}}{3} = 30{,}000 \text{ lbf/in}^2$$

From Eq. 52.61, the face width of the pinion is

$$w = \frac{P F_t}{k_d \sigma_a Y} = \frac{(1.5)(10{,}485 \text{ lbf})}{(0.257)\left(30{,}000 \ \dfrac{\text{lbf}}{\text{in}^2}\right)(0.2)}$$

$$= \boxed{10.2 \text{ in}}$$

Each gear would be 11.1 in wide or larger. This disregards stress concentration factors.

SI Solution

(a) Let gear 1 be the gear and gear 2 be the pinion.

$$\frac{d_1}{2} + \frac{d_2}{2} = \text{center distance} = 380 \text{ mm}$$

From Eq. 52.39,

$$\frac{d_1}{d_2} = \frac{n_2}{n_1} = \frac{1200 \text{ rpm}}{270 \text{ rpm}} = 4.44$$

Solving these two equations simultaneously gives

$$d_1 = \boxed{620.4 \text{ mm}}$$

$$d_2 = \boxed{139.6 \text{ mm}}$$

(b) From Eq. 52.31, the pitch circle velocity is

$$v_t = \pi d_1 n_1$$

$$= \pi(0.6204 \text{ m})(270 \text{ rpm})\left(\frac{1 \text{ min}}{60 \text{ sec}}\right) = 8.77 \text{ m/s}$$

From Eq. 52.46, the transmitted load is

$$F_t = \frac{P_{\text{kW}}\left(1000 \ \dfrac{\text{W}}{\text{kW}}\right)}{v_t} = \frac{(410 \text{ kW})\left(1000 \ \dfrac{\text{W}}{\text{kW}}\right)}{8.77 \ \dfrac{\text{m}}{\text{s}}}$$

$$= 46\,750 \text{ N} \quad (46.75 \text{ kN})$$

The allowable bending stress for the pinion is

$$\sigma_a = \frac{S_e}{\text{FS}} = \frac{620 \text{ MPa}}{3} = 206.7 \text{ MPa}$$

From Eq. 52.62, the Barth speed factor is

$$k_d = \frac{a}{a + v_t} = \frac{600 \ \dfrac{\text{ft}}{\text{min}}}{600 \ \dfrac{\text{ft}}{\text{min}} + \left(8.77 \ \dfrac{\text{m}}{\text{s}}\right)\left(196.8 \ \dfrac{\dfrac{\text{ft}}{\text{min}}}{\dfrac{\text{m}}{\text{s}}}\right)}$$

$$= 0.258$$

Select a pinion width of $w = 150$ mm and an approximate form factor of $Y = 0.3$.

From Eq. 52.61, the diametral pitch is

$$P = \frac{k_d \sigma_a w Y}{F_t}$$

$$= \frac{(0.258)(206.7 \text{ MPa}) \left(1000 \ \dfrac{\text{kPa}}{\text{MPa}}\right) \times (150 \text{ mm})(0.3) \left(\dfrac{1 \text{ m}}{10^3 \text{ mm}}\right)^2}{46.75 \text{ kN}}$$

$$= \boxed{0.051 \ \frac{1}{\text{mm}}}$$

(c) The number of teeth on the pinion is

$$N_2 = \frac{d_2}{m} = \frac{139.6 \text{ mm}}{17 \text{ mm}} = 8.21 \text{ teeth}$$

[say 8 teeth]

The number of teeth on the gear is

$$N_1 = \frac{d_1}{m} = \frac{620.4 \text{ mm}}{17 \text{ mm}} = 36.5 \text{ teeth}$$

[say 36 teeth]

For a $14\frac{1}{2}°$, 36-tooth gear, the form factor is $Y = 0.33$. The allowable bending stress for the gear is

$$\sigma_a = \frac{S_e}{\text{FS}} = \frac{345 \text{ MPa}}{3} = 115 \text{ MPa}$$

From Eq. 52.61, the face width of the gear is

$$w = \frac{P F_t}{k_d \sigma_a Y} = \frac{F_t}{m k_d \sigma_a Y}$$

$$= \frac{46.75 \text{ kN}}{(17 \text{ mm})(0.258)(115 \text{ MPa})} \times \left(1000 \ \frac{\text{kPa}}{\text{MPa}}\right)(0.29) \left(\frac{1 \text{ m}}{10^3 \text{ mm}}\right)^2$$

$$= 319.6 \text{ mm}$$

For a $14\frac{1}{2}$, eight-tooth gear, the form factor is $Y \approx 0.2$. The allowable bending stress for the pinion is

$$\sigma_a = \frac{620 \text{ MPa}}{3} = 206.7 \text{ MPa}$$

From Eq. 52.61, the face width of the pinion is

$$w = \frac{P F_t}{k_d \sigma_a Y} = \frac{F_t}{m k_d \sigma_a Y}$$

$$= \frac{46.75 \text{ kN}}{(17 \text{ mm})(0.258)(206.7 \text{ MPa})} \times \left(1000 \ \frac{\text{kPa}}{\text{MPa}}\right)(0.20) \left(\frac{1 \text{ m}}{1000 \text{ mm}}\right)^2$$

$$= \boxed{257.8 \text{ mm}}$$

Each gear would be 320 mm wide or larger. This disregards stress concentration factors.

7. *Customary U.S. Solution*

(a) Let gear 1 be the gear and gear 2 be the pinion. The center distance is

$$\frac{d_1}{2} + \frac{d_2}{2} = 15 \text{ in}$$

From Eq. 52.39,

$$\frac{d_1}{d_2} = \frac{n_2}{n_1} = \frac{250 \text{ rpm}}{83.33 \text{ rpm}} = 3.0$$

$$d_1 = \boxed{22.5 \text{ in}}$$

$$d_2 = \boxed{7.5 \text{ in}}$$

(b) From Eq. 52.31, the pitch circle velocity is

$$v_t = \pi d_1 n_1 = \pi (22.5 \text{ in})(83.33 \text{ rpm}) \left(\frac{1 \text{ ft}}{12 \text{ in}}\right)$$

$$= 490.9 \text{ ft/min}$$

From Eq. 52.46, the transmitted load is

$$F_t = \frac{P_{\text{hp}} \left(33,000 \ \dfrac{\text{ft-lbf}}{\text{hp-min}}\right)}{v_t}$$

$$= \frac{(250 \text{ hp}) \left(33,000 \ \dfrac{\text{ft-lbf}}{\text{hp-min}}\right)}{490.9 \ \dfrac{\text{ft}}{\text{min}}}$$

$$= 16,806 \text{ lbf}$$

From Eq. 52.62, the Barth speed factor is

$$k_d = \frac{a}{a + v_t} = \frac{600 \ \dfrac{\text{ft}}{\text{min}}}{600 \ \dfrac{\text{ft}}{\text{min}} + 490.9 \ \dfrac{\text{ft}}{\text{min}}} = 0.55$$

Select a pinion width of $w = 6$ in and a form factor of $Y = 0.3$.

From Eq. 52.61, the diametral pitch is

$$P = \frac{k_d \sigma_a w Y}{F_t} = \frac{(0.55) \left(30,000 \ \dfrac{\text{lbf}}{\text{in}^2}\right)(6 \text{ in})(0.3)}{16,806 \text{ lbf}}$$

$$= 1.77 \text{ 1/in}$$

$$\boxed{\text{Select } P = 2 \text{ 1/in as a standard size.}}$$

(c) The number of teeth on the pinion is

$$N_{\text{pinion}} = P d_2 = \left(2 \ \frac{1}{\text{in}}\right)(7.5 \text{ in}) = \boxed{15 \text{ teeth}}$$

The number of teeth on the gear is

$$N_{\text{gear}} = Pd_1 = \left(2\,\frac{1}{\text{in}}\right)(22.5\text{ in}) = \boxed{45\text{ teeth}}$$

(d) For a 20°, 15-tooth pinion, the form factor is $Y = 0.29$.

From Eq. 52.61, the minimum face width of the pinion is

$$w = \frac{PF_t}{k_d\sigma_a Y} = \frac{\left(2\,\frac{1}{\text{in}}\right)(16{,}806\text{ lbf})}{(0.55)\left(30{,}000\,\frac{\text{lbf}}{\text{in}^2}\right)(0.29)}$$

$$= \boxed{7.0\text{ in}}$$

(e) For a 20°, 45-tooth gear, the form factor is $Y = 0.40$.

The allowable bending stress for the gear is

$$\sigma_a = \frac{\sigma_{\max}}{\text{FS}} = \frac{50{,}000\,\frac{\text{lbf}}{\text{in}^2}}{3} = 16{,}667\text{ lbf/in}^2$$

From Eq. 52.61, the minimum face width of the gear is

$$w = \frac{PF_t}{k_d\sigma_a Y} = \frac{\left(2\,\frac{1}{\text{min}}\right)(16{,}806\text{ lbf})}{(0.55)\left(16{,}667\,\frac{\text{lbf}}{\text{in}^2}\right)(0.40)}$$

$$= \boxed{9.2\text{ in}}$$

SI Solution

(a) Let gear 1 be the gear and gear 2 be the pinion. The center distance is

$$\frac{d_1}{2} + \frac{d_2}{2} = 380\text{ mm}$$

From Eq. 52.39,

$$\frac{d_1}{d_2} = \frac{n_2}{n_1} = \frac{250\text{ rpm}}{83.33\text{ rpm}} = 3.0$$

$$d_1 = \boxed{570\text{ mm}}$$

$$d_2 = \boxed{190\text{ mm}}$$

(b) From Eq. 52.31, the pitch circle velocity is

$$v_t = \pi d_1 n_1 = \pi(0.57\text{ m})(83.33\text{ rpm})\left(\frac{1\text{ min}}{60\text{ sec}}\right)$$

$$= 2.49\text{ m/s}$$

From Eq. 52.46, the transmitted load is

$$F_t = \frac{P_{\text{kW}}\left(1000\,\frac{\text{W}}{\text{kW}}\right)}{v_t} = \frac{(190\text{ kW})\left(1000\,\frac{\text{W}}{\text{kW}}\right)}{2.49\,\frac{\text{m}}{\text{s}}}$$

$$= 76{,}305\text{ W}\quad(76.3\text{ kW})$$

From Eq. 52.62, the Barth speed factor is

$$k_d = \frac{a}{a + v_t} = \frac{600\,\frac{\text{ft}}{\text{min}}}{600\,\frac{\text{ft}}{\text{min}} + \left(2.49\,\frac{\text{m}}{\text{s}}\right)\left(196.8\,\frac{\frac{\text{ft}}{\text{min}}}{\frac{\text{m}}{\text{s}}}\right)}$$

$$= 0.55$$

Select a pinion width of $w = 150$ mm and a form factor of $Y = 0.3$.

From Eq. 52.61, the diametral pitch is

$$P = \frac{k_d\sigma_a w Y}{F_t}$$

$$= \frac{(0.55)(210\text{ MPa})\left(1000\,\frac{\text{kPa}}{\text{MPa}}\right)}{76.3\text{ kN}}$$
$$\quad\times(150\text{ mm})(0.3)\left(\frac{1\text{ m}}{10^3\text{ mm}}\right)^2$$

$$= \boxed{0.068\text{ 1/mm}}$$

(c) The number of teeth on the pinion is

$$N_{\text{pinion}} = Pd_2 = \left(0.068\,\frac{1}{\text{mm}}\right)(190\text{ mm}) = 12.9\text{ teeth}$$

$$\boxed{[\text{say 13 teeth}]}$$

The number of teeth on the gear is

$$N_{\text{gear}} = Pd_1 = \left(0.068\,\frac{1}{\text{mm}}\right)(570\text{ mm}) = 38.8\text{ teeth}$$

$$\boxed{[\text{say 39 teeth}]}$$

(d) For a 20°, 13-tooth pinion, the form factor is $Y = 0.26$.

From Eq. 52.61, the minimum face width of the pinion is

$$w = \frac{PF_t}{k_d\sigma_a Y}$$

$$= \frac{\left(0.068\,\frac{1}{\text{mm}}\right)(76.3\text{ kN})}{(0.55)(210\text{ MPa})\left(1000\,\frac{\text{kPa}}{\text{MPa}}\right)(0.26)\left(\frac{1\text{ m}}{10^3\text{ mm}}\right)^2}$$

$$= \boxed{173\text{ mm}}$$

(e) For a 20°, 39-tooth gear, the form factor is $Y = 0.38$.

The allowable bending stress for the gear is

$$\sigma_a = \frac{\sigma_{\max}}{\text{FS}} = \frac{345 \text{ MPa}}{3} = 115 \text{ MPa}$$

From Eq. 52.61, the minimum face width of the gear is

$$w = \frac{PF_t}{k_d \sigma_a Y}$$

$$= \frac{\left(0.068 \, \frac{1}{\text{mm}}\right)(76.3 \text{ kN})}{(0.55)(115 \text{ MPa})\left(1000 \, \frac{\text{kPa}}{\text{MPa}}\right)(0.38)\left(\frac{1 \text{ m}}{10^3 \text{ mm}}\right)^2}$$

$$= \boxed{216 \text{ mm}}$$

8. *Customary U.S. Solution*

The contact surface area for M contact surfaces is

$$A = M\left(\frac{\pi}{4}\right)\left(d_o^2 - d_i^2\right)$$
$$= M\left(\frac{\pi}{4}\right)\left((4.5 \text{ in})^2 - (2.5 \text{ in})^2\right) = 11M \quad [\text{in in}^2]$$

The normal force is

$$N = Ap = (11M)\left(100 \, \frac{\text{lbf}}{\text{in}^2}\right) = 1100M \quad [\text{in lbf}]$$

From Eq. 52.85, the frictional force is

$$F_f = fN = (0.12)(1100M) = 132M \quad [\text{in lbf}]$$

The axial application force is equal to the normal force.

$$F = N = 1100M \quad [\text{in lbf}]$$

From Eq. 52.94, the torque per contact surface is

$$T = \tfrac{1}{2}fF(r_o + r_i) = \tfrac{1}{2}F_f(r_o + r_i)$$
$$= \left(\tfrac{1}{2}\right)(132M)\left(\frac{4.5 \text{ in}}{2} + \frac{2.5 \text{ in}}{2}\right)$$
$$= 231M \quad [\text{in in-lbf}]$$

The slipping torque is

$$T_{\text{slip}} = 3T_{\text{rated}} = (3)(300 \text{ in-lbf}) = 900 \text{ in-lbf}$$

The slipping torque is equal to the torque per contact surface.

$$T_{\text{slip}} = T$$
$$900 \text{ in-lbf} = 231M \quad [\text{in in-lbf}]$$
$$M = 3.9$$

Use four contact surfaces. The arrangement is

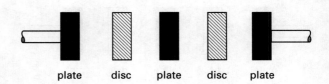

plate   disc   plate   disc   plate

(a) [Use three plates.]

(b) [Use two discs.]

SI Solution

The contact surface area for M contact surfaces is

$$A = M\left(\frac{\pi}{4}\right)\left(d_o^2 - d_i^2\right)$$
$$= M\left(\frac{\pi}{4}\right)\left((115 \text{ mm})^2 - (65 \text{ mm})^2\right) = 7069M$$
$$[\text{in mm}^2]$$

The normal force is

$$N = AP = (7069M)(700 \text{ kPa})\left(\frac{1 \text{ m}}{10^3 \text{ mm}}\right)^2$$
$$= 4.95M \quad [\text{in kN}]$$

From Eq. 52.85, the frictional force is

$$F_f = fN = (0.12)(4.95M) = 0.594M \quad [\text{in kN}]$$

The axial application force is equal to the normal force.

$$F = N = 4.95M \quad [\text{in kN}]$$

From Eq. 52.94, the torque per contact surface is

$$T = \tfrac{1}{2}fF(r_o + r_i) = \tfrac{1}{2}F_f(r_o + r_i)$$
$$= \left(\tfrac{1}{2}\right)(0.594M)\left(1000 \, \frac{\text{N}}{\text{kN}}\right)$$
$$\times \left(\frac{115 \text{ mm}}{2} + \frac{65 \text{ mm}}{2}\right)\left(\frac{1 \text{ m}}{10^3 \text{ mm}}\right)$$
$$= 26.73M \quad [\text{in N·m}]$$

The slipping torque is

$$T_{\text{slip}} = 3T_{\text{rated}} = (3)(33 \text{ N·m}) = 99 \text{ N·m}$$

The slipping torque is equal to the torque per contact surface.

$$T_{\text{slip}} = T$$
$$99 \text{ N·m} = 26.73M \quad [\text{in N·m}]$$
$$M = 3.7 \text{ N·m}$$

Use four contact surfaces. The arrangement is

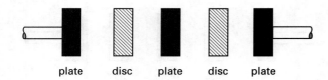

plate   disc   plate   disc   plate

(a) | Use three plates. |

(b) | Use two discs. |

9. *Customary U.S. Solution*

From Eq. 52.111, the bearing pressure is

$$p = \frac{\text{lateral shaft load}}{Ld} = \frac{880 \text{ lbf}}{(3.5 \text{ in})(3 \text{ in})} = 83.81 \text{ lbf/in}^2$$

From Eq. 52.110, the ratio c_d/d is

$$\frac{c_d}{d} = \frac{2c_r}{d} = \frac{2c_r}{r} = \frac{c_r}{r} = 0.001$$

This is the radial clearance ratio.

From Eq. 52.117, the bearing characteristic number is

$$S = \left(\frac{d}{c_d}\right)^2 \left(\frac{\mu n_{\text{rps}}}{p}\right)$$
$$= \left(\frac{r}{c_r}\right)^2 \left(\frac{\mu n_{\text{rps}}}{p}\right)$$
$$= \left(\frac{1}{0.001}\right)^2 \left(\frac{\left(1.184 \times 10^{-6} \frac{\text{lbf-sec}}{\text{in}^2}\right) \times \left(1200 \frac{\text{rev}}{\text{min}}\right)\left(\frac{1 \text{ min}}{60 \text{ sec}}\right)}{83.81 \frac{\text{lbf}}{\text{in}^2}}\right)$$
$$= 0.283$$

The axial length-to-diameter ratio is

$$\frac{L}{d} = \frac{3.5 \text{ in}}{3 \text{ in}} = 1.17$$

(a) From App. 52.B, the minimum film thickness variable is approximately 0.64. From Eq. 52.119, the minimum film thickness is

$$h_o = r \left(\frac{c_d}{d}\right) (\text{minimum film thickness variable})$$
$$= \left(\frac{3 \text{ in}}{2}\right)(0.001)(0.64) = \boxed{0.00096 \text{ in}}$$

(b) From App. 52.B, the coefficient of friction variable is approximately 6.

From Eq. 52.118, the coefficient of friction is

$$f = \left(\frac{c_d}{d}\right) (\text{coefficient of friction variable})$$
$$= (0.001)(6) = 0.006$$

The friction torque is

$$T = fF_r = (0.006)(880 \text{ lbf})\left(\frac{3 \text{ in}}{2}\right)$$
$$= 7.92 \text{ in-lbf}$$

From Eq. 52.32, the power lost to friction is

$$P_{\text{hp}} = \frac{T_{\text{in-lbf}} n_{\text{rpm}}}{63{,}025} = \frac{(7.92 \text{ in-lbf})\left(1200 \frac{\text{rev}}{\text{min}}\right)}{63{,}025}$$
$$= \boxed{0.151 \text{ hp}}$$

(c) Since the minimum film thickness variable is out of the shaded area of the figure in App. 52.B and to the right of the maximum load-carrying ability curve, the bearing is operating above its capacity.

SI Solution

From Eq. 52.111, the bearing pressure is

$$p = \frac{\text{lateral shaft load}}{Ld}$$
$$= \frac{4 \text{ kN}}{(90 \text{ mm})(76 \text{ mm})\left(\frac{1 \text{ m}}{10^3 \text{ mm}}\right)^2}$$
$$= 0.585 \text{ MPa}$$

From Eq. 52.110, the ratio c_d/d is

$$\frac{c_d}{d} = \frac{2c_r}{d} = \frac{2c_r}{2r} = \frac{c_r}{r}$$

This is the radial clearance ratio.

From Eq. 52.117, the bearing characteristic number is

$$S = \left(\frac{d}{c_d}\right)^2 \left(\frac{\mu n_{\text{rps}}}{p}\right)$$
$$= \left(\frac{r}{c_r}\right)^2 \left(\frac{\mu n_{\text{rps}}}{p}\right)$$
$$= \left(\frac{1}{0.001}\right)^2$$
$$\times \left(\frac{(8.16 \text{ cp})\left(1 \frac{\frac{\text{N·s}}{\text{m}^2}}{10^3 \text{ cp}}\right)\left(1200 \frac{\text{rev}}{\text{min}}\right)\left(\frac{1 \text{ min}}{60 \text{ s}}\right)}{(0.585 \text{ MPa})\left(10^6 \frac{\text{Pa}}{\text{MPa}}\right)}\right)$$
$$= 0.279$$

The axial length-to-diameter ratio is

$$\frac{L}{d} = \frac{90 \text{ mm}}{76 \text{ mm}} = 1.18$$

(a) From App. 52.B, the minimum film thickness variable is approximately 0.64.

From Eq. 52.119, the minimum film thickness is

$$h_o = r\left(\frac{cd}{d}\right) \text{ (minimum film thickness variable)}$$

$$= \left(\frac{76 \text{ mm}}{2}\right)(0.001)(0.64) = \boxed{0.0243 \text{ mm}}$$

(b) From App. 52.B, the coefficient of friction variable is approximately 6. From Eq. 52.118, the coefficient of friction is

$$f = \left(\frac{c_d}{d}\right) \text{ (coefficient of friction variable)}$$

$$= (0.001)(6) = 0.006$$

The friction torque is

$$T = fF_r$$

$$= (0.006)(4 \text{ kN})\left(1000 \frac{\text{N}}{\text{kN}}\right)\left(\frac{76 \text{ mm}}{2}\right)\left(\frac{1 \text{ m}}{10^3 \text{ mm}}\right)$$

$$= 0.912 \text{ N·m}$$

From Eq. 52.32(a), the power lost to friction is

$$P_{\text{kW}} = \frac{T_{\text{N·m}} n_{\text{rpm}}}{9549} = \frac{(0.912 \text{ N·m})\left(1200 \frac{\text{rev}}{\text{min}}\right)}{9549}$$

$$= \boxed{0.115 \text{ kW}}$$

(c) Since the minimum film thickness variable is out of the shaded area of the figure in App. 52.B and to the right of the maximum load-carrying ability curve, the bearing is operating above its capacity.

10. *Customary U.S. Solution*

From Table 52.4, the number of active coils are as follows.

For the inner spring,

$$n_a = n_t - 2 = 12.75 - 2 = 10.75$$

For the outer spring,

$$n_a = n_t - 2 = 10.25 - 2 = 8.25$$

From Eq. 52.8, the spring indices are as follows.

For the inner spring,

$$C = \frac{D}{d} = \frac{1.5 \text{ in}}{0.177 \text{ in}} = 8.47$$

For the outer spring,

$$C = \frac{D}{d} = \frac{2.0 \text{ in}}{0.2253 \text{ in}} = 8.88$$

From Eq. 52.12, the spring constants are as follows.
For the inner spring,

$$k_i = \frac{Gd}{8C^3 n_a} = \frac{\left(11.5 \times 10^6 \frac{\text{lbf}}{\text{in}^2}\right)(0.177 \text{ in})}{(8)(8.47)^3(10.75)}$$

$$= 38.95 \text{ lbf/in}$$

For the outer spring,

$$k_o = \frac{Gd}{8C^3 n_a} = \frac{\left(11.5 \times 10^6 \frac{\text{lbf}}{\text{in}^2}\right)(0.2253 \text{ in})}{(8)(8.88)^3(8.25)}$$

$$= 56.06 \text{ lbf/in}$$

Since the inner spring is longer by $\delta_i = 4.5 \text{ in} - 3.75 \text{ in} = 0.75 \text{ in}$, the force absorbed by the inner spring over this distance is

$$F_i = k_i \delta_i = \left(38.95 \frac{\text{lbf}}{\text{in}}\right)(0.75 \text{ in}) = 29.2 \text{ lbf}$$

The force shared by both springs is

$$F = F_s - F_i = 150 \text{ lbf} - 29.2 \text{ lbf} = 120.8 \text{ lbf}$$

The composite spring constant for both springs is

$$k = k_i + k_o = 38.95 \frac{\text{lbf}}{\text{in}} + 56.06 \frac{\text{lbf}}{\text{in}} = 95.0 \text{ lbf/in}$$

The deflection of the composite spring is

$$\delta_c = \frac{F}{k} = \frac{120.8 \text{ lbf}}{95.0 \frac{\text{lbf}}{\text{in}}} = 1.27 \text{ in}$$

(a) The total deflection of the inner spring is

$$\delta_{\text{total}} = \delta_i + \delta_c = 0.75 \text{ in} + 1.27 \text{ in} = \boxed{2.02 \text{ in}}$$

(b) The maximum force exerted by the inner spring is

$$F = k_i \delta_{\text{total}} = \left(38.95 \frac{\text{lbf}}{\text{in}}\right)(2.02 \text{ in}) = \boxed{78.7 \text{ lbf}}$$

(c) From Eq. 52.13, the Wahl correction factor for the inner spring is

$$W = \frac{4C - 1}{4C - 4} + \frac{0.615}{C}$$

$$= \frac{(4)(8.47) - 1}{(4)(8.47) - 4} + \frac{0.615}{8.47}$$

$$= 1.173$$

From Eq. 52.14, the maximum shear stress in the inner spring is

$$\tau_{\max} = \frac{8FCW}{\pi d^2}$$

$$= \frac{(8)(78.7 \text{ lbf})(8.47)(1.173)}{\pi(0.177 \text{ in})^2}$$

$$= \boxed{63{,}555 \text{ lbf/in}^2}$$

(d) The yield strength is 75% of the ultimate strength.

$$S_{yt} = 0.75 S_{ut}$$

$$= (0.75)\left(204{,}000 \ \frac{\text{lbf}}{\text{in}^2}\right)$$

$$= 153{,}000 \text{ lbf/in}^2$$

According to the maximum shear stress failure theory, the maximum allowable shear stress is

$$\tau_{\max,a} = 0.5 S_{yt}$$

$$= (0.5)\left(153{,}000 \ \frac{\text{lbf}}{\text{in}^2}\right)$$

$$= 76{,}500 \text{ lbf/in}^2$$

The factor of safety in shear for the inner spring is

$$\text{FS} = \frac{\tau_{\max,a}}{\tau_{\max}}$$

$$= \frac{76{,}500 \ \dfrac{\text{lbf}}{\text{in}^2}}{63{,}555 \ \dfrac{\text{lbf}}{\text{in}^2}}$$

$$= \boxed{1.20}$$

(e) The inner and outer springs should be wound with opposite direction helixes. This configuration will minimize resonance and prevent coils from one spring from entering the other spring's gaps.

SI Solution

From Table 52.4, the number of active coils are as follows.

For the inner spring,

$$n_a = n_t - 2 = 12.75 - 2 = 10.75$$

For the outer spring,

$$n_1 = n_t - 2 = 10.25 - 2 = 8.25$$

From Eq. 52.8, the spring indices are as follows.

For the inner spring,

$$C = \frac{D}{d} = \frac{38 \text{ mm}}{4.5 \text{ mm}} = 8.44$$

For the outer spring,

$$C = \frac{D}{d} = \frac{51 \text{ mm}}{5.723 \text{ mm}} = 8.91$$

From Eq. 52.12, the spring constants are as follows.

For the inner spring,

$$k_i = \frac{Gd}{8C^3 n_a} = \frac{(79 \times 10^9 \text{ Pa})(4.5 \text{ mm})\left(\dfrac{1 \text{ m}}{10^3 \text{ mm}}\right)}{(8)(8.44)^3(10.75)}$$

$$= 6876 \text{ N/m}$$

For the outer spring,

$$k_o = \frac{Gd}{8C^3 n_a} = \frac{(79 \times 10^9 \text{ Pa})(5.723 \text{ mm})\left(\dfrac{1 \text{ m}}{10^3 \text{ mm}}\right)}{(8)(8.91)^3(8.25)}$$

$$= 9684 \text{ N/m}$$

Since the inner spring is longer by $\delta_i = 115 \text{ mm} - 95.3 \text{ mm} = 19.7 \text{ mm}$, the force absorbed by the inner spring over this distance is

$$F_i = k_i \delta_i = \left(6876 \ \frac{\text{N}}{\text{m}}\right)(19.7 \text{ mm})\left(\frac{1 \text{ m}}{10^3 \text{ m}}\right)$$

$$= 135.5 \text{ N}$$

The force shared by both springs is

$$F = F_s - F_i$$

$$= 600 \text{ N} - 135.5 \text{ N} = 464.5 \text{ N}$$

The composite spring constant for both springs is

$$k = k_i + k_o = 6876 \ \frac{\text{N}}{\text{m}} + 9684 \ \frac{\text{N}}{\text{m}}$$

$$= 16\,560 \text{ N/m}$$

The deflection of the composite spring is

$$\delta_c = \frac{F}{k} = \frac{464.5 \text{ N}}{\left(16\,560\ \frac{\text{N}}{\text{m}}\right)\left(\frac{1 \text{ m}}{10^3 \text{ mm}}\right)} = 28.0 \text{ mm}$$

(a) The total deflection of the inner spring is

$$\delta_{\text{total}} = \delta_i + \delta_c = 19.7 \text{ mm} + 28.0 \text{ mm}$$

$$= \boxed{47.7 \text{ mm}}$$

(b) The maximum force exerted by the inner spring is

$$F = k_i \delta_{\text{total}} = \left(6876\ \frac{\text{N}}{\text{m}}\right)(47.7 \text{ mm})\left(\frac{1 \text{ m}}{10^3 \text{ mm}}\right)$$

$$= \boxed{328.0 \text{ N}}$$

(c) From Eq. 52.13, the Wahl correction factor for the inner spring is

$$W = \frac{4C - 1}{4C - 4} + \frac{0.615}{C} = \frac{(4)(8.44) - 1}{(4)(8.44) - 4} + \frac{0.615}{8.44}$$

$$= 1.174$$

From Eq. 52.14, the maximum shear stress in the inner spring is

$$\tau_{\text{max}} = \frac{8FCW}{\pi d^2} = \frac{(8)(328.0 \text{ N})(8.44)(1.174)}{\pi(4.5 \text{ mm})^2 \left(\frac{1 \text{ m}}{10^3 \text{ mm}}\right)^2}$$

$$= 4.087 \times 10^6 \text{ Pa} \quad \boxed{(408.7 \text{ MPa})}$$

(d) The yield strength is 75% of the ultimate strength.

$$S_{yt} = 0.75 S_{ut}$$
$$= (0.75)(1.4 \times 10^9 \text{ Pa}) = 1.05 \times 10^9 \text{ Pa}$$

According to the maximum shear stress failure theory, the maximum allowable shear stress is

$$\tau_{\text{max},a} = 0.5 S_{yt} = (0.5)(1.05 \times 10^9 \text{ Pa})$$
$$= 5.25 \times 10^8 \text{ Pa} \quad (525 \text{ MPa})$$

The factor of safety in shear for the inner spring is

$$\text{FS} = \frac{\tau_{\text{max},a}}{\tau_{\text{max}}} = \frac{525 \text{ MPa}}{408.7 \text{ MPa}} = \boxed{1.28}$$

(e) The inner and outer springs should be wound with opposite direction helixes. This configuration will minimize resonance and prevent coils from the spring entering from the other spring's gaps.

11. *Customary U.S. Solution*

(a) From Eq. 52.39, the speed of the intermediate shaft is

$$n_{\text{int}} = n_{\text{input}} \left(\frac{N_{\text{input}}}{N_{\text{int at input}}}\right)$$
$$= \left(1800\ \frac{\text{rev}}{\text{min}}\right)\left(\frac{50 \text{ teeth}}{25 \text{ teeth}}\right) = 3600 \text{ rev/min}$$

The speed of the output shaft is

$$n_o = n_{\text{int}} \left(\frac{N_{\text{int at output}}}{N_o}\right)$$
$$= \left(3600\ \frac{\text{rev}}{\text{min}}\right)\left(\frac{60 \text{ teeth}}{20 \text{ teeth}}\right) = \boxed{10{,}800 \text{ rev/min}}$$

(b) From Eq. 52.32, the torque output is

$$T_o = \frac{P_o(63{,}025)}{n_o} = \frac{(\eta_{\text{mesh}})^2 P_i(63{,}025)}{n_o}$$
$$= \frac{(0.98)^2(50 \text{ hp})(63{,}025)}{10{,}800\ \frac{\text{rev}}{\text{min}}} = \boxed{280.2 \text{ in-lbf}}$$

(c) For the gear at section A-A, the pitch diameter is

$$d = \frac{N}{P} = \frac{60 \text{ teeth}}{5\ \frac{\text{teeth}}{\text{in}}} = 12 \text{ in}$$

From Eq. 52.31, the pitch circle velocity is

$$v_t = \pi d n_{\text{rpm}} = \pi(12 \text{ in})\left(\frac{1 \text{ ft}}{12 \text{ in}}\right)\left(3600\ \frac{\text{rev}}{\text{min}}\right)$$
$$= 11{,}310 \text{ ft/min}$$

From Eq. 52.43, the horsepower transmitted is

$$P = \eta_{\text{mesh}} P_i = (0.98)(50 \text{ hp}) = 49 \text{ hp}$$

From Eq. 52.46, the transmitted load is

$$F_t = \frac{P_{\text{hp}}\left(33{,}000\ \frac{\text{ft-lbf}}{\text{hp-min}}\right)}{v_t}$$
$$= \frac{(49 \text{ hp})\left(33{,}000\ \frac{\text{ft-lbf}}{\text{hp-min}}\right)}{11{,}310\ \frac{\text{ft}}{\text{min}}}$$
$$= 143.0 \text{ lbf}$$

From Eq. 52.49, the tangential pressure angle is

$$\phi_t = \arctan\left(\frac{\tan \phi_n}{\cos \psi}\right)$$
$$= \arctan\left(\frac{\tan 20°}{\cos 25°}\right) = 21.9°$$

From Eq. 52.53, the radial force is

$$F_r = F_t \tan \phi_t = (143.0 \text{ lbf})(\tan 21.9°) = 57.5 \text{ lbf}$$

The bending moment on the shaft is

$$M = F_r L = (57.5 \text{ lbf})(4 \text{ in}) = 230 \text{ in-lbf}$$

The torsional moment on the shaft is

$$T = F_t\left(\frac{d}{2}\right) = (143.0 \text{ lbf})\left(\frac{12 \text{ in}}{2}\right) = 858 \text{ in-lbf}$$

According to the maximum shear stress failure theory, the maximum shear stress is

$$\tau_{max} = 0.5 S_{yt} = (0.5)\left(69,000 \frac{\text{lbf}}{\text{in}^2}\right) = 34,500 \text{ lbf/in}^2$$

With a factor of safety of 2, the allowable shear stress is

$$\tau_a = \frac{\tau_{max}}{2} = \frac{34,500 \frac{\text{lbf}}{\text{in}^2}}{2}$$
$$= 17,250 \text{ lbf/in}^2$$

Disregarding the axial loading, from Eq. 51.52, the minimum shaft diameter is

$$d_s = \left(\frac{16\sqrt{M^2 + T^2}}{\pi \tau_{max}}\right)^{\frac{1}{3}}$$
$$= \left(\frac{16\sqrt{(230 \text{ in-lbf})^2 + (858 \text{ in-lbf})^2}}{\pi\left(17,250 \frac{\text{lbf}}{\text{in}^2}\right)}\right)^{\frac{1}{3}}$$
$$= 0.64 \text{ in}$$

Check the normal stress criterion. The maximum allowable normal stress is

$$\sigma_{max} = \frac{S_{yt}}{\text{FS}}$$
$$= \frac{69,000 \frac{\text{lbf}}{\text{in}^2}}{2} = 34,500 \text{ lbf/in}^2$$

From Eq. 51.53, the minimum diameter is

$$d = \left(\left(\frac{16}{\pi \tau_{max}}\right)\sqrt{4M^2 + 3T^2}\right)^{\frac{1}{3}}$$
$$= \left(\frac{16}{\pi\left(34,500 \frac{\text{lbf}}{\text{in}^2}\right)}\right.$$
$$\left.\times \sqrt{((4)(230 \text{ in-lbf}))^2 + ((3)(858 \text{ in-lbf}))^2}\right)^{\frac{1}{3}}$$
$$= 0.739 \text{ in}$$

This is larger than the diameter calculated from the shear stress criterion, so $d = \boxed{0.739 \text{ in.}}$

Check the axial stress.
From Eq. 52.54, the axial force is

$$F_a = F_t \tan \psi = (143.0 \text{ lbf})(\tan 25°) = 66.7 \text{ lbf}$$

The cross-sectional area of the shaft is

$$A = \frac{\pi}{4}d_s^2 = \left(\frac{\pi}{4}\right)(0.739 \text{ in})^2 = 0.429 \text{ in}^2$$

The axial stress is

$$\sigma_{axial} = \frac{F_a}{A} = \frac{66.7 \text{ lbf}}{0.429 \text{ in}^2} = 155 \text{ lbf/in}^2$$

Since σ_{axial} is much less than the yield strength, it is insignificant in this problem.

SI Solution

(a) From Eq. 52.39, the speed of the intermediate shaft is

$$n_{int} = n_{input}\left(\frac{N_{input}}{N_{int at input}}\right)$$
$$= \left(1800 \frac{\text{rev}}{\text{min}}\right)\left(\frac{50 \text{ teeth}}{25 \text{ teeth}}\right) = 3600 \text{ rev/min}$$

The speed of the output shaft is

$$n_o = n_{int}\left(\frac{N_{int at output}}{N_o}\right)$$
$$= \left(3600 \frac{\text{rev}}{\text{min}}\right)\left(\frac{60 \text{ teeth}}{20 \text{ teeth}}\right) = \boxed{10,800 \text{ rev/min}}$$

(b) From Eq. 52.32, the torque output is

$$T_o = \frac{P_o(9549)}{n_o} = \frac{(\eta_{mesh})^2 P_i(9549)}{n_o}$$
$$= \frac{(0.98)^2(38 \text{ kW})(9549)}{10,800 \frac{\text{rev}}{\text{min}}} = \boxed{32.27 \text{ N·m}}$$

(c) For the gear at section A-A, the pitch diameter is

$$d = Nm = (60 \text{ teeth})\left(5 \frac{\text{mm}}{\text{tooth}}\right) = 300 \text{ mm}$$

From Eq. 52.31, the pitch circle velocity is

$$v_t = \pi d n_{rpm} = \pi(300 \text{ mm})\left(\frac{1 \text{ m}}{1000 \text{ mm}}\right)$$
$$\times \left(3600 \frac{\text{rev}}{\text{min}}\right)\left(\frac{1 \text{ min}}{60 \text{ sec}}\right)$$
$$= 56.55 \text{ m/s}$$

From Eq. 52.43, the power transmitted is

$$P = \eta_{\text{mesh}} P_i = (0.98)(38 \text{ kW}) = 37.24 \text{ kW}$$

From Eq. 52.46, the transmitted load is

$$F_t = \frac{P_{\text{kW}} \left(1000 \dfrac{\text{W}}{\text{kW}}\right)}{v_t}$$

$$= \frac{(37.24 \text{ kW}) \left(1000 \dfrac{\text{W}}{\text{kW}}\right)}{56.55 \dfrac{\text{m}}{\text{s}}}$$

$$= 658.5 \text{ N}$$

From Eq. 52.49, the tangential pressure angle is

$$\phi_t = \arctan \left(\frac{\tan \phi_n}{\cos \psi}\right)$$

$$= \arctan \left(\frac{\tan 20°}{\cos 25°}\right) = 21.9°$$

From Eq. 52.53, the radial force is

$$F_r = F_t \tan \phi_t = (658.5 \text{ N})(\tan 21.9°) = 264.7 \text{ N}$$

The bending moment on the shaft is

$$M = F_r L = (264.7 \text{ N})(100 \text{ mm}) \left(\frac{1 \text{ m}}{1000 \text{ mm}}\right)$$

$$= 26.47 \text{ N·m}$$

The torsional moment on the shaft is

$$T = F_t \left(\frac{d}{2}\right) = (658.5 \text{ N}) \left(\frac{300 \text{ mm}}{2}\right) \left(\frac{1 \text{ m}}{1000 \text{ mm}}\right)$$

$$= 98.78 \text{ N·m}$$

According to the maximum shear stress failure theory, the maximum shear stress is

$$\tau_{\max} = 0.5 S_{yt} = (0.5)(480 \text{ MPa}) = 240 \text{ MPa}$$

With a factor of safety of 2, the allowable shear stress is

$$\tau_a = \frac{\tau_{\max}}{2} = \frac{240 \text{ MPa}}{2}$$

$$= 120 \text{ MPa}$$

Disregarding the axial loading, from Eq. 51.52, the minimum shaft diameter is

$$d_s = \left(\frac{16\sqrt{M^2 + T^2}}{\pi \tau_{\max}}\right)^{\frac{1}{3}}$$

$$= \left(\frac{16\sqrt{(26.47 \text{ N·m})^2 + (98.78 \text{ N·m})^2}}{\pi (120 \times 10^6 \text{ Pa})}\right)^{\frac{1}{3}}$$

$$= 0.0163 \text{ m}$$

Check the normal stress criterion. The maximum allowable normal stress is

$$\sigma_{\max} = \frac{S_{yt}}{\text{FS}}$$

$$= \frac{480 \text{ MPa}}{2} = 240 \text{ MPa}$$

From Eq. 51.53, the minimum diameter is

$$d = \left(\left(\frac{16}{\pi \tau_{\max}}\right) \sqrt{4M^2 + 3T^2}\right)^{\frac{1}{3}}$$

$$= \left(\left(\frac{16}{\pi (240 \times 10^6 \text{ Pa})}\right)\right.$$

$$\left. \times \sqrt{\left((4)(26.47 \text{ N·m})\right)^2 + \left((3)(197.6 \text{ N·m})\right)^2}\right)^{\frac{1}{3}}$$

$$= 0.0234 \text{ m}$$

This is larger than the diameter calculated from the shear stress criterion, so $d = \boxed{0.0234 \text{ m.}}$

Check the axial stress.

From Eq. 52.54, the axial force is

$$F_a = F_t \tan \psi = (658.5 \text{ N})(\tan 25°) = 307.1 \text{ N}$$

The cross-sectional area of the shaft is

$$A = \frac{\pi}{4} d_s^2 = \left(\frac{\pi}{4}\right)(0.0234 \text{ m})^2 = 4.301 \times 10^{-4} \text{ m}$$

The axial stress is

$$\sigma_{\text{axial}} = \frac{F_a}{A} = \frac{307.1 \text{ N}}{4.301 \times 10^{-4} \text{ m}} = 7.14 \times 10^5 \text{ Pa}$$

Since σ_{axial} is much less than the yield strength, it is insignificant in this problem.

12. *Customary U.S. Solution*

(a) For a B-type v-belt, the belt length correction is 1.8 in. The pitch length is

$$L_p = L_{\text{inside}} + \text{correction}$$

$$= 90 \text{ in} + 1.8 \text{ in}$$

$$= \boxed{91.8 \text{ in}}$$

(b) The ratio of speeds determines the sheave sizes.

$$d_{\text{equipment}} = d_{\text{motor}} \left(\frac{n_{\text{motor}}}{n_{\text{equipment}}}\right)$$

$$= (10 \text{ in}) \left(\frac{1750 \dfrac{\text{rev}}{\text{min}}}{800 \dfrac{\text{rev}}{\text{min}}}\right)$$

$$= \boxed{21.875 \text{ in} \quad (21.9 \text{ in})}$$

SI Solution

(a) For a B-type v-belt, the belt length correction is 1.8 in. The pitch length is

$$L_p = L_{\text{inside}} + \text{correction}$$
$$= (90 \text{ in} + 1.8 \text{ in}) \left(25.4 \, \frac{\text{mm}}{\text{in}} \right)$$
$$= \boxed{2332 \text{ mm}}$$

(b) The ratio of speeds determines the sheave sizes.

$$d_{\text{equipment}} = d_{\text{motor}} \left(\frac{n_{\text{motor}}}{n_{\text{equipment}}} \right)$$
$$= (254 \text{ mm}) \left(\frac{1750 \, \dfrac{\text{rev}}{\text{min}}}{800 \, \dfrac{\text{rev}}{\text{min}}} \right)$$
$$= \boxed{555.625 \text{ mm} \ (556 \text{ mm})}$$

54 Properties of Solid Bodies

1. Customary U.S. Solution

From the hollow circular cylinder in App. 54.A, the mass moment of inertia of the rim is

$$I_{x,1} = \left(\frac{\pi \rho L}{2}\right)\left(r_o^4 - r_i^4\right)$$

$$= \left(\frac{\pi}{2}\right)\left(0.256 \ \frac{\text{lbm}}{\text{in}^3}\right)(12 \ \text{in})$$

$$\times \left(\left(\frac{60 \ \text{in}}{2}\right)^4 - \left(\frac{60 \ \text{in} - 12 \ \text{in}}{2}\right)^4\right)\left(\frac{1 \ \text{ft}^2}{144 \ \text{in}^2}\right)$$

$$= 16{,}025 \ \text{lbm-ft}^2$$

From the hollow circular cylinder in App. 54.A, the mass moment of inertia of the hub is

$$I_{x,2} = \left(\frac{\pi \rho L}{2}\right)\left(r_o^4 - r_i^4\right)$$

$$= \left(\frac{\pi}{2}\right)\left(0.256 \ \frac{\text{lbm}}{\text{in}^3}\right)(12 \ \text{in})$$

$$\times \left(\left(\frac{12 \ \text{in}}{2}\right)^4 - \left(\frac{12 \ \text{in} - 6 \ \text{in}}{2}\right)^4\right)\left(\frac{1 \ \text{ft}^2}{144 \ \text{in}^2}\right)$$

$$= 42 \ \text{lbm-ft}^2$$

The length of a cylindrical spoke is

$$L = 24 \ \text{in} - 6 \ \text{in} = 18 \ \text{in}$$

The mass of a spoke is

$$m = \rho A L = \rho \pi r^2 L$$

$$= \left(0.256 \ \frac{\text{lbm}}{\text{in}^3}\right)\pi \left(\frac{4.25 \ \text{in}}{2}\right)^2 (18 \ \text{in})$$

$$= 65.37 \ \text{lbm}$$

From the solid circular cylinder in App. 54.A, the mass moment of inertia of a spoke about its own centroidal axis is

$$I_z = \frac{m(3r^2 + L^2)}{12}$$

$$= \frac{(65.37 \ \text{lbm})\left((3)\left(\frac{4.25 \ \text{in}}{2}\right)^2 + (18 \ \text{in})^2\right)\left(\frac{1 \ \text{ft}^2}{144 \ \text{in}^2}\right)}{12}$$

$$= 13 \ \text{lbm-ft}^2$$

Use the parallel axis theorem, Eq. 54.12, to find the mass moment of inertia of a spoke about the axis of the flywheel.

$$I_{x,3} \ \text{per spoke} = I_z + md^2$$

$$= 13 \ \text{lbm-ft}^2 + (65.37 \ \text{lbm})\left(\frac{15 \ \text{in}}{12 \ \frac{\text{in}}{\text{ft}}}\right)^2$$

$$= 115 \ \text{lbm-ft}^2$$

The total for six spokes is

$$I_{x,3} = 6 I_{x,3} \ \text{per spoke}$$

$$= (6)(115 \ \text{lbm-ft}^2) = 690 \ \text{lbm-ft}^2$$

Finally, the total rotational mass moment of inertia of the flywheel is

$$I = I_{x,1} + I_{x,2} + I_{x,3}$$

$$= 16{,}025 \ \text{lbm-ft}^2 + 42 \ \text{lbm-ft}^2 + 690 \ \text{lbm-ft}^2$$

$$= \boxed{16{,}757 \ \text{lbm-ft}^2}$$

SI Solution

From the hollow circular cylinder in App. 54.A, the mass moment of inertia of the rim is

$$I_{x,1} = \left(\frac{\pi \rho L}{2}\right)\left(r_o^4 - r_i^4\right)$$

$$= \left(\frac{\pi \left(7080 \ \frac{\text{kg}}{\text{m}^3}\right)(0.3 \ \text{m})}{2}\right)$$

$$\times \left(\left(\frac{1.5 \ \text{m}}{2}\right)^4 - \left(\frac{1.5 \ \text{m} - 0.30 \ \text{m}}{2}\right)^4\right)$$

$$= 623.3 \ \text{kg·m}^2$$

From the hollow circular cylinder in App. 54.A, the mass moment of inertia of the hub is

$$
\begin{aligned}
I_{x,2} &= \left(\frac{\pi \rho L}{2}\right)\left(r_o^4 - r_i^4\right) \\
&= \left(\frac{\pi \left(7080 \ \frac{kg}{m^3}\right)(0.3 \ m)}{2}\right) \\
&\quad \times \left(\left(\frac{0.3 \ m}{2}\right)^4 - \left(\frac{0.3 \ m - 0.15 \ m}{2}\right)^4\right) \\
&= 1.6 \ kg \cdot m^2
\end{aligned}
$$

The length of a cylindrical spoke is

$$
L = 0.6 \ m - 0.15 \ m = 0.45 \ m
$$

The mass of a spoke is

$$
\begin{aligned}
m = \rho A L &= \rho \pi r^2 L \\
&= \left(7080 \ \frac{kg}{m^3}\right) \pi \left(\frac{0.11 \ m}{2}\right)^2 (0.45 \ m) \\
&= 30.3 \ kg
\end{aligned}
$$

From the solid circular cylinder in App. 54.A, the mass moment of inertia of a spoke about its own centroidal axis is

$$
\begin{aligned}
I_z &= \frac{m(3r^2 + L^2)}{12} \\
&= \frac{(30.3 \ kg)\left((3)\left(\frac{0.11 \ m}{2}\right)^2 + (0.45 \ m)^2\right)}{12} \\
&= 0.53 \ kg \cdot m^2
\end{aligned}
$$

Use the parallel axis theorem, Eq. 54.12, to find the mass moment of inertia of a spoke about the axis of the flywheel.

$$
\begin{aligned}
I_{x,3} \text{ per spoke} &= I_z + md^2 \\
&= 0.53 \ kg \cdot m^2 + (30.3 \ kg)(0.375 \ m)^2 \\
&= 4.8 \ kg \cdot m^2
\end{aligned}
$$

The total for six spokes is

$$
\begin{aligned}
I_{x,3} &= 6 I_{x3} \text{ per spoke} \\
&= (6)(4.8 \ kg \cdot m^2) = 28.8 \ kg \cdot m^2
\end{aligned}
$$

Finally, the total rotational mass moment of inertia of the flywheel is

$$
\begin{aligned}
I &= I_{x,1} + I_{x,2} + I_{x,3} \\
&= 623.3 \ kg \cdot m^2 + 1.6 \ kg \cdot m^2 + 28.8 \ kg \cdot m^2 \\
&= \boxed{653.7 \ kg \cdot m^2}
\end{aligned}
$$

55 Kinematics

1. *Customary U.S. Solution*

The angular velocity of the wheel is

$$\omega = \frac{v_c}{r}$$

$$= \frac{\left(28 \ \frac{mi}{hr}\right)\left(5280 \ \frac{ft}{mi}\right)\left(12 \ \frac{in}{ft}\right)\left(\frac{1 \ hr}{3600 \ sec}\right)}{12 \ in}$$

$$= 41.07 \ rad/sec$$

The distance from the valve stem to the instant center of the point of contact of the wheel and the surface is determined from the law of cosines for the triangle defined by the valve stem, instant center, and center of wheel.

$$l^2 = (12 \ in)^2 + (6 \ in)^2 - (2)(12 \ in)(6 \ in)(\cos 135°)$$

$$l = 16.79 \ in$$

Use Eq. 55.52.

$$v = l\omega$$

$$= (16.79 \ in)\left(\frac{1 \ ft}{12 \ in}\right)\left(41.07 \ \frac{rad}{sec}\right)$$

$$= \boxed{57.46 \ ft/sec}$$

The direction is perpendicular to the direction of l.

SI Solution

The angular velocity of the wheel is

$$\omega = \frac{v_c}{r} = \frac{12.5 \ \frac{m}{s}}{0.305 \ m} = 40.98 \ rad/s$$

The distance from the valve stem to the instant center at the point of contact of the wheel and the surface is determined from the law of cosines for the triangle defined by the valve stem, instant center, and center of wheel.

$$l^2 = (0.305 \ m)^2 + (0.150 \ m)^2$$
$$\quad - (2)(0.305 \ m)(0.150 \ m)(\cos 135°)$$

$$l = 0.425 \ m$$

Use Eq. 55.52.

$$v = l\omega$$

$$= (0.425 \ m)\left(40.98 \ \frac{rad}{s}\right)$$

$$= \boxed{17.4 \ m/s}$$

The direction is perpendicular to the direction of l.

2. *Customary U.S. Solution*

From Table 55.2, the x-distance is

$$x = (v_0 \cos \phi)t$$

Solve for t.

$$t = \frac{x}{v_0 \cos \phi} = \frac{12,000 \ ft}{\left(900 \ \frac{ft}{sec}\right)(\cos \phi)} = \frac{13.33}{\cos \phi}$$

From Table 55.2, the y-distance is

$$y = (v_0 \sin \phi)t - \tfrac{1}{2}gt^2$$

Substitute t and the value for y.

$$2000 \ ft = \left(900 \ \frac{ft}{sec}\right)(\sin \phi)\left(\frac{13.33}{\cos \phi}\right)$$
$$\quad - \left(\tfrac{1}{2}\right)\left(32.2 \ \frac{ft}{sec^2}\right)\left(\frac{13.33}{\cos \phi}\right)$$

Simplify.

$$1 = (6.0)(\tan \phi) - \frac{1.43}{\cos^2 \phi}$$

Use the identity.

$$\frac{1}{\cos^2 \phi} = 1 + \tan^2 \phi$$

$$1 = (6.0)(\tan \phi) - 1.43 - (1.43)(\tan^2 \phi)$$

Simplify.

$$\tan^2 \phi - (4.20)(\tan \phi) + 1.70 = 0$$

Use the quadratic formula.

$$\tan \phi = \frac{4.20 \pm \sqrt{(4.20)^2 - (4)(1)(1.70)}}{(2)(1)}$$

$$= 3.75, \ 0.454$$

$$\phi = \tan^{-1}(3.75), \ \tan^{-1}(0.454)$$

$$= \boxed{75.1°, \ 24.4°}$$

SI Solution

From Table 55.2, the x-distance is

$$x = (v_0 \cos \phi)t$$

Solve for t.

$$t = \frac{x}{v_0 \cos \phi} = \frac{3600 \text{ m}}{\left(270 \ \frac{\text{m}}{\text{s}}\right)(\cos \phi)} = \frac{13.33}{\cos \phi}$$

From Table 55.2, the y-distance is

$$y = (v_0 \sin \phi)t - \tfrac{1}{2}gt^2$$

Substitute t and the value of y.

$$600 \text{ m} = \left(270 \ \frac{\text{m}}{\text{s}}\right)(\sin \phi)\left(\frac{13.33}{\cos \phi}\right)$$

$$- \left(\tfrac{1}{2}\right)\left(9.81 \ \frac{\text{m}}{\text{s}^2}\right)\left(\frac{13.33}{\cos \phi}\right)^2$$

Simplify.

$$1 = (6.0)(\tan \phi) - \frac{1.45}{\cos^2 \phi}$$

Use the identity.

$$\frac{1}{\cos^2 \phi} = 1 + \tan^2 \phi$$

$$1 = (6.0)(\tan \phi) - 1.45 - (1.45)(\tan^2 \phi)$$

Simplify.

$$\tan^2 \phi - (4.14)(\tan \phi) + 1.69 = 0$$

Use the quadratic formula.

$$\tan \phi = \frac{4.14 \pm \sqrt{(4.14)^2 - (4)(1)(1.69)}}{(2)(1)}$$

$$= 3.68, \ 0.459$$

$$\phi = \tan^{-1}(3.68), \ \tan^{-1}(0.459)$$

$$= \boxed{74.8°, \ 24.7°}$$

56 Kinetics

1. *Customary U.S. Solution*

The angular velocity of the flywheel at the start of the cycle is

$$\omega_1 = \frac{\left(2\pi \frac{\text{rad}}{\text{rev}}\right)\left(200 \frac{\text{rev}}{\text{min}}\right)}{60 \frac{\text{sec}}{\text{min}}} = 20.94 \text{ rad/sec}$$

The angular velocity of the flywheel at the end of the cycle is

$$\omega_2 = \frac{\left(2\pi \frac{\text{rad}}{\text{rev}}\right)\left(175 \frac{\text{rev}}{\text{min}}\right)}{60 \frac{\text{sec}}{\text{min}}} = 18.33 \text{ rad/sec}$$

By the work-energy principle, the decrease in kinetic energy is equal to the work supplied by the flywheel.

$$\Delta \text{KE} = W$$

$$\left(\tfrac{1}{2}\right)\left(\frac{I}{g_c}\right)\omega_1^2 - \left(\tfrac{1}{2}\right)\left(\frac{I}{g_c}\right)\omega_2^2 = W$$

Solve for the mass moment of inertia, I.

$$I = \frac{2g_c W}{\omega_1^2 - \omega_2^2}$$

$$= \frac{(2)\left(32.2 \frac{\text{ft-lbm}}{\text{lbf-sec}^2}\right)(1500 \text{ ft-lbf})}{\left(20.94 \frac{\text{rad}}{\text{sec}}\right)^2 - \left(18.33 \frac{\text{rad}}{\text{sec}}\right)^2}$$

$$= 942.5 \text{ lbm-ft}^2$$

Assume all of the rim mass is concentrated at the mean radius. The mean circumference is

$$L_{\text{mean}} = 2\pi r_{\text{mean}}$$

$$= 2\pi\left(\frac{30 \text{ in}}{2}\right) = 94.25 \text{ in}$$

The mass moment of inertia of the rim is

$$I_{\text{rim}} = m r_{\text{mean}}^2 = \rho t w L_{\text{mean}} r_{\text{mean}}^2$$

$$= \left(0.26 \frac{\text{lbm}}{\text{in}^3}\right) t (12 \text{ in})(94.25 \text{ in})$$

$$\times \left(\frac{30 \text{ in}}{2}\right)^2 \left(\frac{1 \text{ ft}^2}{144 \text{ in}^2}\right)$$

$$= 459.5t$$

Adding 10% for the hub and arms,

$$I_{\text{total}} = 1.10 I_{\text{rim}} = (1.10)(459.5t)$$

$$= 505.5t$$

Solve for t.

$$t = \frac{I}{I_{\text{total}}} = \frac{942.5 \text{ lbm-ft}^2}{505.5 \frac{\text{lbm-ft}^2}{\text{in}}}$$

$$= \boxed{1.86 \text{ in}}$$

SI Solution

The angular velocity of the flywheel at the start of the cycle is

$$\omega_1 = \frac{\left(2\pi \frac{\text{rad}}{\text{rev}}\right)\left(200 \frac{\text{rev}}{\text{min}}\right)}{60 \frac{\text{sec}}{\text{min}}} = 20.94 \text{ rad/sec}$$

The angular velocity of the flywheel at the end of the cycle is

$$\omega_2 = \frac{\left(2\pi \frac{\text{rad}}{\text{rev}}\right)\left(175 \frac{\text{rev}}{\text{min}}\right)}{60 \frac{\text{sec}}{\text{min}}} = 18.33 \text{ rad/sec}$$

By the work-energy principle, the decrease in kinetic energy is equal to the work supplied by the flywheel.

$$\Delta \text{KE} = W$$

$$\tfrac{1}{2}I\omega_1^2 - \tfrac{1}{2}I\omega_2^2 = W$$

Solve for the mass moment of inertia, I.

$$I = \frac{2W}{\omega_1^2 - \omega_2^2}$$

$$= \frac{(2)(2 \text{ kJ})\left(1000 \frac{\text{J}}{\text{kJ}}\right)}{\left(20.94 \frac{\text{rad}}{\text{sec}}\right)^2 - \left(18.33 \frac{\text{rad}}{\text{sec}}\right)^2}$$

$$= 39.03 \text{ kg·m}^2$$

Assume all of the rim mass is concentrated at the mean radius. The mean circumference is

$$L_{\text{mean}} = 2\pi r_{\text{mean}}$$
$$= 2\pi \left(\frac{0.762 \text{ m}}{2}\right) = 2.394 \text{ m}$$

The mass moment of inertia of the rim is

$$I_{\text{rim}} = m r_{\text{mean}}^2 = \rho t w L_{\text{mean}} r_{\text{mean}}^2$$
$$= \left(7200 \ \frac{\text{kg}}{\text{m}^3}\right) t (0.305 \text{ m})(2.394 \text{ m}) \left(\frac{0.762 \text{ m}}{2}\right)^2$$
$$= 763.1t$$

Adding 10% for the hub and arms,

$$I_{\text{total}} = 1.10 I_{\text{rim}} = (1.10)(763.1t)$$
$$= 839.4t$$

Solve for t.

$$t = \frac{I}{I_{\text{total}}} = \frac{39.03 \text{ kg}\cdot\text{m}^2}{839.4 \ \frac{\text{kg}\cdot\text{m}^2}{\text{m}}}$$
$$= \boxed{0.0465 \text{ m}}$$

57 Mechanisms and Power Transmission Systems

1. If the arm was locked and the ring was free to rotate, the sun and ring gears would rotate in different directions. Therefore, the train value is negative.

From Eq. 57.29,

$$\text{TV} = -\frac{N_{\text{ring}}}{N_{\text{sun}}} = -\frac{104 \text{ teeth}}{24 \text{ teeth}} = -4.333$$

From Eq. 57.30, the rotational velocity of the sun is

$$\omega_{\text{sun}} = (\text{TV})\omega_{\text{ring}} + (1 - \text{TV})\omega_{\text{carrier}}$$

Since the ring gear is fixed, $\omega_{\text{ring}} = 0$ and the rotational velocity of the carrier are

$$\omega_{\text{carrier}} = \frac{\omega_{\text{sun}}}{1 - \text{TV}} = \frac{50 \dfrac{\text{rev}}{\text{min}}}{1 - (-4.333)}$$

$$= \boxed{9.38 \text{ rev/min}}$$

2. Since the ring gear rotates in a different direction from year A, the rotational velocity of the ring gear is

$$\omega_{\text{ring}} = \omega_{\text{A}}\left(-\frac{N_{\text{A}}}{N_{\text{ring}}}\right)$$

$$= \left(-100 \frac{\text{rev}}{\text{min}}\right)\left(-\frac{30 \text{ teeth}}{100 \text{ teeth}}\right)$$

$$= 30 \text{ rev/min} \quad [\text{clockwise}]$$

Since the ring and sun gears rotate in different directions, the train value is negative. From Eq. 57.29,

$$\text{TV} = -\frac{N_{\text{ring}}}{N_{\text{sun}}} = -\frac{80 \text{ teeth}}{40 \text{ teeth}} = -2$$

From Eq. 57.30, the rotational velocity of the sun gear is

$$\omega_{\text{sun}} = (\text{TV})\omega_{\text{ring}} + (1 - \text{TV})\omega_{\text{carrier}}$$

$$= (-2)\left(30 \frac{\text{rev}}{\text{min}}\right) + (1 - (-2))\left(60 \frac{\text{rev}}{\text{min}}\right)$$

$$= \boxed{120 \text{ rev/min}} \quad [\text{clockwise}]$$

3. *Customary U.S. Solution*

(a) From Eq. 52.34, the number of teeth are as follows. For the sun gear,

$$N_{\text{sun}} = Pd = \left(10 \frac{\text{teeth}}{\text{in}}\right)(5 \text{ in}) = \boxed{50 \text{ teeth}}$$

For the planet gears,

$$N_{\text{planet}} = Pd = \left(10 \frac{\text{teeth}}{\text{in}}\right)(2.5 \text{ in}) = \boxed{25 \text{ teeth}}$$

For the ring gear,

$$N_{\text{ring}} = Pd = \left(10 \frac{\text{teeth}}{\text{in}}\right)(10 \text{ in}) = \boxed{100 \text{ teeth}}$$

(b) Since the sun gear is fixed, its rotational speed is zero ($\omega_{\text{sun}} = 0$).

The rotational speed of the ring gear is $\omega_{\text{ring}} = 1500 \text{ rev/min}$.

Since the ring and sun gears rotate in different directions, the train value is negative. From Eq. 57.29,

$$\text{TV} = -\frac{N_{\text{ring}}}{N_{\text{sun}}} = -\frac{100 \text{ teeth}}{50 \text{ teeth}} = -2$$

From Eq. 57.30, the rotational speed of the sun gear is

$$\omega_{\text{sun}} = (\text{TV})\omega_{\text{ring}} + (1 - \text{TV})\omega_{\text{carrier}}$$

$$0 \frac{\text{rev}}{\text{min}} = (-2)\left(1500 \frac{\text{rev}}{\text{min}}\right) + (1 - (-2))\omega_{\text{carrier}}$$

Solve for the rotational speed of the carrier gear.

$$\omega_{\text{carrier}} = \frac{(2)\left(1500 \dfrac{\text{rev}}{\text{min}}\right)}{3} = \boxed{1000 \text{ rev/min}}$$

(c) From part (b), the direction of rotation of the ring and carrier gears is clockwise. The direction of the sun gear is counterclockwise.

(d) From Eq. 52.32, the torque on the input shaft is

$$T_{\text{in-lbf}} = \frac{P_{\text{hp}}(63,025)}{n_{\text{rpm}}}$$

$$= \frac{P_{\text{hp}}(63,025)}{n_{\text{sun}}} = \left(\frac{(15 \text{ hp})(63,025)}{1500 \dfrac{\text{rev}}{\text{min}}}\right)\left(\frac{1 \text{ ft}}{12 \text{ in}}\right)$$

$$= \boxed{52.52 \text{ ft-lbf}}$$

The torque on the output shaft is

$$T_{\text{in-lbf}} = \frac{P_{\text{hp}}(63{,}025)}{n_{\text{carrier}}} = \left(\frac{(15 \text{ hp})(63{,}025)}{1000 \frac{\text{rev}}{\text{min}}}\right)\left(\frac{1 \text{ ft}}{12 \text{ in}}\right)$$

$$= \boxed{78.78 \text{ ft-lbf}}$$

SI Solution

(a) From Eq. 52.34, the number of teeth are as follows.

For the sun gear,

$$N_{\text{sun}} = Pd = \left(10 \frac{\text{teeth}}{\text{in}}\right)\left(\frac{1 \text{ in}}{25.4 \text{ mm}}\right)(127 \text{ mm})$$

$$= \boxed{50 \text{ teeth}}$$

For the planet gears,

$$N_{\text{planet}} = Pd = \left(10 \frac{\text{teeth}}{\text{in}}\right)\left(\frac{1 \text{ in}}{25.4 \text{ mm}}\right)(63.5 \text{ mm})$$

$$= \boxed{25 \text{ teeth}}$$

For the ring gear,

$$N_{\text{ring}} = Pd = \left(10 \frac{\text{teeth}}{\text{in}}\right)\left(\frac{1 \text{ in}}{25.4 \text{ mm}}\right)(254 \text{ mm})$$

$$= \boxed{100 \text{ teeth}}$$

(b) Since the sun gear is fixed, its rotational speed is zero ($\omega_{\text{sun}} = 0$).

The rotational speed of the ring gear is $\omega_{\text{ring}} = 1500$ rev/min.

Since the ring and sun gears rotate in different directions, the train value is negative.

From Eq. 57.29,

$$\text{TV} = -\frac{N_{\text{ring}}}{N_{\text{sun}}} = -\frac{100 \text{ teeth}}{50 \text{ teeth}} = -2$$

From Eq. 57.30, the rotational speed of the sun gear is

$$\omega_{\text{sun}} = (\text{TV})\omega_{\text{ring}} + (1 - \text{TV})\omega_{\text{carrier}}$$

$$0 \frac{\text{rev}}{\text{min}} = (-2)\left(1500 \frac{\text{rev}}{\text{min}}\right) + (1 - (-2))\omega_{\text{carrier}}$$

Solve for the rotational speed of the carrier gear.

$$\omega_{\text{carrier}} = \frac{(2)\left(1500 \frac{\text{rev}}{\text{min}}\right)}{3} = \boxed{1000 \text{ rev/min}}$$

(c) From part (b), the direction of rotation of the ring and carrier gears is clockwise. The sun gear moves in the opposite direction of the ring gear, so the sun gear rotates counterclockwise.

(d) From Eq. 52.32, the torque on the input shaft is

$$T_{\text{N·m}} = \frac{P_{\text{kW}}(9549)}{n_{\text{sun}}}$$

$$= \frac{(11 \text{ kW})(9549)}{1500 \frac{\text{rev}}{\text{min}}} = \boxed{70.03 \text{ N·m}}$$

The torque on the output shaft is

$$T_{\text{N·m}} = \frac{P_{\text{kW}}(9549)}{n_{\text{carrier}}} = \frac{(11 \text{ kW})(9549)}{1000 \frac{\text{rev}}{\text{min}}} = \boxed{105.0 \text{ N·m}}$$

4. *Customary U.S. Solution*

Treat the flywheel as a rotating hub. First, consider the maximum tangential stress.

For a safety factor of 10,

$$\sigma_{t,\text{max}} = \frac{30{,}000 \frac{\text{lbf}}{\text{in}^2}}{10} = 3000 \text{ lbf/in}^2$$

Use Eq. 57.14 to solve for ω.

$$\omega = \sqrt{\frac{4g_c\sigma_{t,\text{max}}}{\rho\left((3+\nu)r_o^2 + (1-\nu)r_i^2\right)}}$$

$$= \sqrt{\frac{(4)\left(32.2 \frac{\text{ft-lbm}}{\text{lbf-sec}^2}\right)\left(12 \frac{\text{in}}{\text{ft}}\right)\left(3000 \frac{\text{lbf}}{\text{in}^2}\right)}{\left(0.26 \frac{\text{lbm}}{\text{in}^3}\right)\left((3+0.27)\left(\frac{20 \text{ in}}{2}\right)^2 + (1-0.27)\left(\frac{4 \text{ in}}{2}\right)^2\right)}}$$

$$= 232.5 \text{ rad/sec}$$

$$n = \frac{\omega}{2\pi} = \left(232.5 \frac{\text{rad}}{\text{sec}}\right)\left(\frac{1 \text{ rev}}{2\pi \text{ rad}}\right)\left(60 \frac{\text{sec}}{\text{min}}\right)$$

$$= 2220 \text{ rev/min}$$

Next, consider the maximum radial stress. Use Eq. 57.15 to solve for ω.

$$\omega = \sqrt{\frac{8 g_c \sigma_{r,\text{max}}}{\rho(3+\nu)(r_o - r_i)^2}}$$

$$= \sqrt{\frac{(8)\left(32.2 \,\frac{\text{ft-lbm}}{\text{lbf-sec}^2}\right)\left(12 \,\frac{\text{in}}{\text{ft}}\right)\left(3000 \,\frac{\text{lbf}}{\text{in}^2}\right)}{\left(0.26 \,\frac{\text{lbm}}{\text{in}^3}\right)(3+0.27)\left(\frac{20 \text{ in}}{2} - \frac{4 \text{ in}}{2}\right)^2}}$$

$$= 412.8 \text{ rad/sec}$$

$$n = \frac{\omega}{2\pi} = \left(412.8 \,\frac{\text{rad}}{\text{sec}}\right)\left(\frac{1 \text{ rev}}{2\pi \text{ rad}}\right)\left(60 \,\frac{\text{sec}}{\text{min}}\right)$$

$$= 3942 \text{ rev/min}$$

The maximum safe speed for the flywheel is

$$\boxed{2220 \text{ rev/min.}}$$

SI Solution

Treat the flywheel as a rotating hub. First, consider the maximum tangential stress.

For a safety factor of 10,

$$\sigma_{t,\text{max}} = \frac{207 \times 10^6 \text{ Pa}}{10} = 20.7 \times 10^6 \text{ Pa}$$

Use Eq. 57.14 to solve for ω.

$$\omega = \sqrt{\frac{4\sigma_{t,\text{max}}}{\rho\left((3+\nu)r_o^2 + (1-\nu)r_i^2\right)}}$$

$$= \sqrt{\frac{(4)(20.7 \times 10^6 \text{ Pa})}{\left(7200 \,\frac{\text{kg}}{\text{m}^3}\right)\left((3+0.27)\left(\frac{0.51 \text{ m}}{2}\right)^2 + (1-0.27)\left(\frac{0.102 \text{ m}}{2}\right)^2\right)}}$$

$$= 231.5 \text{ rad/s}$$

$$n = \frac{\omega}{2\pi} = \left(231.5 \,\frac{\text{rad}}{\text{s}}\right)\left(\frac{1 \text{ rev}}{2\pi \text{ rad}}\right)\left(60 \,\frac{\text{s}}{\text{min}}\right)$$

$$= 2211 \text{ rev/min}$$

Next, consider the maximum radial stress as the worst case. Use Eq. 57.15 to solve for ω.

For a safety factor of 10,

$$\sigma_{r,\text{max}} = \frac{207 \times 10^6 \text{ Pa}}{10} = 20.7 \times 10^6 \text{ Pa}$$

$$\omega = \sqrt{\frac{8\sigma_{r,\text{max}}}{\rho(3+\nu)(r_o - r_i)^2}}$$

$$= \sqrt{\frac{(8)(20.7 \times 10^6 \text{ Pa})}{\left(7200 \,\frac{\text{kg}}{\text{m}^3}\right)(3+0.27)\left(\frac{0.51 \text{ m}}{2} - \frac{0.102 \text{ m}}{2}\right)^2}}$$

$$= 411.1 \text{ rad/s}$$

$$n = \frac{\omega}{2\pi} = \left(411.1 \,\frac{\text{rad}}{\text{s}}\right)\left(\frac{1 \text{ rev}}{2\pi \text{ rad}}\right)\left(60 \,\frac{\text{s}}{\text{min}}\right)$$

$$= 3926 \text{ rev/min}$$

The maximum safe speed for the flywheel is

$$\boxed{2211 \text{ rev/min.}}$$

5. (This problem can be solved quite quickly with Eq. 57.33.) The automobile differential is equivalent to the following imaginary gear set.

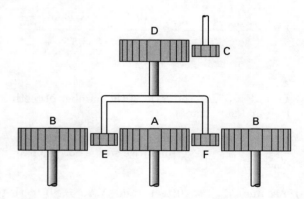

This is the same as a conventional epicyclic gear train except that the ring gear is replaced with two external gears B.

(a) Start with $\omega_C = +600$ rev/min.

Gear D rotates in the opposite direction of gear C.

$$\omega_D = -\left(\frac{N_C}{N_D}\right)\omega_C = -\left(\frac{18 \text{ teeth}}{54 \text{ teeth}}\right)\left(600 \,\frac{\text{rev}}{\text{min}}\right)$$

$$= -200 \text{ rev/min}$$

Gear A rotates in the same direction as gear D.

$$\omega_A = -50 \text{ rev/min}$$

From the actual gear set, turn gear A. Then gear B moves in the opposite direction of gear A. Thus, the train value is negative. From Eq. 57.29,

$$\text{TV} = -\frac{N_B}{N_A} = -\frac{30 \text{ teeth}}{30 \text{ teeth}} = -1.0$$

From Eq. 57.30,

$$\omega_A = (TV)\omega_B + (1 - TV)\omega_D$$

$$\omega_B = \frac{\omega_A - (1 - TV)\omega_D}{TV}$$

$$= \frac{-50\,\frac{rev}{min} - \left(1 - (-1.0)\right)\left(-200\,\frac{rev}{min}\right)}{-1.0}$$

$$= \boxed{-350\ rev/min}$$

(b) Gear B rotates in a direction opposite to gear C; that is, it rotates clockwise.

6. From the overall speed reduction of 3:1, the speed of the carrier is

$$\omega_{carrier} = \frac{\omega_{sun}}{3} = \frac{1000\,\frac{rev}{min}}{3}$$

$$= 333.3\ rev/min$$

The speed of the ring gear is zero. From Eq. 57.29,

$$TV = \frac{\omega_{sun} - \omega_{carrier}}{\omega_{ring} - \omega_{carrier}} = \frac{1000\,\frac{rev}{min} - 333.3\,\frac{rev}{min}}{0 - 333.3\,\frac{rev}{min}}$$

$$= -2$$

(a) From Eq. 57.29, the ratio of the number of teeth on the ring and sun gears is

$$\frac{N_{ring}}{N_{sun}} = TV = \boxed{2}\quad \text{[negative sign is not required]}$$

(b) Assume $N_{sun} = 40$ teeth and $N_{ring} = 80$ teeth to satisfy part (a).

Then, from Eq. 52.34,

$$d_{sun} = \frac{N_{sun}}{P} = \frac{40\ teeth}{10\,\frac{teeth}{in}} = 4\ in$$

$$d_{ring} = \frac{N_{ring}}{P} = \frac{80\ teeth}{10\,\frac{teeth}{in}} = 8\ in$$

$$d_{planet} = \frac{N_{planet}}{P} = \frac{20\ teeth}{10\,\frac{teeth}{in}} = 2\ in$$

Check the sum of the gear diameters.

$$d_{ring} = d_{sun} + 2d_{planet}$$
$$8\ in = 4\ in + (2)(2\ in) = 8\ in$$

Since the gears fit, $N_{sun} = 40$ teeth and $N_{ring} = 80$ teeth is a valid solution. Use Eq. 57.31 to solve for $\omega_{planets}$.

$$\omega_{planets} = \omega_{carrier} - \left(\frac{N_{sun}}{N_{planets}}\right)(\omega_{sun} - \omega_{carrier})$$

$$= 333.3\,\frac{rev}{min}$$

$$- \left(\frac{40\ teeth}{20\ teeth}\right)\left(1000\,\frac{rev}{min} - 333.3\,\frac{rev}{min}\right)$$

$$= \boxed{-1000\ rev/min}$$

7. First, simplify the problem. Input #2 causes gear D–E to rotate at

$$(-75\ rpm)\left(-\frac{N_F}{N_E}\right) = (-75\ rpm)\left(-\frac{28\ teeth}{32\ teeth}\right)$$
$$= 65.625\ rpm$$

Thus, $\omega_D = 65.625$ rpm.

Use the eight-step procedure from Chap. 57, Sec. 14.

step 1: Gears A and D have the same center of rotation as the arm.

	A	D
row 1		
row 2		
row 3		

step 2: Write $\omega_{carrier}$ in the first row.

	A	D
row 1	$\omega_{carrier}$	$\omega_{carrier}$
row 2		
row 3		

step 3: Arbitrarily select gear D as the gear with unknown speed.

	A	D
row 1	$\omega_{carrier}$	$\omega_{carrier}$
row 2		
row 3		ω_D

step 4:

	A	D
row 1	$\omega_{carrier}$	$\omega_{carrier}$
row 2		$\omega_D - \omega_{carrier}$
row 3		ω_D

step 5: The translational path D to A is a compound mesh.

From Fig. 57.8,

$$\omega_A = \omega_D \left(\frac{N_B N_D}{N_A N_C} \right)$$

$$= \omega_D \left(\frac{(63 \text{ teeth})(56 \text{ teeth})}{(68 \text{ teeth}) N_C} \right)$$

$$= 51.8823 \omega_D / N_C$$

step 6:

	A		D
row 1	ω_{carrier}		ω_{carrier}
row 2	$\left(\dfrac{51.8823}{N_C} \right) (\omega_D - \omega_{\text{carrier}})$		$\omega_D - \omega_{\text{carrier}}$
row 3			ω_D

step 7: Insert the known values for ω_{carrier} and ω_D.

	A		D
row 1	150		150
row 2	$\left(\dfrac{51.8823}{N_C} \right)(65.625 - 150)$		$65.625 - 150$
row 3	-250		65.625

step 8: From Eq. 57.32, the characteristic equation for column 1 is

row 1 + row 2 = row 3

$$150 \text{ rpm} + \left(\frac{51.8823}{N_C} \right)(65.625 \text{ rpm} - 150 \text{ rpm})$$

$$= -250 \text{ rpm}$$

$$N_C = \boxed{10.94 \quad (11 \text{ teeth})}$$

8. *Customary U.S. Solution*

The angular velocity is

$$\omega = 2\pi n_{\text{rps}} = \frac{(2\pi)\left(120 \dfrac{\text{rev}}{\text{min}}\right)}{60 \dfrac{\text{sec}}{\text{min}}} = 12.57 \text{ rad/sec}$$

(b) The time to turn 60° is

$$t = \frac{\theta}{\omega} = \frac{(60°)\left(\dfrac{\pi \text{ rad}}{180°}\right)}{12.57 \dfrac{\text{rad}}{\text{sec}}} = 0.08331 \text{ sec}$$

The constant acceleration during the first 60° is

$$a = \frac{2x}{t^2} = \frac{(2)(0.5 \text{ in})}{(0.08331 \text{ sec})^2} = \boxed{144.08 \text{ in/sec}^2}$$

(c) The velocity during the first 60° is

$$\mathrm{v} = at = \left(144.08 \frac{\text{in}}{\text{sec}^2}\right)(0.08331 \text{ sec})$$

$$= 12.0 \text{ in/sec}$$

The time between $\theta = 60°$ and $\theta = 150°$ is

$$\Delta t = \frac{\Delta \theta}{\omega} = \frac{(150° - 60°)\left(\dfrac{\pi \text{ rad}}{180°}\right)}{12.57 \dfrac{\text{rad}}{\text{sec}}} = 0.1250 \text{ sec}$$

Since the cam follower returns to rest at $\theta = 150°$, its velocity is zero there. The constant deceleration during the last 90° is

$$a = \frac{\Delta \mathrm{v}}{\Delta t} = \frac{0 \dfrac{\text{in}}{\text{sec}} - 12.0 \dfrac{\text{in}}{\text{sec}}}{0.1250 \text{ sec}} = \boxed{-96 \text{ in/sec}^2}$$

(a) The distance moved by the cam follower from $\theta = 60°$ to $\theta = 150°$ is

$$x = \tfrac{1}{2}at^2 = \left(\tfrac{1}{2}\right)\left(95.92 \frac{\text{in}}{\text{sec}^2}\right)(0.1250 \text{ sec})^2$$

$$= 0.75 \text{ in}$$

The total follower movement for 150° of rotation is

$$x_{\text{total}} = 0.50 \text{ in} + 0.75 \text{ in} = \boxed{1.25 \text{ in}}$$

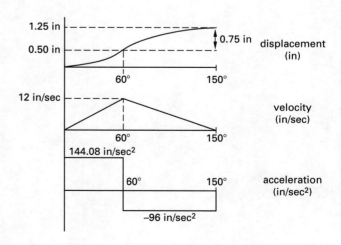

SI Solution

The angular velocity is

$$\omega = 2\pi n_{\text{rps}} = \frac{(2\pi)\left(120 \ \dfrac{\text{rev}}{\text{min}}\right)}{60 \ \dfrac{\text{s}}{\text{min}}} = 12.57 \ \text{rad/s}$$

(b) The time it takes to turn 60° is

$$t = \frac{\theta}{\omega} = \frac{(60°)\left(\dfrac{\pi \ \text{rad}}{180°}\right)}{12.57 \ \dfrac{\text{rad}}{\text{s}}} = 0.08331 \ \text{s}$$

The constant acceleration during the first 60° is

$$a = \frac{2x}{t^2} = \frac{(2)(0.012 \ \text{m})}{(0.08331 \ \text{s})^2} = \boxed{3.458 \ \text{m/s}^2}$$

(c) The velocity during the first 60° is

$$\text{v} = at = \left(3.458 \ \frac{\text{m}}{\text{s}^2}\right)(0.08331 \ \text{s})$$
$$= 0.288 \ \text{m/s}$$

The time between $\theta = 60°$ and $\theta = 150°$ is

$$\Delta t = \frac{\Delta \theta}{\omega} = \frac{(150° - 60°)\left(\dfrac{\pi \ \text{rad}}{180°}\right)}{12.57 \ \dfrac{\text{rad}}{\text{s}}} = 0.1250 \ \text{s}$$

Since the cam follower returns to rest at $\theta = 150°$, its velocity is zero there. The constant deceleration during the last 90° is

$$a = \frac{\Delta \text{v}}{\Delta t} = \frac{0 \ \dfrac{\text{m}}{\text{s}} - 0.288 \ \dfrac{\text{m}}{\text{s}}}{0.1250 \ \text{s}} = \boxed{-2.30 \ \text{m/s}^2}$$

(a) The distance moved by the cam follower from $\theta = 60°$ to $\theta = 150°$ is

$$x = \tfrac{1}{2}at^2 = \left(\tfrac{1}{2}\right)\left(2.30 \ \frac{\text{m}}{\text{s}^2}\right)(0.1250 \ \text{s})^2\left(1000 \ \frac{\text{mm}}{\text{m}}\right)$$
$$= 18.0 \ \text{mm}$$

The total follower movement for 150° of rotation is

$$x_{\text{total}} = 12.0 \ \text{mm} + 18.0 \ \text{mm} = \boxed{30.0 \ \text{mm}}$$

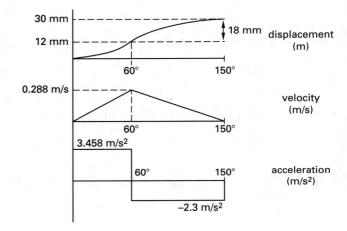

58 Vibrating Systems

1. *Customary U.S. Solution*

The moment of inertia of the circular cross section is

$$I = \frac{\pi r^4}{4} = \frac{\pi \left(\dfrac{2.0 \text{ in}}{2}\right)^4}{4} = 0.7854 \text{ in}^4$$

The deflection due to the 100 lbm disk at the 100 lbm disk is

$$\delta = \frac{F a^2 b^2}{3EIL}$$

$$= \frac{(100 \text{ lbm}) \left(\dfrac{32.2 \dfrac{\text{ft}}{\text{sec}^2}}{32.2 \dfrac{\text{ft-lbm}}{\text{lbf-sec}^2}}\right) (15 \text{ in})^2 (25 \text{ in})^2}{(3) \left(30 \times 10^6 \dfrac{\text{lbf}}{\text{in}^2}\right) (0.7854 \text{ in}^4)(40 \text{ in})}$$

$$= 0.00497 \text{ in}$$

The deflection due to the 100 lbm disk at the 75 lbm disk is

$$\delta = \left(\frac{F b x}{6EIL}\right) (L^2 - b^2 - x^2)$$

$$= \frac{\begin{array}{c}(100 \text{ lbm}) \left(\dfrac{32.2 \dfrac{\text{ft}}{\text{sec}^2}}{32.2 \dfrac{\text{ft-lbm}}{\text{lbf-sec}^2}}\right) (15 \text{ in})(15 \text{ in}) \\ \times \ ((40 \text{ in})^2 - (15 \text{ in})^2 - (15 \text{ in})^2)\end{array}}{(6) \left(30 \times 10^6 \dfrac{\text{lbf}}{\text{in}^2}\right) (0.7854 \text{ in}^4)(40 \text{ in})}$$

$$= 0.00458 \text{ in}$$

The deflection due to the 75 lbm disk at the 75 lbm disk is

$$\delta = \frac{F a^2 b^2}{3EIL}$$

$$= \frac{(75 \text{ lbm}) \left(\dfrac{32.2 \dfrac{\text{ft}}{\text{sec}^2}}{32.2 \dfrac{\text{ft-lbm}}{\text{lbf-sec}^2}}\right) (25 \text{ in})^2 (15 \text{ in})^2}{(3) \left(30 \times 10^6 \dfrac{\text{lbf}}{\text{in}^2}\right) (0.7854 \text{ in}^4)(40 \text{ in})}$$

$$= 0.00373 \text{ in}$$

The deflection due to the 75 lbm disk at the 100 lbm disk is

$$\delta = \left(\frac{F b x}{6EIL}\right) (L^2 - b^2 - x^2)$$

$$= \frac{\begin{array}{c}(75 \text{ lbm}) \left(\dfrac{32.2 \dfrac{\text{ft}}{\text{sec}^2}}{32.2 \dfrac{\text{ft-lbm}}{\text{lbf-sec}^2}}\right) (15 \text{ in})(15 \text{ in}) \\ \times \ ((40 \text{ in})^2 - (15 \text{ in})^2 - (15 \text{ in})^2)\end{array}}{(6) \left(30 \times 10^6 \dfrac{\text{lbf}}{\text{in}^2}\right) (0.7854 \text{ in}^4)(40 \text{ in})}$$

$$= 0.00343 \text{ in}$$

The total deflection at the 100 lbm disk is

$$\delta_{\text{st},1} = 0.00497 \text{ in} + 0.00343 \text{ in} = 0.00840 \text{ in}$$

The total deflection at the 75 lbm disk is

$$\delta_{\text{st},2} = 0.00458 \text{ in} + 0.00373 \text{ in} = 0.00831 \text{ in}$$

Use Eq. 58.60 to find the natural frequency.

$$f = \left(\frac{1}{2\pi}\right) \sqrt{\frac{g \sum m_i \delta_{\text{st},i}}{\sum m_i \delta_{\text{st},i}^2}}$$

$$= \left(\frac{1}{2\pi}\right) \sqrt{\frac{\begin{array}{c}\left(386.4 \dfrac{\text{in}}{\text{sec}^2}\right) ((100 \text{ lbm})(0.00840 \text{ in}) \\ + (75 \text{ lbm})(0.00831 \text{ in}))\end{array}}{\begin{array}{c}(100 \text{ lbm})(0.00840 \text{ in})^2 \\ + (75 \text{ lbm})(0.00831 \text{ in})^2\end{array}}}$$

$$= 34.21 \text{ Hz}$$

The critical speed of the shaft is

$$n = (34.21 \text{ Hz}) \left(60 \ \frac{\text{sec}}{\text{min}}\right)$$

$$= \boxed{2053 \text{ rpm}}$$

SI Solution

The moment of inertia of the circular cross section is

$$I = \frac{\pi r^4}{4} = \frac{\pi \left(\frac{0.05\ \text{m}}{2}\right)^4}{4} = 3.068 \times 10^{-7}\ \text{m}^4$$

The deflection due to the 45 kg disk at the 45 kg disk is

$$\delta = \frac{Fa^2b^2}{3EIL}$$
$$= \frac{(45\ \text{kg})\left(9.81\ \frac{\text{m}}{\text{s}^2}\right)(0.38\ \text{m})^2(0.64\ \text{m})^2}{(3)\,(200 \times 10^9\ \text{Pa})\,(3.068 \times 10^{-7}\ \text{m}^4)(1.02\ \text{m})}$$
$$= 0.000139\ \text{m}$$

The deflection due to the 45 kg disk at the 34 kg disk is

$$\delta = \left(\frac{Fbx}{6EIL}\right)(L^2 - b^2 - x^2)$$
$$= \frac{\begin{array}{c}(45\ \text{kg})\left(9.81\ \frac{\text{m}}{\text{s}^2}\right)(0.38\ \text{m})(0.38\ \text{m}) \\ \times\,\left((1.02\ \text{m})^2 - (0.38\ \text{m})^2 - (0.38\ \text{m})^2\right)\end{array}}{(6)\,(200 \times 10^9\ \text{Pa})\,(3.068 \times 10^{-7}\ \text{m}^4)(1.02\ \text{m})}$$
$$= 0.000128\ \text{m}$$

The deflection due to the 34 kg disk at the 34 kg disk is

$$\delta = \frac{Fa^2b^2}{3EIL}$$
$$= \frac{(34\ \text{kg})\left(9.81\ \frac{\text{m}}{\text{s}^2}\right)(0.64\ \text{m})^2(0.38\ \text{m})^2}{(3)\,(200 \times 10^9\ \text{Pa})\,(3.068 \times 10^{-7}\ \text{m}^4)(1.02\ \text{m})}$$
$$= 0.000105\ \text{m}$$

The deflection due to the 34 kg disk at the 45 kg disk is

$$\delta = \left(\frac{Fbx}{6EIL}\right)(L^2 - b^2 - x^2)$$
$$= \frac{\begin{array}{c}(34\ \text{kg})\left(9.81\ \frac{\text{m}}{\text{s}^2}\right)(0.38\ \text{m})(0.38\ \text{m}) \\ \times\,\left((1.02\ \text{m})^2 - (0.38\ \text{m})^2 - (0.38\ \text{m})^2\right)\end{array}}{(6)\,(200 \times 10^9\ \text{Pa})\,(3.068 \times 10^{-7}\ \text{m}^4)(1.02\ \text{m})}$$
$$= 0.000096\ \text{m}$$

The total deflection at the 45 kg disk is

$$\delta_{\text{st},1} = 0.000139\ \text{m} + 0.000096\ \text{m} = 0.000235\ \text{m}$$

The total deflection at the 34 kg disk is

$$\delta_{\text{st},2} = 0.000128\ \text{m} + 0.000105\ \text{m} = 0.000233\ \text{m}$$

Use Eq. 58.60 to find the natural frequency.

$$f = \left(\frac{1}{2\pi}\right)\sqrt{\frac{g\sum m_i \delta_{\text{st},i}}{\sum m_i \delta_{\text{st},i}^2}}$$
$$= \left(\frac{1}{2\pi}\right)\sqrt{\frac{\begin{array}{c}\left(9.81\ \frac{\text{m}}{\text{s}^2}\right)\big((45\ \text{kg})(0.000235\ \text{m}) \\ +\,(34\ \text{kg})(0.000233\ \text{m})\big)\end{array}}{\begin{array}{c}(45\ \text{kg})(0.000235\ \text{m})^2 \\ +\,(34\ \text{kg})(0.000233\ \text{m})^2\end{array}}}$$
$$= 32.6\ \text{Hz}$$

The critical speed of the shaft is

$$n = (32.6\ \text{Hz})\left(60\ \frac{\text{sec}}{\text{min}}\right)$$
$$= \boxed{1956\ \text{rpm}}$$

2. *Customary U.S. Solution*

The static deflection caused by the electromagnet is

$$\delta_{\text{st}} = \frac{\text{weight}}{k} = \frac{m\left(\frac{g}{g_c}\right)}{k}$$
$$= \left(\frac{300\ \text{lbm}}{1000\ \frac{\text{lbf}}{\text{in}}}\right)\left(\frac{32.2\ \frac{\text{ft}}{\text{sec}^2}}{32.2\ \frac{\text{ft-lbm}}{\text{lbf-sec}^2}}\right)$$
$$= 0.3\ \text{in}$$

(a) From Eqs. 58.4 and 58.7, the natural frequency is

$$f = \frac{\omega}{2\pi} = \left(\frac{1}{2\pi}\right)\sqrt{\frac{g}{\delta_{\text{st}}}} = \left(\frac{1}{2\pi}\right)\sqrt{\frac{386.4\ \frac{\text{in}}{\text{sec}^2}}{0.3\ \text{in}}}$$
$$= \boxed{5.71\ \text{Hz}}$$

(b) The minimum tension occurs at the upper limit of travel. The decrease in tension at that point is the same as the increase in tension at the lower limit caused by the scrap.

$$F_{\text{min}} = (300\ \text{lbm} - 200\ \text{lbm})\left(\frac{32.2\ \frac{\text{ft}}{\text{sec}^2}}{32.2\ \frac{\text{ft-lbm}}{\text{lbf-sec}^2}}\right)$$
$$= \boxed{100\ \text{lbf}}$$

SI Solution

The static deflection caused by the electromagnet is

$$\delta_{st} = \frac{mg}{k} = \frac{(140 \text{ kg})\left(9.81 \frac{m}{s^2}\right)}{\left(175 \frac{kN}{m}\right)\left(1000 \frac{N}{kN}\right)}$$

$$= 0.00785 \text{ m}$$

(a) From Eqs. 58.4 and 58.7, the natural frequency is

$$f = \frac{\omega}{2\pi} = \left(\frac{1}{2\pi}\right)\sqrt{\frac{g}{\delta_{st}}} = \left(\frac{1}{2\pi}\right)\sqrt{\frac{9.81 \frac{m}{s^2}}{0.00785 \text{ m}}}$$

$$= \boxed{5.63 \text{ Hz}}$$

(b) The minimum tension occurs at the upper limit of travel. The decrease in tension at that point is the same as the increase in tension at the lower limit caused by the scrap.

$$F_{min} = (140 \text{ kg} - 90 \text{ kg})\left(9.81 \frac{m}{s^2}\right) = \boxed{490.5 \text{ N}}$$

3. *Customary U.S. Solution*

The transmissibility is

$$\text{TR} = \frac{|F_{transmitted}|}{F_{applied}} = \frac{3 \text{ lbf}}{25 \text{ lbf}} = 0.12$$

The forcing frequency is

$$\omega_f = \frac{\left(1200 \frac{rev}{min}\right)\left(2\pi \frac{rad}{rev}\right)}{60 \frac{sec}{min}} = 125.7 \text{ rad/sec}$$

For negligible damping, Eqs. 58.55 and 58.56 can be simplified.

$$\text{TR} = \frac{1}{|1 - r^2|} = \frac{1}{\left|1 - \left(\frac{\omega_f}{\omega}\right)^2\right|}$$

$$= \frac{1}{\left(\frac{\omega_f}{\omega}\right)^2 - 1} \quad [\text{for } \omega_f > \omega]$$

$$\frac{\omega_f}{\omega} = \sqrt{\frac{1}{\text{TR}} - 1} = \sqrt{\frac{1}{0.12} - 1} = 2.708$$

The required natural frequency is

$$\omega = \frac{\omega_f}{2.71} = \frac{125.7 \frac{rad}{sec}}{2.708} = 46.42 \text{ rad/sec}$$

From Eq. 58.3, the equivalent stiffness of the springs is

$$k = \frac{m\omega^2}{g_c} = \frac{(800 \text{ lbm})\left(46.42 \frac{rad}{sec}\right)^2}{32.2 \frac{ft\text{-}lbm}{lbf\text{-}sec^2}}$$

$$= 53,536 \text{ lbf/ft}$$

The pseudo-static deflection is

$$\frac{F_0}{k} = \frac{3 \text{ lbf}}{53,536 \frac{lbf}{ft}} = 5.60 \times 10^{-5} \text{ ft}$$

From Eq. 58.50, the magnification factor is

$$\beta = \frac{D}{\frac{F_0}{k}} = \left|\frac{1}{1 - \left(\frac{\omega_f}{\omega}\right)^2}\right| = \text{TR} = 0.12$$

The new maximum oscillation is

$$D = \left(\frac{F_0}{k}\right)\beta = (5.60 \times 10^{-5} \text{ ft})\left(12 \frac{in}{ft}\right)(0.12)$$

$$= \boxed{8.06 \times 10^{-5} \text{ in}}$$

SI Solution

The transmissibility is

$$\text{TR} = \frac{|F_{transmitted}|}{F_{applied}} = \frac{13 \text{ N}}{110 \text{ N}} = 0.118$$

The forcing frequency is

$$\omega_f = \frac{\left(1200 \frac{rev}{min}\right)\left(2\pi \frac{rad}{rev}\right)}{60 \frac{s}{min}} = 125.7 \text{ rad/s}$$

For negligible damping, Eqs. 58.55 and 58.56 can be simplified.

$$\text{TR} = \frac{1}{|1 - r^2|} = \frac{1}{\left|1 - \left(\frac{\omega_f}{\omega}\right)^2\right|}$$

$$= \frac{1}{\left(\frac{\omega_f}{\omega}\right)^2 - 1} \quad [\text{for } \omega_f > \omega]$$

$$\frac{\omega_f}{\omega} = \sqrt{\frac{1}{\text{TR}} - 1} = \sqrt{\frac{1}{0.118} - 1} = 2.734$$

The required natural frequency is

$$\omega = \frac{\omega_f}{2.73} = \frac{125.7 \frac{rad}{s}}{2.734} = 45.98 \text{ rad/s}$$

From Eq. 58.3, the equivalent stiffness of the springs is

$$k = m\omega^2 = (300 \text{ kg})\left(45.98 \frac{\text{rad}}{\text{s}}\right)^2$$
$$= 634\,248 \text{ N/m}$$

The pseudo-static deflection is

$$\frac{F_0}{k} = \frac{13 \text{ N}}{634\,428 \frac{\text{N}}{\text{m}}} = 2.05 \times 10^{-5} \text{ m}$$

From Eq. 58.50, the magnification factor is

$$\beta = \frac{D}{\frac{F_0}{k}} = \left| \frac{1}{1 - \left(\frac{\omega_f}{\omega}\right)^2} \right| = \text{TR} = 0.118$$

The new maximum oscillation is

$$D = \left(\frac{F_0}{k}\right)\beta = (2.05 \times 10^{-5} \text{ m})(0.118)$$
$$= \boxed{2.42 \times 10^{-6} \text{ m}}$$

4. *Customary U.S. Solution*

First, consider static equilibrium. The bar mass is considered concentrated at 12 in from the hinge.

$$\sum M_{\text{A}} = 0$$

$$(3 \text{ lbm})\left(\frac{32.2 \frac{\text{ft}}{\text{sec}^2}}{32.2 \frac{\text{ft-lbm}}{\text{lbf-sec}^2}}\right)(24 \text{ in})$$

$$+ (5 \text{ lbm})\left(\frac{32.2 \frac{\text{ft}}{\text{sec}^2}}{32.2 \frac{\text{ft-lbm}}{\text{lbf-sec}^2}}\right)(12 \text{ in}) - M_{\text{spring}}$$

$$= 0$$

$$M_{\text{spring}} = 132 \text{ in-lbf}$$

The angle of rotation is

$$\theta = \frac{\delta}{L} = \frac{0.55 \text{ in}}{16 \text{ in}} = 0.0344 \text{ rad}$$

The equivalent torsional spring constant is

$$k_r = \frac{M_{\text{spring}}}{\theta} = \frac{132 \text{ in-lbf}}{0.0344 \text{ rad}} = 3837 \text{ in-lbf}$$

The mass moment of inertia of the bar is

$$I_{\text{bar}} = \tfrac{1}{3}mL^2$$
$$= \left(\tfrac{1}{3}\right)(5 \text{ lbm})(24 \text{ in})^2$$
$$= 960 \text{ lbm-in}^2$$

The mass moment of inertia of the concentrated mass is

$$I_{\text{mass}} = mL^2 = (3 \text{ lbm})(24 \text{ in})^2 = 1728 \text{ lbm-in}^2$$

The total mass moment of inertia of the system is

$$I = I_{\text{bar}} + I_{\text{mass}} = 960 \text{ lbm-in}^2 + 1728 \text{ lbm-in}^2$$
$$= 2688 \text{ lbm-in}^2$$

From Eq. 58.22, the natural frequency is

$$\omega = \sqrt{\frac{k_r g_c}{I}} = \sqrt{\frac{(3837 \text{ in-lbf})\left(386.4 \frac{\text{lbm-in}}{\text{lbf-sec}^2}\right)}{2688 \text{ lbm-in}^2}}$$
$$= 23.49 \text{ rad/sec}$$

From Eq. 58.4,

$$f = \frac{\omega}{2\pi} = \frac{23.49 \frac{\text{rad}}{\text{sec}}}{2\pi \frac{\text{rad}}{\text{rev}}} = \boxed{3.74 \text{ Hz}}$$

SI Solution

First, consider static equilibrium. The bar mass is considered concentrated at 0.30 m from the hinge.

$$\sum M_{\text{A}} = 0$$

$$(1.4 \text{ kg})\left(9.81 \frac{\text{m}}{\text{s}^2}\right)(0.6 \text{ m})$$

$$+ (2.3 \text{ kg})\left(9.81 \frac{\text{m}}{\text{s}^2}\right)(0.3 \text{ m}) - M_{\text{spring}} = 0$$

$$M_{\text{spring}} = 15.01 \text{ N·m}$$

The angle of rotation is

$$\theta = \frac{\delta}{L} = \frac{0.014 \text{ m}}{0.40 \text{ m}} = 0.035 \text{ rad}$$

The equivalent torsional spring constant is

$$k_r = \frac{M_{\text{spring}}}{\theta} = \frac{15.01 \text{ N·m}}{0.035 \text{ rad}} = 428.9 \text{ N·m}$$

The mass moment of inertia of the bar is

$$I_{\text{bar}} = \frac{1}{3}mL^2$$
$$= \left(\frac{1}{3}\right)(2.3 \text{ kg})(0.60 \text{ m})^2$$
$$= 0.276 \text{ kg}\cdot\text{m}^2$$

The mass moment of inertia of the concentrated mass is

$$I_{\text{mass}} = mL^2 = (1.4 \text{ kg})(0.60 \text{ m})^2 = 0.504 \text{ kg}\cdot\text{m}^2$$

The total mass moment of inertia of the system is

$$I = I_{\text{bar}} + I_{\text{mass}} = 0.276 \text{ kg}\cdot\text{m}^2 + 0.504 \text{ kg}\cdot\text{m}^2$$
$$= 0.78 \text{ kg}\cdot\text{m}^2$$

From Eq. 58.22, the natural frequency is

$$\omega = \sqrt{\frac{k_r}{I}} = \sqrt{\frac{428.9 \text{ N}\cdot\text{m}}{0.78 \text{ kg}\cdot\text{m}^2}} = 23.45 \text{ rad/s}$$

From Eq. 58.4,

$$f = \frac{\omega}{2\pi} = \frac{23.45 \dfrac{\text{rad}}{\text{s}}}{2\pi \dfrac{\text{rad}}{\text{rev}}} = \boxed{3.73 \text{ Hz}}$$

5. *Customary U.S. Solution*

The static deflection is

$$\delta_{\text{st}} = \frac{\text{weight}}{k} = \frac{m\left(\dfrac{g}{g_c}\right)}{k}$$

$$k = \frac{m\left(\dfrac{g}{g_c}\right)}{\delta_{\text{st}}}$$

$$= \left(\frac{8 \text{ lbm}}{5.9 \text{ in}}\right)\left(\frac{32.2 \dfrac{\text{ft}}{\text{sec}^2}}{32.2 \dfrac{\text{ft-lbm}}{\text{lbf-sec}^2}}\right)$$

$$= 1.356 \text{ lbf/in}$$

(a) From Eqs. 58.3 and 58.7, the natural frequency is

$$\omega = \sqrt{\frac{kg_c}{m}} = \sqrt{\frac{g}{\delta_{\text{st}}}} = \sqrt{\frac{386.4 \dfrac{\text{in}}{\text{sec}^2}}{5.9 \text{ in}}}$$

$$= \boxed{8.09 \text{ rad/sec}}$$

(b) The damping ratio is

$$\zeta = \frac{C}{2\sqrt{\dfrac{km}{g_c}}}$$

$$= \frac{0.50 \dfrac{\text{lbf-sec}}{\text{ft}}}{2\sqrt{\begin{array}{c}\left(1.356 \dfrac{\text{lbf}}{\text{in}}\right)\left(12 \dfrac{\text{in}}{\text{ft}}\right)\\ \times (8 \text{ lbm})\left(\dfrac{1}{32.2 \dfrac{\text{ft-lbm}}{\text{lbf-sec}^2}}\right)\end{array}}}$$

$$= \boxed{0.124}$$

(c) The forcing frequency is $\omega_f = 2$ rad/sec.

The pseudo-static deflection is

$$\frac{F_0}{k} = \frac{4 \text{ lbf}}{1.356 \dfrac{\text{lbf}}{\text{in}}}$$

$$= 2.95 \text{ in}$$

The ratio of frequencies is

$$r = \frac{\omega_f}{\omega}$$

$$= \frac{2 \dfrac{\text{rad}}{\text{sec}}}{8.09 \dfrac{\text{rad}}{\text{sec}}}$$

$$= 0.247$$

From Eq. 58.53, the magnification factor is

$$\beta = \frac{D}{\dfrac{F_0}{k}}$$

$$= \left|\frac{1}{\sqrt{(1-r^2)^2 + (2\zeta r)^2}}\right|$$

$$= \left|\frac{1}{\sqrt{\left(1-(0.247)^2\right)^2 + \left((2)(0.124)(0.247)\right)^2}}\right|$$

$$= 1.063$$

The maximum excursion of the system is

$$D = \beta\left(\frac{F_0}{k}\right)$$

$$= (1.063)(2.95 \text{ in})$$

$$= \boxed{3.14 \text{ in}}$$

(d) From Eq. 58.52, the differential equation of motion is

$$\left(\frac{m}{g_c}\right)\left(\frac{d^2x}{dt^2}\right) = -kx - C\left(\frac{dx}{dt}\right) + F(t)$$

$$\left(\frac{8\,\text{lbm}}{32.2\,\dfrac{\text{ft-lbm}}{\text{lbf-sec}^2}}\right)x'' = \frac{-(8\,\text{lbm})\left(\dfrac{32.2\,\dfrac{\text{ft}}{\text{sec}^2}}{32.2\,\dfrac{\text{ft-lbm}}{\text{lbf-sec}^2}}\right)\left(12\,\dfrac{\text{in}}{\text{ft}}\right)x}{5.9\,\text{in}}$$

$$- 0.50\,\frac{\text{lbf-sec}}{\text{ft}}x' + 4\cos 2t$$

$$0.25x'' + 0.50x' + 16.27x = 4\cos 2t$$

$$x'' + 2x' + 65x = 16\cos 2t$$

[coefficients rounded for convenience]

Initial conditions are

$$x_0 = 0$$
$$x_0' = 0$$

There are a variety of methods to solve this differential equation. Use Laplace transforms.

Taking the Laplace transform of both sides,

$$\mathcal{L}(x'') + \mathcal{L}(2x') + \mathcal{L}(65x) = \mathcal{L}(16\cos 2t)$$

$$s^2\mathcal{L}(x) - sx_0 - x_0' + 2s\mathcal{L}(x) - 2x_0 + 65\mathcal{L}(x) = (16)\left(\frac{s}{s^2+4}\right)$$

$$\mathcal{L}(x) = \frac{16s}{(s^2+4)(s^2+2s+65)}$$

Use partial fractions.

$$\mathcal{L}(x) = \frac{16s}{(s^2+4)(s^2+2s+65)}$$
$$= \frac{As+B}{s^2+4} + \frac{Cs+D}{s^2+2s+65}$$
$$16s = As^2 + Bs^2 + 2As^2 + 2Bs + 65As + 65B$$
$$\qquad + Cs^3 + Ds^2 + 4Cs + 4D$$

Then,

$$A + C = 0 \qquad C = -A = -\frac{61}{8}B$$

$$B + 2A + D = 0 \quad B + 2A - \frac{65}{4}B = 0 \rightarrow A = \frac{61}{8}B$$

$$65B + 4D = 0 \qquad D = -\frac{65}{4}B$$

$$2B + 65A + 4C = 16$$

$$2B + (65)\left(\frac{61}{8}B\right) + (4)\left(-\frac{61}{8}B\right) = 16$$

$$B = 0.0342521$$
$$A = 0.2611721$$
$$C = -0.2611721$$
$$D = -0.5565962$$

$$\mathcal{L}(x) = \frac{0.2611721s + 0.0342521}{s^2+4} - \frac{0.2611721s + 0.5566}{(s+1)^2+(8)^2}$$

$$= (0.26)\left(\frac{s}{s^2+(2)^2}\right) + (0.017)\left(\frac{2}{s^2+(2)^2}\right)$$

$$- (0.26)\left(\frac{s-(-1)}{\left(s-(-1)\right)^2+(8)^2} + \frac{1.1311472}{\left(s-(-1)\right)^2+(8)^2}\right)$$

Take the inverse transform. The response is

$$\boxed{\begin{aligned}x(t) &= 0.26\cos 2t + 0.017\sin 2t\\ &\quad - (0.26)(e^{-t}\cos 8t + 0.14e^{-t}\sin 8t)\end{aligned}}$$

Compare the values here with those obtained previously.

$$D = (0.26\,\text{ft})\left(12\,\frac{\text{in}}{\text{ft}}\right) = 3.12\,\text{in}$$

This checks with part (c).

The natural frequency is 8 rad/sec, which corresponds to ω from part (a). (The coefficient of 0.25 in the differential equation was rounded from 0.248, which accounts for the difference.)

SI Solution

The static deflection is

$$\delta_{\text{st}} = \frac{\text{weight}}{k} = \frac{mg}{k}$$

$$k = \frac{mg}{\delta_{\text{st}}} = \frac{(3.6\,\text{kg})\left(9.81\,\dfrac{\text{m}}{\text{s}^2}\right)}{0.15\,\text{m}} = 235.4\,\text{N/m}$$

(a) From Eqs. 58.3 and 58.7, the natural frequency is

$$\omega = \sqrt{\frac{k}{m}} = \sqrt{\frac{g}{\delta_{\text{st}}}} = \sqrt{\frac{9.81\,\dfrac{\text{m}}{\text{s}^2}}{0.15\,\text{m}}}$$

$$= \boxed{8.09\,\text{rad/s}}$$

(b) The damping ratio is

$$\zeta = \frac{C}{2\sqrt{km}} = \frac{7.3\,\dfrac{\text{N·s}}{\text{m}}}{2\sqrt{\left(235.4\,\dfrac{\text{N}}{\text{m}}\right)(3.6\,\text{kg})}} = \boxed{0.125}$$

(c) The forcing frequency is $\omega_f = 2$ rad/s.

The pseudo-static deflection is

$$\frac{F_0}{k} = \frac{18 \text{ N}}{235.4 \frac{\text{N}}{\text{m}}} = 0.0765 \text{ m}$$

The ratio of frequencies is

$$r = \frac{\omega_f}{\omega} = \frac{2 \frac{\text{rad}}{\text{s}}}{8.09 \frac{\text{rad}}{\text{s}}} = 0.247$$

From Eq. 58.53, the magnification factor is

$$\beta = \frac{D}{\frac{F_0}{k}} = \left| \frac{1}{\sqrt{(1-r^2)^2 + (2\zeta r)^2}} \right|$$

$$= \left| \frac{1}{\sqrt{(1-(0.247)^2)^2 + ((2)(0.125)(0.247))^2}} \right|$$

$$= 1.063$$

The response of the system is

$$D = \beta\left(\frac{F_0}{k}\right) = (1.063)(0.0765 \text{ m}) = \boxed{0.0813 \text{ m}}$$

(d) From Eq. 58.52, the differential equation of motion is

$$m\left(\frac{d^2x}{dt^2}\right) = -kx - C\left(\frac{dx}{dt}\right) + F(t)$$

$$(3.6 \text{ kg})x'' = \left(\frac{(-3.6 \text{ kg})\left(9.81 \frac{\text{m}}{\text{s}^2}\right)}{0.15 \text{ m}}\right)x$$

$$- \left(7.3 \frac{\text{N·m}}{\text{s}}\right)x' + 18\cos 2t$$

$$3.6x'' + 7.3x' + 235.4x = 18\cos 2t$$

$$x'' + 2x' + 65x = 5\cos 2t$$

[coefficients rounded for convenience]

Initial conditions are

$$x_0 = 0$$
$$x_0' = 0$$

There are a variety of methods to solve this differential equation. Use Laplace transforms.

Take the Laplace transform of both sides.

$$\mathcal{L}(x'') + \mathcal{L}(2x') + \mathcal{L}(65x) = \mathcal{L}(5\cos 2t)$$

$$s^2\mathcal{L}(x) - sx_0 - x_0' + 2s\mathcal{L}(x) - 2x_0 + 65\mathcal{L}(x) = (5)\left(\frac{s}{s^2+4}\right)$$

$$\mathcal{L}(x) = \frac{5s}{(s^2+4)(s^2+2s+65)}$$

Use partial fractions.

$$\mathcal{L}(x) = \frac{5s}{(s^2+4)(s^2+2s+65)}$$

$$= \frac{As+B}{s^2+4} + \frac{Cs+D}{s^2+2s+65}$$

$$5s = As^2 + Bs^2 + 2As^2 + 2Bs + 65As + 65B$$
$$+ Cs^3 + Ds^2 + 4Cs + 4D$$

Then,

$$A + C = 0 \qquad C = -A = -\frac{61}{8}B$$

$$B + 2A + D = 0 \quad B + 2A - \frac{65}{4}B = 0 \rightarrow A = \frac{61}{8}B$$

$$65B + 4D = 0 \qquad D = -\frac{65}{4}B$$

$$2B + 65A + 4C = 5$$

$$2B + (65)\left(\frac{61}{8}B\right) + (4)\left(-\frac{61}{8}B\right) = 5$$

$$B = 0.0107$$
$$A = 0.0816$$
$$C = -0.0816$$
$$D = -0.1739$$

$$\mathcal{L}(x) = \frac{0.0816s + 0.0107}{s^2+4} - \frac{0.0816 + 0.1739}{(s+1)^2+(8)^2}$$

$$= (0.0816)\left(\frac{s}{s^2+(2)^2}\right) + (0.00535)\left(\frac{2}{s^2+(2)^2}\right)$$

$$- (0.0816)\left(\frac{s-(-1)}{(s-(-1))^2+(8)^2}\right)$$

$$+ \frac{1.1311}{(s-(-1))^2+(8)^2}$$

Take the inverse transform. The response is

$$\boxed{\begin{array}{l} x(t) = 0.0816\cos 2t + 0.00535\sin 2t \\ \quad -(0.0816)(e^{-t}\cos 8t + 0.14e^{-t}\sin 8t) \end{array}}$$

Compare the values here with those obtained previously.

$$D = 0.0816 \text{ m}$$

This checks with part (c).

The natural frequency is 8 rad/sec, which corresponds to ω from part (a).

6. *Customary U.S. Solution*

The equivalent spring constant is

$$k_{eq} = (4)\left(1000 \ \frac{\text{lbf}}{\text{in}}\right) = 4000 \ \text{lbf/in}$$

From Eq. 58.3, the natural frequency of the system is

$$\omega = \sqrt{\frac{k_{eq}g_c}{m}} = \sqrt{\frac{\left(4000 \ \frac{\text{lbf}}{\text{in}}\right)\left(386.4 \ \frac{\text{in-lbm}}{\text{lbf-sec}^2}\right)}{50 \ \text{lbm}}}$$

$$= 175.8 \ \text{rad/sec}$$

The forcing frequency is

$$\omega_f = \frac{\left(800 \ \frac{\text{rev}}{\text{min}}\right)\left(2\pi \ \frac{\text{rad}}{\text{rev}}\right)}{60 \ \frac{\text{sec}}{\text{min}}} = 83.77 \ \text{rad/sec}$$

The out-of-balance force caused by the rotating eccentric mass is

$$F_0 = \frac{m_0\omega^2 e}{g_c} = \frac{\left(\frac{1 \ \text{oz}}{16 \ \frac{\text{oz}}{\text{lbm}}}\right)\left(83.77 \ \frac{\text{rad}}{\text{sec}}\right)^2(5 \ \text{in})}{386.4 \ \frac{\text{in-lbm}}{\text{lbf-sec}^2}}$$

$$= 5.675 \ \text{lbf}$$

The pseudo-static deflection is

$$\frac{F_0}{k_{eq}} = \frac{5.675 \ \text{lbf}}{4000 \ \frac{\text{lbf}}{\text{in}}} = 0.00142 \ \text{in}$$

The ratio of frequencies is

$$r = \frac{\omega_f}{\omega} = \frac{83.77 \ \frac{\text{rad}}{\text{sec}}}{175.8 \ \frac{\text{rad}}{\text{sec}}} = 0.477$$

From Eq. 58.53, the magnification factor is

$$\beta = \frac{D}{\frac{F_0}{k}} = \left| \frac{1}{\sqrt{(1-r^2)^2 + (2\zeta r)^2}} \right|$$

$$= \left| \frac{1}{\sqrt{\left(1-(0.477)^2\right)^2 + \left((2)(0.125)(0.477)\right)^2}} \right|$$

$$= 1.28$$

The maximum vertical displacement is

$$D = \beta\left(\frac{F_0}{k_{eq}}\right) = (1.28)(0.00142 \ \text{in}) = \boxed{0.00182 \ \text{in}}$$

SI Solution

The equivalent spring constant is

$$k_{eq} = (4)\left(175 \ \frac{\text{kN}}{\text{m}}\right)\left(1000 \ \frac{\text{N}}{\text{kN}}\right) = 700\,000 \ \text{N/m}$$

From Eq. 58.3, the natural frequency of the system is

$$\omega = \sqrt{\frac{k_{eq}}{m}} = \sqrt{\frac{700\,000 \ \frac{\text{N}}{\text{m}}}{23 \ \text{kg}}} = 174.5 \ \text{rad/s}$$

The forcing frequency is

$$\omega_f = \frac{\left(800 \ \frac{\text{rev}}{\text{min}}\right)\left(2\pi \ \frac{\text{rad}}{\text{rev}}\right)}{60 \ \frac{\text{s}}{\text{min}}} = 83.77 \ \text{rad/s}$$

The out-of-balance force caused by the rotating eccentric mass is

$$F_0 = m_0\omega^2 e$$

$$= (30 \ \text{g})\left(\frac{1 \ \text{kg}}{1000 \ \text{g}}\right)\left(83.77 \ \frac{\text{rad}}{\text{s}}\right)^2(0.130 \ \text{m})$$

$$= 27.37 \ \text{N}$$

The pseudo-static deflection is

$$\frac{F_0}{k_{eq}} = \frac{27.37 \ \text{N}}{700\,000 \ \frac{\text{N}}{\text{m}}} = 3.91 \times 10^{-5} \ \text{m}$$

The ratio of frequencies is

$$r = \frac{\omega_f}{\omega} = \frac{83.77 \ \frac{\text{rad}}{\text{s}}}{174.5 \ \frac{\text{rad}}{\text{s}}} = 0.48$$

From Eq. 58.53, the magnification factor is

$$\beta = \frac{D}{\frac{F_0}{k}} = \left| \frac{1}{\sqrt{(1-r^2)^2 + (2\zeta r)^2}} \right|$$

$$= \left| \frac{1}{\sqrt{\left(1-(0.48)^2\right)^2 + \left((2)(0.125)(0.48)\right)^2}} \right|$$

$$= 1.28$$

The maximum vertical displacement is

$$D = \beta\left(\frac{F_0}{k_{eq}}\right) = (1.28)(3.91\times10^{-5} \ \text{m}) = \boxed{5.0 \times 10^{-5} \ \text{m}}$$

7. *Customary U.S. Solution*

The forcing frequency is

$$\omega_f = \frac{\left(1200 \frac{\text{rev}}{\text{min}}\right)\left(2\pi \frac{\text{rad}}{\text{rev}}\right)}{60 \frac{\text{sec}}{\text{min}}} = 125.7 \text{ rad/sec}$$

The out-of-balance force caused by the rotating imbalance is

$$F_0 = \frac{m_0\omega^2 e}{g_c} = \frac{(3.6 \text{ lbm})\left(125.7 \frac{\text{rad}}{\text{sec}}\right)^2 (3 \text{ in})}{386.4 \frac{\text{in-lbm}}{\text{lbf-sec}^2}}$$

$$= 441.6 \text{ lbf}$$

The transmissibility is

$$\text{TR} = \frac{|F_{\text{transmitted}}|}{F_{\text{applied}}} = 0.05$$

From Eqs. 58.55 and 58.56, the transmissibility for negligible damping and a value of TR < 1 is

$$\text{TR} = \frac{1}{\left(\frac{\omega_f}{\omega}\right)^2 - 1}$$

$$\frac{\omega_f}{\omega} = \sqrt{\frac{1}{\text{TR}} - 1} = \sqrt{\frac{1}{0.05} - 1} = 4.36$$

The required natural frequency is

$$\omega = \frac{\omega_f}{4.36} = \frac{125.7 \frac{\text{rad}}{\text{sec}}}{4.36} = 28.83 \text{ rad/sec}$$

(a) From Eq. 58.3, the required stiffness of the system is

$$k_{\text{eq}} = \frac{m\omega^2}{g_c} = \frac{(175 \text{ lbm})\left(28.83 \frac{\text{rad}}{\text{sec}}\right)^2}{386.4 \frac{\text{in-lbm}}{\text{lbf-sec}^2}} = 376.4 \text{ lbf/in}$$

For four identical springs in parallel, the required stiffness for an individual spring is

$$k = \frac{k_{\text{eq}}}{4} = \frac{376.4 \frac{\text{lbf}}{\text{in}}}{4} = \boxed{94.1 \text{ lbf/in}}$$

(b) The pseudo-static deflection is

$$\frac{F_0}{k_{\text{eq}}} = \frac{441.6 \text{ lbf}}{376.4 \frac{\text{lbf}}{\text{in}}} = 1.17 \text{ in}$$

From Eq. 58.50, the amplitude of vibration is

$$D = \left(\frac{F_0}{k_{\text{eq}}}\right)\left|\frac{1}{1 - \left(\frac{\omega_f}{\omega}\right)^2}\right| = \left(\frac{F_0}{k_{\text{eq}}}\right)(\text{TR})$$

$$= (1.17 \text{ in})(0.05)$$

$$= \boxed{0.059 \text{ in}}$$

SI Solution

The forcing frequency is

$$\omega_f = \frac{\left(1200 \frac{\text{rev}}{\text{min}}\right)\left(2\pi \frac{\text{rad}}{\text{rev}}\right)}{60 \frac{\text{s}}{\text{min}}} = 125.7 \text{ rad/s}$$

The out-of-balance force caused by the rotating imbalance is

$$F_0 = m_0\omega^2 e = (1.6 \text{ kg})\left(125.7 \frac{\text{rad}}{\text{s}}\right)^2 (0.075 \text{ m})$$

$$= 1896 \text{ N}$$

The transmissibility is

$$\text{TR} = \frac{|F_{\text{transmitted}}|}{F_{\text{applied}}} = 0.05$$

From Eqs. 58.55 and 58.56, the transmissibility for negligible damping and a value of TR < 1 is

$$\text{TR} = \frac{1}{\left(\frac{\omega_f}{\omega}\right)^2 - 1}$$

$$\frac{\omega_f}{\omega} = \sqrt{\frac{1}{\text{TR}} - 1} = \sqrt{\frac{1}{0.05} - 1} = 4.36$$

The required natural frequency is

$$\omega = \frac{\omega_f}{4.36} = \frac{125.7 \frac{\text{rad}}{\text{s}}}{4.36} = 28.83 \text{ rad/s}$$

(a) From Eq. 58.3, the required stiffness of the system is

$$k_{\text{eq}} = m\omega^2 = (80 \text{ kg})\left(28.83 \frac{\text{rad}}{\text{s}}\right)^2 = 66\,494 \text{ N/m}$$

For four identical springs in parallel, the required stiffness for an individual spring is

$$k = \frac{k_{\text{eq}}}{4} = \frac{66\,494 \frac{\text{N}}{\text{m}}}{4} = \boxed{16\,624 \text{ N/m}}$$

(b) The pseudo-static deflection is

$$\frac{F_0}{k_{eq}} = \frac{1896 \text{ N}}{66\,494 \, \dfrac{\text{N}}{\text{m}}} = 0.0285 \text{ m}$$

From Eq. 58.50, the amplitude of vibration is

$$D = \left(\frac{F_0}{k_{eq}}\right)\left|\frac{1}{1 - \left(\dfrac{\omega_f}{\omega}\right)^2}\right| = \left(\frac{F_0}{k_{eq}}\right)(\text{TR})$$

$$= (0.0285 \text{ m})(0.05)$$

$$= \boxed{0.00143 \text{ m}}$$

8. *Customary U.S. Solution*

The first plate under the load is a simple beam with two concentrated forces and may be modeled as in case 8 of App. 49.A.

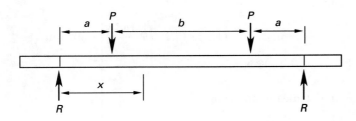

The load P is

$$P = \frac{20,000 \text{ lbf}}{2} = 10,000 \text{ lbf}$$

The locations of P are

$$a = \frac{36 \text{ in} - 24 \text{ in}}{2} = 6 \text{ in}$$

$$b = 24 \text{ in} \quad [\text{given}]$$

The moment of inertia of the cross section of the plate is

$$I = \frac{bh^3}{12} = \frac{(30 \text{ in})(0.5 \text{ in})^3}{12} = 0.3125 \text{ in}^4$$

The overhangs do not contribute to the rigidity of the plate. The length of the beam model is

$$L = 2a + b = (2)(6 \text{ in}) + 24 \text{ in} = 36 \text{ in}$$

(a) The deflection at the load $P(x = a)$ is

$$y = \left(\frac{P}{6EI}\right)(3Lax - 3a^2x - x^3)$$

$$= \left(\frac{Px}{6EI}\right)\left((3a)(L - a) - x^2\right)$$

$$= \frac{(10,000 \text{ lbf})(6 \text{ in})\left((3)(6 \text{ in})(36 \text{ in} - 6 \text{ in}) - (6 \text{ in})^2\right)}{(6)\left(2.9 \times 10^7 \, \dfrac{\text{lbf}}{\text{in}^2}\right)(0.3125 \text{ in}^4)}$$

$$= 0.556 \text{ in}$$

The second plate is loaded exactly the same as the first plate, only upside down. Therefore, its deflection is also 0.556 in at the load. Since plates 3, 5, and 7 are loaded the same as plate 1 and since plates 4, 6, and 8 are loaded the same as plate 2, the total static deflection for the eight plates is

$$y_{\text{total}} = (4)(0.556 \text{ in}) + (4)(0.556 \text{ in})$$

$$= \boxed{4.448 \text{ in}}$$

(b) The maximum moment in the plates is at the load P and is

$$M_{\max} = Pa = (10,000 \text{ lbf})(6 \text{ in}) = 60,000 \text{ in-lbf}$$

The maximum stress in the plates is at the extreme fiber and is

$$\sigma_{\max} = \frac{M_{\max}c}{I}$$

$$= \frac{(60,000 \text{ in-lbf})\left(\dfrac{0.50 \text{ in}}{2}\right)}{0.3125 \text{ in}^4}$$

$$= \boxed{48,000 \text{ lbf/in}^2}$$

(c) From Eqs. 58.4 and 58.7, the natural frequency of oscillation is

$$f = \left(\frac{1}{2\pi}\right)\sqrt{\frac{g}{\delta_{\text{st}}}}$$

$$= \left(\frac{1}{2\pi}\right)\sqrt{\frac{g}{y_{\text{total}}}}$$

$$= \left(\frac{1}{2\pi}\right)\sqrt{\frac{386.4 \, \dfrac{\text{in}}{\text{sec}^2}}{4.448 \text{ in}}}$$

$$= \boxed{1.48 \text{ Hz}}$$

SI Solution

The first plate under the load is a simple beam with two concentrated forces and may be modeled as in case 8 of App. 49.A.

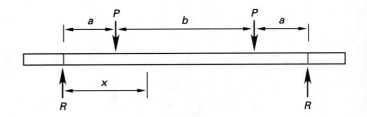

The load P is

$$P = \frac{(9100 \text{ kg}) \left(9.81 \frac{\text{m}}{\text{s}^2}\right)}{2} = 44\,636 \text{ N}$$

The locations of P are

$$a = \frac{0.92 \text{ m} - 0.60 \text{ m}}{2} = 0.16 \text{ m}$$
$$b = 0.60 \text{ m} \quad \text{[given]}$$

The moment of inertia of the cross section of the plate is

$$I = \frac{bh^3}{12} = \frac{(0.76 \text{ m})(0.012 \text{ m})^3}{12} = 1.094 \times 10^{-7} \text{ m}^4$$

The overhangs do not contribute to the rigidity of the plate. The length of the beam model is

$$L = 2a + b = (2)(0.16 \text{ m}) + 0.60 \text{ m} = 0.92 \text{ m}$$

(a) The deflection at the load $P(x = a)$ is

$$y = \left(\frac{P}{6EI}\right)(3Lax - 3a^2x - x^3)$$
$$= \left(\frac{Px}{6EI}\right)\left((3a)(L - a) - x^2\right)$$
$$= \frac{\begin{array}{c}(44\,636 \text{ N})(0.16 \text{ m})\big((3)(0.16 \text{ m}) \\ \times (0.92 \text{ m} - 0.16 \text{ m}) - (0.16 \text{ m})^2\big)\end{array}}{(6)(200 \times 10^9 \text{ Pa})(1.094 \times 10^{-7} \text{ m}^4)}$$
$$= 0.01845 \text{ m}$$

The second plate is loaded exactly the same as the first plate, only upside down. Therefore, its deflection is also 0.01845 m at the load. Since plates 3, 5, and 7 are loaded the same as plate 1 and since plates 4, 6, and 8 are loaded the same as plate 2, the total static deflection for the eight plates is

$$y_{\text{total}} = (4)(0.01845 \text{ m}) + (4)(0.01845 \text{ m}) = \boxed{0.1476 \text{ m}}$$

(b) The maximum moment in the plates is at the load P and is

$$M_{\text{max}} = Pa = (44\,636 \text{ N})(0.16 \text{ m}) = 7142 \text{ N·m}$$

The maximum stress in the plates is at the extreme fiber and is

$$\sigma_{\text{max}} = \frac{M_{\text{max}}c}{I} = \frac{(7142 \text{ N·m})\left(\dfrac{0.012 \text{ m}}{2}\right)}{1.094 \times 10^{-7} \text{ m}^4}$$
$$= 3.92 \times 10^8 \text{ Pa} \quad \boxed{(392 \text{ MPa})}$$

(c) From Eqs. 58.4 and 58.7, the natural frequency of oscillation is

$$f = \left(\frac{1}{2\pi}\right)\sqrt{\frac{g}{\delta_{\text{st}}}} = \left(\frac{1}{2\pi}\right)\sqrt{\frac{g}{y_{\text{total}}}}$$
$$= \left(\frac{1}{2\pi}\right)\sqrt{\frac{9.81 \frac{\text{m}}{\text{s}^2}}{0.1476 \text{ m}}}$$
$$= \boxed{1.30 \text{ Hz}}$$

9. *Customary U.S. Solution*

From the fan rotation,

$$\frac{600 \frac{\text{rev}}{\text{min}}}{60 \frac{\text{sec}}{\text{min}}} = \boxed{10 \text{ Hz}}$$

From the driving blades,

$$\frac{\left(600 \frac{\text{rev}}{\text{min}}\right)(8)}{60 \frac{\text{sec}}{\text{min}}} = \boxed{80 \text{ Hz}}$$

From the fan blades,

$$\frac{\left(600 \frac{\text{rev}}{\text{min}}\right)(64)}{60 \frac{\text{sec}}{\text{min}}} = \boxed{640 \text{ Hz}}$$

From the motor rotation,

$$\frac{1725 \frac{\text{rev}}{\text{min}}}{60 \frac{\text{sec}}{\text{min}}} \approx \boxed{29 \text{ Hz}}$$

From the poles,

$$\frac{\left(1725 \frac{\text{rev}}{\text{min}}\right)(4)}{60 \frac{\text{sec}}{\text{min}}} = \boxed{115 \text{ Hz}}$$

The electrical hum is $\boxed{60 \text{ Hz.}}$

The pulleys are

$$\text{motor pulley (same as motor)} = \boxed{29 \text{ Hz}}$$
$$\text{fan pulley (same as fan)} = \boxed{10 \text{ Hz}}$$

For the belt,

$$\text{belt speed} = \pi D n = \pi(4 \text{ in})\left(\frac{1725 \frac{\text{rev}}{\text{min}}}{60 \frac{\text{sec}}{\text{min}}}\right)$$

$$= 361.3 \text{ in/sec}$$

The frequency is

$$f = \frac{361.3 \frac{\text{in}}{\text{sec}}}{72 \text{ in}} \approx \boxed{5 \text{ Hz}}$$

SI Solution

From the fan rotation,

$$\frac{600 \frac{\text{rev}}{\text{min}}}{60 \frac{\text{sec}}{\text{min}}} = \boxed{10 \text{ Hz}}$$

From the driving blades,

$$\frac{\left(600 \frac{\text{rev}}{\text{min}}\right)(8)}{60 \frac{\text{sec}}{\text{min}}} = \boxed{80 \text{ Hz}}$$

From the fan blades,

$$\frac{\left(600 \frac{\text{rev}}{\text{min}}\right)(64)}{60 \frac{\text{sec}}{\text{min}}} = \boxed{640 \text{ Hz}}$$

From the motor rotation,

$$\frac{1725 \frac{\text{rev}}{\text{min}}}{60 \frac{\text{sec}}{\text{min}}} \approx \boxed{29 \text{ Hz}}$$

From the poles,

$$\frac{\left(1725 \frac{\text{rev}}{\text{min}}\right)(4)}{60 \frac{\text{sec}}{\text{min}}} = \boxed{115 \text{ Hz}}$$

The electrical hum is $\boxed{60 \text{ Hz.}}$

The pulleys are

$$\text{motor pulley (same as motor)} = \boxed{29 \text{ Hz}}$$

$$\text{fan pulley (same as fan)} = \boxed{10 \text{ Hz}}$$

For the belt,

$$\text{belt speed} = \frac{(\pi)(100 \text{ mm})\left(\frac{1725 \frac{\text{rev}}{\text{min}}}{60 \frac{\text{s}}{\text{min}}}\right)}{1000 \frac{\text{mm}}{\text{m}}}$$

$$= \boxed{9.032 \text{ m/s}}$$

The frequency is

$$f = \frac{9.032 \frac{\text{m}}{\text{s}}}{1.83 \text{ m}} = \boxed{4.94 \text{ Hz}}$$

10. *Customary U.S. Solution*

The forcing frequency is

$$f_f = \frac{1725 \frac{\text{rev}}{\text{min}}}{60 \frac{\text{sec}}{\text{min}}} = 28.75 \text{ Hz}$$

The natural frequency is

$$f = \left(\frac{1}{2\pi}\right)\sqrt{\frac{g}{\delta_{\text{st}}}} = \left(\frac{1}{2\pi}\right)\sqrt{\frac{386.4 \frac{\text{in}}{\text{sec}^2}}{0.02 \text{ in}}}$$

$$= 22.12 \text{ Hz}$$

From Eq. 58.56 with negligible damping,

$$\text{TR} = \frac{1}{\sqrt{(1-r^2)^2}} = \frac{1}{\sqrt{\left(1-\left(\frac{f_f}{f}\right)^2\right)^2}}$$

$$= \frac{1}{\sqrt{\left(1-\left(\frac{28.75 \text{ Hz}}{22.12 \text{ Hz}}\right)^2\right)^2}}$$

$$= 1.451$$

$$\boxed{\text{This is a 45.1\% increase in force.}}$$

SI Solution

The forcing frequency is

$$f_f = \frac{1725 \frac{\text{rev}}{\text{min}}}{60 \frac{\text{sec}}{\text{min}}} = 28.75 \text{ Hz}$$

The natural frequency is

$$f = \left(\frac{1}{2\pi}\right)\sqrt{\frac{g}{\delta_{\text{st}}}} = \left(\frac{1}{2\pi}\right)\sqrt{\frac{9.81\,\dfrac{\text{m}}{\text{s}^2}}{(0.5\text{ mm})\left(\dfrac{1\text{ m}}{1000\text{ mm}}\right)}}$$

$$= 22.29\text{ Hz}$$

From Eq. 58.56 with negligible damping,

$$\text{TR} = \frac{1}{\sqrt{(1-r^2)^2}} = \frac{1}{\sqrt{\left(1-\left(\dfrac{f_f}{f}\right)^2\right)^2}}$$

$$= \frac{1}{\sqrt{\left(1-\left(\dfrac{28.75\text{ Hz}}{22.29\text{ Hz}}\right)^2\right)^2}}$$

$$= 1.507$$

This is a 50.7% increase in force.

Dynamics and Vibrations

59 Modeling of Engineering Systems

1. (a) The velocity of the plunger is v_1. The velocity of the body of the damper is the same as the upper part of the spring, v_2. By Rule 59.2, the other end of the force and the spring is attached to the stationary wall at $v = 0$. The system diagram is

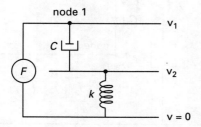

(b) By Rule 59.3, the force from the source is the same force experienced by the dashpot. One of the system equations is based on node 1. Using Rule 59.4 and expanding with Eq. 59.5,

$$F = F_C = C(v_1 - v_2) = C(x'_1 - x'_2)$$

By Rule 59.3, the force from the source is the same force experienced by the spring. A second system equation is based on node 2. Using Rule 59.4 and expanding with Eq. 59.4,

$$F = F_k = k(x_2 - 0) = kx_2$$

2. (a) The velocity of the ends of the springs connected to m_i is v_1. The velocity of the ends of the springs connected to m_2 is v_2. By Rule 59.1, the other end of each mass connects to $v = 0$. The system diagram is

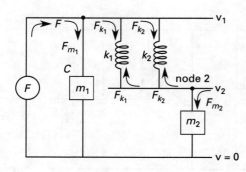

(b) The force leaving the source splits: some of it goes through m_1, some of it goes through k_1, and some of it goes through k_2. One of the system equations is based on node 1.

$$F = F_{m_1} + F_{k_1} + F_{k_2}$$

Using Rule 59.4 and expanding with Eqs. 59.3 and 59.4,

$$\begin{aligned} F &= m_1 a_1 + k_1(x_1 - x_2) + k_2(x_1 - x_2) \\ &= m_1 x''_1 + (k_1 + k_2)(x_1 - x_2) \end{aligned}$$

A second system equation is based on node 2. The conservation law is written to conserve force in the v_2 line.

$$0 = F_{m_2} + F_{k_2} + F_{k_1}$$

Using Rule 59.4 and expanding with Eqs. 59.3 and 59.4,

$$\begin{aligned} 0 &= m_2 a_2 + k_2(x_2 - x_1) + k_1(x_2 - x_1) \\ &= m_2 x''_2 + (k_1 + k_2)(x_2 - x_1) \end{aligned}$$

3. (a) Treat this as a rotational system. The applied rotational torque is

$$T = FL$$

The equivalent torsional spring constant is

$$k_r = \frac{M_{\text{resisting}}}{\theta} = \frac{F_k l}{\theta} = \frac{kx_2 l}{\theta}$$

However, $x_2 = l \sin \theta$ and $\theta \approx \sin \theta$ for small angles.

$$k_r = kl^2$$

The moment of inertia of the beam about the hinge point is

$$I = \tfrac{1}{3}mL^2$$

The equivalent rotational system is

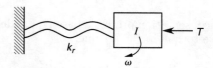

Control Systems

The angular velocity of the end of the spring connected to the inertial element is ω. By Rule 59.2, the other end of the spring is attached to the stationary wall at $\omega = 0$. The system diagram is

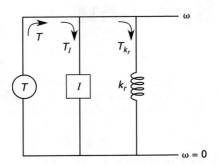

(b) The torque leaving the source splits: some of it goes through I and some of it goes through k_r. The conservation law is written to conserve torque in the ω line.

$$T = T_I + T_{k_r}$$

Using Rule 59.4 and expanding with Eqs. 59.6 and 59.7,

$$T = I\alpha + k_r(\theta - 0)$$
$$FL = \left(\tfrac{1}{3}mL^2\right)\theta'' + kl^2\theta$$

4. (a) The angular velocity of the small gear is ω_m, and the angular velocity of the large gear is ω_f. By Rule 59.2, the other end of each inertia connects to $\omega = 0$. The gearing transforms the torque and angular displacement from gear 1 to gear 2. The system diagram is

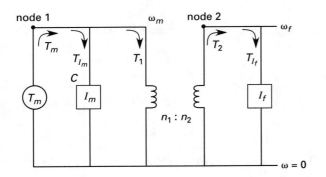

(b) The conservation law based on node 1 is written to conserve torque in the ω_m line.

$$T_m = T_{I_m} + T_1 = I_m\alpha_m + T_1 = I_m\theta''_m + T_1$$

The same conservation principle based on node 2 is used to conserve torque in the ω_f line.

$$T_2 = T_{I_f} = I_f\alpha_f = I_f\theta''_f$$

The transformer equations are

$$T_2 = \left(\frac{n_2}{n_1}\right)T_1$$
$$\theta_m = \left(\frac{n_2}{n_1}\right)\theta_f$$

5. (a) Consider the fluid to act as a damper with coefficient C_r. The plunger is connected to velocity ω_1, and the body is connected to velocity ω_2. By Rule 59.2, the ends of the inertia elements are connected to $\omega = 0$. The system diagram is

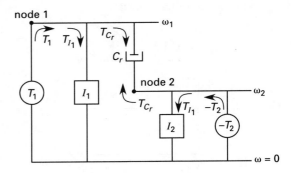

(b) One of the system equations is based on conservation of torque at node 1.

$$T_1 = T_{I_1} + T_{C_r}$$

Using Rule 59.4 and expanding with Eqs. 59.6 and 59.8,

$$T_1 = I_1\alpha_1 + C_r(\omega_1 - \omega_2) = I_1\theta''_1 + C_r(\theta'_1 - \theta'_2)$$

The second system equation is based on conservation of torque at node 2.

$$-T_2 = T_{I_2} + T_{C_r} = I_2\alpha_2 + C_r(\omega_2 - \omega_1)$$
$$= I_2\theta''_2 + C_r(\theta'_2 - \theta'_1)$$

6. (a) The velocity of the end of the spring connected to m_1 is v_1. This is also the velocity of the plunger and the velocity of the viscous damper, C_1. The velocity of the end of the spring connected to m_2 is v_2. This is also the velocity of the body of the damper and the velocity of the viscous damper C_2. By Rule 59.2, the other end of each mass connects to $v = 0$. The system diagram is

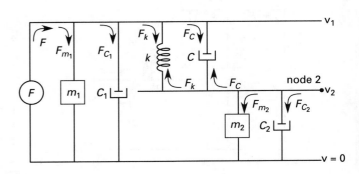

(b) The force leaving the source splits: some of it goes through m_1, C_1, k, and C. The conservation law is written to conserve force in the v_1 line. The equation is based on node 1.

$$F = F_{m_1} + F_{C_1} + F_k + F_C$$

Using Rule 59.4 and expanding with Eqs. 59.3, 59.4, and 59.5,

$$F = m_1 a_1 + C_1(v_1 - 0) + C(v_1 - v_2) + k(x_1 - x_2)$$
$$= m_1 x_1'' + C_1 x_1' + C(x_1' + x_2') + k(x_1 - x_2)$$

The same conservation principle based on node 2 is used to conserve force in the v_2 line. Using Rule 59.4 and expanding with Eqs. 59.3, 59.4, and 59.5,

$$0 = F_{C_2} + F_{m_2} + F_C + F_k$$
$$= C_2(v_2 - 0) + m_2 a_2 + C(v_2 - v_1) + k(x_2 - x_1)$$
$$= C_2 x_2' + m_2 x_2'' + C(x_2' - x_1') + k(x_2 - x_1)$$

7. (a) The fluid capacitance of the water in the tank is C_f. From Rule 59.2, one end of each of the two energy sources Q_1 and Q_2 connects to $p = 0$. The system diagram is

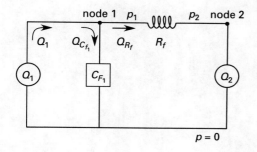

(b) From Eq. 59.10, the flow through the capacitor is

$$Q_{C_{f_1}} = C_{f_1}\left(\frac{dp_1}{dt}\right)$$

From Eq. 59.12, the flow through the resistor is

$$Q_{R_f} = \frac{p_1 - p_2}{R_f}$$

One of the system equations is based on conservation of flow at node 1.

$$Q_1 = Q_{f_1} + Q_{R_f} = C_{f_1}\left(\frac{dp_1}{dt}\right) + \left(\frac{1}{R_f}\right)(p_1 - p_2)$$

The second system equation is based on conservation of flow at node 2.

$$Q_2 = \left(\frac{1}{R_f}\right)(p_1 - p_2)$$

8. (a) The fluid resistance in the entrance pipe is R_f. The pressure at the entrance is p_1, and the pressure in the tank is p_2. The fluid capacitance of the water is C_f. The pressure at the open top of the tank is $p = 0$. The system diagram is

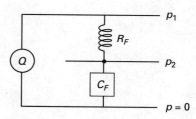

(b) By Rule 59.3, the source flow Q is the same flow through the resistor and the capacitor. Use Eq. 59.12 for the resistor.

$$Q = \frac{p_1 - p_2}{R_f}$$

Use Eq. 59.10 for the capacitor.

$$Q = C_f\left(\frac{dp_2}{dt}\right)$$

60 Analysis of Engineering Systems

1. (a) Draw the first block diagram.

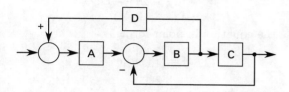

From the rules of simplifying block diagrams, use case 7 to move the extreme right pick-off point to the left of C.

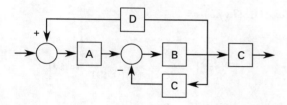

Use case 6 to combine the two summing points on the left.

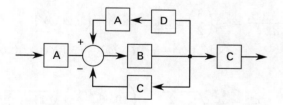

Use case 1 to combine boxes in series in the upper feedback loop.

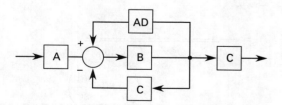

Use case 2 to combine the two feedback loops.

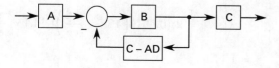

Use case 3 to simplify the remaining feedback loop.

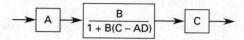

Use case 1 to combine boxes in series to determine the system gain.

$$G_{\text{loop}} = \frac{ABC}{1 + BC - ABD}$$

(b) Draw the second block diagram.

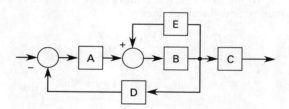

From the rules of simplifying block diagrams, use case 6 to combine the two summing points on the left.

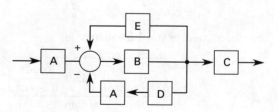

Use case 1 to combine boxes in series in the lower feedback loop.

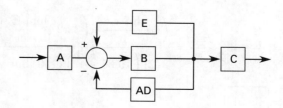

Use case 2 to combine the two feedback loops.

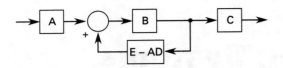

Use case 3 to simplify the remaining feedback loop.

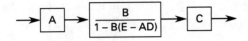

Use case 1 to combine boxes in series to determine the system gain.

$$G_{\text{loop}} = \frac{ABC}{1 - BE + ABD}$$

2. *Customary U.S. Solution*

The system differential equation for a force input f is

$$mx'' + Bx' + kx = f$$

Divide by m to write the equation in terms of natural frequency and damping factor.

$$x'' + \left(\frac{B}{m}\right)x' + \left(\frac{k}{m}\right)x = \frac{f}{m}$$

$$x'' + 2\zeta\omega_n x' + \omega_n^2 x = \frac{f}{\frac{k}{\omega_n^2}} = \omega_n^2\left(\frac{f}{k}\right)$$

Define the forcing function as $h = f/k$.

The equation is the same as Eq. 60.3.

$$x'' + 2\zeta\omega_n x' + \omega_n^2 x = \omega_n^2 h$$

(a) The undamped natural frequency is

$$\omega_n = \sqrt{\frac{kg_c}{m}} = \sqrt{\frac{\left(1200\ \frac{\text{lbf}}{\text{ft}}\right)\left(32.2\ \frac{\text{lbm-ft}}{\text{lbf-sec}^2}\right)}{100\ \text{lbm}}}$$

$$= \boxed{19.66\ \text{rad/sec}}$$

(b) The damping ratio is

$$\zeta = \frac{\frac{B}{m}}{2\omega_n} = \frac{B}{2\omega_n m} = \frac{\left(60\ \frac{\text{lbf-sec}}{\text{ft}}\right)\left(32.2\ \frac{\text{lbm-ft}}{\text{lbf-sec}^2}\right)}{(2)\left(19.66\ \frac{\text{rad}}{\text{sec}}\right)(100\ \text{lbm})}$$

$$= \boxed{0.491}$$

(c) Take the Laplace transform of Eq. 60.3. Consider zero initial conditions.

$$s^2 x(s) + 2\zeta\omega_n s x(s) + \omega_n^2 x(s) = \omega_n^2 H(s)$$

Determine the transfer function.

$$T(s) = \frac{x(s)}{H(s)} = \frac{\omega_n^2}{s^2 + 2\zeta\omega_n s + \omega_n^2}$$

The frequency response is obtained by letting $s = j\omega$.

$$T(j\omega) = \frac{\omega_n^2}{(\omega_n^2 - \omega^2) + j2\zeta\omega_n\omega}$$

Write the equation in polar form.

$$T(j\omega) = |T(j\omega)|e^{j\phi(\omega)}$$

The magnitude is

$$|T(j\omega)| = \frac{\omega_n^2}{\sqrt{(\omega_n^2 - \omega^2)^2 + (2\zeta\omega_n\omega)^2}}$$

At $\omega = 0$, $|T(j\omega)| = 1$.

At $\omega = \omega_n$,

$$|T(j\omega)| = \frac{1}{2\zeta} = \frac{1}{(2)(0.491)} \approx 1.0$$

At $\omega \to \infty$, $|T(j\omega)| \to 0$.

A peak occurs near $\omega = \omega_n$. To obtain the location ω_p, set the derivative of $|T(j\omega)|$ equal to zero.

$$\frac{d|T(j\omega)|}{d\omega} = -\left(\frac{3}{2}\right)\omega_n^2[(\omega_n^2 - \omega^2) + (2\zeta\omega_n\omega)^2]^{-\frac{3}{2}}$$
$$\times [(2)(\omega_n^2 - \omega^2)(-2\omega) + (2)(2\zeta\omega_n\omega)(2\zeta\omega_n)]$$
$$= 0$$

$$\omega_p = \omega_n\sqrt{1 - 2\zeta^2} = \left(19.66\ \frac{\text{rad}}{\text{sec}}\right)\sqrt{1 - (2)(0.491)^2}$$

$$= 14.15\ \text{rad/sec}$$

At $\omega = \omega_p$,

$$|T(j\omega)| = \frac{\omega_n^2}{\sqrt{(\omega_n^2 - \omega_p^2)^2 + (2\zeta\omega_n\omega_p)^2}}$$

$$= \frac{\left(19.66\ \frac{\text{rad}}{\text{sec}}\right)^2}{\sqrt{\left[\left(19.66\ \frac{\text{rad}}{\text{sec}}\right)^2 - \left(14.15\ \frac{\text{rad}}{\text{sec}}\right)^2\right]^2 + \left[(2)(0.491)\left(19.66\ \frac{\text{rad}}{\text{sec}}\right)\left(14.15\ \frac{\text{rad}}{\text{sec}}\right)\right]^2}}$$

$$= 1.17$$

A sketch of the frequency response magnitude is

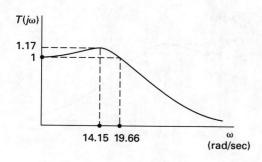

The phase is

$$\phi(\omega) = \tan^{-1}\left(\frac{-2\zeta\omega_n\omega}{\omega_n^2 - \omega^2}\right)$$

At $\omega = 0$, $\phi(\omega) = 0$.

At $\omega = \omega_n$, $\phi(\omega) = -\pi/2$.

At $\omega \to \infty$, $\phi(\omega) = -\pi$.

A sketch of the phase is

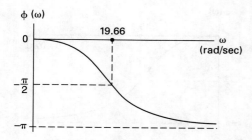

(d) The final value of the step response is obtained from the final value theorem.

$$x_{\text{final}} = \lim_{s \to 0} sx(s) = \lim_{s \to 0} sT(s)H(s)$$

$$= \lim_{s \to 0} sT(s)\left(\frac{1 \text{ ft}}{s}\right) = \left(\frac{\omega_n^2}{\omega_n^2}\right)(1 \text{ ft})$$

$$= 1.0 \text{ ft}$$

From Eq. 60.7, the fraction of overshoot is

$$M_p = \exp\left(\frac{-\pi\zeta}{\sqrt{1-\zeta^2}}\right) = \exp\left(\frac{-\pi(0.491)}{\sqrt{1-(0.491)^2}}\right)$$

$$= 0.17$$

The peak is $x_{\max} = 1.17$ ft.

The damped natural frequency is

$$\omega_d = \omega_n\sqrt{1-\zeta^2} = \left(19.66 \frac{\text{rad}}{\text{sec}}\right)\sqrt{1-(0.491)^2}$$

$$= 17.1 \text{ rad/sec}$$

The peak time from Eq. 60.6 is

$$t_p = \frac{\pi}{\omega_d} = \frac{\pi}{17.1 \dfrac{\text{rad}}{\text{sec}}} = 0.18 \text{ sec}$$

The 5% criterion settling time from Eq. 60.9 is

$$t_s = \frac{3.00}{\zeta\omega_n} = \frac{3.00}{(0.491)\left(19.66 \dfrac{\text{rad}}{\text{sec}}\right)} = 0.31 \text{ sec}$$

The sketch of the response to a unit step input is obtained from Fig. 60.2 and the preceding calculations.

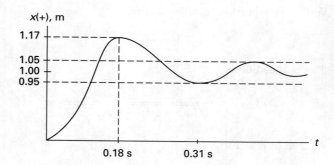

SI Solution

The system differential equation for a force input f is

$$mx'' + Bx' + kx = f$$

Divide by m to write the equation in terms of natural frequency and damping factor.

$$x'' + \left(\frac{B}{m}\right)x' + \left(\frac{k}{m}\right)x = \frac{f}{m}$$

$$x'' + 2\zeta\omega_n x' + \omega_n^2 x = \frac{f}{\dfrac{k}{\omega_n^2}} = \omega_n^2\left(\frac{f}{k}\right)$$

Define the forcing function as $h = f/k$.

The equation is the same as Eq. 60.3.

$$x'' + 2\zeta\omega_n x' + \omega_n^2 x = \omega_n^2 h$$

(a) The undamped natural frequency is

$$\omega_n = \sqrt{\frac{k}{m}} = \sqrt{\frac{17\,500 \dfrac{\text{N}}{\text{m}}}{45 \text{ kg}}} = \boxed{19.7 \text{ rad/s}}$$

(b) The damping ratio is

$$\zeta = \frac{\dfrac{B}{m}}{2\omega_n} = \frac{\dfrac{880 \dfrac{\text{N·s}}{\text{m}}}{45 \text{ kg}}}{(2)\left(19.7 \dfrac{\text{rad}}{\text{s}}\right)} = \boxed{0.50}$$

(c) Take the Laplace transform of Eq. 60.3. Consider zero initial conditions.

$$s^2 x(s) + 2\zeta\omega_n s x(s) + \omega_n^2 x(s) = \omega_n^2 H(s)$$

Determine the transfer function.

$$T(s) = \frac{x(s)}{H(s)} = \frac{\omega_n^2}{s^2 + 2\zeta\omega_n s + \omega_n^2}$$

The frequency response is obtained by letting $s = j\omega$.

$$T(j\omega) = \frac{\omega_n^2}{(\omega_n^2 - \omega^2) + j2\zeta\omega_n\omega}$$

Write the equation in polar form.

$$T(j\omega) = |T(j\omega)|e^{j\phi(\omega)}$$

The magnitude is

$$|T(j\omega)| = \frac{\omega_n^2}{\sqrt{(\omega_n^2 - \omega^2)^2 + (2\zeta\omega_n\omega)^2}}$$

At $\omega = 0$, $|T(j\omega)| = 1$.

At $\omega = \omega_n$,

$$|T(j\omega)| = \frac{1}{2s} = \frac{1}{(2)(0.50)} = 1.0$$

At $\omega \to \infty$, $|T(j\omega)| \to 0$.

A peak occurs near $\omega = \omega_n$. To obtain the location ω_p, set the derivative of $|T(j\omega)|$ equal to zero.

$$\frac{d|T(j\omega)|}{d\omega} = -\left(\frac{3}{2}\right)\omega_n^2[(\omega_n^2 - \omega^2) + (2\zeta\omega_n\omega)^2]^{-\frac{3}{2}}$$
$$\times [(2)(\omega_n^2 - \omega^2)(-2\omega) + (2)(2\zeta\omega_n\omega)2\zeta\omega_n]$$
$$= 0$$

$$\omega_p = \omega_n\sqrt{1 - 2\zeta^2} = \left(19.7\,\frac{\text{rad}}{\text{s}}\right)\sqrt{1 - (2)(0.50)^2}$$
$$= 13.9\text{ rad/s}$$

At $\omega = \omega_p$,

$$|T(j\omega)| = \frac{\omega_n^2}{\sqrt{(\omega_n^2 - \omega_p^2)^2 + (2\zeta\omega_n\omega_p)^2}}$$

$$= \frac{\left(19.7\,\frac{\text{rad}}{\text{s}}\right)^2}{\sqrt{\left[\left(19.7\,\frac{\text{rad}}{\text{s}}\right)^2 - \left(13.9\,\frac{\text{rad}}{\text{s}}\right)^2\right]^2 + \left[(2)(0.50)\left(19.7\,\frac{\text{rad}}{\text{s}}\right)\left(13.9\,\frac{\text{rad}}{\text{s}}\right)\right]^2}}$$

$$= 1.16$$

A sketch of the frequency response magnitude is

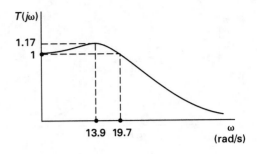

The phase is

$$\phi(\omega) = \tan^{-1}\left(\frac{-2\zeta\omega_n\omega}{\omega_n^2 - \omega^2}\right)$$

At $\omega = 0$, $\phi(\omega) = 0$.

At $\omega = \omega_n$, $\phi(\omega) = -\pi/2$.

At $\omega \to \infty$, $\phi(\omega) = -\pi$.

A sketch of the phase is

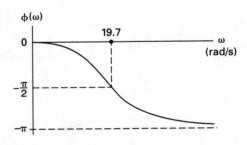

(d) The final value of the step response is obtained from the final value theorem.

$$x_{\text{final}} = \lim_{s\to 0} sx(s) = \lim_{s\to 0} sT(s)H(s)$$
$$= \lim_{s\to 0} sT(s)\left(\frac{1\text{ m}}{s}\right) = \left(\frac{\omega_n^2}{\omega_n^2}\right)(1\text{ m})$$
$$= 1.0\text{ m}$$

From Eq. 60.7, the fraction of overshoot is

$$M_p = \exp\left(\frac{-\pi\zeta}{\sqrt{1 - \zeta^2}}\right) = \exp\left(\frac{-\pi(0.50)}{\sqrt{1 - (0.50)^2}}\right)$$
$$= 0.16$$

The peak is $x_{\text{max}} = 1.16$ m.

The damped natural frequency is

$$\omega_d = \omega_n\sqrt{1 - \zeta^2} = \left(19.7\,\frac{\text{rad}}{\text{s}}\right)\sqrt{1 - (0.50)^2}$$
$$= 17.1\text{ rad/s}$$

The peak time from Eq. 60.6 is

$$t_p = \frac{\pi}{\omega_d} = \frac{\pi}{17.1 \, \frac{\text{rad}}{\text{s}}} = 0.18 \text{ s}$$

The 5% criterion settling time from Eq. 60.9 is

$$t_s = \frac{3.00}{\zeta\omega_n} = \frac{3.00}{(0.50)\left(19.7 \, \frac{\text{rad}}{\text{s}}\right)} = 0.30 \text{ s}$$

The sketch of the response to a unit step input is obtained from Fig. 60.2 and the preceding calculations.

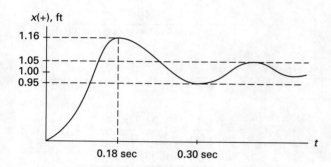

3. First, redraw the system in more traditional form.

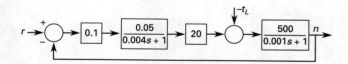

From Fig. 60.5, use case 1 to combine boxes in series.

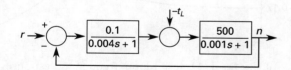

Use case 5 to combine the two summing points.

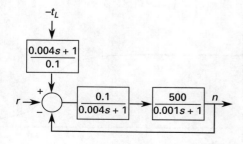

Use case 1 to combine boxes in series.

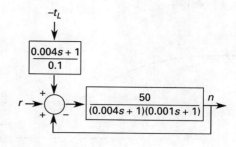

(a) Ignoring the feedback loop, the open-loop transfer function from r to n is

$$T_1(s) = \frac{N(s)}{R(s)}$$
$$= \frac{50}{(0.004s+1)(0.001s+1)}$$

The open-loop transfer function from $-t_L$ to n is

$$T_2(s) = \frac{N(s)}{-T_L(s)}$$
$$= \left(\frac{0.004s+1}{0.1}\right)\left(\frac{50}{(0.004s+1)(0.001s+1)}\right)$$
$$= \frac{500}{0.001s+1}$$

The open-loop frequency response for $T_1(s)$ is

$$T_1(j\omega) = |T_1(j\omega)|e^{j\phi_1(\omega)}$$

From Eq. 60.34, the gain is $20\log|T_1(j\omega)|$ (in dB).

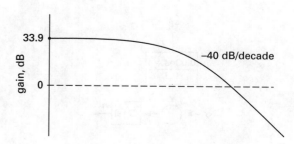

The phase is $\phi_1(\omega)$.

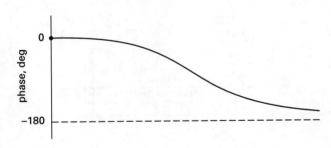

The open-loop frequency response for $T_2(s)$ is

$$T_2(j\omega) = |T_2(j\omega)|e^{j\phi_2(\omega)}$$

From Eq. 63.34, the gain is $20\log|T_2(j\omega)|$ (in dB).

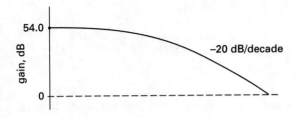

The phase is $\phi_2(\omega)$.

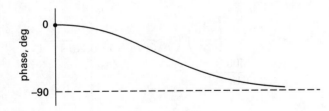

(b) The open-loop steady-state gain for $T_1(s)$ is

$$T_1(0) = \frac{50}{\big((0.004)(0)+1\big)\big((0.001)(0)+1\big)} = \boxed{50}$$

The open-loop steady-state gain for $T_2(s)$ is

$$T_2(0) = \frac{500}{(0.001)(0)+1} = \boxed{500}$$

(c) From Fig. 60.5, use case 3 to simplify the feedback loop.

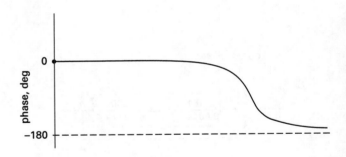

$$G_c(s) = \cfrac{\cfrac{50}{(0.004s+1)(0.001s+1)}}{1 + \cfrac{50}{(0.004s+1)(0.001s+1)}}$$

$$= \frac{50}{(0.004s+1)(0.001s+1)+50}$$

$$= \frac{50}{(4\times10^{-6})s^2 + 0.005s + 51}$$

The closed-loop transfer function from r to n is

$$T_1(s) = \frac{N(s)}{R(s)} = G_c(s)$$

$$= \frac{50}{(4\times10^{-6})s^2 + 0.005s + 51}$$

The closed-loop transfer function from $-t_L$ to n is

$$T_2(s) = \frac{N(s)}{-T_L(s)} = \left(\frac{0.004s+1}{0.1}\right)G_c(s)$$

$$= \frac{(500)(0.004s+1)}{(4\times10^{-6})s^2 + 0.005s + 51}$$

The gain for the closed-loop frequency response of $T_1(s)$ is

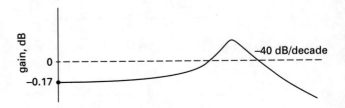

The phase for the closed-loop frequency response of $T_1(s)$ is

The gain for the closed-loop frequency response of $T_2(s)$ is

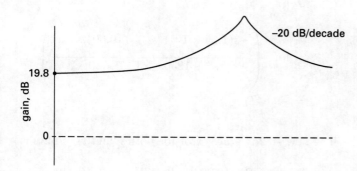

The phase for the closed-loop frequency response of $T_2(s)$ is

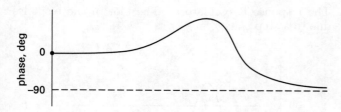

(d) The closed-loop steady-state gain for $T_1(s)$ is

$$T_1(0) = \frac{50}{(4 \times 10^{-6})(0)^2 + (0.005)(0) + 51} = \boxed{0.98}$$

The closed-loop steady-state gain for $T_2(s)$ is

$$T_2(0) = \frac{(500)[(0.004)(0) + 1]}{(4 \times 10^{-6})(0)^2 + (0.005)(0) + 51} = \boxed{9.80}$$

(e) From Fig. 60.4, use Eq. 60.22 to find the system sensitivity.

$$S = \frac{1}{1 + GH} = \frac{1}{1 + \left[\dfrac{50}{(0.004s + 1)(0.001s + 1)}\right]} \quad (1)$$

$$= \frac{(0.004s + 1)(0.001s + 1)}{50 + (0.004s + 1)(0.001s + 1)}$$

$$= \frac{(0.004s + 1)(0.001s + 1)}{(4 \times 10^{-6})s^2 + 0.005s + 51}$$

The frequency response for S is

$$S(j\omega) = |S(j\omega)|e^{j\phi(\omega)}$$

From Eq. 60.34, the gain is $20 \log |S(j\omega)|$ (in dB).

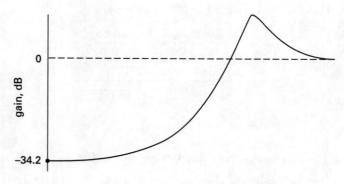

The phase is $\phi(\omega)$.

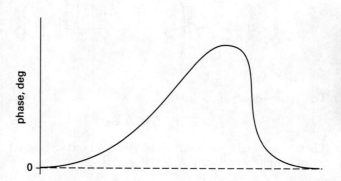

(f) From part (c), the response to a step change in input r is

$$N(s) = R(s)G_c(s)$$

$$= \left(\frac{R}{s}\right)\left(\frac{50}{4 \times 10^{-6}s^2 + 0.005s + 51}\right)$$

$$= \frac{(1.25 \times 10^7)\left(\dfrac{R}{s}\right)}{s^2 + 1250s + 1.275 \times 10^7}$$

Equate the denominator of $N(s)$ to the standard second-order form $s^2 + 2\zeta\omega_n s + \omega_n^2$.

$$\omega_n = \sqrt{1.275 \times 10^7 \, \frac{\text{rad}^2}{\text{sec}^2}} = 3570.7 \text{ rad/sec}$$

Set $2\zeta\omega_n$ equal to 1250 and solve for ζ.

$$\zeta = \frac{1250 \, \dfrac{\text{rad}}{\text{sec}}}{2\omega_n} = \frac{1250 \, \dfrac{\text{rad}}{\text{sec}}}{(2)\left(3570.7 \, \dfrac{\text{rad}}{\text{sec}}\right)} = 0.175$$

Since ζ is less than one, the response is oscillatory.

Use Eq. 60.7 to find the fraction overshoot.

$$M_p = \exp\left(\frac{-\pi\zeta}{\sqrt{1 - \zeta^2}}\right) = \exp\left(\frac{-\pi(0.175)}{\sqrt{1 - (0.175)^2}}\right)$$

$$= 0.57$$

Use Eq. 60.5 to find the 90% rise time.

$$t_r = \frac{\pi - \arccos \zeta}{\omega_d} = \frac{\pi - \arccos \zeta}{\omega_n \sqrt{1 - \zeta^2}}$$

$$= \frac{\pi - \arccos (0.175)}{\left(3570.7 \dfrac{\text{rad}}{\text{sec}}\right) \sqrt{1 - (0.175)^2}}$$

$$= 4.97 \times 10^{-4} \text{ sec}$$

The response is very fast but highly oscillatory.

Use the final value theorem, Eq. 60.27, to find the steady-state value.

$$n = \lim_{s \to 0} sN(s) = \lim_{s \to 0} \left(\frac{s(1.25 \times 10^7)\left(\dfrac{R}{s}\right)}{s^2 + 1250s + 1.275 \times 10^7} \right)$$

$$= 0.98R$$

The steady-state error is

$$e = R - n = R - 0.98R = 0.02R$$

There is a steady-state error proportional to the desired output angular velocity R.

The plot for $n(t)$ is

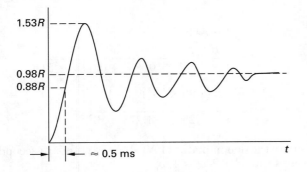

(g) From part (c), the response to a step change in input t_L is

$$N(s) = -T_L(s)\left(\frac{0.004s + 1}{0.1}\right) G_c(s)$$

$$= \left(\frac{-T_L}{s}\right)\left(\frac{(500)(0.004s + 1)}{(4 \times 10^{-6})s^2 + 0.005s + 51}\right)$$

$$= \frac{-(1.25 \times 10^8)\left(\dfrac{T_L}{s}\right)(0.004s + 1)}{s^2 + 1250s + 1.275 \times 10^7}$$

Since the denominator is the same as that for $N(s)$ in part (f), the response to a step change in t_L will be similar to a step change in r. However, the numerator, $0.004s + 1$, will cause the response to deviate from second order. The response will still be oscillatory and very fast.

Use the final value theorem, Eq. 60.27, to find the steady-state error.

$$n = \lim_{s \to 0} sN(s)$$

$$= \lim_{s \to 0} \left(\frac{-s(1.25 \times 10^8)\left(\dfrac{T_L}{s}\right)(0.004s + 1)}{s^2 + 1250s + 1.27 \times 10^7} \right)$$

$$= -9.84T_L$$

The new steady-state error for both r and t_L inputs is

$$e = R - n = R - (0.98R - 9.84T_L) = 0.02R + 9.84T_L$$

Thus the load torque, $-t_L$, contributes to the steady-state error.

The response is oscillatory. The plot of the response due to a step change in $-t_L$ is

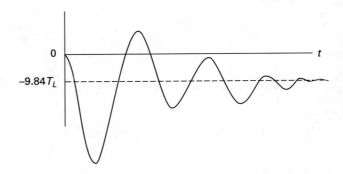

(h) Replace the comparator gain of 0.1 with K. The reduced system is

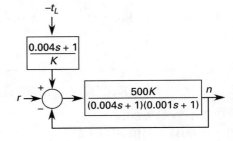

The closed-loop transfer function from r to n is

$$T_1(s) = \frac{N(s)}{R(s)} = \frac{\dfrac{500K}{(0.004s + 1)(0.001s + 1)}}{1 + \dfrac{500K}{(0.004s + 1)(0.001s + 1)}}$$

$$= \frac{500K}{(4 \times 10^{-6})s^2 + 0.005s + 1 + 500K}$$

The Routh-Hurwitz table is

$$\begin{bmatrix} a_0 & a_2 \\ a_1 & a_3 \\ b_1 & b_2 \end{bmatrix} = \begin{bmatrix} 4 \times 10^{-6} & 1 + 500K \\ 0.005 & 0 \\ b_1 & b_2 \end{bmatrix}$$

Use Eq. 60.40.

$$\begin{aligned} b_1 &= \frac{a_1 a_2 - a_0 a_3}{a_1} \\ &= \frac{(0.005)(1 + 500K) - (4 \times 10^{-6})(0)}{0.005} \\ &= 1 + 500K \end{aligned}$$

For a stable system, there can be no sign changes in the first column of the table.

Thus,

$$1 + 500K > 0$$
$$K > -0.002$$

(i) The closed-loop system steady-state response can be improved by adding integral control. This will effectively compensate for any steady-state disturbances due to t_L and will provide a zero steady-state error for a step input for r. This addition has a side effect of reducing the stability margin of the system. However, if properly designed, the system will still be stable.

Control Systems

61 Management Science

1. Assume the following.

$$5 \; \frac{\text{work days}}{\text{week}}; \; 52 \; \frac{\text{weeks}}{\text{year}}$$

$$\left(5 \; \frac{\text{work days}}{\text{week}}\right) \left(52 \; \frac{\text{weeks}}{\text{year}}\right)$$

$$= 260 \; \text{work days/year}$$

Let t equal production time, in minutes/unit, for 1 unit.

Let m equal the minutes/day available for production.

Note:

$$\left(8 \; \frac{\text{hours}}{\text{day}}\right) \left(60 \; \frac{\text{minutes}}{\text{hour}}\right) = 480 \; \text{minutes/day}$$

$$m = 480 \; \frac{\text{minutes}}{\text{day}} - \left(\frac{\text{setup time}}{\text{day}} + \frac{\text{downtime}}{\text{day}}\right.$$

$$\left. + \frac{\text{maintenance time}}{\text{day}} + \frac{\text{recordkeeping time}}{\text{day}}\right)$$

$$\left(900{,}000 \; \frac{\text{units}}{\text{year}}\right) \left(\frac{1 \; \text{year}}{260 \; \text{work days}}\right)$$

$$= 3462 \; \text{units/work day}$$

n = number of machines needed to reach a production rate of 3462 units/day

e = efficiency of each department

$$= \frac{\begin{array}{c}\text{number of units}\\\text{produced in each department}\end{array}}{\begin{array}{c}\text{maximum possible number of units}\\\text{produced in each department}\end{array}}$$

p = percentage of defective units

$\left(\dfrac{m}{t}\right)(1-p)$ = maximum production in each department using one machine

Based on the preceding definitions,

$$n = \frac{3462}{\left(\dfrac{m}{t}\right)(1-p)} + 1 \quad \text{[greatest integer function]}$$

$$e = \frac{3462}{n\left(\dfrac{m}{t}\right)(1-p)}$$

dept	t	m	$\left(\frac{m}{t}\right)(1-p)$	n	e
1	6/60	438	4204	1	89.2%
2	10/60	444	2504	2	74.9%
3	11/60	431	2280	2	82.2%
4	45/60	445	581	6	92.2%

(a) Since each circuit board must go through all four departments, maximum production is 581 units/day.

$$\left(581 \; \frac{\text{units}}{\text{day}}\right) \left(260 \; \frac{\text{work days}}{\text{year}}\right) = \boxed{151{,}060 \; \text{units/year}}$$

(b) The values of n are computed in the chart.

(c) The values of e are computed in the chart.

2. For the time being, disregard the 10 min per hour shift break since this break reduces the capacity of all stations by the same percentage.

Determine the maximum output per hour for each station.

station	output
1	$\dfrac{60 \; \frac{\text{min}}{\text{hr}}}{0.6 \; \frac{\text{min}}{\text{unit}}} = 100 \; \text{units/hr}$
2	$\dfrac{60 \; \frac{\text{min}}{\text{hr}}}{0.6 \; \frac{\text{min}}{\text{unit}}} = 100 \; \text{units/hr}$
3	$\dfrac{60 \; \frac{\text{min}}{\text{hr}}}{0.9 \; \frac{\text{min}}{\text{unit}}} = 66.67 \; \text{units/hr}$
4	$\dfrac{60 \; \frac{\text{min}}{\text{hr}}}{0.8 \; \frac{\text{min}}{\text{unit}}} = 75 \; \text{units/hr}$

Stations 3 and 4 are the bottleneck operations. Intuitively, we would want to help operation 3 the most, followed by helping operation 4.

Start by allocating station 5 capacity to the slowest operation, operation 3. Try to bring station 3 up to the same capacity as stations 1 and 2. To do so requires station 5 to produce $100 - 66.67 = 33.33$ units per hour.

Since station 5 works at the same speed as station 3, the fraction of time station 5 needs to assist station 3 is $33.33/66.67 = 0.5$ (50%). This leaves 50% of station 5's time available to assist other stations.

Next, allocate the remaining station 5 time to station 4. To bring station 4 up to 100 units per hour will require station 5 to produce $100 - 75 = 25$ units per hour. Since station 5 works at the same rate as station 4, the fraction of time station 5 needs to assist station 4 is $25/75 = 0.3333$ (33.33%).

So, we have brought all of the stations up to 100 units per hour. Station 5 still has some remaining capacity: $100\% - 50\% - 33.33\% = 16.67\%$. This remaining capacity needs to be allocated to all of the remaining stations to bring them all up to the same output rate.

Suppose we want to raise the output of the assembly line by 1 unit (i.e., from 100 to 101 units/hr). How much time would this take? It would take 0.6 min for operation 1, 0.6 min for operation 2, 0.9 min for operation 3, and 0.8 min for operation 4. Suppose we want to raise the output by 2 units/hr. That would take 1.2 min for operation 1, 1.2 min for operation 2, 1.8 min for operation 3, and 1.6 min for operation 4. Notice that the ratios of times between stations remain the same. The additional time for operation 2, for example, is always the same as for operation 1.

All of the extra time must come from the remaining capacity of station 5, since all other stations are working at their individual capacities. Station 5 has 17% of its time left, and it must allocate its time in the same fraction (ratio) as the assembly times.

operation	time	fraction of total	ratio × 17%
1	0.6	0.2069	3.52%
2	0.6	0.2069	3.52%
3	0.9	0.3103	5.27%
4	0.8	0.2759	4.69%
totals	2.9	1.0000	17.00%

Therefore, 3.52% of station 5's time will be given to operations 1 and 2. Operation 3 will receive $50\% + 5.27\% = 55.27\%$ of station 5's time. Operation 4 will receive $33.33\% + 4.69\% = 38.02\%$.

The production rates of each of the operations are as follows.

operations 1 and 2:
$$\frac{(1.0352)\left(60\ \dfrac{\text{min}}{\text{hr}}\right)}{0.6\ \dfrac{\text{min}}{\text{unit}}} = 103.5\ \text{units/hr}$$

operation 3:
$$\frac{(1.5527)\left(60\ \dfrac{\text{min}}{\text{hr}}\right)}{0.9\ \dfrac{\text{min}}{\text{unit}}} = 103.5\ \text{units/hr}$$

operation 4:
$$\frac{(1.3802)\left(60\ \dfrac{\text{min}}{\text{hr}}\right)}{0.8\ \dfrac{\text{min}}{\text{unit}}} = 103.5\ \text{units/hr}$$

So, the capacity of the assembly line is 103 units per hour.

(Check: The total time required per product is 2.9 minutes. With all five 5 stations working optimally, the total available time per hour is (5 stations)(60 min/station) = 300 min. The optimal production rate would be (300 min/hr)/(2.9 min/unit) = 103.5 units/hr. This checks.)

However, everybody takes a 10 min break per hour, and the stations only work 50 min per hour. So, the overall capacity is reduced proportionally.

$$\text{capacity} = \left(103.5\ \frac{\text{units}}{\text{hr}}\right)\left(\frac{50\ \text{min}}{60\ \text{min}}\right) = \boxed{86.3\ \text{units/hr}}$$

3. (a) The critical path network diagram is as follows.

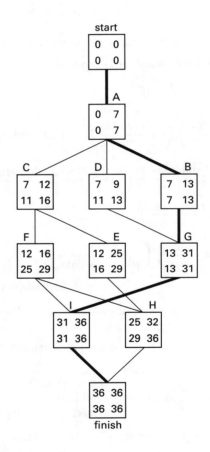

ES (earliest start) Rule: The earliest start time for an activity leaving a particular node is equal to the largest of the earliest finish times for all activities entering the node.

LF (latest finish) Rule: The latest finish time for an activity entering a particular node is equal to the smallest of the latest start times for all activities leaving the node.

The activity is critical if the earliest start equals the latest start.

(b) The critical path is $\boxed{\text{A-B-G-I.}}$

(c) The earliest finish is $\boxed{36.}$

(d) The latest finish is $\boxed{36.}$

(e) The slack along the critical path is $\boxed{0.}$

(f) The float along the critical path is $\boxed{0.}$

4. From Eq. 61.1,

$$\mu = \frac{t_{\text{minimum}} + 4t_{\text{likely}} + t_{\text{maximum}}}{6}$$

From Eq. 61.2,

$$\sigma^2 = \left(\frac{t_{\text{maximum}} - t_{\text{minimum}}}{6}\right)^2$$

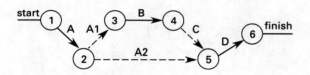

The critical path is A-A1-B-C-D.

The following probability calculations assume that all activities are independent. Use the following theorems for the sum of independent random variables and use the normal distribution for T (project time).

$$\mu_{\text{total}} = t_{\text{A}} + t_{\text{B}} + t_{\text{C}} + t_{\text{D}}$$
$$\sigma^2_{\text{total}} = \sigma^2_{\text{A}} + \sigma^2_{\text{B}} + \sigma^2_{\text{C}} + \sigma^2_{\text{D}}$$

The variance is 10.52778 and the standard deviation is 3.244654.

$$\mu_{\text{total}} = 43.83333$$
$$\sigma^2_{\text{total}} = 10.52778$$
$$\sigma_{\text{total}} = 3.244654$$
$$z = \frac{t - \mu_{\text{total}}}{\sigma} = \left|\frac{42 - 43.83333}{3.244654}\right| = 0.565$$

The probability of finishing for $T \leq 42$ is 0.286037 $\boxed{(28.6\%).}$

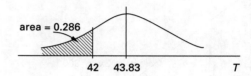

5. This is a two-dimensional linear programming problem.

x_1 = no. of B-1 buses produced
x_2 = no. of B-2 buses produced
Z = total profit

The objective function is

$$\text{maximize } Z = 800{,}000x_1 + 650{,}000x_2$$

The constraints are

$$8x_1 + 10x_2 \leq 2000$$
$$6x_1 + 4x_2 \leq 1800$$
$$3x_1 + 2x_2 \leq 3600$$
$$x_1 \geq 0, x_2 \geq 0$$

PERT Analysis for Prob. 4

no.	name	activity exp. time	variance	earliest start	latest start	earliest finish	latest finish	slack LS-ES
1	A	+2.33333	+0.44444	15	15	+17.3333	+17.3333	0
2	A1	0	0	+17.3333	+17.3333	+17.3333	+17.3333	0
3	A2	0	0	+17.3333	+39.6667	+17.3333	+39.6667	+22.3333
4	B	+10.5000	+4.69444	+17.3333	+17.3333	+27.8333	+27.8333	0
5	C	+11.8333	+4.69444	+27.8333	+27.8333	+39.6667	+39.6667	0
6	D	+4.16667	+0.69444	+39.6667	+39.6667	+43.8333	+43.8333	0

expected completion time = 43.83333

The simplex theory states that the optimal solution will be a feasible corner point.

feasible corner points (x_1, x_2)	Z
$(0,0)$	0
$(0,200)$	$130,000,000$
optimal solution → $(250,0)$	$200,000,000$

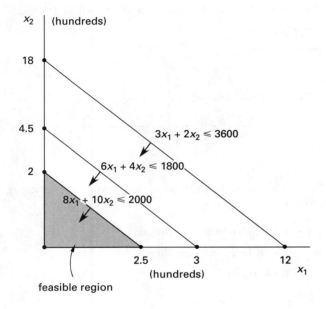

6. x_1 = no. of units of C-1 produced/month
x_2 = no. of units of C-2 produced/month
Z = total profit

The objective function is

$$\text{maximize } Z = 3000x_1 + 5000x_2$$

The constraints are

$$10x_1 + 20x_2 \le 300$$
$$8x_1 + 3x_2 \le 120$$
$$x_1 \ge 0, x_2 \ge 0$$

The simplex theory states that the optimal solution will be a feasible corner point.

feasible corner points (x_1, x_2)	Z
$(0,0)$	0
$(0,15)$	$75,000$
optimal solution → $\left(\dfrac{150}{13}, \dfrac{120}{13}\right)$	$80,769.23$
$(15,0)$	$45,000$

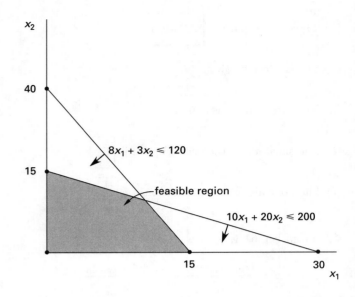

At the intersection point of the two constraints,

$$65x_2 = 600$$
$$x_2 = \frac{600}{65} = 120/13$$

Substituting x_2 into the first constraint yields

$$10x_1 + (20)\left(\frac{120}{13}\right) \le 300$$
$$x_1 = 150/13$$
$$(x_1, x_2) = \left(\frac{150}{13}, \frac{120}{13}\right)$$

(Note: The best integer solution is $(11,9)$; $Z = 78,000$.)

7.   RE = relative earnings
From Eq. 61.70,

$$\text{bonus factor} = \frac{\text{standard bonus}}{\text{participation}}$$
$$\text{productivity} = \frac{\text{standard time}}{\text{actual time}}$$

From Eq. 61.71,

$$\text{RE} = 1 + (\text{productivity})(\text{participation})$$
$$\times (1 + \text{bonus factor}) - (\text{participation})$$
$$\text{bonus factor} = \frac{0.667}{0.500} = 1.334$$
$$\text{productivity} = \frac{0.004 \text{ hour}}{\frac{8}{1900} \text{ hour}} = 0.95$$
$$\text{RE} = 1 + (0.95)(0.50)(1 + 1.334) - 0.5$$
$$= 1.60865 \quad \boxed{(161\%)}$$

63 Manufacturing Processes

1.

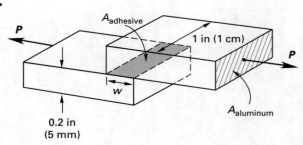

P

A_adhesive

1 in (1 cm)

P

w

A_aluminum

0.2 in
(5 mm)

Customary U.S. Solution

step 1: Assume the unit length ($L = 1$ in) for the joint.

$$A_{\text{adhesive}} = wL = w_{\text{in}}(1 \text{ in}) = w$$
$$A_{\text{aluminum}} = Lt = (1 \text{ in})(0.2 \text{ in}) = 0.2 \text{ in}^2$$

step 2: Find the tensile force P as follows.

The yield strength is

$$P = S_y A_{\text{aluminum}}$$
$$= \left(15{,}000 \ \frac{\text{lbf}}{\text{in}^2}\right)(0.2 \text{ in}^2)$$
$$= 3000 \text{ lbf}$$

step 3: Find the required width, w, with a stress concentration factor of 2.

The shear stress is

$$\tau = \frac{2P}{A_{\text{adhesive}}}$$
$$1500 \ \frac{\text{lbf}}{\text{in}^2} = \frac{(2)(3{,}000 \text{ lbf})}{w}$$
$$w = \boxed{4 \text{ in}}$$

SI Solution

step 1: Assume the unit length ($L = 1$ cm) for the joint.

$$A_{\text{adhesive}} = wL = w_{\text{in}}(0.01 \text{ m}) = 0.01w$$
$$A_{\text{aluminum}} = Lt = (0.01 \text{ m})(0.005 \text{ m})$$
$$= 0.00005 \text{ m}^2$$

step 2: Find the tensile force P as follows.

The yield strength is

$$P = S_y A_{\text{aluminum}}$$
$$= (100 \times 10^6 \text{ Pa})(0.00005 \text{ m}^2)$$
$$= 5000 \text{ N}$$

step 3: Find the required width, w, with a stress concentration factor of 2.

The shear stress is

$$\tau = \frac{2P}{A_{\text{adhesive}}}$$
$$10 \times 10^6 \text{ Pa} = \frac{(2)(5000 \text{ N})}{0.01w}$$
$$w = \boxed{0.1 \text{ m}}$$

68 Illumination and Sound

1. Use Eq. 68.16.

$$L = 10 \log \sum 10^{\frac{W_i}{10}} = 10 \log \left(10^{\frac{40}{10}} + 10^{\frac{35}{10}} \right)$$

$$= \boxed{41.2 \text{ dB}}$$

2. Use Eq. 68.16.

$$L = 10 \log \sum 10^{\frac{W_i}{10}} = 10 \log \left(10^{\frac{43}{10}} + 10^{\frac{W}{10}} \right) = 45 \text{ dB}$$

Solve for the unknown machinery sound pressure level, W.

$$10^{\frac{W}{10}} = 10^{\frac{45}{10}} - 10^{\frac{43}{10}}$$

$$W = 10 \log \left(10^{\frac{45}{10}} - 10^{\frac{43}{10}} \right) = \boxed{40.7 \text{ dB}}$$

3. Define $L_{W,1}$ as the sound pressure level inside the enclosure, and define $L_{W,2}$ as the sound pressure level outside the enclosure. Use Eq. 68.23.

$$L_{W,2} = L_{W,1} - \text{TL} = 110 \text{ dB} - 30 \text{ dB} = 80 \text{ dB}$$

Define $L_{W,1}$ as the sound pressure level for the un-enclosed source, and define $L_{W,2}$ as the sound pressure level for the enclosed source.

Use Eq. 68.22 to solve for the insertion loss.

$$\text{IL} = 100 \text{ dB} - 80 \text{ dB} = \boxed{20 \text{ dB}}$$

4. From Eq. 68.15, the free-field sound pressure is inversely proportional to the square of the distance from the source.

$$\frac{p_2}{p_1} = \left(\frac{r_1}{r_2} \right)^2$$

From Eq. 68.13,

$$L_{p,2} = L_{p,1} + 10 \log \left(\frac{r_1}{r_2} \right)^2$$

$$= L_{p,1} + 20 \log \left(\frac{r_1}{r_2} \right)$$

Customary U.S. Solution

$$L_{p,2} = 92 \text{ dB} + 20 \log \left(\frac{4 \text{ ft}}{12 \text{ ft}} \right)$$

$$= 92 \text{ dB} - 9.5 \text{ dB}$$

$$= \boxed{82.5 \text{ dB}}$$

SI Solution

$$L_{p,2} = 92 \text{ dB} + 20 \log \left(\frac{1.2 \text{ m}}{3.6 \text{ m}} \right)$$

$$= 92 \text{ dB} - 9.5 \text{ dB}$$

$$= \boxed{82.5 \text{ dB}}$$

5. Add the corrections from Table 68.5 to the measurements.

frequency	measurement	correction	corrected value
63	85	−26.2	58.8
125	90	−16.1	73.9
250	92	−8.6	83.4
500	87	−3.2	83.8
1000	82	0	82.0
2000	78	+1.2	79.2
4000	65	+1.0	66.0
8000	54	−1.1	52.9

Use Eq. 68.16.

$$L = 10 \log \sum 10^{\frac{W_i}{10}}$$
$$= 10 \log \left(10^{5.88} + 10^{7.39} + 10^{8.34} + 10^{8.38} + 10^{8.2} \right.$$
$$\left. + 10^{7.92} + 10^{6.6} + 10^{5.29} \right)$$

$$= \boxed{88.6 \text{ dBA}}$$

6. Define A as the total room area.

$$\sum S_1 = 0.50A$$

The maximum number of sabins is equal to the room area.

$$\sum S_2 = A$$

Use Eq. 68.21.

$$\text{NR} = 10\log\left(\frac{\sum S_1}{\sum S_2}\right) = 10\log\left(\frac{0.50A}{A}\right)$$
$$= 10\log(0.50)$$
$$= \boxed{-3.0 \text{ dB} \quad [\text{decrease}]}$$

7. *Customary U.S. Solution*

The surface area of the room walls is

$$A_1 = \big((2)(100 \text{ ft}) + (2)(400 \text{ ft})\big)(20 \text{ ft}) = 20{,}000 \text{ ft}^2$$

The surface area of the room floor and ceiling is

$$A_2 = (2)(100 \text{ ft})(400 \text{ ft}) = 80{,}000 \text{ ft}^2$$

The sound absorption coefficient of precast concrete is the NRC value of 0.02 from App. 68.A.

Define the sound absorption coefficient of precast concrete as α_{concrete}.

The sabin area of the room with all precast concrete is

$$\sum S_2 = \alpha_{\text{concrete}}(A_1 + A_2)$$
$$= (0.02)(20{,}000 \text{ ft}^2 + 80{,}000 \text{ ft}^2)$$
$$= 2000 \text{ ft}^2$$

Define the sound absorption coefficient of the wall acoustical treatment as α_{wall}.

The sabin area of the room with 40% of the walls treated with $\alpha_{\text{wall}} = 0.8$ is

$$\sum S_1 = \alpha_{\text{concrete}}A_2 + \alpha_{\text{concrete}}(0.6A_1) + \alpha_{\text{wall}}(0.4A_1)$$
$$= (0.02)(80{,}000 \text{ ft}^2) + (0.02)(0.6)(20{,}000 \text{ ft}^2)$$
$$\quad + (0.8)(0.4)(20{,}000 \text{ ft}^2)$$
$$= 8240 \text{ ft}^2$$

Use Eq. 68.21.

$$\text{NR} = 10\log\left(\frac{\sum S_1}{\sum S_2}\right)$$
$$= 10\log\left(\frac{8240 \text{ ft}^2}{2000 \text{ ft}^2}\right) = \boxed{6.1 \text{ dB}}$$

SI Solution

The surface area of the room walls is

$$A_1 = \big((2)(30 \text{ m}) + (2)(120 \text{ m})\big)(6 \text{ m}) = 1800 \text{ m}^2$$

The surface area of the room floor and ceiling is

$$A_2 = (2)(30 \text{ m})(120 \text{ m}) = 7200 \text{ m}^2$$

The sound absorption coefficient of precast concrete is the NRC value of 0.02 from App. 68.A.

Define the sound absorption coefficient of precast concrete as α_{concrete}.

The sabin area of the room with all precast concrete is

$$\sum S_2 = \alpha_{\text{concrete}}(A_1 + A_2)$$
$$= (0.02)(1800 \text{ m}^2 + 7200 \text{ m}^2)$$
$$= 180 \text{ m}^2$$

Define the sound absorption coefficient of the wall acoustical treatment as α_{wall}.

The sabin area of the room with 40% of the walls treated with $\alpha_{\text{wall}} = 0.8$ is

$$\sum S_1 = \alpha_{\text{concrete}}A_2 + \alpha_{\text{concrete}}(0.6A_1) + \alpha_{\text{wall}}(0.4A_1)$$
$$= (0.02)(7200 \text{ m}^2) + (0.02)(0.6)(1800 \text{ m}^2)$$
$$\quad + (0.8)(0.4)(1800 \text{ m}^2)$$
$$= 741.6 \text{ m}^2$$

Use Eq. 68.21.

$$\text{NR} = 10\log\left(\frac{\sum S_1}{\sum S_2}\right)$$
$$= 10\log\left(\frac{741.6 \text{ m}^2}{180 \text{ m}^2}\right) = \boxed{6.1 \text{ dB}}$$

8. *Customary U.S. Solution*

The area of the walls is

$$A_1 = \big((2)(20 \text{ ft}) + (2)(50 \text{ ft})\big)(10 \text{ ft}) = 1400 \text{ ft}^2$$

From App. 68.A, the sound absorption coefficient of sheetrock and glass is $\alpha_1 = 0.03$.

The area of the floor is

$$A_2 = (20 \text{ ft})(50 \text{ ft}) = 1000 \text{ ft}^2$$

From App. 68.A, the sound absorption coefficient of roll vinyl is $\alpha_2 = 0.03$.

The area of the ceiling is

$$A_3 = (20 \text{ ft})(50 \text{ ft}) = 1000 \text{ ft}^2$$

The sound absorption coefficient of the sheetrock is $\alpha_3 = 0.03$.

From App. 68.A, the desks have approximately 1.5 sabins each and the occupants have approximately 5.0 sabins each.

The total sabin area of the untreated room is

$$\sum S_2 = \alpha_1 S_1 + \alpha_2 S_2 + \alpha_3 S_3 + \text{desks} + \text{occupants}$$
$$+ \text{miscellaneous}$$
$$= (0.03)(1400 \text{ ft}^2) + (0.03)(1000 \text{ ft}^2)$$
$$+ (0.03)(1000 \text{ ft}^2) + (15)(1.5 \text{ ft}^2)$$
$$+ (15)(5.0 \text{ ft}^2) + 5.0 \text{ ft}^2$$
$$= 204.5 \text{ ft}^2$$

The total sabin area excluding the ceiling is

$$204.5 \text{ ft}^2 - \alpha_3 S_3 = 204.5 \text{ ft}^2 - (0.03)(1000 \text{ ft}^2)$$
$$= 174.5 \text{ ft}^2$$

The total sabin area of the room with the ceiling treated with $\alpha_3 = 0.7$ sound absorption is

$$\sum S_1 = 174.5 \text{ ft}^2 + \alpha_3 S_3$$
$$= 174.5 \text{ ft}^2 + (0.7)(1000 \text{ ft}^2)$$
$$= 874.5 \text{ ft}^2$$

Use Eq. 68.21.

$$\text{NR} = 10 \log \left(\frac{\sum S_1}{\sum S_2} \right)$$
$$= 10 \log \left(\frac{874.5 \text{ ft}^2}{204.5 \text{ ft}^2} \right) = \boxed{6.3 \text{ dB}}$$

SI Solution

The area of the walls is

$$A_1 = ((2)(6 \text{ m}) + (2)(15 \text{ m}))(3 \text{ m}) = 126 \text{ m}^2$$

From App. 68.A, the sound absorption coefficient of sheetrock and glass is $\alpha_1 = 0.03$.

The area of the floor is

$$A_2 = (6 \text{ m})(15 \text{ m}) = 90 \text{ m}^2$$

From App. 68.A, the sound absorption coefficient of roll vinyl is $\alpha_2 = 0.03$.

The area of the ceiling is

$$A_3 = (6 \text{ m})(15 \text{ m}) = 90 \text{ m}^2$$

The sound absorption coefficient of the sheetrock is $\alpha_3 = 0.03$.

From App. 68.A, the desks have approximately 1.5 sabins each and the occupants have approximately 5.0 sabins each.

The total sabin area (m^2) of the untreated room is

$$\sum S_2 = \alpha_1 S_1 + \alpha_2 S_2 + \alpha_3 S_3 + \text{desks} + \text{occupants}$$
$$+ \text{miscellaneous}$$
$$= (0.03)(126 \text{ m}^2) + (0.03)(90 \text{ m}^2)$$
$$+ (0.03)(90 \text{ m}^2) + (15)(1.5 \text{ ft}^2)$$
$$\times \left(\frac{1 \text{ m}}{3.28 \text{ ft}} \right)^2 + (15)(5.0 \text{ ft}^2) \left(\frac{1 \text{ m}}{3.28 \text{ ft}} \right)^2$$
$$+ (5.0 \text{ ft}^2) \left(\frac{1 \text{ m}}{3.28 \text{ ft}} \right)^2$$
$$= 18.7 \text{ m}^2$$

The total sabin area excluding the ceiling is

$$18.7 \text{ m}^2 - \alpha_3 S_3 = 18.7 \text{ m}^2 - (0.03)(90 \text{ m}^2)$$
$$= 16.0 \text{ m}^2$$

The total sabin area of the room with the ceiling treated with $\alpha_3 = 0.7$ sound absorption is

$$\sum S_1 = 16.0 \text{ m}^2 + \alpha_3 S_3$$
$$= 16.0 \text{ m}^2 + (0.7)(90 \text{ m}^2)$$
$$= 79.0 \text{ m}^2$$

Use Eq. 68.21.

$$\text{NR} = 10 \log \left(\frac{\sum S_1}{\sum S_2} \right) = 10 \log \left(\frac{79.0 \text{ m}^2}{18.7 \text{ m}^2} \right) = \boxed{6.3 \text{ dB}}$$

9. *Customary U.S. Solution*

Define the sound absorption coefficients of the floor, ceiling, and walls as α_1, α_2, and α_3, respectively.

The floor area is

$$A_1 = (15 \text{ ft})(20 \text{ ft}) = 300 \text{ ft}^2$$

The ceiling area is

$$A_2 = (15 \text{ ft})(20 \text{ ft}) = 300 \text{ ft}^2$$

Plant Engineering

The area of the walls is

$$A_3 = \big((2)(15\text{ ft}) + (2)(20\text{ ft})\big)(10\text{ ft}) = 700\text{ ft}^2$$

The total surface area of the room is

$$\begin{aligned}A = \sum A_i &= A_1 + A_2 + A_3 \\ &= 300\text{ ft}^2 + 300\text{ ft}^2 + 700\text{ ft}^2 \\ &= 1300\text{ ft}^2\end{aligned}$$

From Eq. 68.18, the average sound absorption coefficient of the room is

$$\begin{aligned}\overline{\alpha} = \frac{\sum S_i}{\sum A_i} &= \frac{\alpha_1 A_1 + \alpha_2 A_2 + \alpha_3 A_3}{A} \\ &= \frac{(0.03)(300\text{ ft}^2) + (0.5)(300\text{ ft}^2) + (0.06)(700\text{ ft}^2)}{1300\text{ ft}^2} \\ &= 0.155\end{aligned}$$

From Eq. 68.19, the room constant is

$$R = \frac{\overline{\alpha}A}{1-\overline{\alpha}} = \frac{(0.155)(1300\text{ ft}^2)}{1-0.155} = 238.5\text{ ft}^2$$

From Eq. 68.15, the sound pressure level due to the machine is

$$\begin{aligned}L_{p,\text{dB}} &= 10.5 + L_W + 10\log\left(\frac{Q}{4\pi r^2} + \frac{4}{R}\right) \\ &= 10.5 + 65 + 10\log\left(\frac{4}{4\pi(5\text{ ft})^2} + \frac{4}{238.5\text{ ft}^2}\right) \\ &= 60.2\text{ dB}\end{aligned}$$

Use Eq. 68.16 to combine the machine sound pressure level with the ambient sound pressure level.

$$L = 10\log\sum 10^{\frac{W_i}{10}} = 10\log\left(10^{\frac{60.2}{10}} + 10^{\frac{50}{10}}\right)$$

$$= \boxed{60.6\text{ dB}}$$

The area of the walls is

$$A_3 = \big((2)(4.5\text{ m}) + (2)(6\text{ m})\big)(3\text{ m}) = 63\text{ m}^2$$

The total surface area of the room is

$$\begin{aligned}A = \sum A_i &= A_1 + A_2 + A_3 \\ &= 27\text{ m}^2 + 27\text{ m}^2 + 63\text{ m}^2 \\ &= 117\text{ m}^2\end{aligned}$$

From Eq. 68.18, the average sound absorption coefficient of the room is

$$\begin{aligned}\overline{\alpha} = \frac{\sum S_i}{\sum A_i} &= \frac{\alpha_1 A_1 + \alpha_2 A_2 + \alpha_3 A_3}{A} \\ &= \frac{(0.03)(27\text{ m}^2) + (0.5)(27\text{ m}^2) + (0.06)(63\text{ m}^2)}{117\text{ m}^2} \\ &= 0.155\end{aligned}$$

From Eq. 68.19, the room constant is

$$R = \frac{\overline{\alpha}A}{1-\overline{\alpha}} = \frac{(0.155)(117\text{ m}^2)}{1-0.155} = 21.5\text{ m}^2$$

From Eq. 68.15, the sound pressure level due to the machine is

$$\begin{aligned}L_{p,\text{dB}} &= L_W + 10\log\left(\frac{Q}{4\pi r^2} + \frac{4}{R}\right) \\ &= 65 + 10\log\left(\frac{4}{4\pi(1.5\text{ m})^2} + \frac{4}{21.5\text{ m}^2}\right) \\ &= 60.2\text{ dB}\end{aligned}$$

Use Eq. 68.16 to combine the machine sound pressure level with the ambient sound pressure level.

$$L = 10\log\sum_{10}^{\frac{W_i}{10}} = 10\log\left(10^{\frac{60.2}{10}} + 10^{\frac{50}{10}}\right) = \boxed{60.6\text{ dB}}$$

SI Solution

Define the sound absorption coefficients of the floor, ceiling, and walls as α_1, α_2, and α_3, respectively.

The floor area is

$$A_1 = (4.5\text{ m})(6\text{ m}) = 27\text{ m}^2$$

The ceiling area is

$$A_2 = (4.5\text{ m})(6\text{ m}) = 27\text{ m}^2$$

69 Engineering Economic Analysis

1.

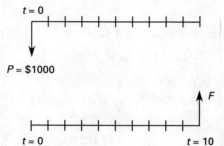

i = 6% a year

By the formula from Table 69.1,

$$F = P(1+i)^n = (\$1000)(1 + 0.06)^{10} = \boxed{\$1790.85}$$

By the factor converting P to F, $(F/P, i, n) = 1.7908$ for $i = 6\%$ a year and $n = 10$ years.

$$F = P(F/P, 6\%, 10) = (\$1000)(1.7908) = \boxed{\$1790.80}$$

2.

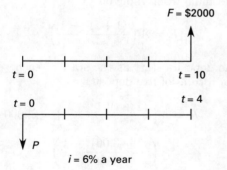

i = 6% a year

By the formula from Table 69.1,

$$P = \frac{F}{(1+i)^n} = \frac{\$2000}{(1+0.06)^4} = \boxed{\$1584.19}$$

From the factor converting F to P, $(P/F, i, n) = 0.7921$ for $i = 6\%$ a year and $n = 4$ years.

$$P = F(P/F, 6\%, 4) = (\$2000)(0.7921) = \boxed{\$1584.20}$$

3.

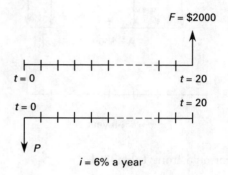

i = 6% a year

By the formula from Table 69.1,

$$P = \frac{F}{(1+i)^n} = \frac{\$2000}{(1+0.06)^{20}} = \boxed{\$623.61}$$

From the factor converting F to P, $(P/F, i, n) = 0.3118$ for $i = 6\%$ a year and $n = 20$ years.

$$P = F(P/F, 6\%, 20) = (\$2000)(0.3118) = \boxed{\$623.60}$$

4.

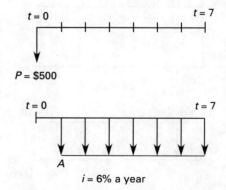

i = 6% a year

By the formula from Table 69.1,

$$A = P\left(\frac{i(1+i)^n}{(1+i)^n - 1}\right) = (\$500)\left(\frac{(0.06)(1+0.06)^7}{(1+0.06)^7 - 1}\right)$$

$$= \boxed{\$89.57}$$

Economics

By the factor converting P to A, $(A/P, i, n) = 0.17914$ for $i = 6\%$ a year and $n = 7$ years.

$$A = P(A/P, 6\%, 7) = (\$500)(0.17914) = \boxed{\$89.57}$$

5.

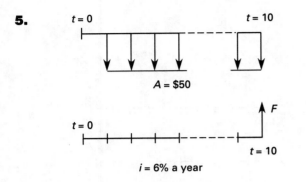

By the formula from Table 69.1,

$$F = A\left(\frac{(1+i)^n - 1}{i}\right) = (\$50)\left(\frac{(1+0.06)^{10} - 1}{0.06}\right)$$

$$= \boxed{\$659.04}$$

By the factor converting A to F, $(F/A, i, n) = 13.181$ for $i = 6\%$ a year and $n = 10$ years.

$$F = A(F/A, 6\%, 10) = (\$50)(13.181) = \boxed{\$659.05}$$

6.

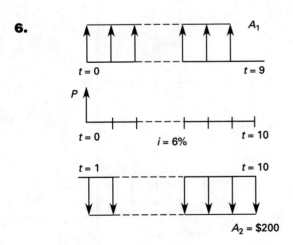

By the formula from Table 69.1, for each cash flow diagram,

$$P = (A_1 + A_1)\left(\frac{(1+0.06)^9 - 1}{(0.06)(1+0.06)^9}\right)$$

$$= (A_2)\left(\frac{(1+0.06)^{10} - 1}{(0.06)(1+0.06)^{10}}\right)$$

Therefore for $A_2 = \$200$,

$$(A_1 + A_1)\left(\frac{(1+0.06)^9 - 1}{(0.06)(1+0.06)^9}\right)$$

$$= (\$200)\left(\frac{(1+0.06)^{10} - 1}{(0.06)(1+0.06)^{10}}\right)$$

$$7.80 A_1 = \$1472.02$$

$$A_1 = \boxed{\$188.72}$$

By the factor converting A to P,

$$(P/A, 6\%, 9) = 6.8017$$
$$(P/A, 6\%, 10) = 7.3601$$
$$(A_1 + A_1)(6.8017) = (\$200)(7.3601)$$
$$7.8017 A_1 = \$1472.02$$
$$A_1 = \frac{\$1472.02}{7.8017} = \boxed{\$188.68}$$

7.

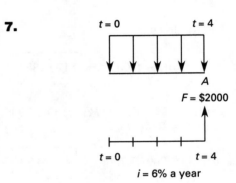

By the formula from Table 69.1,

$$F = A\left(\frac{(1+i)^n - 1}{i}\right)$$

Since the deposits start at the start of each year, $n = 4 + 1$, for a total of five deposits.

$$F = A\left(\frac{(1+i)^{n+1} - 1}{i}\right) = \$2000$$

$$= A\left(\frac{(1+0.06)^5 - 1}{0.06}\right)$$

$$\$2000 = 5.6371 A$$

$$A = \frac{\$2000}{5.6371} = \boxed{\$354.79}$$

By the factor converting P and A to F,

$$F = A\big[(F/P, 6\%, 4) + (F/A, 6\%, 4)\big]$$
$$\$2000 = A(1.2625 + 4.3746)$$
$$A = \boxed{\$354.79}$$

8.

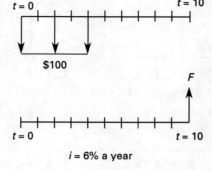

$i = 6\%$ a year

By the formula from Table 69.1, $F = P(1+i)^n$. If each deposit is considered as P, each will accumulate interest for periods of 10, 8, and 6 years.

Therefore,

$$F = (\$100)(1 + 0.06)^{10} + (\$100)(1 + 0.06)^8$$
$$+ (\$100)(1 + 0.06)^6$$
$$= (\$100)(1.7908 + 1.5938 + 1.4185)$$
$$= (\$100)(4.8031)$$
$$= \boxed{\$480.31}$$

By the factor converting P to F,

$$(F/P, i, n) = 1.7908 \text{ for } i = 6\% \text{ and } n = 10$$
$$= 1.5938 \text{ for } i = 6\% \text{ and } n = 8$$
$$= 1.4185 \text{ for } i = 6\% \text{ and } n = 6$$

By summation,

$$F = (\$100)(1.7908 + 1.5938 + 1.4185)$$
$$= (\$100)(4.8031)$$
$$= \boxed{\$480.31}$$

9.

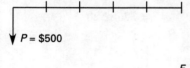

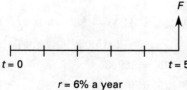

$r = 6\%$ a year

Since the deposit is compounded monthly, the effective interest rate should be calculated as shown by Eq. 69.54.

$$i = \left(1 + \frac{r}{k}\right)^k - 1 = \left(1 + \frac{0.06}{12}\right)^{12} - 1$$
$$= \boxed{0.061677 \ (6.1677\%)}$$

By the formula from Table 69.1,

$$F = P(1+i)^n = (\$500)(1 + 0.061677)^5 = \$674.42$$

To use a table of factors, interpolation is required.

$i\%$	factor F/P
6	1.3382
6.1677	desired
7	1.4026

$$i = \left(\frac{6.1677 - 6}{7 - 6}\right)(1.4026 - 1.3382)$$
$$= 0.0108$$

Therefore,

$$F/P = 1.3382 + 0.0108 = 1.3490$$
$$F = P(F/P, 6.1677\%, 5) = (\$500)(1.3490)$$
$$= \boxed{\$674.50}$$

10.

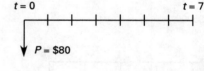

By the formula from Table 69.1,

$$F = P(1+i)^n$$

Therefore,

$$(1+i)^n = F/P$$
$$i = (F/P)^{\frac{1}{n}} - 1 = \left(\frac{\$120}{\$80}\right)^{\frac{1}{7}} - 1$$
$$= 0.059 \approx \boxed{6\%}$$

By the factor coverting P to F,

$$F = P(F/P, i\%, 7)$$
$$(F/P, i\%, 7) = F/P = \frac{\$120}{\$80} = 1.5$$

Economics

By checking the interest tables,

$$(F/P, i\%, 7) = 1.4071 \text{ for } i = 5\%$$
$$= 1.5036 \text{ for } i = 6\%$$
$$= 1.6058 \text{ for } i = 7\%$$

Therefore, $i = \boxed{6\%}$.

11.

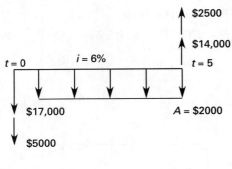

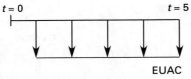

Annual cost of ownership, EUAC, can be obtained by the factors converting P to A and F to A.

$$P = \$17,000 + \$5000$$
$$= \$22,000$$
$$F = \$14,000 + \$2500$$
$$= \$16,500$$
$$\text{EUAC} = A + P(A/P, 6\%, 5) - F(A/F, 6\%, 5)$$
$$(A/P, 6\%, 5) = 0.23740$$
$$(A/F, 6\%, 5) = 0.17740$$
$$\text{EUAC} = \$2000 + (\$22,000)(0.23740)$$
$$- (\$16,500)(0.17740)$$
$$= \boxed{\$4295.70}$$

12.

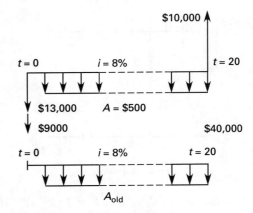

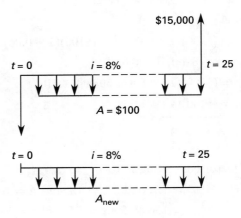

Consider the salvage value as a benefit lost (cost).

$$\text{EUAC}_{\text{old}} = \$500 + (\$22,000)(A/P, 8\%, 20)$$
$$- (\$10,000)(A/F, 8\%, 20)$$
$$(A/P, 8\%, 20) = 0.10185$$
$$(A/F, 8\%, 20) = 0.02185$$
$$\text{EUAC}_{\text{old}} = \$500 + (\$22,000)(0.10185)$$
$$- (\$10,000)(0.02185)$$
$$= \$2522.20$$

Similarly,

$$\text{EUAC}_{\text{new}} = \$100 + (\$40,000)(A/P, 8\%, 25)$$
$$- (\$15,000)(A/F, 8\%, 25)$$
$$(A/P, 8\%, 25) = 0.09368$$
$$(A/F, 8\%, 25) = 0.01368$$
$$\text{EUAC}_{\text{new}} = \$100 + (\$40,000)(0.09368)$$
$$- (\$15,000)(0.01368)$$
$$= \$3642$$

Therefore, the new bridge is going to be more costly. The best alternative is to strengthen the old bridge.

13.

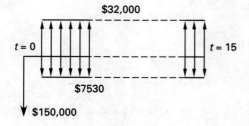

The annual depreciation is

$$D = \frac{C - S_n}{n} = \frac{\$150,000}{15}$$
$$= \$10,000/\text{year}$$

The taxable income is

$$\$32,000 - \$7530 - \$10,000 = \$14,470/\text{year}$$

Taxes paid are

$$(\$14,470)(0.48) = \$6945.60/\text{year}$$

The after-tax cash flow is

$$\$24,470 - \$6945.60 = \$17,524.40$$

The present worth of the alternate is zero when evaluated at its ROR.

$$0 = -\$150,000 + (\$17,524.40)(P/A, i\%, 15)$$

Therefore,

$$(P/A, i\%, 15) = \frac{\$150,000}{\$17,524.40} = 8.55949$$

By checking the tables, this factor matches $i = 8\%$.

$$\boxed{\text{ROR} = 8\%}$$

14. The conventional benefit/cost ratio is

$$B/C = \frac{B - D}{D}$$

(a) The benefit/cost ratio will be

$$B/C = \frac{\$1,500,000 - \$300,000}{\$1,000,000} = \boxed{1.2}$$

(b) The excess of benefits over cost are $\boxed{\$200,000.}$

15.

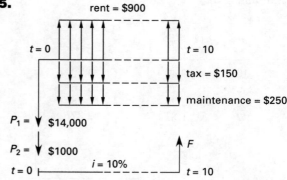

The annual rent is

$$(\$75)\left(12\,\frac{\text{months}}{\text{year}}\right) = \$900$$
$$P = P_1 + P_2 = \$15,000$$
$$A_1 = -\$900$$
$$A_2 = \$250 + \$150 = \$400$$

By the factors converting P to F and A to F,

$$F = (\$15,000)(F/P, 10\%, 10)$$
$$+ (\$400)(F/A, 10\%, 10)$$
$$- (\$900)(F/A, 10\%, 10)$$
$$(F/P, 10\%, 10) = 2.5937$$
$$(F/A, 10\%, 10) = 15.937$$
$$F = (\$15,000)(2.5937) + (\$400)(15.937)$$
$$- (\$900)(15.937)$$
$$= \boxed{\$30,937}$$

16.

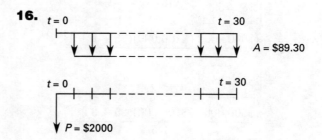

By the formula relating P to A,

$$P = A\left(\frac{(1 + i)^n - 1}{i(1 + i)^n}\right)$$
$$\frac{(1 + i)^{30} - 1}{i(1 + i)^{30}} = \frac{\$2000}{\$89.30} = 22.30$$

By trial and error,

i	$(1+i)^{30}$	$\dfrac{(1+i)^{30}-1}{i(1+i)^{30}}$
10	17.45	9.42
6	5.74	13.76
4	3.24	17.28
2	1.81	22.37

2% per month is close.

$$i = (1+0.02)^{12} - 1 = \boxed{0.2682 \quad (26.82\%)}$$

17. (a) Use the straight line method, Eq. 69.25.

$$D = \frac{C - S_n}{n}$$

Each year depreciation will remain the same.

$$D = \frac{\$500{,}000 - \$100{,}000}{25} = \boxed{\$16{,}000}$$

(b) Sum-of-the years digits (SOYD) can be calculated as shown by Eq. 69.28,

$$D_j = \frac{(C - S_n)(n - j + 1)}{T}$$

Use Eq. 69.27.

$$T = \tfrac{1}{2}n(n+1) = \left(\tfrac{1}{2}\right)(25)(25+1) = 325$$

$$D_1 = \frac{(\$500{,}000 - \$100{,}000)(25 - 1 + 1)}{325}$$

$$= \boxed{\$30{,}769}$$

$$D_2 = \frac{(\$500{,}000 - \$100{,}000)(25 - 2 + 1)}{325}$$

$$= \boxed{\$29{,}538}$$

$$D_3 = \frac{(\$500{,}000 - \$100{,}000)(25 - 3 + 1)}{325}$$

$$= \boxed{\$28{,}308}$$

(c) The double-declining balance (DDB) method can be used. By Eq. 69.32,

$$D_j = dC(1 - d)^{j-1}$$

Use Eq. 69.31.

$$d = \frac{2}{n}$$

$$= \frac{2}{25}$$

$$D_1 = \left(\frac{2}{25}\right)(\$500{,}000)\left(1 - \frac{2}{25}\right)^0 = \boxed{\$40{,}000}$$

$$D_2 = \left(\frac{2}{25}\right)(\$500{,}000)\left(1 - \frac{2}{25}\right)^1 = \boxed{\$36{,}800}$$

$$D_3 = \left(\frac{2}{25}\right)(\$500{,}000)\left(1 - \frac{2}{25}\right)^2 = \boxed{\$33{,}856}$$

18.

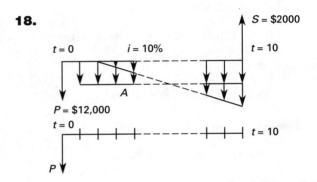

$A = \$1000$ and $G = \$200$ for $t = n - 1 = 9$ years.

$$F = S = \$2000$$
$$P = \$12{,}000 + A(P/A, 10\%, 10) + G(P/G, 10\%, 10)$$
$$\quad - F(P/F, 10\%, 10)$$
$$= \$12{,}000 + (\$1000)(6.1446) + (\$200)(22.8913)$$
$$\quad - (\$2000)(0.3855)$$
$$= \boxed{\$21{,}952}$$

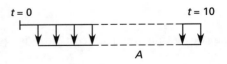

$$A = (\$12{,}000)(A/P, 10\%, 10) + \$1000$$
$$\quad + (\$200)(A/G, 10\%, 10) - (\$2000)(A/F, 10\%, 10)$$
$$= (\$12{,}000)(0.16275) + \$1000 + (\$200)(3.7255)$$
$$\quad - (\$2000)(0.06275)$$
$$= \boxed{\$3572.60}$$

19. An increase in rock removal capacity can be achieved by a 20-year loan (investment). Different cases available can be compared by equivalent uniform annual cost (EUAC).

$$EUAC = \text{annual loan cost}$$
$$+ \text{expected annual damage}$$
$$= \text{cost } (A/P, 10\%, 20)$$
$$+ (\$25{,}000)(\text{probability})$$
$$(A/P, 10\%, 20) = 0.11746$$

A table can be prepared for different cases.

rock removal rate	cost ($)	annual loan cost ($)	expected annual damage ($)	EUAC ($)
7	0	0	3750	3750.00
8	15,000	1761.90	2500	4261.90
9	20,000	2349.20	1750	4099.20
10	30,000	3523.80	750	4273.80

It is cheapest to do nothing.

20. Calculate the cost of owning and operating for each year.

$$A_1 = (\$10{,}000)(A/P, 20\%, 1) + \$2000$$
$$- (\$8000)(A/F, 20\%, 1)$$
$$(A/P, 20\%, 1) = 1.2$$
$$(A/F, 20\%, 1) = 1.0$$
$$A_1 = (\$10{,}000)(1.2) + \$2000 - (\$8000)(1.0)$$
$$= \$6000$$
$$A_2 = (\$10{,}000)(A/P, 20\%, 2) + \$2000$$
$$+ (\$1000)(A/G, 20\%, 2)$$
$$- (\$7000)(A/F, 20\%, 2)$$
$$(A/P, 20\%, 2) = 0.6545$$
$$(A/G, 20\%, 2) = 0.4545$$
$$(A/F, 20\%, 2) = 0.4545$$
$$A_2 = (\$10{,}000)(0.6545) + \$2000$$
$$+ (\$1000)(0.4545) - (\$7000)(0.4545)$$
$$= \$5818$$
$$A_3 = (\$10{,}000)(A/P, 20\%, 3) + \$2000$$
$$+ (\$1000)(A/G, 20\%, 3)$$
$$- (\$6000)(A/F, 20\%, 3)$$
$$(A/P, 20\%, 3) = 0.4747$$
$$(A/G, 20\%, 3) = 0.8791$$
$$(A/F, 20\%, 3) = 0.2747$$

$$A_3 = (\$10{,}000)(0.4747) + \$2000$$
$$+ (\$1000)(0.8791)$$
$$- (\$6000)(0.2747)$$
$$= \$5977.90$$
$$A_4 = (\$10{,}000)(A/P, 20\%, 4)$$
$$+ \$2000 + (\$1000)(A/G, 20\%, 4)$$
$$- (\$5000)(A/F, 20\%, 4)$$
$$(A/P, 20\%, 4) = 0.3863$$
$$(A/G, 20\%, 4) = 1.2762$$
$$(A/F, 20\%, 4) = 0.1863$$
$$A_4 = (\$10{,}000)(0.3863) + \$2000$$
$$+ (\$1000)(1.2762) - (\$5000)(0.1863)$$
$$= \$6207.70$$
$$A_5 = (\$10{,}000)(A/P, 20\%, 5) + \$2000$$
$$+ (\$1000)(A/G, 20\%, 5)$$
$$- (\$4000)(A/F, 20\%, 5)$$
$$(A/P, 20\%, 5) = 0.3344$$
$$(A/G, 20\%, 5) = 1.6405$$
$$(A/F, 20\%, 5) = 0.1344$$
$$A_5 = (\$10{,}000)(0.3344) + \$2000$$
$$+ (\$1000)(1.6405) - (\$4000)(0.1344)$$
$$= \$6446.90$$

(a) Since the annual owning and operating cost is smallest after two years of operation, it is advantageous to sell the mechanism after the second year.

The economic life is two years.

(b) After four years of operation, the owning and operating cost of the mechanism for one more year will be

$$A = \$6000 + (\$5000)(1 + i) - \$4000$$
$$i = 0.2 \ (20\%)$$
$$A = \$6000 + (\$5000)(1.2) - \$4000$$
$$= \boxed{\$8000}$$

21. To find out if the reimbursement is adequate, calculate the business-related expense.

Charge the company for business travel.

$$\text{insurance: } \$3000 - \$2000 = \$1000$$
$$\text{maintenance: } \$2000 - \$1500 = \$500$$
$$\text{drop in salvage value: } \$10{,}000 - \$5000 = \$5000$$

The annual portion of the drop in salvage value is

$$A = (\$5000)(A/F, 10\%, 5)$$
$$(A/F, 10\%, 5) = 0.1638$$
$$A = (\$5000)(0.1638) = \$819/\text{year}$$

The cost of gas is

$$\left(\frac{50,000 \text{ mi}}{15 \frac{\text{mi}}{\text{gal}}}\right)\left(\frac{\$1.50}{\text{gal}}\right) = \$5000/\text{yr}$$

$$\text{EUAC per mile} = \frac{\$1000 + \$500 + \$819 + \$5000}{50,000 \text{ mi}}$$

$$= \boxed{\$0.14638/\text{mi}}$$

Since the reimbursement per mile was $0.30 and since $0.30 > $0.14638, the reimbursement is adequate.

Next, determine (with reimbursement) how many miles must the car be driven to break even.

If the car is driven M miles per year,

$$\left(\frac{\$0.30}{1 \text{ mi}}\right)M = (\$50,000)(A/P, 10\%, 5) + \$2500$$
$$+ \$2000 - (\$8000)(A/F, 10\%, 5)$$
$$+ \left(\frac{M}{15 \frac{\text{mi}}{\text{gal}}}\right)(\$1.50)$$

$$(A/P, 10\%, 5) = 0.2638$$
$$(A/F, 10\%, 5) = 0.1638$$
$$0.3M = (\$50,000)(0.2638) + \$2500 + \$2000$$
$$- (\$8000)(0.1638) + 0.1M$$
$$0.2M = \$16,379.60$$
$$M = \frac{\$16,379.60}{0.2 \frac{\$}{\text{mi}}} = \boxed{81,898 \text{ mi}}$$

22.

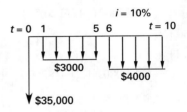

$$P_A = \$80,000 + (\$1000)(P/A, 10\%, 5)$$
$$+ (\$1500)(P/A, 10\%, 5)(P/F, 10\%, 5)$$
$$+ (\$2000)(P/A, 10\%, 10)(P/F, 10\%, 10)$$
$$+ (\$5000)(P/F, 10\%, 10)$$
$$- (\$7000)(P/F, 10\%, 20)$$

$$(P/A, 10\%, 5) = 3.7908$$
$$(P/F, 10\%, 5) = 0.6209$$
$$(P/A, 10\%, 10) = 6.1446$$
$$(P/F, 10\%, 10) = 0.3855$$
$$(P/F, 10\%, 10) = 0.3855$$
$$(P/F, 10\%, 20) = 0.1486$$
$$P_A = \$80,000 + (\$1000)(3.7908)$$
$$+ (\$1500)(3.7908)(0.6209)$$
$$+ (\$2000)(6.1446)(0.3855)$$
$$+ (\$5000)(0.3855) - (\$7000)(0.1486)$$
$$= \$92,946.15$$

Since the lives are different, compare by EUAC.

$$\text{EUAC}(A) = (\$92,946.14)(A/P, 10\%, 20)$$
$$= (\$92,946.14)(0.1175) = \$10,921$$

Similarly, evaluate alternative B.

$$P_B = \$35,000 + (\$3000)(P/A, 10\%, 5)$$
$$+ (\$4000)(P/A, 10\%, 5)(P/F, 10\%, 6)$$
$$(P/A, 10\%, 5) = 3.7908$$
$$(P/F, 10\%, 5) = 0.6209$$
$$P_B = \$35,000 + (\$3000)(3.7908)$$
$$+ (\$4000)(3.7908)(0.6209)$$
$$= \$55,787.23$$
$$\text{EUAC}(B) = (\$55,787.23)(A/P, 10\%, 10)$$
$$= (\$55,787.23)(0.1627) = \$9077$$

Since $\text{EUAC}(B) < \text{EUAC}(A)$,

$$\boxed{\text{alternative B is economically superior.}}$$

23. For both cases, if the annual cost is compared with a total annual mileage of M,

$$A_{\rm A} = \$0.25M$$

$$A_{\rm B} = (\$30{,}000)(A/P, 10\%, 3) + \$0.14M$$
$$+ \$500 - (\$7200)(A/F, 10\%, 3)$$

$$(A/P, 10\%, 3) = 0.40211$$

$$(A/F, 10\%, 3) = 0.30211$$

$$A_{\rm B} = (\$30{,}000)(0.40211) + \$0.14M + \$500$$
$$- (\$7200)(0.30211)$$
$$= \$12{,}063.30 + \$0.14M$$
$$+ \$500 - \$2175.19$$
$$= \$10{,}388.11 + \$0.14M$$

For an equal annual cost $A_{\rm A} = A_{\rm B}$,

$$\$0.25M = \$10{,}388.11 + \$0.14M$$

An annual mileage would be $M = 94{,}437$ mi.

For an annual mileage less than that, $A_{\rm A} < A_{\rm B}$.

> Plan A is economically superior until that mileage is exceeded.

24. Method A:

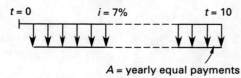

A = yearly equal payments

24 hours/day
365 days/year
total of $(24)(365) = 8760$ hours/year
\$10.50 operational cost/hour
total of $(8760)(\$10.50) = \$91{,}890$ operational cost/year

$$A = \$91{,}980 + (\$23{,}000)(A/P, 7\%, 10)$$
$$- (\$5000)(A/F, 7\%, 10)$$

$$(A/P, 7\%, 10) = 0.14238$$

$$(A/F, 7\%, 10) = 0.07238$$

$$A = \$91{,}980 + (\$23{,}000)(0.14238)$$
$$- (\$5000)(0.07238)$$
$$= \$94{,}892.84/\text{yr}$$

Therefore, the uniform annual cost per ton each year will be

$$\frac{\$94{,}892.84}{50 \text{ ton}} = \boxed{\$1897.86}$$

Method B:

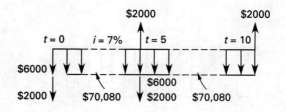

equivalent model

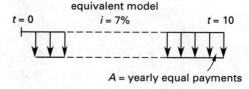

A = yearly equal payments

8760 hours/year
\$8 operational cost/hour
total of \$70,080 operational cost/year

$$A = \$70{,}080 + (\$8000)(F/P, 7\%, 10)$$
$$\times (A/F, 7\%, 10)$$
$$- (\$2000)(F/P, 7\%, 5)(A/F, 7\%, 10)$$
$$+ (\$8000)(F/P, 7\%, 5)(A/F, 7\%, 10)$$
$$- (\$2000)(A/F, 7\%, 10)$$

$$(F/P, 7\%, 10) = 1.9672$$

$$(A/F, 7\%, 10) = 0.07238$$

$$(F/P, 7\%, 5) = 1.4026$$

$$A = \$70{,}080 + (\$8000)(1.9672)(0.07238)$$
$$- (\$2000)(1.4026)(0.07238)$$
$$+ (\$8000)(1.4026)(0.07238)$$
$$- (\$2000)(0.07238)$$
$$= \$71{,}683.45/\text{yr}$$

Therefore, the uniform annual cost per ton each year will be

$$\frac{\$71{,}683.45}{20 \text{ ton}} = \$3584.17$$

tons/hr	cost of using A		cost of using B		cheapest
0–20	\$94,893	(1x)	\$71,683	(1x)	B
20–40	\$94,893	(1x)	\$143,366	(2x)	A
40–50	\$94,893	(1x)	\$215,049	(3x)	A
50–60	\$189,786	(2x)	\$215,049	(3x)	A
60–80	\$189,786	(2x)	\$286,732	(4x)	A

25.

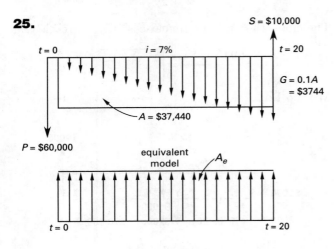

$$A_e = (\$60,000)(A/P, 7\%, 20) + A$$
$$+ G(P/G, 7\%, 20)(A/P, 7\%, 20)$$
$$- (\$10,000)(A/F, 7\%, 20)$$

$$(A/P, 7\%, 20) = 0.09439$$

$$A = (37,440 \text{ mi}) \left(\frac{\$1.0}{1 \text{ mi}} \right) = \$37,440$$

$$G = 0.1A = (0.1)(\$37,440) = \$3744$$

$$(P/G, 7\%, 20) = 77.509$$

$$(A/F, 7\%, 20) = 0.02439$$

$$A_e = (\$60,000)(0.09439) + \$37,440$$
$$+ (\$3744)(77.509)(0.09439)$$
$$- (\$10,000)(0.02439)$$

$$= \$70,250.88$$

(a) With 80,000 passengers a year, the break-even fare per passenger would be

$$\text{fare} = \frac{A_e}{80,000} = \frac{\$70,250.88}{80,000} = \boxed{\$0.878}$$

(b) $\qquad \$0.878 = \$0.35 + G(A/G, 7\%, 20)$

$$G = \frac{\$0.878 - \$0.35}{7.3163}$$

$$= \boxed{\$0.072 \text{ increase per year}}$$

(c) As in part (b), the subsidy should be

$$\text{subsidy} = \text{cost} - \text{revenue}$$
$$P = \$0.878 - \big(\$0.35 + (\$0.05)(A/G, 7\%, 20)\big)$$
$$= \$0.878 - \big(\$0.35 + (\$0.05)(7.3163)\big)$$
$$= \boxed{\$0.162}$$

NO POSTAGE
NECESSARY
IF MAILED
IN THE
UNITED STATES

BUSINESS REPLY MAIL

FIRST CLASS MAIL   PERMIT NO. 33   BELMONT, CA

POSTAGE WILL BE PAID BY ADDRESSEE

PROFESSIONAL PUBLICATIONS INC
1250 FIFTH AVE
BELMONT CA 94002-9979

NO POSTAGE
NECESSARY
IF MAILED
IN THE
UNITED STATES

BUSINESS REPLY MAIL

FIRST CLASS MAIL   PERMIT NO. 33   BELMONT, CA

POSTAGE WILL BE PAID BY ADDRESSEE

PROFESSIONAL PUBLICATIONS INC
1250 FIFTH AVE
BELMONT CA 94002-9979

NO POSTAGE
NECESSARY
IF MAILED
IN THE
UNITED STATES

BUSINESS REPLY MAIL

FIRST CLASS MAIL   PERMIT NO. 33   BELMONT, CA

POSTAGE WILL BE PAID BY ADDRESSEE

PROFESSIONAL PUBLICATIONS INC
1250 FIFTH AVE
BELMONT CA 94002-9979